# IARC MONOGRAPHS
## ON THE
# EVALUATION OF THE
# CARCINOGENIC RISK
# OF CHEMICALS TO HUMANS

## Some Monomers, Plastics and Synthetic Elastomers, and Acrolein

**VOLUME 19**

This publication represents the views and expert opinions
of an IARC Working Group on the
Evaluation of the Carcinogenic Risk of Chemicals to Humans
which met in Lyon,
7-13 February 1978

February 1979

INTERNATIONAL AGENCY FOR RESEARCH ON CANCER

IARC MONOGRAPHS

In 1971, the International Agency for Research on Cancer (IARC) initiated a programme on the evaluation of the carcinogenic risk of chemicals to humans involving the production of critically evaluated monographs on individual chemicals.

The objective of the programme is to elaborate and publish in the form of monographs critical reviews of data on carcinogenicity for groups of chemicals to which humans are known to be exposed, to evaluate these data in terms of human risk with the help of international working groups of experts in chemical carcinogenesis and related fields, and to indicate where additional research efforts are needed.

International Agency for Research on Cancer 1979

ISBN 92 832 1219 3

PRINTED IN SWITZERLAND

# CONTENTS

    The following compounds were considered but no monograph was prepared because of lack of carcinogenicity data: adipic acid, hexamethylenediamine and nylon 6/6; dimethylterephthalate, terephthalic acid and polyethylene terephthalate; isoprene and polyisoprene; methacrylic acid; vinylidene fluoride and polyvinylidene fluoride.

IARC WORKING GROUP ON THE EVALUATION OF THE CARCINOGENIC
RISK OF CHEMICALS TO HUMANS:

SOME MONOMERS, PLASTICS AND
SYNTHETIC ELASTOMERS AND ACROLEIN

Lyon, 7-13 February 1978

## Members[1]

J. Autian, Director, Materials Science Toxicology Laboratories, College
of Dentistry & College of Pharmacy, University of Tennessee Center
for the Health Sciences, Memphis, Tennessee 38163, United States of
America

L. Elbling, Institut für Krebsforschung der Universität Wien,
Borschkegasse 8a, 1090 Vienna, Austria

V.J. Feron, Central Institute for Nutrition and Food Research (TNO),
Utrechtseweg 48, Postbus 360, 3700 AJ Zeist, The Netherlands

L. Fishbein, Assistant to the Director for Environmental Surveillance,
National Center for Toxicological Research, Jefferson, Arkansas 72079,
United States of America (*Vice-Chairman*)

R. Griesemer, Carcinogenesis Testing Program, Division of Cancer Cause
and Prevention, Room 3A22, National Cancer Institute, Bethesda,
Maryland 20014, United States of America

T. Matsushima, Professor, Department of Molecular Oncology, The Institute
of Medical Science, The University of Tokyo, Minato-ku, Tokyo 108,
Japan

R. Owen, Medical Adviser, Trades Union Congress, Congress House,
Great Russell Street, London WC1B 3LS, United Kingdom

G. Parmiani, Division of Experimental Oncology A, Istituto Nazionale per
lo Studio e la Cura dei Tumori, Via Venezian 1, 20133 Milan, Italy

M. Roberfroid, Université Catholique de Louvain, Faculté de Médecine,
Ecole de Pharmacie, Unité de Chimie Médicale, Toxicologie et
Bromatologie, Avenue Emmanuel Mounier 73, 1200 Brussels, Belgium

---

[1]Unable to attend:  C. Maltoni, Director, Istituto di Oncologia
'Felice Addarii', Viale Ercolani 4/2, 40138 Bologna, Italy

V.S. Turusov, Cancer Research Center, USSR Academy of Medical Sciences, Karshirskoye Shosse 6, Moscow 115478, USSR (*Chairman*)

H.A. Tyroler, Professor of Epidemiology, Department of Epidemiology, The School of Public Health, The University of North Carolina, Rosenau Hall 201 H, Chapel Hill, North Carolina 27514, United States of America

H. Vainio, Department of Industrial Hygiene and Toxicology, Institute of Occupational Health, Haartmaninkatu 1, 00290 Helsinki 29, Finland

J.K. Wagoner, Special Assistant for Occupational Carcinogenesis, Office of the Assistant Secretary of Labor, Occupational Safety & Health Administration, US Department of Labor, 200 Constitution Avenue N.W., Washington DC 20210, USA

F. Zajdela, Unité No. 22, Institut National de la Santé et de la Recherche Médicale, Institut du Radium, Bâtiment 110, Faculté des Sciences, 91405 Orsay, France

G. Zetterberg, Department of General Genetics, University of Uppsala, Box 7003, S-750 07 Uppsala 7, Sweden

Representative from the National Cancer Institute

S. Siegel, Coordinator, Technical Information Activities, Technical Information Resources Branch, Room 3A-06, Landow Building, Carcinogenesis Bioassay Testing Program, Division of Cancer Cause and Prevention, National Cancer Institute, Bethesda, Maryland 20014, United States of America

Representative from SRI International

K.E. McCaleb, Director, Chemical-Environmental Program, SRI International, 333 Ravenswood Avenue, Menlo Park, California 94025, United States of America (*Rapporteur sections 2.1 and 2.2*)

Representative from the Commission of the European Communities

M.-T. van der Venne, Commission of the European Communities, Health and Safety Directorate, Bâtiment Jean Monnet, Plateau du Kirchberg, Luxembourg, Great Duchy of Luxembourg

Representative from the United Nations Environment Programme

H.E. Christensen, Chief, Information Processing Unit, International Register of Potentially Toxic Chemicals, United Nations Environment Programme, World Health Organization, 1211 Geneva 27, Switzerland

Representative from C.E.F.I.C. (Conseil Européen des Fédérations de l'Industrie Chimique/European Council of Chemical Manufacturers' Federations)

W. Freiesleben, Director, Wacker-Chemie GmbH, Prinzregentenstrasse 22, 8000 Munich 22, Federal Republic of Germany

Observers

A.M. Kaplan, Chief, Oral Toxicology, Haskell Laboratory for Toxicology and Industrial Medicine, E.I. Du Pont de Nemours & Co., Inc., Elkton Road, Newark, Delaware 19711, United States of America

E. Loser, Bayer AG, Institut für Toxikologie, Friedrich-Ebert-Strasse 217-319, 5600 Wuppertal 1, Federal Republic of Germany

A. Yamamoto, Visiting Fellow from Japanese Government, Division of Prophylactic, Diagnostic and Therapeutic Substances, World Health Organization, 1211 Geneva 27, Switzerland

Secretariat

H. Bartsch, Unit of Chemical Carcinogenesis (*Rapporteur section 3.2*)

M. Castegnaro, Unit of Environmental Carcinogens

J.A. Cooper, Unit of Epidemiology and Biostatistics (*Co-rapporteur section 3.3*)

L. Griciute, Chief, Unit of Environmental Carcinogens

J.E. Huff, Unit of Chemical Carcinogenesis (*Secretary*)

T. Kuroki, Unit of Chemical Carcinogenesis

D. Mietton, Unit of Chemical Carcinogenesis (*Library assistant*)

R. Montesano, Unit of Chemical Carcinogenesis (*Rapporteur section 3.1*)

C. Partensky, Unit of Chemical Carcinogenesis (*Technical editor*)

I. Peterschmitt, Unit of Chemical Carcinogenesis, WHO, Geneva (*Bibliographic researcher*)

V. Ponomarkov, Unit of Chemical Carcinogenesis

R. Saracci, Unit of Epidemiology and Biostatistics (*Rapporteur section 3.3*)

L. Tomatis, Chief, Unit of Chemical Carcinogenesis (*Head of the Programme*)

E.A. Walker, Unit of Environmental Carcinogens (*Rapporteur sections 1 and 2.3*)

E. Ward, Montignac, France (*Editor*)

J.D. Wilbourn, Unit of Chemical Carcinogenesis (*Co-secretary*)

Secretarial assistance

A.V. Anderson

M.J. Ghess

R.B. Johnson

The term 'carcinogenic risk' in the *IARC Monograph* series is taken to mean the probability that exposure to the chemical will lead to cancer in humans.

Inclusion of a chemical in the monographs does not imply that it is a carcinogen, only that the published data have been examined. Equally, the fact that a chemical has not yet been evaluated in a monograph does not mean that it is not carcinogenic.

Anyone who is aware of published data that may alter the evaluation of the carcinogenic risk of a chemical for humans is encouraged to make this information available to the Unit of Chemical Carcinogenesis, International Agency for Research on Cancer, Lyon, France, in order that the chemical may be considered for re-evaluation by a future Working Group.

Although every effort is made to prepare the monographs as accurately as possible, mistakes may occur. Readers are requested to communicate any errors to the Unit of Chemical Carcinogenesis, so that corrections can be reported in future volumes.

PREAMBLE

## BACKGROUND

In 1971, the International Agency for Research on Cancer (IARC) initiated a programme on the evaluation of the carcinogenic risk of chemicals to humans with the object of producing monographs on individual chemicals*. The criteria established at that time to evaluate carcinogenic risk to humans were adopted by all the working groups whose deliberations resulted in the first 16 volumes of the *IARC Monograph* series. In October 1977, a joint IARC/WHO *ad hoc* Working Group met to re-evaluate these guiding criteria; this preamble reflects the results of their deliberations(1) and those of a subsequent IARC *ad hoc* Working Group which met in April 1978(2).

## OBJECTIVE AND SCOPE

The objective of the programme is to elaborate and publish in the form of monographs critical reviews of data on carcinogenicity for groups of chemicals to which humans are known to be exposed, to evaluate these data in terms of human risk with the help of international working groups of experts in chemical carcinogenesis and related fields, and to indicate where additional research efforts are needed.

The monographs summarize the evidence for the carcinogenicity of individual chemicals and other relevant information. The critical analyses of the data are intended to assist national and international authorities in formulating decisions concerning preventive measures. No recommendations are given concerning legislation, since this depends on risk-benefit evaluations, which seem best made by individual governments and/or international agencies. In this connection, WHO recommendations on food additives(3), drugs(4), pesticides and contaminants(5) and occupational carcinogens(6) are particularly informative.

---

*Since 1972, the programme has undergone considerable expansion, primarily with the scientific collaboration and financial support of the US National Cancer Institute.

The *IARC Monographs* are recognized as an authoritative source of information on the carcinogenicity of environmental chemicals. The first users' survey, made in 1976, indicates that the monographs are consulted routinely by various agencies in 24 countries.

Since the programme began in 1971, 19 volumes have been published(7) in the *IARC Monograph* series, and 420 separate chemical substances have been evaluated (see also cumulative index to the monographs, p. 497). Each volume is printed in 4000 copies and distributed *via* the WHO publications service (see inside covers for a listing of IARC publications and back outside cover for distribution and sales services).

## SELECTION OF CHEMICALS FOR MONOGRAPHS

The chemicals (natural and synthetic, including those which occur as mixtures and in manufacturing processes) are selected for evaluation on the basis of two main criteria: (a) there is evidence of human exposure, and (b) there is some experimental evidence of carcinogenicity and/or there is some evidence or suspicion of a risk to humans. In certain instances, chemical analogues were also considered.

Inclusion of a chemical in a volume does not imply that it is carcinogenic, only that the published data have been examined. The evaluations must be consulted to ascertain the conclusions of the Working Group. Equally, the fact that a chemical has not appeared in a monograph does not mean that it is without carcinogenic hazard.

The scientific literature is surveyed for published data relevant to the monograph programme. In addition, the IARC Survey of Chemicals Being Tested for Carcinogenicity(8) often indicates those chemicals that are to be scheduled for future meetings. The major aims of the survey are to prevent unnecessary duplication of research, to increase communication among scientists, and to make a census of chemicals that are being tested and of available research facilities.

As new data on chemicals for which monographs have already been prepared and new principles for evaluating carcinogenic risk receive acceptance, re-evaluations will be made at subsequent meetings, and revised monographs will be published as necessary.

## WORKING PROCEDURES

Approximately one year in advance of a meeting of a working group, a list of the substances to be considered is prepared by IARC staff in consultation with other experts. Subsequently, all relevant biological data are collected by IARC; in addition to the published literature, US Public Health Service Publication No. 149(9) has been particularly valuable and has been used in conjunction with other recognized sources

of information on chemical carcinogenesis and systems such as MEDLINE and
TOXLINE. The major collection of data and the preparation of first drafts
for the sections on chemical and physical properties, on production, use,
occurrence and on analysis are carried out by SRI International under a
separate contract with the US National Cancer Institute. Most of the data
so obtained on production, use and occurrence refer to the United States
and Japan; SRI International and IARC supplement this information with
that from other sources in Europe. Bibliographical sources for data on
mutagenicity and teratogenicity are the Environmental Mutagen Information
Center and the Environmental Teratology Information Center, both located
at the Oak Ridge National Laboratory, USA.

Six to nine months before the meeting, reprints of articles containing relevant biological data are sent to an expert(s), or are used by the
IARC staff, for the preparation of first drafts of the monographs. These
drafts are edited by IARC staff and are sent prior to the meeting to all
participants of the Working Group for their comments. The Working Group
then meets in Lyon for seven to eight days to discuss and finalize the
texts of the monographs and to formulate the evaluations. After the
meeting, the master copy of each monograph is verified by consulting the
original literature, then edited and prepared for reproduction. The
monographs are usually published within six months after the Working Group
meeting.

## DATA FOR EVALUATIONS

With regard to biological data, only reports that have been published
or accepted for publication are reviewed by the working groups, although
a few exceptions have been made. The monographs do not cite all of the
literature on a particular chemical: only those data considered by the
Working Group to be relevant to the evaluation of the carcinogenic risk
of the chemical to humans are included.

Anyone who is aware of data that have been published or are in press
which are relevant to the evaluations of the carcinogenic risk to humans
of chemicals for which monographs have appeared is urged to make them
available to the Unit of Chemical Carcinogenesis, International Agency
for Research on Cancer, Lyon, France.

## THE WORKING GROUP

The tasks of the Working Group are five-fold: (a) to ascertain that
all data have been collected; (b) to select the data relevant for the
evaluation; (c) to ensure that the summaries of the data enable the reader
to follow the reasoning of the committee; (d) to judge the significance
of the results of experimental and epidemiological studies; and (e) to
make an evaluation of the carcinogenic risk of the chemical.

Working Group participants who contributed to the consideration and evaluation of chemicals within a particular volume are listed, with their addresses, at the beginning of each publication (see p. 7). Each member serves as an individual scientist and not as a representative of any organization or government. In addition, observers are often invited from national and international agencies, organizations and industries.

## GENERAL PRINCIPLES FOR EVALUATING THE CARCINOGENIC RISK OF CHEMICALS

The widely accepted meaning of the term 'chemical carcinogenesis', and that used in these monographs, is the induction by chemicals of neoplasms that are not usually observed, the earlier induction by chemicals of neoplasms that are usually observed, and/or the induction by chemicals of more neoplasms than are usually found - although fundamentally different mechanisms may be involved in these three situations. Etymologically, the term 'carcinogenesis' means the induction of cancer, that is, of malignant neoplasms; however, the commonly accepted meaning is the induction of various types of neoplasms or of a combination of malignant and benign tumours. In the monographs, the words 'tumour' and neoplasm' are used interchangeably (In scientific literature the terms 'tumourigen', 'oncogen' and 'blastomogen' have all been used synonymously with 'carcinogen', although occasionally 'tumourigen' has been used specifically to denote the induction of benign tumours).

### Experimental Evidence

*Qualitative aspects*

Both the interpretation and evaluation of a particular study as well as the overall assessment of the carcinogenic activity of a chemical involve several qualitatively important considerations, including: (a) the experimental parameters under which the chemical was tested, including route of administration and exposure, species, strain, sex, age, etc.; (b) the consistency with which the chemical has been shown to be carcinogenic, e.g., in how many species and at which target organ(s); (c) the spectrum of neoplastic response, from benign neoplasia to multiple malignant tumours; (d) the stage of tumour formation in which a chemical may be involved: some chemicals act as complete carcinogens and have initiating and promoting activity, while others are promoters only; and (e) the possible role of modifying factors.

There are problems not only of differential survival but of differential toxicity, which may be manifested by unequal growth and weight gain in treated and control animals. These complexities should also be considered in the interpretation of data, or, better, in the experimental design.

Many chemicals induce both benign and malignant tumours; few instances are recorded in which only benign neoplasms are induced by chemicals that have been studied extensively. Benign tumours may represent a stage in the evolution of a malignant neoplasm or they may be 'end-points' that do not readily undergo transition to malignancy. If a substance is found to induce only benign tumours in experimental animals, the chemical should be suspected of being a carcinogen and requires further investigation.

*Hormonal carcinogenesis*

Hormonal carcinogenesis presents certain distinctive features: the chemicals involved occur both endogenously and exogenously; in many instances, long exposure is required; tumours occur in the target tissue in association with a stimulation of non-neoplastic growth, but in some cases, hormones promote the proliferation of tumour cells in a target organ. Hormones that occur in excessive amounts, hormone-mimetic agents and agents that cause hyperactivity or imbalance in the endocrine system may require evaluative methods comparable with those used to identify chemical carcinogens; particular emphasis must be laid on quantitative aspects and duration of exposure. Some chemical carcinogens have significant side effects on the endocrine system, which may also result in hormonal carcinogenesis. Synthetic hormones and anti-hormones can be expected to possess other pharmacological and toxicological actions in addition to those on the endocrine system, and in this respect they must be treated like any other chemical with regard to intrinsic carcinogenic potential.

*Quantitative aspects*

Dose-response studies are important in the evaluation of carcinogenesis: the confidence with which a carcinogenic effect can be established is strengthened by the observation of an increasing incidence of neoplasms with increasing exposure.

The assessment of carcinogenicity in animals is frequently complicated by recognized differences among the test animals (species, strain, sex, age), in route(s) of administration and in dose/duration of exposure; often, target organs at which a cancer occurs and its histological type may vary with these parameters. Nevertheless, indices of carcinogenic potency in particular experimental systems (for instance, the dose-rate required under continuous exposure to halve the probability of the animals remaining tumourless(10)) have been formulated in the hope that, at least among categories of fairly similar agents, such indices may be of some predictive value in other systems, including humans.

Chemical carcinogens differ widely in the dose required to produce a given level of tumour induction, although many of them share common biological properties which include metabolism to reactive (electrophilic (11-13)) intermediates capable of interacting with DNA. The reason for this variation in dose-response is not understood but may be due either to differences within a common metabolic process or to the operation of qualitatively distinct mechanisms.

## Statistical analysis of animal studies

Tumours which would have arisen had an animal lived longer may not be observed because of the death of the animal from unrelated causes, and this possibility must be allowed for. Various analytical techniques have been developed which use the assumption of independence of competing risks to allow for the effects of intercurrent mortality on the final numbers of tumour-bearing animals in particular treatment groups.

For externally visible tumours and for neoplasms that cause death, methods such as Kaplan-Meier (i.e., 'life-table', 'product-limit' or 'actuarial') estimates(10), with associated significance tests(14,15), are recommended.

For internal neoplasms which are discovered 'incidentally'(14) at autopsy but which did not cause the death of the host, different estimates (16) and significance tests(14,15) may be necessary for the unbiased study of the numbers of tumour-bearing animals.

All of these methods(10,14-16) can be used to analyse the numbers of animals bearing particular tumour types, but they do not distinguish between animals with one or many such tumours. In experiments which end at a particular fixed time, with the simultaneous sacrifice of many animals, analysis of the total numbers of internal neoplasms per animal found at autopsy at the end of the experiment is straightforward. However, there are no adequate statistical methods for analysing the numbers of particular neoplasms that kill an animal host.

## Evidence of Carcinogenicity in Humans

Evidence of carcinogenicity in humans can be derived from three types of study, the first two of which usually provide only suggestive evidence: (1) reports concerning individual cancer patients (case reports), including a history of exposure to the supposed carcinogenic agent; (2) descriptive epidemiological studies in which the incidence of cancer in human populations is found to vary (spatially or temporally) with exposure to the agent; and (3) analytical epidemiological studies (e.g., case-control or cohort studies) in which individual exposure to the agent is found to be associated with an increased risk of cancer.

An analytical study that shows a positive association between an agent and a cancer may be interpreted as implying causality to a greater or lesser extent, if the following criteria are met: (a) there is no identifiable positive bias (By 'positive bias' is meant the operation of factors in study design or execution which lead erroneously to a more strongly positive association between an agent and disease than in fact exists. Examples of positive bias include, in case-control studies, better documentation of exposure to the agent for cases than for controls, and, in cohort studies, the use of better means of detecting cancer in individuals exposed to the agent than in individuals not exposed);

(b) the possibility of positive confounding has been considered (By 'positive confounding' is meant a situation in which the relationship between an agent and a disease is rendered more strongly positive than it truly is as a result of an association between that agent and another agent which either causes or prevents the disease. An example of positive confounding is the association between coffee consumption and lung cancer, which results from their joint association with cigarette smoking); (c) the association is unlikely to be due to chance alone; (d) the association is strong; and (e) there is a dose-response relationship.

In some instances, a single epidemiological study may be strongly indicative of a cause-effect relationship; however, the most convincing evidence of causality comes when several independent studies done under different circumstances result in 'positive' findings.

Analytical epidemiological studies that show no association between an agent and a cancer ('negative' studies) should be interpreted according to criteria analogous to those listed above: (a) there is no identifiable negative bias; (b) the possibility of negative confounding has been considered; and (c) the possible effects of misclassification of exposure or outcome have been weighed.

In addition, it must be recognized that in any study there are confidence limits around the estimate of association or relative risk. In a study regarded as 'negative', the upper confidence limit may indicate a relative risk substantially greater than unity; in that case, the study excludes only relative risks that are above this upper limit. This usually means that a 'negative' study must be large to be convincing. Confidence in a 'negative' result is increased when several independent studies carried out under different circumstances are in agreement.

Finally, a 'negative' study may be considered to be relevant only to dose levels within or below the range of those observed in the study and is pertinent only if sufficient time has elapsed since first human exposure to the agent. Experience with human cancers of known etiology suggests that the period from first exposure to a chemical carcinogen to development of clinically observed cancer is usually measured in decades and may be in excess of 30 years.

## Experimental Data Relevant to the Evaluation of Carcinogenic Risk to Humans

No adequate criteria are presently available to interpret experimental carcinogenicity data directly in terms of carcinogenic potential for humans. Nonetheless, utilizing data collected from appropriate tests in animals, positive extrapolations to possible human risk can be approximated.

Information compiled from the first 17 volumes of the *IARC Monographs* (17-19) shows that of about 26 chemicals or manufacturing processes now generally accepted to cause cancer in humans, all but possibly two (arsenic and benzene) of those which have been tested appropriately produce cancer in at least one animal species. For several (aflatoxins, 4-aminobiphenyl, diethylstilboestrol, melphalan, mustard gas and vinyl chloride), evidence of carcinogenicity in experimental animals preceded evidence obtained from epidemiological studies or case reports.

In general, the evidence that a chemical produces tumours in experimental animals is of two degrees:   (a) *sufficient evidence* of carcinogenicity is provided by the production of malignant tumours;   and (b) *limited evidence* of carcinogenicity reflects qualitative and/or quantitative limitations of the experimental results.

For many of the chemicals evaluated in the first 18 volumes of the *IARC Monographs* for which there is *sufficient evidence* of carcinogenicity in animals, data relating to carcinogenicity for humans are either insufficient or nonexistent.   In the absence of adequate data on humans, it is reasonable, for practical purposes, to regard such chemicals as if they were carcinogenic to humans.

*Sufficient evidence* of carcinogenicity is provided by experimental studies that show an increased incidence of malignant tumours:   (i) in multiple species or strains, and/or (ii) in multiple experiments (routes and/or doses), and/or (iii) to an unusual degree (with regard to incidence, site, type and/or precocity of onset).   Additional evidence may be provided by data concerning dose-response, mutagenicity or structure.

In the present state of knowledge, it would be difficult to define a predictable relationship between the dose (mg/kg bw/day) of a particular chemical required to produce cancer in test animals and the dose which would produce a similar incidence of cancer in humans.   The available data suggest, however, that such a relationship may exist(20,21), at least for certain classes of carcinogenic chemicals.   Data that provide *sufficient evidence* of carcinogenicity in test animals may therefore be used in an approximate quantitative evaluation of the human risk at some given exposure level, provided that the nature of the chemical concerned and the physiological, pharmacological and toxicological differences between the test animals and humans are taken into account.   However, no acceptable methods are currently available for quantifying the possible errors in such a procedure, whether it is used to generalize between species or to extrapolate from high to low doses.   The methodology for such quantitative extrapolation to humans requires further development.

Evidence for the carcinogenicity of some chemicals in experimental animals may be *limited* for two reasons.   Firstly, experimental data may be restricted to such a point that it is not possible to determine a causal relationship between administration of a chemical and the development of a particular lesion in the animals.   Secondly, there are certain neoplasms, including lung tumours and hepatomas in mice, which have been considered of lesser significance than neoplasms occurring at other sites for the purpose of evaluating the carcinogenic risk of chemicals to humans.   Such tumours occur spontaneously in high incidence in these animals, and their malignancy is often difficult to establish. An evaluation of the significance of these tumours following administration of a chemical is the responsibility of particular Working Groups preparing individual monographs, and it has not been possible to set down rigid guidelines; the relevance of these tumours must be determined by considerations which include experimental design and completeness of reporting.

Some chemicals for which there is *limited evidence* of carcinogenicity in animals have also been studied in humans with, in general, inconclusive results. While such chemicals may indeed be carcinogenic to humans, more experimental and epidemiological investigation is required.

Hence, '*sufficient evidence*' of carcinogenicity and '*limited evidence*' of carcinogenicity do not indicate categories of chemicals: the inherent definitions of those terms indicate varying degrees of experimental evidence, which may change if and when new data on the chemicals become available. The main drawback to any rigid classification of chemicals with regard to their carcinogenic capacity is the as yet incomplete knowledge of the mechanism(s) of carcinogenesis.

In recent years, several short-term tests for the detection of potential carcinogens have been developed. When only inadequate experimental data are available, positive results in validated short-term tests (see p. 24) are an indication that the compound is a potential carcinogen and that it should be tested in animals for an assessment of its carcinogenicity. Negative results from short-term tests cannot be considered sufficient evidence to rule out carcinogenicity. Whether short-term tests will eventually be as reliable as long-term tests in predicting carcinogenicity in humans will depend on further demonstrations of consistency with long-term experiments and with data from humans.

## EXPLANATORY NOTES ON THE MONOGRAPH CONTENTS

### Chemical and Physical Data (Section 1)

The Chemical Abstracts Service Registry Number and the latest Chemical Abstracts Primary Name (9th Collective Index)(22) are recorded in section 1. Other synonyms and trade names are given, but no comprehensive list is provided. Further, some of the trade names are those of mixtures in which the compound being evaluated is only one of the ingredients.

The structural and molecular formulae, molecular weight and chemical and physical properties are given. The properties listed refer to the pure substance, unless otherwise specified, and include, in particular, data that might be relevant to carcinogenicity (e.g., lipid solubility) and those that concern identification. A separate description of the composition of technical products includes available information on impurities and formulated products.

## Production, Use, Occurrence and Analysis (Section 2)

The purpose of section 2 is to provide indications of the extent of past and present human exposure to the chemical.

### Synthesis

Since cancer is a delayed toxic effect, the dates of first synthesis and of first commercial production of the chemical are provided. In addition, methods of synthesis used in past and present commercial production are described. This information allows a reasonable estimate to be made of the date before which no human exposure could have occurred.

### Production

Since Europe, Japan and the United States are reasonably representative industrialized areas of the world, most data on production, foreign trade and uses are obtained from those countries. It should not, however, be inferred that those nations are the sole or even the major sources or users of any individual chemical.

Production and foreign trade data are obtained from both governmental and trade publications by chemical economists in the three geographical areas. In some cases, separate production data on organic chemicals manufactured in the United States are not available because their publication could disclose confidential information. In such cases, an indication of the minimum quantity produced can be inferred from the number of companies reporting commercial production. Each company is required to report on individual chemicals if the sales value or the weight of the annual production exceeds a specified minimum level. These levels vary for chemicals classified for different uses, e.g., medicinals and plastics; in fact, the minimal annual sales value is between $1000 and $50 000 and the minimal annual weight of production is between 450 and 22 700 kg. Data on production in some European countries are obtained by means of general questionnaires sent to companies thought to produce the compounds being evaluated. Information from the completed questionnaires is compiled by country, and the resulting estimates of production are included in the individual monographs.

### Use

Information on uses is meant to serve as a guide only and is not complete. It is usually obtained from published data but is often complemented by direct contact with manufacturers of the chemical. In the case of drugs, mention of their therapeutic uses does not necessarily represent current practice nor does it imply judgement as to their clinical efficacy.

Statements concerning regulations and standards (e.g., pesticide registrations, maximum levels permitted in foods, occupational standards and allowable limits) in specific countries are mentioned as examples only. They may not reflect the most recent situation, since such legislation is in a constant state of change;  nor should it be taken to imply that other countries do not have similar regulations.

## Occurrence

Information on the occurrence of a chemical in the environment is obtained from published data, including that derived from the monitoring and surveillance of levels of the chemical in occupational environments, air, water, soil, foods and tissues of animals and humans.  When available, data on the generation, persistence and bioaccumulation of a chemical are also included.

## Analysis

The purpose of the section on analysis is to give the reader an indication, rather than a complete review, of methods cited in the literature. No attempt is made to evaluate critically or to recommend any of the methods.

## Biological Data Relevant to the Evaluation of Carcinogenic Risk to Humans (Section 3)

In general, the data recorded in section 3 are summarized as given by the author;  however, comments made by the Working Group on certain shortcomings of reporting, of statistical analysis or of experimental design are given in square brackets.  The nature and extent of impurities/ contaminants in the chemicals being tested are given when available.

## Carcinogenicity studies in animals

The monographs are not intended to cover all reported studies.  Some studies are purposely omitted (a) because they are inadequate, as judged from previously described criteria(23-26) (e.g., too short a duration, too few animals, poor survival);  (b) because they only confirm findings that have already been fully described;  or (c) because they are judged irrelevant for the purpose of the evaluation.  In certain cases, however, such studies are mentioned briefly, particularly when the information is considered to be a useful supplement to other reports or when it is the only data available.  Their inclusion does not, however, imply acceptance of the adequacy of their experimental design and/or of the analysis and interpretation of their results.

Mention is made of all routes of administration by which the compound has been adequately tested and of all species in which relevant tests have been done(5,26).  In most cases, animal strains are given (General characteristics of mouse strains have been reviewed(27)).  Quantitative data are given to indicate the order of magnitude of the effective carcinogenic doses.  In general, the doses and schedules are indicated as they appear in the original paper;  sometimes units have been converted for easier comparison.  Experiments on the carcinogenicity of known metabolites, chemical precursors, analogues and derivatives, and experiments on factors that modify the carcinogenic effect are also reported.

*Other relevant biological data*

Lethality data are given when available, and other data on toxicity are included when considered relevant. The metabolic data are restricted to studies that show the metabolic fate of the chemical in animals and humans, and comparisons of data from animals and humans are made when possible. Information is also given on absorption, distribution, excretion and placental transfer.

*Embryotoxicity and teratogenicity*

Data on teratogenicity from studies in experimental animals and from observations in humans are also included. There appears to be no causal relationship between teratogenicity(28) and carcinogenicity, but chemicals often have both properties. Evidence of teratogenicity suggests transplacental transfer, which is a prerequisite for transplacental carcinogenesis.

*Indirect tests (mutagenicity and other short-term tests)*

Data from indirect tests are also included. Since most of these tests have the advantage of taking less time and being less expensive than mammalian carcinogenicity studies, they are generally known as 'short-term' tests. They comprise assay procedures which rely on the induction of biological and biochemical effects in *in vivo* and/or *in vitro* systems. The end-point of the majority of these tests is the production not of neoplasms in animals but of changes at the molecular, cellular or multicellular level: these include the induction of DNA damage and repair, mutagenesis in bacteria and other organisms, transformation of mammalian cells in culture, and other systems.

The short-term tests are proposed for use (a) in predicting potential carcinogenicity in the absence of carcinogenicity data in animals, (b) as a contribution in deciding which chemicals should be tested in animals, (c) in identifying active fractions of complex mixtures containing carcinogens, (d) for recognizing active metabolites of known carcinogens in human and/or animal body fluids and (e) to help elucidate mechanisms of carcinogenesis.

Although the theory that cancer is induced as a result of somatic mutation suggests that agents which damage DNA *in vivo* may be carcinogens, the precise relevance of short-term tests to the mechanism by which cancer is induced is not known. Predictions of potential carcinogenicity are currently based on correlations between responses in short-term tests and data from animal carcinogenicity and/or human epidemiological studies. This approach is limited because the number of chemicals known to be carcinogenic in humans is insufficient to provide a basis for validation, and most validation studies involve chemicals that have been evaluated for carcinogenicity only in animals. The selection of chemicals is in turn limited to those classes for which data on carcinogenicity are available. The results of validation studies could be strongly influenced by such selection of chemicals and by the proportion of carcinogens in the series of chemicals tested; this should be kept in mind when evaluating the predictivity of a particular test. The usefulness of any test is reflected by its ability to classify carcinogens and noncarcinogens, using the animal data as a standard; however, animal tests may not always provide a perfect standard. The attainable level of correlation between short-term tests and animal bioassays is still under investigation.

Since many chemicals require metabolism to an active form, tests that do not take this into account may fail to detect certain potential carcinogens. The metabolic activation systems used in short-term tests (e.g., the cell-free systems used in bacterial tests) are meant to approximate the metabolic capacity of the whole organism. Each test has its advantages and limitations; thus, more confidence can be placed in the conclusions when negative or positive results for a chemical are confirmed in several such test systems. Deficiencies in metabolic competence may lead to misclassification of chemicals, which means that not all tests are suitable for assessing the potential carcinogenicity of all classes of compounds.

The present state of knowledge does not permit the selection of a specific test(s) as the most appropriate for identifying potential carcinogenicity. Before the results of a particular test can be considered to be fully acceptable for predicting potential carcinogenicity, certain criteria should be met: (a) the test should have been validated with respect to known animal carcinogens and found to have a high capacity for discriminating between carcinogens and noncarcinogens, and (b), when possible, a structurally related carcinogen(s) and noncarcinogen(s) should have been tested simultaneously with the chemical in question. The results should have been reproduced in different laboratories, and a prediction of carcinogenicity should have been confirmed in additional test systems. Confidence in positive results is increased if a mechanism of action can be deduced and if appropriate dose-response data are available. For optimum usefulness, data on purity must be given.

The short-term tests in current use that have been the most extensively validated are the *Salmonella typhimurium* plate-incorporation assay(29-33), the X-linked recessive lethal test in *Drosophila melanogaster*(34), unscheduled DNA synthesis(35) and *in vitro* transformation(33,36). Each is compatible with current concepts of the possible mechanism(s) of carcinogenesis.

An adequate assessment of the genetic activity of a chemical depends on data from a wide range of test systems. The monographs include, therefore, data not only from those already mentioned, but also on the induction of point mutations in other systems(37-42), on structural(43) and numerical chromosome aberrations, including dominant lethal effects(44), on mitotic recombination in fungi(37) and on sister chromatid exchanges(45-46).

The existence of a correlation between quantitative aspects of mutagenic and carcinogenic activity has been suggested(5,44-50), but it is not sufficiently well established to allow general use.

Further information about mutagenicity and other short-term tests is given in references 45-53.

*Case reports and epidemiological studies*

Observations in humans are summarized in this section.

## Summary of Data Reported and Evaluation (Section 4)

Section 4 summarizes the relevant data from animals and humans and gives the critical views of the Working Group on those data.

*Experimental data*

Data relevant to the evaluation of the carcinogenicity of a chemical in animals are summarized in this section. Results from validated mutagenicity and other short-term tests are reported if the Working Group considered the data to be relevant. Dose-response data are given when available. An assessment of the carcinogenicity of the chemical in animals is made on the basis of all of the available data.

The animal species mentioned are those in which the carcinogenicity of the substance was clearly demonstrated. The route of administration used in experimental animals that is similar to the possible human exposure is given particular mention. Tumour sites are also indicated. If the substance has produced tumours after prenatal exposure or in single-dose experiments, this is indicated.

*Human data*

Case reports and epidemiological studies that are considered to be pertinent to an assessment of human carcinogenicity are described. Human exposure to the chemical is summarized on the basis of data on production, use and occurrence. Other biological data which are considered to be relevant are also mentioned. An assessment of the carcinogenicity of the chemical in humans is made on the basis of all of the available evidence.

*Evaluation*

This section comprises the overall evaluation by the Working Group of the carcinogenic risk of the chemical to humans. All of the data in the monograph, and particularly the summarized information on experimental and human data, are considered in order to make this evaluation.

References

1.   IARC (1977)   IARC Monograph Programme on the Evaluation of the
     Carcinogenic Risk of Chemicals to Humans.   Preamble.
     IARC intern. tech. Rep. No. 77/002

2.   IARC (1978)   Chemicals with *sufficient evidence* of carcinogenicity
     in experimental animals - *IARC Monographs* volumes 1-17.
     IARC intern. tech. Rep. No. 78/003

3.   WHO (1961)   Fifth Report of the Joint FAO/WHO Expert Committee on
     Food Additives.   Evaluation of carcinogenic hazard of food addi-
     tives.   WHO tech. Rep. Ser., No. 220, pp. 5, 18, 19

4.   WHO (1969)   Report of a WHO Scientific Group.   Principles for the
     testing and evaluation of drugs for carcinogenicity.   WHO tech.
     Rep. Ser., No. 426, pp. 19, 21, 22

5.   WHO (1974)   Report of a WHO Scientific Group.   Assessment of the
     carcinogenicity and mutagenicity of chemicals.   WHO tech. Rep.
     Ser., No. 546

6.   WHO (1964)   Report of a WHO Expert Committee.   Prevention of cancer.
     WHO tech. Rep. Ser., No. 276, pp. 29, 30

7.   IARC (1972-1978)   IARC Monographs on the Evaluation of the
     Carcinogenic Risk of Chemicals to Humans, Volumes 1-18, Lyon,
     France

     Volume 1 (1972)   Some Inorganic Substances, Chlorinated Hydrocarbons,
     Aromatic Amines, *N*-Nitroso Compounds and Natural Products
     (19 monographs), 184 pages

     Volume 2 (1973)   Some Inorganic and Organometallic Compounds
     (7 monographs), 181 pages

     Volume 3 (1973)   Certain Polycyclic Aromatic Hydrocarbons and
     Heterocyclic Compounds (17 monographs), 271 pages

     Volume 4 (1974)   Some Aromatic Amines, Hydrazine and Related
     Substances, *N*-Nitroso Compounds and Miscellaneous Alkylating
     Agents (28 monographs), 286 pages

     Volume 5 (1974)   Some Organochlorine Pesticides (12 monographs),
     241 pages

     Volume 6 (1974)   Sex Hormones (15 monographs), 243 pages

     Volume 7 (1974)   Some Anti-thyroid and Related Substances,
     Nitrofurans and Industrial Chemicals (23 monographs), 326 pages

Volume 8 (1975)  Some Aromatic Azo Compounds (32 monographs),
357 pages

Volume 9 (1975)  Some Aziridines, *N*-, *S*- and *O*-Mustards and
Selenium (24 monographs), 268 pages

Volume 10 (1976)  Some Naturally Occurring Substances
(32 monographs), 353 pages

Volume 11 (1976)  Cadmium, Nickel, Some Epoxides, Miscellaneous
Industrial Chemicals and General Considerations on Volatile
Anaesthetics (24 monographs), 306 pages

Volume 12 (1976)  Some Carbamates, Thiocarbamates and Carbazides
(24 monographs), 282 pages

Volume 13 (1977)  Some Miscellaneous Pharmaceutical Substances
(17 monographs), 255 pages

Volume 14 (1977)  Asbestos (1 monograph), 106 pages

Volume 15 (1977)  Some Fumigants, the Herbicides 2,4-D and
2,4,5-T, Chlorinated Dibenzodioxins and Miscellaneous
Industrial Chemicals (18 monographs), 354 pages

Volume 16 (1978)  Some Aromatic Amines and Related Nitro Compounds -
Hair Dyes, Colouring Agents and Miscellaneous Industrial
Chemicals (32 monographs), 400 pages

Volume 17 (1978)  Some *N*-Nitroso Compounds (17 monographs),
365 pages

Volume 18 (1978)  Polychlorinated Biphenyls and Polybrominated
Biphenyls (2 monographs), 140 pages

Volume 19 (1979)  Some Monomers, Plastics and Synthetic Elastomers,
and Acrolein (17 monographs), 513 pages

8.  IARC (1973-1978)  Information Bulletin on the Survey of Chemicals
Being Tested for Carcinogenicity, Numbers 1-7, Lyon, France

Number 1 (1973) 52 pages
Number 2 (1973) 77 pages
Number 3 (1974) 67 pages
Number 4 (1974) 97 pages
Number 5 (1975) 88 pages
Number 6 (1976) 360 pages
Number 7 (1978) 460 pages

9.   PHS 149 (1951-1976)  Public Health Service Publication No. 149,
     Survey of Compounds which have been Tested for Carcinogenic
     Activity, Washington DC, US Government Printing Office

     1951  Hartwell, J.L., 2nd ed., Literature up to 1947 on 1329
           compounds, 583 pages

     1957  Shubik, P. & Hartwell, J.L., Supplement 1, Literature for
           the years 1948-1953 on 981 compounds, 388 pages

     1969  Shubik, P. & Hartwell, J.L., edited by Peters, J.A.,
           Supplement 2, Literature for the years 1954-1960 on 1048
           compounds, 655 pages

     1971  National Cancer Institute, Literature for the years
           1968-1969 on 882 compounds, 653 pages

     1973  National Cancer Institute, Literature for the years
           1961-1967 on 1632 compounds, 2343 pages

     1974  National Cancer Institute, Literature for the years
           1970-1971 on 750 compounds, 1667 pages

     1976  National Cancer Institute, Literature for the years
           1972-1973 on 966 compounds, 1638 pages

10.  Pike, M.C. & Roe, F.J.C. (1963)  An actuarial method of analysis
     of an experiment in two-stage carcinogenesis. Br. J. Cancer,
     17, 605-610

11.  Miller, E.C. & Miller, J.A. (1966)  Mechanisms of chemical carcino-
     genesis: nature of proximate carcinogens and interactions with
     macromolecules. Pharmacol. Rev., 18, 805-838

12.  Miller, J.A. (1970)  Carcinogenesis by chemicals: an overview –
     G.H.A. Clowes Memorial Lecture. Cancer Res., 30, 559-576

13.  Miller, J.A. & Miller, E.C. (1976)  The metabolic activation of
     chemical carcinogens to reactive electrophiles. In:
     Yuhas, J.M., Tennant, R.W. & Reagon, J.D., eds, Biology of
     Radiation Carcinogenesis, New York, Raven Press

14.  Peto, R. (1974)  Guidelines on the analysis of tumours rates and
     death rates in experimental animals. Br. J. Cancer, 29, 101-105

15.  Peto, R. (1975)  Letter to the editor. Br. J. Cancer, 31, 697-699

16.  Hoel, D.G. & Walburg, H.E., Jr (1972)  Statistical analysis of
     survival experiments. J. natl Cancer Inst., 49, 361-372

17.   Tomatis, L. (1977)  The value of long-term testing for the implemen-
      tation of primary prevention. In:  Hiatt, H.H., Watson, J.D.
      & Winsten, J.A., eds, Origins of Human Cancer, Book C, Cold
      Spring Harbour, N.Y., Cold Spring Harbor Laboratory, pp. 1339-
      1357

18.   IARC (1977)  Annual Report 1977, Lyon, International Agency for
      Research on Cancer, p. 94

19.   Tomatis, L., Agthe, C., Bartsch, H., Huff, J., Montesano, R.,
      Saracci, R., Walker, E. & Wilbourn, J. (1978) Evaluation of
      the carcinogenicity of chemicals:  a review of the IARC Monograph
      Programme, 1971-1977. Cancer Res., 38, 877-885

20.   Rall, D.P. (1977)  Species differences in carcinogenesis testing.
      In:  Hiatt, H.H., Watson, J.D. & Winsten, J.A., eds, Origins
      of Human Cancer, Book C, Cold Spring Harbor, N.Y., Cold Spring
      Harbor Laboratory, pp. 1383-1390

21.   National Academy of Sciences (NAS) (1975)  Contemporary Pest Control
      Practices and Prospects:  the Report of the Executive Committee,
      Washington DC

22.   Chemical Abstracts Service (1978)  Chemical Abstracts Ninth Collective
      Index (9CI), 1972-1976, Vols 76-85, Columbus, Ohio

23.   WHO (1958)  Second Report of the Joint FAO/WHO Expert Committee on
      Food Additives. Procedures for the testing of intentional food
      additives to establish their safety and use. WHO tech. Rep.
      Ser., No. 144

24.   WHO (1967)  Scientific Group. Procedures for investigating inten-
      tional and unintentional food additives. WHO tech. Rep. Ser.,
      No. 348

25.   Berenblum, I., ed. (1969)  Carcinogenicity testing. UICC tech. Rep.
      Ser., 2

26.   Sontag, J.M., Page, N.P. & Saffiotti, U. (1976)  Guidelines for
      carcinogen bioassay in small rodents. Natl Cancer Inst.
      Carcinog. tech. Rep. Ser., No. 1

27.   Committee on Standardized Genetic Nomenclature for Mice (1972)
      Standardized nomenclature for inbred strains of mice. Fifth
      listing. Cancer Res., 32, 1609-1646

28.   Wilson, J.G. & Fraser, F.C. (1977)  Handbook of Teratology, New York,
      Plenum Press

29.   Ames, B.N., Durston, W.E., Yamasaki, E. & Lee, F.D. (1973)  Carcino-
      gens are mutagens:  a simple test system combining liver homo-
      genates for activation and bacteria for detection.  Proc. natl
      Acad. Sci. (Wash.), 70, 2281-2285

30.   McCann, J., Choi, E., Yamasaki, E. & Ames, B.N. (1975)  Detection
      of carcinogens as mutagens in the Salmonella/microsome test:
      assay of 300 chemicals.  Proc. natl Acad. Sci. (Wash.), 72,
      5135-5139

31.   McCann, J. & Ames, B.N. (1976)  Detection of carcinogens as mutagens
      in the Salmonella/microsome test:  assay of 300 chemicals:
      discussion.  Proc. natl Acad. Sci. (Wash.), 73, 950-954

32.   Sugimura, T., Sato, S., Nagao, M., Yahagi, T., Matsushima, T.,
      Seino, Y., Takeuchi, M. & Kawachi, T. (1977)  Overlapping of
      carcinogens and mutagens.  In: Magee, P.N., Takayama, S.,
      Sugimura, T. & Matsushima, T., eds, Fundamentals in Cancer
      Prevention, Baltimore, University Park Press, pp. 191-215

33.   Purchase, I.F.M., Longstaff, E., Ashby, J., Styles, J.A.,
      Anderson, D., Lefevre, P.A. & Westwood, F.R. (1976)  Evaluation
      of six short term tests for detecting organic chemical carcino-
      gens and recommendations for their use.  Nature (Lond.), 264,
      624-627

34.   Vogel, E. & Sobels, F.H. (1976)  The function of Drosophila in
      genetic toxicology testing.  In: Hollaender, A., ed.,
      Chemical Mutagens:  Principles and Methods for Their Detection,
      Vol. 4, New York, Plenum Press, pp. 93-142

35.   San, R.H.C. & Stich, H.F. (1975)  DNA repair synthesis of cultured
      human cells as a rapid bioassay for chemical carcinogens.
      Int. J. Cancer, 16, 284-291

36.   Pienta, R.J., Poiley, J.A. & Lebherz, W.B. (1977)  Morphological
      transformation of early passage golden Syrian hamster embryo
      cells derived from cryopreserved primary cultures as a reliable
      in vitro bioassay for identifying diverse carcinogens.  Int. J.
      Cancer, 19, 642-655

37.   Zimmermann, F.K. (1975)  Procedures used in the induction of mitotic
      recombination and mutation in the yeast Saccharomyces cerevisiae.
      Mutat. Res., 31, 71-86

38.   Ong, T.-M. & de Serres, F.J. (1972)  Mutagenicity of chemical
      carcinogens in Neurospora crassa.  Cancer Res., 32, 1890-1893

39.  Huberman, E. & Sachs, L. (1976)  Mutability of different genetic
     loci in mammalian cells by metabolically activated carcinogenic
     polycyclic hydrocarbons. Proc. natl Acad. Sci. (Wash.), 73,
     188-192

40.  Krahn, D.F. & Heidelburger, C. (1977)  Liver homogenate-mediated
     mutagenesis in Chinese hamster V79 cells by polycyclic aromatic
     hydrocarbons and aflatoxins. Mutat. Res., 46, 27-44

41.  Kuroki, T., Drevon, C. & Montesano, R. (1977)  Microsome-mediated
     mutagenesis in V79 Chinese hamster cells by various nitrosamines.
     Cancer Res., 37, 1044-1050

42.  Searle, A.G. (1975)  The specific locus test in the mouse. Mutat.
     Res., 31, 277-290

43.  Evans, H.J. & O'Riordan, M.L. (1975)  Human peripheral blood lympho-
     cytes for the analysis of chromosome aberrations in mutagen
     tests. Mutat. Res., 31, 135-148

44.  Epstein, S.S., Arnold, E., Andrea, J., Bass, W. & Bishop, Y. (1972)
     Detection of chemical mutagens by the dominant lethal assay in
     the mouse. Toxicol. appl. Pharmacol., 23, 288-325

45.  Perry, P. & Evans, H.J. (1975)  Cytological detection of mutagen-
     carcinogen exposure by sister chromatid exchanges. Nature
     (Lond.), 258, 121-125

46.  Stetka, D.G. & Wolff, S. (1976)  Sister chromatid exchanges as an
     assay for genetic damage induced by mutagen-carcinogens. I.
     In vivo test for compounds requiring metabolic activation.
     Mutat. Res., 41, 333-342

47.  Bartsch, H. & Grover, P.L. (1976)  Chemical carcinogenesis and muta-
     genesis. In: Symington, T. & Carter, R.L., eds, Scientific
     Foundations of Oncology, Vol. IX, Chemical Carcinogenesis,
     London, Heinemann Medical Books Ltd, pp. 334-342

48.  Hollaender, A., ed. (1971a,b, 1973, 1976)  Chemical Mutagens:
     Principles and Methods for Their Detection, Vols 1-4, New York,
     Plenum Press

49.  Montesano, R. & Tomatis, L., eds (1974)  Chemical Carcinogenesis
     Essays, Lyon (IARC Scientific Publications No. 10)

50.  Ramel, C., ed. (1973)  Evaluation of genetic risk of environmental
     chemicals:  report of a symposium held at Skokloster, Sweden,
     1972. Ambio Spec. Rep., No. 3

51.   Stoltz, D.R., Poirier, L.A., Irving, C.C., Stich, H.F.,
        Weisburger, J.H. & Grice, H.C. (1974) Evaluation of short-term
        tests for carcinogenicity. Toxicol. appl. Pharmacol., 29,
        157-180

52.   Montesano, R., Bartsch, H. & Tomatis, L., eds (1976) Screening
        Tests in Chemical Carcinogenesis, Lyon (IARC Scientific
        Publications No. 12)

53.   Committee 17 (1976) Environmental mutagenic hazards. Science, 187,
        503-514

In this nineteenth volume of *IARC Monographs*, some monomers, plastics and synthetic elastomers and acrolein have been evaluated. Acrolein is included since it is used in the production of acrylic acid and its esters; it may also be evolved from certain plastics upon heating. Styrene oxide is also included, since it is a metabolite of styrene and is used in curing epoxy resins.

The Working Group considered draft monographs on adipic acid, hexa-methylenediamine and nylon 6/6; dimethylterephthalate, terephthalic acid and polyethylene terephthalate; isoprene and polyisoprene; methacrylic acid; and vinylidene fluoride and polyvinylidene fluoride. However, finalized monographs on these substances are not included in this volume, since no adequate biological data, particularly with respect to carcino-genicity, were available for evaluation. They will be considered at a future date should the results of carcinogenicity studies become available. Testing of the monomers, in particular, is recommended.

A monograph has already been published on styrene oxide, in volume 11 of the *IARC Monographs* (IARC, 1976), and this has been updated. A previous monograph on vinyl chloride, in volume 7 (IARC, 1974), which included an appendix on the physical and chemical properties, production, use, occur-rence and analysis of polyvinyl chloride and vinyl chloride-vinyl acetate copolymers, has also been updated. In this new monograph, carcinogenicity data on the polymer and copolymers have also been evaluated.

It was impossible in these monographs to give complete listings of trade names for polymeric products. Such lists are in a constant state of change, since individual producers may have a number of commercial designations for the same product, and new products are introduced rapidly as old ones are phased out. The overall product line is usually designated by a single name, which is followed by a sequence of numbers and/or letters which indicate the properties of the specific product. The basic name may apply to all polymer products of a single kind (e.g., polyethylene), but it may also be used for related copolymers (e.g., polyethylene-polypropyl-ene copolymers) or polymers prepared from monomer homologues (e.g., poly-propylene).

In general, polymeric materials are composed of a mixture of molecules of similar, but not identical, molecular weight; the molecular weights of such materials are therefore expressed in ranges. The distri-bution of molecular weights may vary greatly from product to product and is a function of particular reaction conditions.

A glossary of technical terms relating to the manufacture of plastics is given in Table 1.

TABLE 1

Glossary of technical terms relating to
the manufacture of plastics

ACRYLIC FIBRE         :    A manufactured fibre in which the fibre-forming substance is any
                           long-chain, synthetic polymer composed of at least 85% by weight
                           acrylonitrile units

ADDITION POLYMER      :    A polymer produced by a particular joining of molecules in which
                           no elements or molecules such as water are obtained as byproducts

BLOCK COPOLYMER       :    A copolymer whose molecules consist of two or more separate
                           chain sequences, each of which has its own properties

COMONOMER             :    One of the monomeric constituents of a copolymer

CONDENSATION          :    A polymer produced by a union between atoms in the same or different
   POLYMER                 molecules with the elimination of a simple molecule such as water or
                           hydrogen chloride

COPOLYMER             :    A product of the polymerization of two or more different monomeric
                           substances

ELASTOMER             :    A polymer characterized by elastic properties, e.g., rubber

EMULSION              :    A process in which a monomer is emulsified in water and polymerized
   POLYMERIZATION          to form an emulsion of polymer in water

FOAM                  :    A plastic or rubber of cellular structure

HOMOPOLYMER           :    A polymer containing only repeating units of a single monomer

LATEX                 :    An aqueous emulsion of an elastomer or plastic resin

MODACRYLIC FIBRE      :    A manufactured fibre in which the fibre-forming substance is any
                           long-chain synthetic polymer composed of less than 85%, but at
                           least 35%, by weight acrylonitrile units

MONOMER               :    The simple, unpolymerized form of a chemical compound, with a
                           relatively low molecular weight

OLIGOMER              :    A low-molecular-weight polymer consisting of a comparatively small
                           number (e.g., 30 to 40) of repeating homologous units and with
                           physical characteristics which differ greatly from those of a
                           corresponding long-chain polymer of high molecular weight

PLASTIC               :    Any of a large group of materials of high molecular weight that
                           contains as the essential ingredient a synthetic organic substance
                           made by polymerization or condensation and that can be moulded,
                           cast or extruded

POLYMER               :    A natural or synthetic chemical compound or mixture of compounds
                           formed by polymerization and consisting essentially of repeating
                           structural units

SARAN                 :    A material composed of at least 80% by weight vinylidene chloride
                           units

TERPOLYMER            :    A product formed by the polymerization of three different
                           monomeric substances

The Working Group noted that the annual production of monomers and polymers over the past 30 years has greatly augmented, and increasing numbers of people are exposed to these compounds (The compounds evaluated in this volume are listed in Table 2, with the date of their first commercial production and an estimate of the latest worldwide annual production figures). It is evident, however, that no corresponding increase in the amount of toxicological testing on these compounds occurred over the same period, and for many monomers there is a notable lack of carcinogenicity studies. In the setting of priorities for toxicological testing, production data and the extent and intensity of human exposure should obviously be taken into consideration.

Plastic materials have an extremely wide range of uses, so that there is a strong likelihood of both occupational and general human exposure through air, water and food. In addition, there is widespread direct physical contact from manufactured products, such as packaging, including that of foods and beverages;  consumer products (e.g., clothing, shoes, houseware, appliances, furniture, containers, household furnishings, toys, sporting goods);  construction materials;  transport applications (e.g., in passenger cars, trains, aeroplanes and ships for such items as seating, padding, coatings, carpeting, miscellaneous mouldings and furniture); textile fibres for clothing and furnishings;  rubber goods;  adhesives; insulation;  electronic and electrical products;  piping;  fumigants; paints;  water treatment;  and in various medical applications, as listed in Table 3.

Originally, polymeric materials were assumed to be biologically inert. This is one of the major reasons why these materials are used extensively in a broad spectrum of applications such as medical devices, pharmaceutical products, packaging and in food products.

It must be borne in mind, however, that the biological effects of the polymer may include those of the monomer, of low-molecular-weight oligomers, or of adsorbed and absorbed substances. Polymers may also contain a variety of other substances, such as plasticizers, stabilizers, curing agents and catalysts.

In comparison with monomers, less is known of the metabolism and/or degradation of polymers;  however, there may be several pathways:  for example, if metabolism occurs, it may take place partly *via* mechanisms analogous to those of the monomer;  or the various additives may contribute to other degradative pathways or rates of degradation. Elucidation of these possibilities would be helpful in understanding the biological reactivities of these materials.

A polymeric material may present potential carcinogenic liabilities to animals and humans because (1) a carcinogenic agent may be present in the material, (2) a carcinogenic agent may be generated through degradation of the polymer, (3) a tumour may develop only as a result of physical effects, and (4) other chemicals may be concentrated in the polymer.

TABLE 2

| Compound | Year of first commercial production (and country) | Latest annual world production[a] |
|---|---|---|
| Acrylic acid | 1954 (USA) | 336.5 million kg |
| Methyl acrylate | 1944 (USA) | 48.4 million kg |
| Ethyl acrylate | 1944 (USA) | 600 million kg (1976) |
| Polyacrylic acid and salts | early 1950's (USA) | 11.0 million kg |
| Acrylic resins | early 1930's (USA) | At least 200 million kg |
| Acrylonitrile | 1940 (USA) | 2400 million kg (1976) |
| Acrylic and modacrylic fibres | 1948-50 (USA) | 1700-1800 million kg (1976) |
| Acrylonitrile-butadiene-styrene copolymers | late 1940's (USA) | 1000 million kg (1976) |
| Styrene-acrylonitrile copolymers | 1947 (USA) | 180 million kg (1976) |
| Caprolactam | 1955 (USA) | 2033 million kg |
| Nylon 6 | 1941 (Germany) | 3420 million kg |
| Chloroprene | Unknown | 300 million kg (1977) |
| Polychloroprene | 1932 (USA) | 300 million kg (1977) |
| Ethylene | 1922 (USA) | 28 465 million kg (1976) |
| Low-density polyethylene | 1941 (USA) | 8281 million kg |
| High-density polyethylene | 1941 (USA) | 4000 million kg (1977) |
| Methyl methacrylate | 1937 (USA) | 582 million kg |
| Propylene | ~1925 (USA) | 19 619 million kg (15 000 for use in chemicals) (1976) |
| Polypropylene | 1958 (USA) | 3500 million kg (1976) |
| Styrene | 1938 (USA) | 7000 million kg (1977) |
| Polystyrene | ~1938 (USA) | 4200 million kg (1976) |
| Styrene-butadiene copolymers | 1942 (USA) | 2791 million kg |
| Styrene oxide | 1964 (Japan) | ~2.5 million kg |

---

[a]A year is given only when an estimate of total world production was available.

Table 2 - continued

| Compound | Year of first commercial production (and country) | Latest annual world production[a] |
|---|---|---|
| Tetrafluoroethylene | 1953 (Japan) | 15-20 million kg (1977) |
| Polytetrafluoroethylene | 1953 (Japan) | 15-20 million kg (1977) |
| 2,4- and 2,6-Toluene diisocyanates | late 1930's (Germany) | 660 million kg (1976) |
| 1,5-Naphthalane diisocyanate | 1967 (Japan) | At least 140 thousand kg |
| 4,4'-Methylenediphenyl diisocyanate and polymethylene polyphenyl isocyanate | 1953 (USA) | At least 180 million kg |
| Polyurethane foams | 1952 (FRG) | 843 million kg |
| Vinyl acetate | 1928 (USA) | 1384 million kg |
| Polyvinyl acetate | 1929 (USA) | 900 million kg (1977) |
| Polyvinyl alcohol | 1920's (Germany) | 2505 million kg |
| Vinyl bromide | 1968 (USA) | Unknown |
| Vinyl chloride | ~1927 (USA) | 7786 million kg |
| Polyvinyl chloride | 1933 | 6854 million kg |
| Vinyl chloride-vinyl acetate copolymers | 1934 | 436 million kg |
| Vinylidene chloride | 1940 (USA) | 148.1 million kg |
| Vinylidene chloride-vinyl chloride copolymers | ~1930's (USA) | 99.9 million kg |
| N-Vinyl-2-pyrrolidone | 1955 (USA) | ) At least 716 thousand kg |
| Polyvinyl pyrrolidone | 1955 (USA) | ) |
| Acrolein | 1955 (USA) | 100-120 million kg (1977) |

---

[a] A year is given only when an estimate of total world production was available.

TABLE 3

Plastic devices used medically[a]

| Device | Examples |
|--------|----------|
| Permanent implants | Heart valves, various vascular grafts, orthopaedic implants, implants for cosmetic reconstruction, artificial organs, etc. |
| Implants in contact with mucosal tissue | Artificial eyes, contact lenses, dentures, intrauterine devices, certain types of catheters |
| Corrective, protective and supportive devices | Splints, braces, films, protective clothing, etc. |
| Collection and administration devices | Blood transfusion sets, various types of catheters, dialysis units, hypodermic devices, other injection devices, etc. |
| Storage devices | Bags or other containers for blood, blood products, drug products, nutritional products, diagnostic agents, etc. |

[a]From Autian & Lawrence (1972)

Unreacted monomers and other additives present in polymeric material can migrate to a food or beverage when the material is used as a container or packaging material. A similar situation may occur when the material is used as a drug container or in various medical and dental applications, such as collection, storage and/or administration devices. In addition, if the material is used as a medical or dental implant, a carcinogenic agent may diffuse from the plastic to surrounding tissues over long periods.

Degradation of a polymer may take place when the material is placed in long contact with tissues, such as when it is implanted into animals and humans; if a carcinogenic chemical moiety is released, the animal or human could be placed at risk.

Since the publication of studies by Turner (1941) and by Oppenheimer et al. (1948), a large number of man-made polymeric materials have been investigated in animals for their carcinogenic properties. Reviews on this subject have been published by Bischoff & Bryson (1964), by Brand et al. (1975), by Bryson & Bischoff (1969) and by Vasiliev et al. (1962). In the majority of these studies, the polymeric material, in one or more forms, was implanted primarily into subcutaneous tissue, although other

routes such as intraperitoneal, intramuscular and intrauterine implantation
have been used.  Many months after implantation, tumours appeared at the
site;  however, the incidence of tumours at sites of implants did not
seem to be related to the nature or to the specific chemical structure of
the test sample.  In the large majority of cases, distant tumours were not
observed.

Tumours usually develop around or near an implant with a frequency
that is dependent on several factors:  (1) the size of the implant (large
implants generally produce more sarcomas than small ones);  (2) their
form (discs are reported to be among the most efficient);  (3) their
smoothness (those with rough surfaces are less carcinogenic than those
with smooth surfaces);  (4) the continuity of the surface area (the larger
the holes or pores in the implant, the lower the tumour incidence);  (5),
for certain materials, their thickness (thicker implants produce more
sarcomas);  and (6) the length of time the implant remains in the tissue.
The same material that produces tumours as a film or sheet will, for the
most part, produce fewer or no tumours when implanted as a powder, a thread
or a porous material.  There are, however, notable exceptions to each of
these conditions;  and the genetic background of the host also influences
the frequency of tumour production by identical implants.

Tumours induced by plastics usually have a long average latent period,
approaching half to two-thirds of the lifespan of experimental animals.
Histologically, most of the tumours induced are sarcomas of various types.

An important problem in these studies is finding proper controls,
since completely inert materials may not exist, and nearly all the compounds
tested have given rise to tumours at the site of implantation when their
size was appropriate.

Bischoff & Bryson (1964), in a critical analysis of their own work
as well as that of other investigators, used the term 'solid state'
carcinogenesis for the induction of tumours by solid materials at the
site of their implantation in experimental animals.

When solid materials which have an uninterrupted surface and meet
the critical size requirement are implanted subcutaneously into rodents,
they lead to a fibrous, poorly cellular capsule.  Oppenheimer *et al.* (1953)
described the consecutive pathological changes that take place around the
implant which lead to precancerous lesions and finally to sarcomas.  If the
implant was removed before 6 months and the animals maintained until old
age or death, tumours generally did not develop at the sites in which the
material had been implanted.  On the other hand, if the implant was removed
after 6 months, tumours occurred many months after the implants had been
removed (Oppenheimer *et al.*, 1958).

Brand *et al.* (1967) implanted films of a vinyl chloride-vinyl acetate
copolymer into the subcutaneous tissues of mice and then transplanted the
film and the surrounding tissue capsule after various intervals.

Tumours developed only when transplantation was carried out 6 or more months after the initial insertion of the film. In addition, tumours that developed from these transplants after a latent period of 8 or more months did so only from the film transplants, whereas tumours with a latent period of 1 month developed from both films and tissue capsules. These findings indicate that the tumour cells are initially firmly attached to the films and that only at a later stage are they present in the surrounding capsule tissue.

On the basis of present information, it seems possible that man-made polymeric materials act by a combination of physical and chemical carcinogenesis; the design of past experiments has not permitted definitive conclusions.

Epidemiological aspects

The rapidly increasing exploitation of man-made materials on a massive scale often involves exposure to many agents; therefore, the carrying out and interpretation of epidemiological studies specific to one agent is most difficult. This is particularly true for the monomers, polymers and copolymers covered in this volume.

For at least one of these (vinyl chloride) there is unequivocal evidence of carcinogenicity in humans; and for another (acrylonitrile) there is evidence of probable carcinogenicity; for a third (chloroprene) a suspicion of carcinogenicity in humans has been raised. However, for the many remaining materials included in this volume there is a paucity or complete absence of human studies bearing on carcinogenesis.

Decisions about the use of plastic and related materials in various medical applications, such as prosthetic devices, dental materials, catheters, administration devices and containers for drugs and biological fluids, require careful consideration of information on both toxicology and carcinogenicity. In the United States alone, hundreds of thousands of prosthetic devices are implanted annually. It is recommended that case reports be made when tumours develop in a way, or at a site, which raises the suspicion of induction by the material used. The possibility of epidemiological assessment of the presence or absence of hazard should also receive attention, although the follow-up periods since first use of some of the materials under consideration may not yet be of long enough duration.

For a number of compounds in these monographs for which no epidemiological data are available, chemical and biological reactivity characteristics, positive mutagenicity tests, and *limited evidence* of carcinogenicity from animal experiments, taken together, indicate that the compound may possess carcinogenic activity. In these cases, the initiation of additional experimental studies and of epidemiological investigations is essential, since the possibility that these compounds are also carcinogenic to humans cannot be excluded.

Where the Working Group has proposed that studies of exposed groups should be conducted, it is important that this not be construed solely to refer to observations extending into the future. Many of the compounds have been in use for two or three decades, so that case identification and specification of appropriate cohorts may already be possible. The Working Group felt that it was important that all possible steps be taken to carry out such retrospective enquiries, so that risk evaluation may be made as rapidly as possible, thus leading to appropriate preventive decisions.

The fact that most plastics and synthetic elastomers are disposed of by incineration and landfill activities raises serious questions as to the nature of possible adverse effects on humans resulting from such exposures.

## References

Autian, J. & Lawrence, W.H. (1972)  Visit to a laboratory. The Materials Science Toxicology Laboratories, University of Tennessee. Med. Res. Eng., September-October, 23-27

Bischoff, F. & Bryson, G. (1964)  Carcinogenesis through solid state surfaces. Prog. exp. Tumour Res., 5, 85-133

Brand, K.G., Buoen, L.C. & Brand, I. (1967)  Premalignant cells in tumorigenesis induced by plastic film. Nature (Lond.), 213, 810

Brand, K.G., Buoen, L.C., Johnson, K.H. & Brand, I. (1975)  Etiological factors, stages, and the role of the foreign body in foreign body tumorigenesis: a review. Cancer Res., 35, 279-286

Bryson, G. & Bischoff, F. (1969)  The limitations of safety testing. Prog. exp. Tumor Res., 11, 100-133

IARC (1974)  IARC Monographs on the Evaluation of Carcinogenic Risk of Chemicals to Man, 7, Some Anti-thyroid and Related Substances, Nitrofurans and Industrial Chemicals, Lyon, pp. 291-326

IARC (1976)  IARC Monographs on the Evaluation of Carcinogenic Risk of Chemicals to Man, 11, Cadmium, Nickel, Some Epoxides, Miscellaneous Industrial Chemicals and General Considerations on Volatile Anaesthetics, Lyon, pp. 201-208

Oppenheimer, B.S., Oppenheimer, E.T. & Stout, A.P. (1948)  Sarcomas induced in rats by implanting cellophane. Proc. Soc. exp. Biol. (N.Y.), 67, 33-34

Oppenheimer, B.S., Oppenheimer, E.T., Stout, A.P. & Danishefsky, I. (1953) Malignant tumors resulting from embedding plastics in rodents. Science, 118, 305-306

Oppenheimer, B.S., Oppenheimer, E.T., Stout, A.P., Willhite, M. & Danishefsky, I. (1958)  The latent period in carcinogenesis by plastics in rats and its relation to the presarcomatous stage. Cancer, 11, 204-213

Turner, F.C. (1941)  Sarcomas at sites of subcutaneously implanted Bakelite disks in rats. J. natl Cancer Inst., 2, 81-83

Vasiliev, J.M., Olshevskaja, L.V., Raikhlin, N.T. & Ivanova, O.J. (1962) Comparative study of alterations induced by 7,12-dimethylbenz[$a$]-anthracene and polymer films in the subcutaneous connective tissue of rats. J. natl Cancer Inst., 28, 515-559

THE MONOGRAPHS

ACRYLIC ACID, METHYL ACRYLATE, ETHYL ACRYLATE and
POLYACRYLIC ACID

Acrylic acid

## 1. Chemical and Physical Data

### 1.1 Synonyms and trade names

Chem. Abstr. Services Reg. No.: 79-10-7

Chem. Abstr. Name: 2-Propenoic acid

Acroleic acid; ethylenecarboxylic acid; vinylformic acid

### 1.2 Structural and molecular formulae and molecular weight

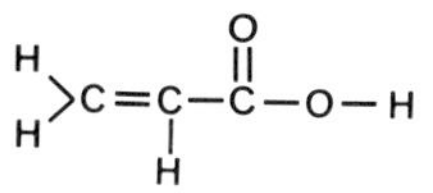

$$\underset{H}{\overset{H}{>}}C=\underset{\underset{H}{|}}{C}-\overset{\overset{O}{\|}}{C}-O-H$$

$C_3H_4O_2$                 Mol. wt: 72.1

### 1.3 Chemical and physical properties of the pure substance

From Weast (1976a), unless otherwise specified

(a) Description: Colourless, fuming, corrosive liquid with an acrid odour (Anon., 1972; Fassett, 1963a; Windholz, 1976a)

(b) Boiling-point: 141.6°C

(c) Melting-point: 13°C

(d) Density: $d_4^{20}$ 1.0511; vapour density, 2.5 (air = 1) (Anon., 1972; Fassett, 1963a)

(e) Refractive index: $n_D^{20}$ 1.4224

(f) Spectroscopy data: $\lambda_{max}$ 252 nm ($E_1^1$ = 13) in methanol; infrared, Raman, nuclear magnetic resonance and mass spectral data have been tabulated (Grasselli & Ritchey, 1975a).

(g) Solubility: Miscible with water, ether and ethanol; moderately soluble in acetone and benzene

(h) Volatility: Vapour pressure is 52 mm at 20°C (Perry & Chilton, 1973a).

(i) Stability: Flash-point (open cup), 54°C (Fassett, 1963a); polymerizes readily in presence of oxygen (Windholz, 1976a)

(j) Reactivity: The glacial acid corrodes iron and steel; reactive at both the carboxylic acid group and the double-bond (Miller, 1964)

(k) Conversion factor: 1 ppm in air = 3 mg/m$^3$

## 1.4 Technical products and impurities

Acrylic acid is commercially available in the US in two grades: (a) a technical grade for esterification and polymerization and (b) a glacial grade for the production of water-soluble resins. A typical commercial glacial acrylic acid contains 98.0% by weight acrylic acid, a maximum of 0.5% by weight water and 0.045-0.055 mg/kg (ppm) of inhibitor (usually hydroquinone monomethyl ether), and is substantially free of suspended matter.

## 2. Production, Use, Occurrence and Analysis

### 2.1 Production and use

#### (a) Production

Acrylic acid was first prepared in 1843 by the oxidation of acrolein (Miller, 1964). Approximately 50% of the acrylic acid made in the US is produced by oxidizing propylene to acrolein, which is then further oxidized to acrylic acid. The other 50% is made by modified Reppe processes involving either acetylene, an alcohol and carbon monoxide (either as gas or in nickel carbonyl form), or acetylene, carbon monoxide and water in the presence of a nickel halide salt.

Acrylic acid is manufactured in Japan by (1) the propylene oxidation process, with acrolein as an intermediate; (2) oxidation of propylene directly to acrylic acid; and (3) hydrolysis of acrylonitrile to acrylamide and conversion to acrylic acid.

Commercial production of acrylic acid in the US was first reported in 1954 (US Tariff Commission, 1955). In 1976, three US companies reported production of 116.5 million kg (US International Trade Commission, 1977a).

US import and export data for acrylic acid are not available; although its derivatives are traded, it is believed that negligible quantities of the acid are imported or exported due to the difficulty in shipping it (e.g., temperature must be controlled) and since almost all acrylic acid is used as acrylates (which are easier to ship).

Production of acrylic acid in the member states of the European Community in 1975 was 150 million kg.

Acrylic acid was first produced commercially in Japan in 1970. In 1976, five companies produced about 70 million kg, of which 3 million kg were exported.

(b) Use

In the US, most acrylic acid is used captively; only 9.5 million kg of the acid were sold in 1975. Approximately 83% was used captively as a precursor of acrylates: 52% for ethyl acrylate and methyl acrylates, 26% for n-butyl and isobutyl acrylates, and 5% for 2-ethylhexyl acrylate. The remaining 17% was used for miscellaneous applications, including the production of water-soluble resins and salts, as a comonomer in acrylic emulsion and solution polymers and in the production of special acrylates.

The largest US market for acrylates is surface coatings, which accounted for about 50% of total acrylate use in 1975; textile applications accounted for approximately 23% of the total use in that year. Ethyl acrylate and n-butyl acrylate were the two major monomers used in both applications. The remaining 27% was used in the production of paper, polishes, acrylic fibres, leather and miscellaneous applications. For more detailed descriptions of the uses of methyl and ethyl acrylates, see p. 55 and p. 59.

The water-soluble resins and salts made from acrylic acid include polyacrylic acid and its salts (usually the sodium salt) and copolymers of acrylamide and acrylic acid. For a detailed description of the uses of polyacrylic acid, see p. 64. Copolymers of acrylamide and acrylic acid are used as dispersants, flocculants, filler-retention aids and dry-strength agents in the manufacture of paper, and as fluid-loss control agents in oil-well drilling muds. Among the specific end uses for these products are paper manufacture (to flocculate solids in paper-mill effluents), recovery and beneficiation of minerals and metal ores (e.g., coal-dust separation), sugar juice flocculation and treatment of potable water and sewage.

Less than 2 million kg acrylic acid are used as comonomer in the production of acrylic emulsion and solution polymers. Small amounts of acrylic acid are commonly used as functional monomer in acrylic emulsion polymers and in thermosetting acrylic solution polymers to provide carboxyl groups. Copolymers of acrylic acid and methyl acrylate are used as thickeners in coatings for rug backings. Acrylic acid is also used as comonomer in ion-exchange resins.

Small amounts of acrylic acid are used as a precursor in the production of special acrylates (e.g., pentaerythritol triacrylate, tetraethylene glycol diacrylate and trimethylolpropane triacrylate). Most special acrylates are used as polymer intermediates to impart specific properties to plastics or resins.

More than 80% of acrylic acid used in the countries of the European Community is for the production of polyacrylates.

In Japan, acrylic acid is used for the production of acrylic esters (90%), as a copolymer with acrylamide (6%) and for the manufacture of the sodium salt of polyacrylic acid (4%). A small amount (less than 500 kg) is used to make polyacrylic acid and other salts.

The US Food and Drug Administration permits the use of acrylic acid polymers and copolymers as components of the following products when they are intended for use in contact with food: (1) resinous and polymeric coatings; (2) paper and paperboard components; (3) rigid, semi-rigid and modified acrylic and vinyl plastics (at a maximum level of 5 wt % of the total polymer); (4) adhesives; (5) resin-bonded filters; and (5) polyolefin films. The amounts present may not exceed that which is reasonably required to produce the intended effect (US Food & Drug Administration, 1977a).

2.2  Occurrence

Acrylic acid has been reported to occur naturally in the following species of marine algae: nine species of *Chlorophyceae*, ten of *Rhodophyceae* and eleven of *Phaeophyceae* (Glombitza, 1970). It has been found in the rumen fluid of sheep (Noble & Czerkawski, 1973); and it has been detected in trace amounts of commercial-grade propionic acid (Kostanyan *et al.*, 1969).

2.3  Analysis

Analytical methods reported to be useful for the detection of acrylic acid include: (1) half-wave potential polarography, (2) gas chromatography, (3) ion-exchange chromatography, (4) paper chromatography and (5) ultraviolet spectrophotometry.

Trace amounts of acrylic acid in commercial propionic acid have been determined by oxidation to dibromopropionic acid using bromine water and polarographic determination of this product; the limit of detection was 10 mg/kg (ppm) (Kostanyan *et al.*, 1969).

A method has been developed for detecting acrylic acid by composite gas chromatography (Linkiewicz & Szocik, 1970; Noble & Czerkawski, 1973).

It has been separated from mixtures of aliphatic acids using either strong cation-exchange chromatography and ultra-violet spectroscopy detection at 210 nm, with a limit of detection of 1 µg/ml (Richards, 1975), or anion exchange with ultra-violet detection at 254 nm (Lefèvre et al., 1976). Acrylic acid has also been determined in polyacrylamide using cation-exchange chromatography and ultra-violet detection at 200 nm, with a limit of detection of 0.5 µg (Schmoetzer, 1971).

The level of acrylic acid in air has been determined by paper chromatography after trapping in ethanolic mercuric acetate; the limit of detection was 0.1 µg (Kaznina, 1972).

Acrylic acid was detected in polyacrylic acid by ultra-violet spectroscopy at 195 nm, with a limit of detection of 300 mg/kg (ppm) (Brunn et al., 1975).

## 3. Biological Data Relevant to the Evaluation of Carcinogenic Risk to Humans

### 3.1 Carcinogenicity studies in animals

No data were available to the Working Group.

### 3.2 Other relevant biological data

(a) Experimental systems

Toxic effects

The $LD_{50}$ of acrylic acid by i.p. injection in rats is 24 mg/kg bw (Majka et al., 1974; Singh et al., 1972); the oral $LD_{50}$ of glacial acrylic acid in rats is 193 mg/kg bw (Union Carbide Corporation, 1977) or 350 mg/kg bw (Carpenter et al., 1974); the oral $LD_{50}$ of acrylic acid in rats is 2520 mg/kg bw (Fassett, 1963a), in the range of 2100-3200 mg/kg bw (Miller, 1964). The $LD_{50}$ in rabbits after single skin application is 750 mg/kg bw (Union Carbide Corporation, 1977), 295 mg/kg bw (Carpenter et al., 1974) or about 950 mg/kg bw (Fassett, 1963a). In rats exposed to acrylic acid vapours in air for 4 hours, the $LC_{50}$ was 3600 mg/m$^3$ (1200 ppm) (Majka et al., 1974). In single inhalation studies in rats, a concentration of 12 mg/l (4000 ppm) acrylic acid killed none of 6 test animals exposed for 4 hours and observed over 14 days. Vapour concentrations approaching saturation in air killed half of a group of test rats in about 3.5 hours (Union Carbide Corporation, 1977).

Strong local irritation, resulting in irreversible changes in skin and eyes of rats, was noted after exposure to vapours in air. Five weeks' exposure to acrylic acid vapours at a concentration of 700 mg/m$^3$ (240 ppm) of air for 4 hours daily led to reduced body weight gain and an increased number of blood reticulocytes. Single and repeated doses caused injury to the gastric mucosa and inflammation of the upper respiratory tract (Majka *et al.*, 1974).

A 1% solution was the lowest concentration of acrylic acid that caused significant injury to the rabbit eye (Union Carbide Corporation, 1977).

### Embryotoxicity and teratogenicity

Four groups of 5 female rats were injected intraperitoneally with 0, 2.5, 4.7 or 8 mg/kg bw acrylic acid three times on days 5, 10 and 15 of pregnancy. Significant increases in the number of gross abnormalities occurred in the offspring of those given the two highest dose levels, and skeletal abnormalities were significantly increased in pups of those given the highest dose level when compared to controls. Embryotoxicity also occurred in animals given the highest dose level (Singh *et al.*, 1972).

No adequate data on the metabolism or mutagenicity of this compound were available to the Working Group.

### (b) Humans

No data were available to the Working Group.

## 3.3 Case reports and epidemiological studies

No data were available to the Working Group.


## Methyl acrylate

### 1.  Chemical and Physical Data

### 1.1 Synonyms and trade names

Chem. Abstr. Services Reg. No.: 96-33-3

Chem. Abstr. Name: 2-Propenoic acid methyl ester

Acrylic acid methyl ester; methoxycarbonylethylene; methyl propenoate; methyl-2-propenoate

## 1.2 Structural and molecular formulae and molecular weight

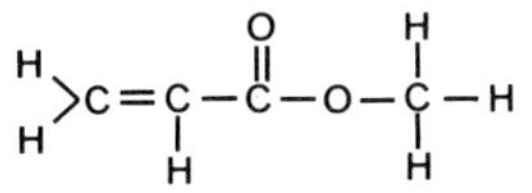

$$\underset{H}{\overset{H}{>}} C = C - \overset{O}{\overset{\|}{C}} - O - \overset{H}{\underset{H}{\overset{|}{C}}} - H$$

$C_4H_6O_2$                     Mol. wt: 86.1

## 1.3 Chemical and physical properties of the pure substance

From Weast (1976b), unless otherwise specified

(a) Description: Colourless liquid with an acrid odour (Anon., 1972; Windholz, 1976b)

(b) Boiling-point: 80.5°C

(c) Melting-point: <-75°C

(d) Density: $d_4^{20}$ 0.9535; vapour-air density at 38°C, 1.5; vapour density, 3 (air = 1) (Anon., 1972)

(e) Refractive index: $n_D^{20}$ 1.4040

(f) Spectroscopy data: Infra-red, Raman, nuclear magnetic resonance and mass spectral data have been tabulated (Grasselli & Ritchey, 1975b).

(g) Solubility: Soluble in water, ethanol, ether, acetone and benzene

(h) Volatility: Vapour pressure is 100 mm at 28°C (Perry & Chilton, 1973b).

(i) Stability: Flash-point (open cup), -2.8°C (Anon., 1972); polymerizes on standing; polymerization is accelerated by heat, light and peroxides (Windholz, 1976b)

(j) Conversion factor: 1 ppm in air = 3.5 mg/m³

## 1.4 Technical products and impurities

Methyl acrylate available commercially in the US has the following typical properties: purity, 98.8%; acidity (as acrylic acid), 0.0008%;

water, 0.06%; inhibitor (hydroquinone monomethyl ether), 15, 200 or 1000 mg/kg (ppm); specific gravity (25/15.6°C), 0.950; refractive index, $n_D^{25}$ 1.4003; distillation range, 95% min at 80.3°C (Glavis & Specht, 1963).

In Japan, commercially available methyl acrylate has the following specifications: purity, 98.5% min; acidity (as acrylic acid), 0.01% max; water, 0.05% max; inhibitor (hydroquinone monomethyl ether), 100 mg/kg (ppm); specific gravity (20°C/4°C), 0.953-0.958; distillation range, 95% min at 77.5-82.5°C.

## 2. Production, Use, Occurrence and Analysis

### 2.1 Production and use

#### (a) Production

Methyl acrylate was first prepared in 1873 by Caspary & Tollens by reacting α,β-dibromopropionic acid methyl ester with zinc and sulphuric acid in small amounts of methanol (Prager et al., 1920).

Methyl acrylate is produced in the US by a propylene oxidation process and by modified Reppe processes. The oxidation of propylene results in acrolein, which is further oxidized to acrylic acid, and methyl acrylate is then produced by reaction with methanol. In the Reppe processes, acetylene is reacted with carbon monoxide (either as gas or in the nickel carbonyl form) and methanol or with carbon monoxide and water in the presence of a nickel halide salt. The resulting acrylic acid is then reacted with methanol.

Commercial production of methyl acrylate in the US was first reported in 1944 (US Tariff Commission, 1946a). Two US companies reported the commercial production of undisclosed amounts (see preamble, p. 22) of methyl acrylate in 1976 (US International Trade Commission, 1977b); but their combined production (excluding any which may have been used to produce higher acrylates) is estimated to have been 20.4 million kg. US imports of methyl acrylate in 1976 (all from Italy) amounted to 82.5 thousand kg (US Department of Commerce, 1977a). Although US exports of methyl acrylate are not reported separately, they are estimated to have been as much as 4.5 million kg in 1976.

Methyl acrylate was first produced commercially in Japan in 1956. In 1976, five Japanese companies used the propylene oxidation process to produce a total of about 28 million kg methyl acrylate.

No data on the production of this compound in Europe were available.

(b) Use

The primary use for methyl acrylate is in the production of acrylic and modacrylic fibres. In the US in 1975, 10.5 million kg were used in this way; about 13.6 million kg were used in 1974. Methyl acrylate is one of several materials used as a comonomer (7-8% of total monomer weight) with acrylonitrile in such fibres. It adds physical properties to the polymer that facilitate fibre spinning and processing. For a detailed description of this end use, see the monograph including acrylic and modacrylic fibres, p. 73.

One resin intended for use in plastic containers is made by copolymerizing acrylonitrile with methyl acrylate and then grafting the copolymer onto a small amount of 'butadiene-derived impact modifier'; the copolymer itself contains about 75% acrylonitrile and 25% methyl acrylate. Intended markets for this so-called 'nitrile barrier resin' include sheet, film and non-pressurized blown bottles for food, pharmaceuticals and toiletries. The US Food and Drug Administration banned the use of nitrile barrier resins as beverage containers on 23 September 1977. In early 1977, one Swiss manufacturer was reported to be marketing the resin in Sweden for use in the manufacture of beer bottles (Anon., 1977).

Very small quantities of methyl acrylate (less than 230 thousand kg in 1975) are used in the manufacture of amphoteric surfactants (e.g., $N$-dodecyl-$\beta$-aminopropionic acid) for use in special industrial cleaners and for a variety of other applications.

In Japan, 70-80% of methyl acrylate is used in acrylic fibres, and 20-30% in miscellaneous uses.

The US Food and Drug Administration considers methyl acrylate to be a GRAS (generally recognized as safe) substance when it is in contact with food and migrates from paper and paperboard products used in food packaging (US Food and Drug Administration, 1977b).

The US Occupational Safety and Health Administration's health standards for exposure to air contaminants require that an employee's exposure to methyl acrylate not exceed an eight-hour time-weighted average of 35 mg/m$^3$ (10 ppm) in the workplace air in any eight-hour work shift of a forty-hour work week (US Occupational Safety and Health Administration, 1976).

The work environment hygiene standard (in terms of an eight-hour time-weighted average) reported by Winell (1975) for methyl acrylate is 35 mg/m$^3$ (10 ppm) in the Federal Republic of Germany and 20 mg/m$^3$ (5.7 ppm) in the German Democratic Republic. The maximum acceptable concentration of methyl acrylate in the USSR is 20 mg/m$^3$ (5.7 ppm).

## 2.2  Occurrence

Methyl acrylate has been reported to be a volatile component of pineapple concentrate (Näf-Müller & Willhalm, 1971).

## 2.3  Analysis

A sampling method using charcoal followed by gas chromatographic analysis has been recommended by the US National Institute for Occupational Safety and Health for determining methyl acrylate concentrations in work-place atmospheres in the range of 13.9-58.4 mg/m$^3$ (4-17 ppm) (National Institute for Occupational Safety and Health, 1975a).

Methyl acrylate has been detected by gas chromatography in pineapple concentrate (Näf-Müller & Willhalm, 1971) and in aqueous polymer latexes, with a limit of detection of 10 mg/kg (ppm) (Zaytseva et al., 1972). Gas chromatography retention data for methyl acrylate have been tabulated for 14 polysiloxane column substrates (Ashes & Haken, 1975).

Methyl acrylate has been separated from cross-linked polyvinyl acetate emulsions by gel chromatography and detected by ultra-violet spectroscopy (Schmoetzer, 1972).

## 3.  Biological Data Relevant to the Evaluation of Carcinogenic Risk to Humans

### 3.1  Carcinogenicity studies in animals

No data were available to the Working Group.

### 3.2  Other relevant biological data

#### (a)  Experimental systems

The oral LD$_{50}$ in rabbits is 200 mg/kg bw, and the LD$_{50}$ by skin application, 1250 mg/kg bw. In rats, the LC$_{50}$ for a 4-hour exposure to the vapours was 3.5 g/m$^3$ (1000 ppm) (Fassett, 1963b).

A single oral dose of 280 mg/kg bw to rabbits resulted in fatal poisoning, characterized by dyspnoea, cyanosis, convulsions and hypothermia. In rabbits, skin application caused local irritation. Inhalation of 1.99 g/m$^3$ (578 ppm) for 7 hours/day for 2-7 days to rabbits, guinea-pigs and rats caused a decrease in body weight, distension of ear veins (only in rabbits), lachrymation (not in rats), salivation, laboured respiration and lethargy; rabbits were more sensitive (Treon et al., 1949).

No data on the embryotoxicity, metabolism or mutagenicity of this compound were available to the Working Group.

(b)  Humans

No data were available to the Working Group.

3.3  Case reports and epidemiological studies

No data were available to the Working Group.


Ethyl acrylate

## 1.  Chemical and Physical Data

1.1  Synonyms and trade names

Chem. Abstr. Services Reg. No.:  140-88-5

Chem. Abstr. Name:  2-Propenoic acid ethyl ester

Acrylic acid ethyl ester;  ethoxycarbonylethylene;  ethyl propenoate;
ethyl 2-propenoate

1.2  Structural and molecular formulae and molecular weight

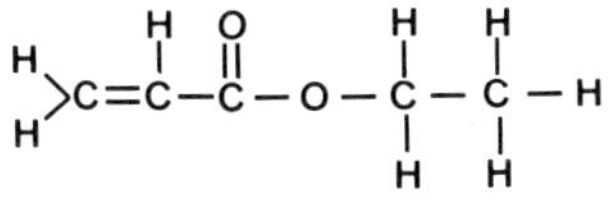

$$\underset{H}{\overset{H}{>}}C=\overset{\overset{H}{|}}{C}-\overset{\overset{O}{||}}{C}-O-\overset{\overset{H}{|}}{\underset{\underset{H}{|}}{C}}-\overset{\overset{H}{|}}{\underset{\underset{H}{|}}{C}}-H$$

$C_5H_8O_2$                    Mol. wt:  100.1

1.3  Chemical and physical properties of the pure substance

From Weast (1976b), unless otherwise specified

(a)  Description:  Colourless liquid with an acrid odour (Anon.,
1972;  Windholz, 1976c)

(b)  Boiling-point:  99.8°C

(c)  Melting-point:  -71.2°C

(d)  Density:  $d_4^{20}$ 0.9234;  vapour-air density at 38°C, 1.2;
vapour density, 3.5 (air = 1) (Anon., 1972)

(e)  Refractive index:  $n_D^{20}$ 1.4068

(f) Spectroscopy data: $\lambda_{max}$ 208 nm ($E_1^1$ = 692); infra-red, nuclear magnetic resonance and mass spectral data have been tabulated (Grasselli & Ritchey, 1975c).

(g) Solubility: Slightly soluble in water; soluble in ethanol, ether and chloroform

(h) Volatility: Vapour pressure is 40 mm at 26°C (Perry & Chilton, 1973c).

(i) Stability: Flash-point (open cup), 15.5°C (Anon., 1972); polymerizes readily on standing; polymerization is accelerated by heat, light and peroxides (Windholz, 1976c).

(j) Conversion factor: 1 ppm in air = 4 mg/m$^3$

1.4  Technical products and impurities

Typical properties for commercial grade ethyl acrylate available in the US are as follows: purity, 99.0%; acidity (as acrylic acid), 0.0008%; water, 0.03%; inhibitors, 15 or 200 mg/kg (ppm) hydroquinone monomethyl ether or 1000 mg/kg (ppm) hydroquinone (see IARC, 1977); specific gravity (25/15.6°C), 0.917; refractive index, $n_D^{25}$ 1.4034; distillation range, 95% min at 100.2°C (Glavis & Specht, 1963).

In Japan, commercially available ethyl acrylate has the following specifications: purity, 98.5% min; acidity (as acrylic acid), 0.01% max; inhibitor (hydroquinone monomethyl ether), 100 mg/kg (ppm); specific gravity (20°C/4°C), 0.919-0.923; distillation range, 95% min at 97-102°C.

## 2.  Production, Use, Occurrence and Analysis

2.1  Production and use

(a)  Production

Ethyl acrylate was first prepared in 1873 by Caspary & Tollens by reacting $\alpha,\beta$-dibromopropionic acid ethyl ester with zinc and sulphuric acid in alcohol (Prager et al., 1920).

Ethyl acrylate is produced commercially in the US by a propylene oxidation process and by modified Reppe processes. The oxidation of propylene results in acrolein, which is further oxidized to acrylic acid, and ethyl acrylate is then produced by reaction with ethanol. In the Reppe processes, acetylene is reacted with carbon monoxide (either as gas or in the form of nickel carbonyl) and ethanol or with carbon monoxide and water in the presence of a nickel halide salt. The resulting acrylic acid is then reacted with ethanol.

Commercial production of ethyl acrylate in the US was first reported in 1944 (US Tariff Commission, 1946b). In 1976, four US companies reported production of 134 million kg ethyl acrylate (US International Trade Commission, 1977c). Imports in that year were 1.5 million kg, from Japan (33% of total imports), The Netherlands (67%) and the UK (negligible) (US Department of Commerce, 1977a); exports were 18.4 million kg, to the following countries (% of total): Argentina (3.2), Australia (5.4), Belgium (18.7), Brazil (18.2), Canada (31.5), Colombia (3.0), The Netherlands (8.2), the UK (4.0) and at least five other countries (7.8) (US Department of Commerce, 1977b).

Production of ethyl acrylate in western Europe in 1976 was 200 million kg.

Ethyl acrylate was first produced commercially in Japan in 1956. In 1976, five companies used the propylene oxidation process to produce a total of about 18.8 million kg ethyl acrylate.

Worldwide production of ethyl acrylate in 1976 is estimated to have been 600 million kg.

(b) Use

Although a specific US use pattern for ethyl acrylate is not available, that in 1975 for all acrylates (ethyl acrylate representing about 50% of the total) was as follows: in emulsion polymers used in surface coatings (39%), textiles (23%), paper and polishes (5% each), leather (3%) and other (2%); in solution polymers used in surface coatings (13%); as comonomers in the production of acrylic fibres (5%); and in miscellaneous non-latex polymer uses (5%).

Ethyl acrylate is a major component of straight acrylic emulsion polymers, which are used in latex paints for exterior house and trim and interior wall semi-gloss and trim. It is also a major monomer used in straight acrylic emulsions for textile applications, including backcoatings, fabric finishes, pigment binders, dirt release agents and thickeners.

Acrylic acid esters, including ethyl acrylate, are also used to make emulsion polymers for the following applications: as paper coatings; as paper pulp additives to improve tensile strength and folding endurance; in industrial and retail floor polishes and sealants; in shoe polishes; in base coatings and surface impregnation of leather to improve scuff resistance and cutting properties; and in miscellaneous applications, including adhesives, sealants, caulking compounds and binders.

Ethyl acrylate is used as a comonomer in solution polymers, which are used to make thermosetting acrylic enamels for industrial product finishes (e.g., automotive and appliance coatings).

Miscellaneous non-latex polymer applications include its use in the production of an acrylic elastomer - a copolymer with chlorethyl vinyl ether. Acrylates in general are used as modifiers for rigid polyvinyl chloride plastics, acrylic films, oil and functional fluid additives, and in the production of special plastics.

Ethyl acrylate was used in western Europe in 1976 as follows: textile applications (45%), leather processing (27%), paints (18%) and miscellaneous uses, e.g., paper adhesives, ion-exchange resins (10%).

In Japan, it is used in fibre processing and in the manufacture of paint.

Ethyl acrylate is considered to be a GRAS (generally recognized as safe) adjuvant in food by the US Food and Drug Administration. Ethyl acrylate polymers and copolymers are also permitted as components of the following products when they are intended for use in contact with food: (1) adhesives, (2) resinous and polymeric coatings, (3) paper and paperboard for aqueous and fatty food, (4) rigid and semi-rigid acrylic plastics, (5) cross-linked polyester resins, and (6) rigid and semi-rigid vinyl chloride plastic modifiers (US Food & Drug Administration, 1977a).

The US Occupational Safety and Health Administration's health standards for exposure to air contaminants require that an employee's exposure to ethyl acrylate not exceed an eight-hour time-weighted average of 100 mg/m$^3$ (25 ppm) in the workplace air in any eight-hour work shift of a forty-hour work week (US Occupational Safety and Health Administration, 1976).

## 2.2  Occurrence

Ethyl acrylate has been reported to be a volatile component of pineapple concentrate (Näf-Müller & Willhalm, 1971).

It has been found as a residual monomer in polyethyl acrylate (Brunn et al., 1975) and, at a concentration of 50 mg/kg (ppm), in aqueous polymer latexes used in the paper and textile industries (Bollini et al., 1975).

Concentrations of 2.89-5.38 mg/m$^3$ ethyl acrylate polymer dust have been found in a factory manufacturing synthetic textile products where fibres were saturated with an ethyl acrylate polymer emulsion in water (Cohen et al., 1974).

## 2.4  Analysis

A sampling method using charcoal followed by gas chromatographic analysis has been recommended by the US National Institute for Occupational

Safety and Health for determining ethyl acrylate concentrations in work-place atmospheres in the range of 50-210 mg/m$^3$ (National Institute for Occupational Safety and Health, 1975b).

Ethyl acrylate has been detected by gas chromatography in pineapple concentrate (Näf-Müller & Willhalm, 1971), in aqueous polymer latexes (Bollini *et al.*, 1975; Zaytseva *et al.*, 1972), and in air with flame-ionization detection (Parsons & Mitzner, 1975). Gas chromatography retention data for ethyl acrylate have been tabulated for 14 polysiloxane column substrates (Ashes & Haken, 1975).

Ethyl acrylate has been determined in technical polymers at levels of $\geq$ 300 mg/kg (ppm), using ultra-violet spectrophotometry at 195 nm (Brunn *et al.*, 1975), and in air, using chromotropic acid, with a sensitivity of 2.5 µg (Gronsberg, 1970).

## 3.  Biological Data Relevant to the Evaluation
## of Carcinogenic Risk to Humans

### 3.1  Carcinogenicity studies in animals[1]

#### Oral administration

Rat:  Groups of 25 male and 25 female Wistar rats were administered 0, 6, 60 or 2000 mg/l (ppm) ethyl acrylate in the drinking-water for 2 years;  no treatment-related lesions were reported (Borzelleca *et al.*, 1964) [The Working Group noted that insufficient details on survival and pathological examinations were given].

### 3.2  Other relevant biological data

#### (a)  Experimental systems

The oral LD$_{50}$ for ethyl acrylate in rats has been reported to be 1000 mg/kg bw (Pozzani *et al.*, 1949) and 2080 mg/kg bw (Union Carbide Corporation, 1971). The i.p. LD$_{50}$ in rats is 450 mg/kg bw (Paulet & Vidal, 1975). In female rabbits, the minimal lethal oral dose is in the range of 280-420 mg/kg bw (Treon *et al.*, 1949). The dermal LD$_{50}$ in rabbits has been reported to be 1950 mg/kg bw (Union Carbide Corporation, 1971).

---

[1]The Working Group was aware of studies in progress to assess the carcinogenicity of this compound in mice and rats by oral administration (IARC, 1978).

Single exposure to vapours of ethyl acrylate approaching saturation in air was found to be lethal to 6/6 rats in a 15-minute period. A concentration of 8 g/m³ (2000 ppm) killed 5/6 rats, but a level of 4 g/m³ (1000 ppm) killed none of 6 rats exposed for a 4-hour period (Union Carbide Corporation, 1971).

Thirteen of 19 rats exposed to vapour concentrations of ethyl acrylate of 2 g/m³ (540 ppm) in air for 7 hrs/day on 5 days/week for 3 weeks died with pneumonic involvement (Pozzani *et al.*, 1949).

In rabbits, the compound produces a mild irritation when applied to the skin and a moderate response when one drop is placed in the eye (Union Carbide Corporation, 1971).

Female, but not male, rats that received 2000 mg/1 (ppm) ethyl acrylate in their drinking-water had decreased body weight. No effect was seen in dogs that were given 1000 mg/kg of diet (Borzelleca *et al.*, 1964).

No data on the embryotoxicity, metabolism or mutagenicity of this compound were available to the Working Group.

(b)  Humans

One case report indicated that a worker exposed to the dust of a polymer of ethyl acrylate was hospitalized for investigation of a respiratory cough; itching of the skin of the face and ears also occurred (Cohen *et al.*, 1974).

3.3  Case reports and epidemiological studies

No data were available to the Working Group.


Polyacrylic acid

1.   Chemical and Physical Data

1.1  Synonyms and trade names

Chem. Abstr. Services Reg. No.:  9003-01-4

Chem. Abstr. Name:  2-Propenoic acid homopolymer

Acrylic acid polymer; acrylic acid resin; acrylic polymer; acrylic resin; atactic poly(acrylic acid); polyacrylate; poly(acrylic acid)

Acrysol A 1;  Acrysol A 3;  Acrysol A 5;  Acrysol AC 5;  Acrysol

ASE-75;  Acrysol WS-24;  Antiprex A;  Aron;  Aron A 10H;  Carbopol

940;  Carbopol 941;  Carbopol 960;  Dispex C40;  Good-rite K 37;

Good-rite K 702;  Good-rite WS 801;  Junlon 110;  Nalfloc 636;

OLD 01;  PA 11M;  PAA-25;  P 11H;  Primal ASE 60;  R968;  Revacryl

A 191;  Rohagit SD 15;  Synthemul 90-588;  Versicol E 7;  Versicol

E9;  Versicol E15;  Versicol S 25;  Viscalex HV 30;  Viscon 103;

WS 24;  WS 801;  XPA

## 1.2  Structural and molecular formulae and molecular weight

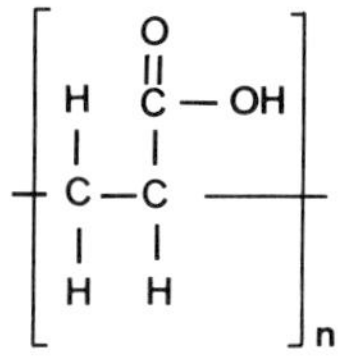

$$(C_3H_4O_2)_n$$          Mol. wt:  10 000-800 000

## 1.3  Chemical and physical properties of the homopolymer

From Miller (1964)

(a)  Description:  Clear, brittle, hygroscopic solid

(b)  Melting-point:  $106^\circ C$ (glass-transition temperature)

(c)  Solubility:  Soluble in water (deliquescent), dioxane,
      dimethylformamide, ethanol, methanol and isopropanol;
      insoluble in ether, benzene and cyclohexane

## 1.4  Technical products and impurities

Polyacrylic acid is available commercially in the US in proprietary
formulations designed for specific end uses.

No detailed information on the possible presence of unreacted monomer
in the polymer was available to the Working Group.

## 2. Production, Use, Occurrence and Analysis

### 2.1 Production and use

#### (a) Production

The polymerization of acrylic acid to polyacrylic acid was first observed in 1872. Polyacrylic acid is produced commercially by polymerizing an aqueous solution of acrylic acid (at concentrations of 25% or less) at 90-100°C in the presence of a peroxydisulphate initiator or at 60°C using redox initiators, i.e., a combination of potassium peroxydisulphate and potassium metabisulphite (Miller, 1964).

Commercial production of polyacrylic acid salts in the US was first reported in the early 1950's (US Tariff Commission, 1955). In 1976, five US companies reported production of 1.1 million kg polyacrylic acid and seven companies reported production of 7.9 million kg polyacrylic acid salts (e.g., sodium or ammonium salts) (US International Trade Commission, 1977a).

Polyacrylic acid sodium salt has been produced commercially in Japan since 1954; five companies produced about 2 million kg in 1976. Japanese imports and exports of this product are negligible.

#### (b) Use

Polyacrylic acid and its salts are primarily used as textile warp sizes for man-made fibre monofilaments (especially for nylon) and as thickeners for use in latex paints, natural and synthetic rubber (particularly in rug backings), textile printing pastes, wallcovering binders and cosmetics. Other applications are as flocculants, fluid-loss control additives in oil-well drilling muds, scale-inhibitor additives in formulations for treating cooling-water systems, sequestrants and as temporary binders for ceramics before firing.

In Japan, polyacrylic acid sodium salt is used in industrial applications (70%) and as a food additive (30%). Its use as a food additive (at a maximum level of 0.2%) was first permitted in 1962.

### 2.2 Occurrence

Polyacrylic acid is not known to occur as a natural product.

### 2.3 Analysis

Polyacrylic acid can be determined by: (1) a turbidimetric method, for concentrations in the range of 5-40 mg/kg (ppm) (Wimberley & Jordan, 1971); (2) a conductometric titration, for aqueous solutions (Crisp et al., 1975); (3) differential thermal analysis (Concilio & Jahnke, 1972); and (4) pyrolysis-gas chromatography (Szocik et al., 1970).

Traces of polyacrylic acid have been determined in fresh and sea water by formation of a methylene blue complex and detection by colorimetry. The method is suitable for determining polyacrylic acid in sea water at concentrations of 1-6 mg/l (ppm), with a mean error of 0.1 mg/l (ppm) (Sweett & Rolfe, 1966).

## 3. Biological Data Relevant to the Evaluation of Carcinogenic Risk to Humans

No data were available to the Working Group.

## 4. Summary of Data Reported and Evaluation

### 4.1 Experimental data

Ethyl acrylate was tested in rats by oral administration; the reporting of the experiment was considered inadequate by the Working Group. No mutagenicity data on ethyl acrylate were available to the Working Group.

No carcinogenicity or mutagenicity data on acrylic acid, methyl acrylate or polyacrylic acid were available to the Working Group.

Acrylic acid is embryotoxic and teratogenic.

### 4.2 Human data

No case reports or epidemiological studies relating to the carcinogenicity of acrylic acid, methyl acrylate, ethyl acrylate or polyacrylic acid were available to the Working Group.

Acrylic acid is used primarily for the production of acrylates and polymers, and human exposure may be expected to occur. The use of methyl acrylate, ethyl acrylate and polyacrylic acid in a variety of textile, surface coating and other applications suggests other occupational exposures. Because methyl and ethyl acrylate as well as polyacrylic acid components are permitted in some countries for use in contact with foods, the general population may be exposed; in addition, polyacrylic acid sodium salt has been used as a food additive in one country.

### 4.3 Evaluation

The data available to the Working Group do not permit an evaluation of the carcinogenicity to humans of acrylic acid, methyl acrylate, ethyl acrylate or polyacrylic acid.

The Working Group noted the absence of data on carcinogenicity and mutagenicity for this group of substances and considered that suitable experiments should be undertaken. Even in the absence of such data in animals, because of the substantial production of these compounds and products containing them as well as the diversity of end-applications, research should be undertaken to identify exposed groups, to measure exposure levels and to conduct the appropriate epidemiological studies (see also 'General Remarks on the Substances Considered', p. 35).

## 5. References

Anon. (1972)  Fire Protection Guide on Hazardous Materials, 4th ed., Boston, Mass., National Fire Protection Association, pp. 49-31, 49-111-49-112, 49-149-49-150, 325M-19, 325M-74, 325M-99

Anon. (1977)  New plastic migration standards aligned in Europe, USA. European Chemical News, 18 March, p. 28

Ashes, J.R. & Haken, J.K. (1975)  Gas chromatography of homologous esters. IX. Structure-retention increments of unsaturated esters. J. Chromatogr., 111, 171-187

Bollini, M., Seves, A. & Focher, B. (1975)  Determination of free monomers in aqueous emulsions of synthetic polymers and copolymers (Ital.). Textilia, 51, 25-28

Borzelleca, J.F., Larson, P.S., Hennigar, G.R., Jr, Huf, E.G., Crawford, E.M. & Blackwell Smith, R., Jr (1964)  Studies on the chronic oral toxicity of monomeric ethyl acrylate and methyl methacrylate. Toxicol. appl. Pharmacol., 6, 29-36

Brunn, J., Doerffel, K., Much, H. & Zimmermann, G. (1975)  Ultraviolet photometric determination of residual monomer content in technical polymers of acrylic acids and acrylic acid ethyl esters (Ger.). Plaste Kautsch., 22, 485-486 [Chem. Abstr., 83, 115163m]

Carpenter, C.P., Weil, C.S. & Smyth, H.F., Jr (1974)  Range-finding toxicity data: list VIII. Toxicol. appl. Pharmacol., 28, 313-319

Cohen, S.R., Maier, A.A. & Flesch, J.P. (1974)  Case reports. Occupational health case report - No. 3: ethyl acrylate. J. occup. Med., 16, 199-200

Concilio, C.B. & Jahnke, B.J. (1972)  Characterization by differential thermal analysis of organic polyelectrolytes and flocculating agents. Thermochim. acta, 4, 249-255 [Chem. Abstr., 77, 116365s]

Crisp, S., Lewis, B.G. & Wilson, A.D. (1975)  Conductometric titration of aqueous solutions of poly(acrylic acid) and its copolymers. J. dent. Res., 54, 1238 [Chem. Abstr., 84, 49878r]

Fassett, D.W. (1963a)  Organic acids, anhydrides, lactones, acid halides and amides, thioacids. In: Patty, F.A., ed., Industrial Hygiene and Toxicology, 2nd revised ed., Vol. 2, New York, Interscience, p. 1794

Fassett, D.W. (1963b)  Esters. In: Patty, F.A., ed., Industrial Hygiene and Toxicology, 2nd revised ed., Vol. 2, New York, Interscience, pp. 1877-1880

Glavis, F.J. & Specht, E.H. (1963) Acrylic acid and derivatives. In:
    Kirk, R.E. & Othmer, D.F., eds, Encyclopedia of Chemical Technology,
    2nd ed., Vol. 1, New York, John Wiley and Sons, p. 301

Glombitza, K.W. (1970) Antimicrobial components of algae. 2. Occurrence
    of acrylic acid in different marine algae (Ger.). Planta med., 18,
    210-221 [Chem. Abstr., 73, 63209c]

Grasselli, J.G. & Ritchey, W.M., eds (1975a) CRC Atlas of Spectral Data
    and Physical Constants for Organic Compounds, 2nd ed., Vol. IV,
    Cleveland, Ohio, Chemical Rubber Co., p. 309

Grasselli, J.G. & Ritchey, W.M., eds (1975b) CRC Atlas of Spectral Data
    and Physical Constants for Organic Compounds, 2nd ed., Vol. IV,
    Cleveland, Ohio, Chemical Rubber Co., p. 316

Grasselli, J.G. & Ritchey, W.M., eds (1975c) CRC Atlas of Spectral Data
    and Physical Constants for Organic Compounds, 2nd ed., Vol. IV,
    Cleveland, Ohio, Chemical Rubber Co., p. 314

Gronsberg, E.S. (1970) Determination of vinyl acetate and ethyl acrylate
    during analysis of air (Russ.). Tr. Khim. Tekhnol., 1, 186-189
    [Chem. Abstr., 75, 88995k]

IARC (1977) IARC Monographs on the Evaluation of the Carcinogenic Risk
    to Man, 15, Some Fumigants, the Herbicides 2,4,-D and 2,4,5-T,
    Chlorinated Dibenzodioxins and Miscellaneous Industrial Chemicals,
    Lyon, pp. 155-175

IARC (1978)  Information Bulletin on the Survey of Chemicals Being Tested
    for Carcinogenicity, No. 7, Lyon, p. 201

Kaznina, N.I. (1972) Determination of unsaturated compounds in the air
    by mercury salt addition (Russ.). Gig. i Sanit., 37, 63-66 [Chem.
    Abstr., 77, 92364n]

Kostanyan, G.G., Dadayan, A.A. & Safaryan, G.E. (1969) Polarographic
    determination of acrylic acid in commercial propionic acid (Russ.).
    Arm. Khim. Zh., 22, 1044 [Chem. Abstr., 72, 86037p]

Lefèvre, J.-P., Caude, M. & Rosset, R. (1976) Analysis of mixtures of
    maleic, fumaric, acrylic and methacrylic acids by ion-exchange
    chromatography (Fr.). Analusis, 4, 16-24

Linkiewicz, M. & Szocik, A. (1970) Analysis of lower acrylic esters, acids,
    and alcohols by gas chromatography (Pol.). Chem. Anal. (Warsaw), 15,
    845-852 [Chem. Abstr., 74, 19165g]

Majka, J., Knobloch, K. & Stetkiewicz, J. (1974) Evaluation of acute and
    subacute toxicity of acrylic acid (Pol.). Med. Pr., 25, 427-435

Miller, M.L. (1964) Acrylic acid polymers. In: Bikales, N.M., ed., Encylopedia of Polymer Science and Technology, Plastics, Resins, Rubbers, Fibers, Vol. 1, New York, Interscience, pp. 197-226

Näf-Müller, R. & Willhalm, B. (1971) On volatile constituents of pineapple (Ger.). Helv. chim. acta, 54, 1880-1890

National Institute of Occupational Safety and Health (1975a) Methyl Acrylate, Method No. S38, Set D, Washington DC (available from Springfield, Va, National Technical Information Service)

National Institute of Occupational Safety and Health (1975b) Ethyl Acrylate, Method No. S35, Set D, Washington DC (available from Springfield, Va, National Technical Information Service)

Noble, R.C. & Czerkawski, J.W. (1973) A gas-chromatographic method for the determination of low concentrations of acrylic acid in mixtures of $C_2$ to $C_5$ fatty acids in biological materials. Analyst, 98, 122-125

Parsons, J.S. & Mitzner, S. (1975) Gas chromatographic method for concentration and analysis of traces of industrial organic pollutants in environmental air and stacks. Environ. Sci. Technol., 9, 1053-1058

Paulet, G. & Vidal, Mme (1975) On the toxicity of some acrylic and methacrylic esters of acrylamide and polyacrylamides (Fr.). Arch. Mal. prof. Méd. Trav. Sécur. Soc., 36, 58-60

Perry, R.H. & Chilton, C.H., eds (1973a) Chemical Engineers' Handbook, 5th ed., New York, McGraw-Hill, p. 3-49

Perry, R.H. & Chilton, C.H., eds (1973b) Chemical Engineers' Handbook, 5th ed., New York, McGraw-Hill, p. 3-56

Perry, R.H. & Chilton, C.H., eds (1973c) Chemical Engineers' Handbook, 5th ed., New York, McGraw-Hill, p. 3-54

Pozzani, U.C., Weil, C.S. & Carpenter, C.P. (1949) Subacute vapor toxicity and range-finding data for ethyl acrylate. J. ind. Hyg. Toxicol., 31, 311-316

Prager, B., Schmidt, P., Jacobson, P. & Stern, D. eds (1920) Beilsteins Handbuch der Organischen Chemie, 4th ed., Vol. 2, Syst. No. 163, Berlin, Springer, pp. 399-400

Richards, M. (1975) Separation of mono- and dicarboxylic acids by liquid chromatography. J. Chromatogr., 115, 259-261

Schmoetzer, G. (1971) Determination of acrylamide and acrylic acid in acrylamide polymers (Ger.). Chromatographia, 4, 391-395 [Chem. Abstr., 76, 25744c]

Schmoetzer, G. (1972)  Determination of residual monomers in emulsion
    polymers (Ger.).  Fresenius' Z. anal. Chem., 260, 10-24 [Chem. Abstr.,
    77, 127080w]

Singh, A.R., Lawrence, W.H. & Autian, J. (1972)  Embryonic-fetal toxicity
    and teratogenic effects of a group of methacrylate esters in rats.
    J. dent. Res., 51, 1632-1638

Sweett, F. & Rolfe, P.F. (1966)  Estimation of traces of poly(acrylic acid)
    and other poly(carboxylic acids) in water and salt solutions by
    complexing with methylene blue.  Anal. Chem., 38, 1958-1959 [Chem.
    Abstr., 66, 29116r]

Szocik, A., Szelejewska, I. & Linkiewicz, M. (1970)  Pyrolysis gas chromato-
    graphy applied to the analysis of polymers of acrolein, acrylic acid,
    and acrylates (Pol.).  Zesz. Nauk., Inst. Ciezkiej Syntezy Organicznej
    Blachowni Slask., 2, 37-45 [Chem. Abstr., 74, 64755k]

Treon, J.F., Sigmon, H., Wright, H. & Kitzmiller, K.V. (1949)  The toxicity
    of methyl and ethyl acrylate.  J. ind. Hyg. Toxicol., 31, 317-326

Union Carbide Corp. (1971)  Toxicology Studies - Ethyl Acrylate,
    14 December, New York, Industrial Medicine and Toxicology Department

Union Carbide Corp. (1977)  Toxicology Studies - Acrylic Acid, Glacial,
    2 May, New York, Industrial Medicine and Toxicology Department

US Department of Commerce (1977a)  US Imports for Consumption and General
    Imports, TSUSA Commodity by Country of Origin, FT 246/Annual 1976,
    Bureau of the Census, Washington DC, US Government Printing Office,
    p. 230

US Department of Commerce (1977b)  US Exports, Schedule B Commodity
    Groupings, Schedule B Commodity by Country, FT 410/December, Bureau
    of the Census, Washington DC, US Government Printing Office, p. 2-84

US Food and Drug Administration (1977a)  Food and drugs.  US Code Fed.
    Regul., Title 21, parts 175.105, 175.300, 175.320, 176.170, 176.180,
    177.1010, 177.2260 and 178.3790, pp. 438, 445, 452, 456, 465, 467,
    471, 479, 481, 486, 488, 496, 545, 546, 596

US Food and Drug Administration (1977b)  Food and drugs.  US Code Fed.
    Regul., Title 21, part 182.90, p. 623

US International Trade Commission (1977a)  Synthetic Organic Chemicals,
    US Production and Sales, 1976, USITC Publication 833, Washington DC,
    US Government Printing Office, pp. 287, 294, 300, 314, 316

US International Trade Commission (1977b)  Synthetic Organic Chemicals,
    US Production and Sales, 1976, USITC Publication 833, Washington DC,
    US Government Printing Office, p. 326

US International Trade Commission (1977c)  Synthetic Organic Chemicals,
    US Production and Sales, 1976, USITC Publication 833, Washington DC,
    US Government Printing Office, pp. 301, 325

US Occupational Safety and Health Administration (1976)  Occupational
    safety and health standards.  Subpart Z - Toxic and hazardous
    substances.  US Code Fed. Regul., Title 29, Chapter XVII,
    Section 1910.1000, p. 31:8303

US Tariff Commission (1946a)  Synthetic Organic Chemicals, US Production
    and Sales, 1944, Report No. 155, Second Series, Washington DC, US
    Government Printing Office, p. 124

US Tariff Commission (1946b)  Synthetic Organic Chemicals, US Production
    and Sales, 1944, Report No. 155, Second Series, Washington DC, US
    Government Printing Office, p. 120

US Tariff Commission (1955)  Synthetic Organic Chemicals, US Production
    and Sales, 1954, Report No. 196, Second Series, Washington DC, US
    Government Printing Office, pp. 142, 151

Weast, R.C., ed. (1976a)  CRC Handbook of Chemistry and Physics, 57th ed.,
    Cleveland, Ohio, Chemical Rubber Co., p. C-464

Weast, R.C., ed. (1976b)  CRC Handbook of Chemistry and Physics, 57th ed.,
    Cleveland, Ohio, Chemical Rubber Co., p. C-465

Wimberley, J.W. & Jordan, D.E. (1971)  Automated method for the deter-
    mination of low concentrations of polyelectrolytes.  Anal. chim. acta,
    56, 308-312 [Chem. Abstr., 76, 46585s]

Windholz, M., ed. (1976a)  The Merck Index, 9th ed., Rahway, NJ, Merck &
    Co., p. 17

Windholz, M., ed. (1976b)  The Merck Index, 9th ed., Rahway, NJ, Merck &
    Co., p. 786

Windholz, M., ed. (1976c)  The Merck Index, 9th ed., Rahway, NJ, Merck &
    Co., p. 495

Winell, M. (1975)  An international comparison of hygienic standards for
    chemicals in the work environment.  Ambio, 4, 34-36

Zaytseva, N.A., Tolstobrova, S.A. & Il'in, D.T. (1972)  Chromatographic
    determination of unreacted monomers in emulsions of acrylic copolymers
    (Russ.).  Soviet chem. Ind., 48, 298-299

ACRYLONITRILE, ACRYLIC and MODACRYLIC FIBRES, and
ACRYLONITRILE-BUTADIENE-STYRENE and
STYRENE-ACRYLONITRILE COPOLYMERS

Acrylonitrile

## 1. Chemical and Physical Data

### 1.1 Synonyms and trade names

Chem. Abstr. Services Reg. No.: 107-13-1

Chem. Abstr. Name: 2-Propenenitrile

AN; cyanoethylene; propenenitrile; VCN; vinyl cyanide

Acrylon; Carbacryl; Fumigrain; Ventox

### 1.2 Structural and molecular formulae and molecular weight

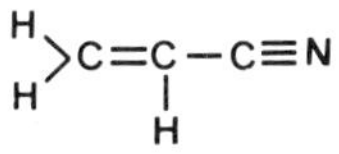

$$\begin{matrix} H \\ H \end{matrix} {>} C{=}C{-}C{\equiv}N \\ \qquad\quad | \\ \qquad\quad H$$

$C_3H_3N$          Mol. wt: 53.1

### 1.3 Chemical and physical properties of the pure substance

From Weast (1976), unless otherwise specified

(a) *Description*: Clear, colourless liquid (Fassett, 1963)

(b) *Boiling-point*: 77.5-79°C

(c) *Melting-point*: -83.5°C

(d) *Density*: $d_4^{20}$ 0.8060; vapour-air density at 37.7°C, 1.2;
vapour density, 1.8 (air = 1) (Anon., 1972)

(e) *Refractive index*: $n_D^{20}$ 1.3911

(f) *Spectroscopy data*: $\lambda_{max}$ 203 nm ($E_1^1$ = 1163); infra-red,
Raman, nuclear magnetic resonance and mass spectral data
have been tabulated (Grasselli & Ritchey, 1975).

(g) Solubility: Soluble in water, acetone and benzene; miscible with ethanol and ether

(h) Volatility: Vapour pressure is 100 mm at $23^\circ C$ (Perry & Chilton, 1973).

(i) Stability: Flash-point (open cup), $0^\circ C$ (Anon., 1972); may release cyanide when burned, especially when the oxygen supply is limited (US Department of Labor, 1978). Polymerizes spontaneously, particularly in the absence of oxygen, on exposure to visible light and in contact with concentrated alkali (Windholz, 1976)

(j) Reactivity: Undergoes reactions at both the nitrile group and the double bond (Maltoni *et al.*, 1977)

(k) Conversion factor: 1 ppm in air = $2.2 \text{ mg/m}^3$

## 1.4 Technical products and impurities

Acrylonitrile is available commercially in the US in 55-gallon drums, tank cars and tank trucks. The technical grade is more than 99% pure and meets the following specifications: a stability of not less than 4 hours when exposed to oxygen at 100 pounds per square inch (7 kg/cm$^2$) and 100$^\circ$C; water content of 0.25-.45%; and with maximum impurities in mg/kg (ppm) as follows: acidity (as acetic acid), 20; aldehydes (as acetaldehyde), 100; divinylacetylene, 5; hydrogen cyanide, 5; iron (soluble), 0.2; methyl vinyl ketone, 100; peroxides (as hydrogen peroxide), 1; non-volatile matter, 100. Hydroquinone monomethyl ether is added as an inhibitor at concentrations of 35-45 mg/kg (ppm).

In Japan, acrylonitrile has a minimum purity of 99% and may contain acetonitrile and acrolein as impurities.

## 2. Production, Use, Occurrence and Analysis

A review article on acrylonitrile has been published recently (US Consumer Product Safety Commission, 1978).

## 2.1 Production and use

### (a) Production

Acrylonitrile was first prepared in 1893 by dehydration of either acrylamide or ethylene cyanohydrin with phosphorus pentoxide (Fugate, 1963).

All US and Japanese acrylonitrile production is now based on the Sohio process, in which propylene, ammonia and air are reacted in the vapour phase in the presence of a bismuth-iron catalyst. Hydrogen cyanide and acetonitrile are the chief by-products formed. Sulphuric acid is used to remove excess ammonia from the reaction mixture, and the nitrile compounds are removed by absorption in water. High-purity acrylonitrile is obtained by a series of distillations.

Commercial production of acrylonitrile in the US was first reported in 1940 (US Tariff Commission, 1941). Four US companies produced 690 million kg acrylonitrile in 1976 (US International Trade Commission, 1977a); production in 1975 amounted to 552 million kg (US International Trade Commission, 1977b). In 1976, US imports of acrylonitrile were 6.1 million kg, with 51.7% from Taiwan, 48.2% from Japan and the remaining 0.1% from the Federal Republic of Germany (US Department of Commerce, 1977a); total exports were 105.9 million kg acrylonitrile, to the following countries (per cent of total): Argentina (6.6), Brazil (11.1), Canada (19.7), the Federal Republic of Germany (4.5), Mexico (14.2), The Netherlands (19.4), Peru (15.0), and at least eight other countries (9.5) (US Department of Commerce, 1977b).

Total western European production in 1976 amounted to 915 million kg, in the following countries (in millions of kg): the Federal Republic of Germany (285), France (125), Italy (185), The Netherlands (95), Spain (45) and the UK (180). Exports from western Europe in that year were 170 million kg, and imports were 155 million kg.

Acrylonitrile has been produced commercially in Japan since 1958. In 1976, six Japanese companies produced 633 million kg; imports amounted to 7 million kg, and exports were 75 million kg.

Total world production of acrylonitrile in 1976 was about 2 400 million kg.

(b) Use

Acrylonitrile was used in the US in 1976 as follows: for the manufacture of acrylic and modacrylic fibres (48%), acrylonitrile-butadiene-styrene and styrene-acrylonitrile resins (21%) (see monograph on styrene, p. 231), adiponitrile (12%) and other applications (mainly the production of butadiene-acrylonitrile copolymers) (19%).

In 1976, 282 million kg acrylonitrile were used to make acrylic and modacrylic fibres. These fibres are used primarily (82%) in clothing and home furnishings; the remainder (18%) was exported. For a detailed description of the uses of acrylic and modacrylic fibres, see p. 89.

Acrylonitrile-butadiene-styrene resins accounted for 88% of the acrylonitrile used for the production of these and styrene-acrylonitrile resins. The major applications for acrylonitrile-butadiene-styrene resins are in pipe fittings, automotive and recreational vehicle components and large appliances. Styrene-acrylonitrile resins are used primarily in automobile instrument panels and in drinking tumblers and other houseware items. For a detailed description of the uses of these two resins, see pp. 95 and 99.

Adiponitrile is used almost exclusively as a chemical intermediate. It is hydrogenated to hexamethylenediamine, which is reacted with adipic acid to produce nylon 6/6.

Other applications for acrylonitrile, and the per cent of total use in the US, are as follows: manufacture of nitrile elastomers (4%), acrylamide (4%), barrier resins (3%) and miscellaneous applications (e.g., polyether polymer polyols, fatty diamines) (8%).

Nitrile elastomers and latexes made by copolymerizing butadiene and acrylonitrile usually contain 30-40% acrylonitrile. Nitrile elastomers are used primarily when resistance to oil and hydrocarbon solvents is required (e.g., well-head packing and drill-pipe protectors in the petroleum industry and hoses, gaskets and belts in the food and automobile industries). Nitrile latexes are used in paper coatings and as pigment binders in leather finishing.

Acrylamide is used primarily to make polyacrylamides used in waste and water treatment and as papermaking strengtheners and retention aids.

Nitrile resins made from copolymers of acrylonitrile and other monomers (e.g., methyl acrylate) have been used to make beverage bottles; however, this usage was banned in the US from September 1977 (US Food & Drug Administration, 1977a). In early 1977, one company was reported to be producing a nitrile resin in Switzerland for use in Sweden in the manufacture of beer bottles (Anon., 1977a).

Acrylonitrile has also been used in a mixture with carbon tetrachloride as a fumigant for stored tobacco (Berg, 1977) and for flour milling and bakery food processing equipment. Although it is a registered pesticide in the US and the Environmental Protection Agency has classified it for restricted use by certified applicators (US Environmental Protection Agency, 1977), most pesticide products containing acrylonitrile have been withdrawn voluntarily by the manufacturers.

In western Europe, acrylonitrile was used in 1977 as follows: acrylic fibres (68%), acrylonitrile-butadiene-styrene/styrene-acrylonitrile resins (15%), nitrile elastomers (5%) and other applications (12%). The total amount used in 1976 was approximately 900 million kg.

In Japan, acrylonitrile was used in 1976 as follows: acrylic fibres (65%), acrylonitrile-butadiene-styrene/styrene-acrylonitrile resins and nitrile elastomers (17%) and other applications (18%).

The US Food and Drug Administration permits the use of acrylonitrile polymers and copolymers as components of the following products when they are intended for use in contact with food:  (1) vinyl resin coatings; (2) adhesives;  (3) cellophane;  (4) paper and paperboard components (limited to use as a size promoter and retention aid in containers for aqueous and fatty foods only);  (5) polyolefin films;  (6) elastomers (for repeated use);  and (7) rigid, semi-rigid and modified acrylic and vinyl plastics (in conjunction with designated polymers and copolymers at maximum levels of 5 wt % - acrylics - and 50 wt % - vinyl - of the total polymer content).  The amounts present may not exceed that which is reasonably required to produce the intended effect (US Food and Drug Administration, 1977b).

Prior to 17 January 1978, the US Occupational Safety and Health Administration's health standards for exposure to air contaminants required that an employee's exposure to acrylonitrile not exceed an eight-hour time-weighted average of 20 ppm (45 mg/m$^3$) in the workplace air in any eight-hour work shift of a forty-hour work week (US Occupational Safety and Health Administration, 1976).  On 17 January 1978, the US Occupational Safety and Health Administration announced an emergency standard for acrylonitrile, which limits employee exposure to an eight-hour time-weighted average of 2 ppm (4.5 mg/m$^3$) acrylonitrile in air.  A ceiling level of 10 ppm was also set for any 15-minute period during the eight-hour shift (US Department of Labor, 1978).

On 3 June 1977, the Federal Republic of Germany placed acrylonitrile in the category of carcinogenic chemicals for which no threshold limit values are established because they induce cancer in experimental animals when administered by the same routes as those involved in human exposure (Senatskommission zur Prüfung gesundheitsschädlicher Arbeitsstoffe, 1977).

The maximum allowable concentration in The Netherlands in 1977 was 20 ppm (45 mg/m$^3$) (Anon., 1977b).

## 2.2  Occurrence

Acrylonitrile is not known to occur as a natural product.

### (a)  Acrylonitrile-derived polymers

Residual acrylonitrile has been reported in a limited number of samples of commercial polymeric materials derived from acrylonitrile at the following levels:  (1) acrylic and modacrylic fibres, generally less than 1 mg/kg;  (2) acrylonitrile-butadiene-styrene resins, 30-50 mg/kg; (3) styrene-acrylonitrile resins, 15 mg/kg;  and (4) nitrile rubbers and latex materials, 0-750 mg/kg (US Consumer Product Safety Commission, 1978). Residual acrylonitrile levels in finished acrylic fibres 'are usually well below 20 ppm' (US Department of Labor, 1978).

Acrylonitrile was reported as one of eleven products formed when styrene-acrylonitrile polymers were pyrolysed under nitrogen at 500°C (Braun & Disselhoff, 1972).

(b)  Water

Acrylonitrile has been detected at a concentration of 0.1 g/l in effluent discharged from a US acrylic fibre manufacturing plant (Eurocop-Cost, 1976) and in effluent discharged from chemical and latex manufacturing plants in Louisville, Kentucky (Shackelford & Keith, 1976).

(c)  Air - Occupational environment

The total emissions of acrylonitrile to the US workplace environment in 1974 are estimated to have been 14.1 million kg. The breakdown by source was: acrylonitrile production, 6.4 million kg; end-product manufacture, 5.9 million kg; and bulk storage, 1.8 million kg (Patterson *et al.*, 1976). It has been estimated that 125 000 persons are potentially exposed to acrylonitrile in US workplaces (National Institute for Occupational Safety and Health, 1977a, 1978).

The stage of acrylic fibre production at which potential employee exposure is greatest is when the solvent is removed from newly-formed fibres. Several steps in the production of acrylonitrile-butadiene-styrene copolymer have been identified as potential employee exposure sources (US Department of Labor, 1978).

In studies in the USSR, acrylonitrile has been detected in workplace air in: (1) a thermosetting plastics plant, at a concentration of 1.4 mg/m$^3$ (Scupakas, 1968); (2) a rubber footwear plant, at concentrations of 1-11 mg/m$^3$ (Volkova & Bagdinov, 1969); and (3) in several sewing factories using fabrics of mixed synthetic and natural fibres (Fedorchuk, 1973).

Acrylonitrile has been reported in the workplace air of an acrylonitrile plant, in the range of 11.2-22.1 g/hr (Musserskaya & Boklag, 1976), and in an acrylic fibre plant in concentrations of 3-20 mg/m$^3$ in air (Orusev *et al.*, 1973). It has also been detected in the workplace atmosphere of a large acrylonitrile plant (Boklag, 1975) and of a polyacrylonitrile fibre plant (Stamova *et al.*, 1976).

(d)  Food

The content of acrylonitrile in containers fabricated from acrylonitrile copolymers and the possible migration of acrylonitrile to foods and beverages have been reviewed (US Food & Drug Administration, 1977a).

Acrylonitrile has been detected in shelled walnuts at concentrations of 0-8.5 mg/kg 38 days after fumigation with a mixture of acrylonitrile and carbon tetrachloride (Berck, 1960).

(e)  Other

Acrylonitrile has been detected: (1) in the smoke of US cigarettes and in the smoke of 100 non-filter cigarettes, at a level of 1-2 mg

(Guerin *et al.*, 1974; Wynder & Hoffmann, 1967); (2) in interstellar space (Gardner & Winnewisser, 1975); (3) as an impurity in organic soil-consolidating agents, in concentrations of 0.3 mg/ml (Matsumura & Arito, 1975); and (4) in commercial acrylamide, at a level of 25-50 mg/kg, and in polyether polymer polyols, at a level of 100-300 mg/kg (US Consumer Product Safety Commission, 1978).

2.3 Analysis

A sampling method using charcoal followed by gas chromatography has been recommended by the National Institute for Occupational Safety and Health in the US for determining acrylonitrile concentrations in workplace atmospheres, with a useful range of 17.5-70 mg/m$^3$ (8-30 ppm) (National Institute for Occupational Safety and Health, 1977b, 1978).

A colorimetric method, which allows a limit of detection of 20 ppm (44 mg/m$^3$), has been adopted by the International Union of Pure and Applied Chemists (IUPAC) for determining acrylonitrile in air (Gage *et al.*, 1962).

Various gas chromatographic packings have been evaluated for the collection and concentration of air pollutants, including acrylonitrile, for subsequent analysis by gas chromatography (Parsons & Mitzner, 1975; Russell, 1975). Head-space analytical methods, including detection by gas chromatography, have been used to determine residual acrylonitrile in its polymers, with a limit of detection of 0.5 mg/kg (Steichen, 1976).

Residual acrylonitrile has been determined by gas chromatography: (1) in latexes (Panova *et al.*, 1969); (2) in polyacrylonitrile by three methods, with limits of detection of 10, 100, and 100 mg/kg (Reichle & Tengler, 1968); (3) in commercial polystyrene plastics, with a limit of detection of 10 mg/kg (Klescheva *et al.*, 1971); (4) in water emulsion latexes used in the paper and textile industry (Bollini *et al.*, 1974); and (5) in emulsions of acrylic copolymers, with a limit of detection of 10 mg/kg (Zaytseva *et al.*, 1972).

Acrylonitrile can also be determined by gas chromatography: (1) as a fumigant residue in cereals and other foods, with a level of detection of 0.1 mg/kg (Heuser & Scudamore, 1969); (2) in blood and urine samples (Sato *et al.*, 1975); (3) after migration from medical polymers into aqueous solutions (Markelov & Semenenko, 1976); (4) as a by-product in the laboratory preparation of acrolein (Ustinovskaya *et al.*, 1977); (5) in the air of a plant producing plastic materials (Korzhova *et al.*, 1974); and (6) in acetone extracts of styrene-acrylonitrile resins, with a limit of detection of 1 mg/kg (US Consumer Product Safety Commission, 1978).

High-pressure liquid chromatography has been used to determine residual acrylonitrile in acrylic polymers and fibres (US Consumer Product Safety Commission, 1978).

Residual monomers, including acrylonitrile, have been determined in emulsion polymers using gel-permeation chromatography and ultra-violet spectrophotometry (Schmoetzer, 1972).

Polarographic methods have been devised to determine acrylonitrile in: (1) aqueous extracts of styrene-acrylonitrile copolymers, with a limit of detection of 0.2 mg/l (Petrova $et$ $al.$, 1972); (2) the volatile fractions of styrene copolymers, with a sensitivity of 2 µg/ml and a limit of detection of 100 mg/kg in the copolymer (Uhde & Koehler, 1967); and (3) industrial waste-water in the concentration range of 3-5 mg/l of water (Ponomarev $et$ $al.$, 1974).

Acrylonitrile has been determined colorimetrically in air with a limit of detection of 0.4-0.5 mg/m$^3$ by formation of cyanogen bromide followed by coupling with benzidine and pyridine to form the polymethine dye (Krynska, 1970; Russkikh, 1972, 1973). A similar method has been used for food (Kroeller, 1970). Colorimetric determination of acrylonitrile in waste-water has been also described, with a limit of detection of 2 mg/l (Ghersin $et$ $al.$, 1969). Kotova $et$ $al.$ (1972) have described the interference of dodecylmercaptan, tert-butyl perbenzoate and surfactants during spectrophotometric determination of acrylonitrile.

Acrylonitrile has been determined by titration methods: (1) in air after collection in sulphuric acid, with a limit of detection of approximately 0.5 ppm (11 mg/m$^3$) (Patterson $et$ $al.$, 1976); (2) in water, with a limit of detection of 0.05 mg/l (Wronski & Smal, 1974); (3) in waste-water, with a limit of detection of less than 2 mg/l (Stefanescu & Ursu, 1973); (4) in 9 samples of styrene-acrylonitrile copolymers (Roy, 1977); and (5) in aqueous copolymer latexes (Taubinger, 1969).

### 3. Biological Data Relevant to the Evaluation of Carcinogenic Risk to Humans

#### 3.1 Carcinogenicity studies in animals

##### (a) Oral administration

Rat: An interim report on oral studies in progress in rats indicates that in a small number of Sprague-Dawley rats administered 0, 35, 100 or 300 mg/l (ppm) acrylonitrile in the drinking-water, and killed after 12 months, squamous-cell papillomas of the forestomach, microgliomas of the central nervous system and Zymbal gland carcinomas occurred. Among male and female rats that ingested 100 or 300 mg/kg diet acrylonitrile for 12 months, stomach papillomas developed in 1/20 given 100 and in 12/20 given 300 mg/kg diet; central nervous system tumours were found in 2/20 given 35, in 6/20 given 100 and in 3/20 given 300 mg/kg diet; and Zymbal gland carcinomas occurred in 2/20 rats given 100 and in 2/20 given 300 mg/kg diet. No such tumours were seen in control animals (US Department of Labor, 1978).

A group of 40 male and 40 female Sprague-Dawley rats, 4-5 weeks of age, were given 5 mg/kg bw acrylonitrile in olive oil by gavage 3 times per week for 52 weeks. At 131 weeks, 21/40 (52.5%) females and 2/40 males had fibroadenomas and/or carcinomas of the mammary gland, compared with 33/75 (44%) female and 2/74 male controls; 1 treated male and 1 female control had a Zymbal gland carcinoma; 4 treated females, 1 treated male and 1 female control had forestomach papillomas and acanthomas; no increase was seen in the incidence of central nervous system gliomas (Maltoni *et al.*, 1977).

(b)  Inhalation and/or intratracheal administration

Rat:  In an interim report on inhalation studies in progress, Sprague-Dawley rats were exposed to 0, 44 or 170 mg/m$^3$ (0, 20 or 80 ppm) acrylonitrile in air for 6 hours a day on 5 days per week. After 1 year, 3/13 rats exposed to the 80 ppm level had tumours of the central nervous system and an increased incidence of Zymbal gland tumours (US Consumer Product Safety Commission, 1978; US Department of Labor, 1978).

Groups of 30 male and 30 female Sprague-Dawley rats, 4-5 weeks of age, were exposed to 88, 44, 22 or 11 mg/m$^3$ (40, 20, 10 or 5 ppm) acrylonitrile by inhalation for 4 hours a day on 5 days per week for 52 weeks. After 136 weeks, 13-23% treated rats had mammary tumours (*versus* 10% in controls); 1 female exposed to 20 ppm and 1 male and 1 female exposed to 10 ppm had a Zymbal gland carcinoma (none in the controls); 1.6-6.6% treated animals had forestomach papillomas and acanthomas (none in the controls); 2 males exposed to 40 ppm and 1 male exposed to 20 ppm had central nervous system gliomas (none in the controls) (Maltoni *et al.*, 1977).

3.2  Other relevant biological data

(a)  Experimental systems

Toxic effects

Table 1 summarizes the acute toxicity of acrylonitrile in experimental animals when given by various routes.

Acrylonitrile causes congestion in all organs of mice, rats and guinea-pigs, as well as damage to the central nervous system, liver and kidneys. I.p. injection of 50 mg/kg bw acrylonitrile daily for three weeks to adult rats resulted in loss of body weight, leucocytosis, functional disturbances in the liver and kidneys, slight damage to the neuronal cells of the brain stem and cortex and parenchymal degeneration of the liver and kidneys (Knobloch *et al.*, 1971).

A single i.v. dose of 150 mg/kg bw (15 mg/animal) acrylonitrile administered to rats produced bilateral adrenocortical haemorrhage and necrosis (Szabó & Selye, 1971).

Table 1

| Route of administration | $LD_{50}$ in mg/kg bw | | | |
|---|---|---|---|---|
| | Mice | Rats | Guinea-pigs | Rabbits |
| Oral | $27^a$ | $78^a$, $93^b$ | – | – |
| Intraperitoneal | $44^c$ | $100^d$ | – | – |
| Intravenous | – | – | – | $69^c$, $50^e$ |
| Skin application | – | – | – | $43^b$ |
| Subcutaneous | $34^d$ | $80^d$ | $130^f$ | – |
| Inhalation ($LC_{50}$ mg/1 (ppm))$^g$ | $0.30\ (140)^d$ | $0.33\ (150)^{h,i}$ $0.93\ (425)^{h,j}$ $0.47\ (220)^d$ | $0.99\ (455)^d$ | |

[a] Beneš & Černá (1959)
[b] Union Carbide Corporation (1970)
[c] Paulet & Desnos (1961)
[d] Knobloch *et al.* (1971)
[e] Hashimoto & Kanai (1965)
[f] Chiringhelli (1954)
[g] Neither the duration of exposure nor the duration of observation was indicated.
[h] Jaeger *et al.* (1974)
[i] Fasted animals
[j] Fed animals

Acrylonitrile applied to the skin of rats at doses of 28 or 14 mg/kg bw for 2 months, or 2.8, 0.56 or 0.11 mg/kg bw for 4.5 months, had a general toxic effect; the dominant changes were in the blood vessels (congestive plethora and haemorrhages) (Zotova, 1976).

Rats and rabbits that inhaled acrylonitrile at concentrations of 250 mg/m$^3$ air (114 ppm) for 6 months exhibited changes in peripheral blood pattern and functional disorders in the respiratory, cardiovascular and renal systems, as well as neuronal lesions in the central nervous system. Some of the same changes were observed after exposure to a concentration of 50 mg/m$^3$ (23 ppm) (Knobloch et al., 1972).

When given to rats subcutaneously at two times its $LD_{50}$, acrylonitrile decreased the glutathione content and reduced the activity of $\alpha$-ketoglutarate (oxoglutarate) dehydrogenase of both liver and kidneys. It increased the content of lactic acid, the production of malonaldehyde and the activity of catalase and glutathione peroxidase in the liver (Dinu, 1975; Dinu & Klein, 1976; Wiśniewska-Knypl et al., 1970). Administered intraperitoneally to rats at a dose of 100 mg/kg bw, acrylonitrile inhibits non-competitively the activity of brain, kidney and liver cytochrome oxidase (Tarkowski, 1968); when injected subcutaneously at a dose of 100-120 mg/kg bw it decreases the ratio between oxidized and reduced nucleotides in the brain and blood (Sokal & Klyszejko-Stefanowicz, 1972); when given as an i.v. dose of 150 mg/kg bw, it reduces the content of glutathione in liver, lung, kidneys, adrenals and brain of rats (Szabó et al., 1977).

I.p. injection of doses ranging from 20-80 mg/kg bw reduces the amount of non-protein SH groups in the liver of mice, guinea-pigs, hamsters and rats; mice were the most sensitive species (Vainio & Mäkinen, 1977).

L-Cysteine greatly reduced both acrylonitrile and hydrogen cyanide concentrations in the blood and protected animals from poisoning (Hashimoto & Kanai, 1965). Cysteine administered intraperitoneally is more effective than cystine, methionine or sodium thiosulphate in protecting rats against the toxic effects of subsequently (30 min later) inhaled or intraperitoneally administered acrylonitrile (Bondarev et al., 1976).

Embryotoxicity and teratogenicity

Acrylonitrile was administered by gavage at doses of 0, 10, 25 or 65 mg/kg bw to pregnant Sprague-Dawley rats on days 6-15 of gestation. Doses of 65 mg/kg bw were toxic to the mothers and produced an increased number of malformations among the foetuses and embryotoxicity. These effects were less apparent in those given 25 mg/kg bw; 10 mg/kg bw had no effect (Murray et al., cited in US Department of Labor, 1978).

Absorption, distribution, excretion and metabolism

After i.v. injection of a lethal dose of acrylonitrile (75 mg/kg bw) in rabbits, the hydrogen cyanide concentration in the blood rose steadily

until the death of the animals;  the thiocyanate concentration in the
blood increased slightly during this period.  After a single i.v. injection
of 15 mg/kg bw, about 3% of the dose was expired for about one hour, and
approximately 10% of the total dose was gradually excreted in the urine
for more than 48 hours after its injection.  The total amount of thiocyanate (formed from hydrogen cyanide) excreted in the urine over 24 hours
after the injection of acrylonitrite was equivalent to about 14% of the
dose (Hashimoto & Kanai, 1965).

In guinea-pigs, elimination of acrylonitrile in the urine was demonstrated within 24 hours and 30 hours after oral and s.c. administration,
respectively (Beneš & Černá, 1959).

Acrylonitrile is metabolized by mammals (mouse, rat, hamster, guinea-
pig, rabbit, dog, monkey) to cyanide, which is then transformed to thiocyanate and eliminated as such in the urine.  There is marked disagreement
as to what percentage is thus metabolized, and values from 4-30% have been
reported (Beneš & Černá, 1959;  Brieger *et al.*, 1952;  Czajkowska, 1971;
Paulet & Desnos, 1961).'

In rats given doses of 26-40 mg/kg bw, the elimination of thiocyanate
in the urine was over 20% of the dose after oral administration, 2-5% after
i.p. or s.c. injection and 1% after i.v. administration.  A greater amount
of acrylonitrile is transfored into thiocyanate after oral than after i.p.
administration in hamsters and mice (Gut *et al.*, 1975).

## Mutagenicity and other short-term tests

Acrylonitrile, in aqueous or gas phases, induced reverse mutations in
*Salmonella typhimurium* TA1530, TA1535, TA1950, TA100, TA1538, TA98 and
TA1978 in the presence of a 9000 x $g$ supernatant of liver from mice or rats
(de Meester *et al.*, 1978a,b;  Milvy, 1978;  Milvy & Wolff, 1977;  Venitt,
1978).  It was also mutagenic to *S. typhimurium* TA1530 in a fluctuation
test in the presence of a 9000 x $g$ supernatant of rat liver (de Meester
*et al.*, 1978a,b).

Acrylonitrile in solution produced reverse mutations in a plate inco-
poration assay using *Escherichia coli* WP2, WP2 *uvrA* and WP2 *uvrApolA*
without a metabolic activation system.  Acrylonitrile was also mutagenic
in the fluctuation test in *E. coli* WP2 and WP2 *uvrApolA* at a concentration
20-40-fold less than that used in the plate assay (Venitt *et al.*, 1977).

(b)  Humans

A review of the toxicity of acrylonitrile in humans is available
(US Department of Labor, 1978).

Several cases of acrylonitrile poisoning were reported in workers by
Wilson (1944).  The most frequent symptoms were slight jaundice, gastritis,
respiratory difficulties and fatigue.  Workers exposed to 35-220 mg/m$^3$

(16-100 ppm) for 20-45 minutes experienced respiratory and nervous system effects (Wilson *et al.*, 1948).

Workers aged 25-39, occupationally exposed to acrylonitrile at concentrations of 3-20 mg/m$^3$ (1.4-9 ppm), showed irritability, headaches and neurasthenic syndrome (Orusev & Popovski, 1973). Among 122 workers exposed to acrylonitrile, 77 showed a fall in the adrenergic activity of the blood with a simultaneous rise in the acetylcholine content; 54 had an astheno-vegetative syndrome (low arterial blood pressure, perspiration) (Ageeva, 1970).

Acrylonitrile was implicated as the causative agent in 4 cases of toxic epidermal necrosis which developed 11-21 days after persons returned to houses fumigated with a 2:1 mixture of carbon tetrachloride and acrylonitrile (the levels were not given). Three patients died of septic shock and gastrointestinal haemorrhage 3-4 weeks after exposure (Radimer *et al.*, 1974).

Examination of 18 workers who had been exposed to acrylonitrile for an average of 15.3 years and 18 workers who had not been exposed to acrylonitrile showed no difference in the incidence of chromosome aberrations (Thiess & Fleig, 1978).

## 3.3 Case reports and epidemiological studies[1]

A preliminary study reported to the Occupational Safety & Health Administration showed that persons occupationally exposed to acrylonitrile at one US textile fibre plant are at a greater risk of cancer morbidity and mortality of the lung and large intestine, as compared with the companywide experience. The increased risk of cancer morbidity and mortality was most evident among wage employees and was restricted to those observed 20 or more years following onset of exposure to acrylonitrile. When compared with the companywide cancer incidence experience, active male employees who were first exposed to acrylonitrile between 1950 and 1952 and observed for 20 or more years following onset of exposure demonstrated a statistically significant excess of total cancers (16 observed *versus* 5.8 expected), of lung cancers (6 observed *versus* 1.5 expected) and of large-intestine cancers (3 observed *versus* 0.5 expected). Similar excesses of cancer mortality were demonstrated when comparisons were made with either companywide or national mortality experience (US Department of Labor, 1978) [No information on cigarette smoking habits was reported,

---

[1]The Working Group was aware of a planned epidemiological study on workers exposed to acrylonitrile (IARC, 1978).

although there is no reason to believe that this could explain a major part of the excess cancer risk observed. No pathological data are presented].

## Acrylic and modacrylic fibres

### 1. Chemical and Physical Data

#### 1.1 Synonyms and trade names

##### Acrylic fibres

Acelan; Acribel; Acrilan; Acryl; Aksa; Anilana; Beslon; Bi-Loft; Bulana; Cashmilon; Courtelle; Creslan; Crilenka; Crumeron; Crylor; Crysel; Dolan; Dralon; Euroacril; Exlan; Fina; Fisisa; Jekrilon; Leacril; Makrolan; Malon; Melana; Nitron; Orlon; Pewlon; Redolen; Redon; R-P Acrylfaser; Safacril; Silpalon; Siracril; Tairylan; Tercryl; Toraylon; Town Flower; Triana; Velicren; Vonnel; Wolpryla; Yalova; Zefran

##### Modacrylic fibres

Elura; Kanecaron; Kanekalon; SEF; Teklan; Verel; Yalova

#### 1.2 Structural and molecular formulae and molecular weight

$$\left[ \begin{array}{cc} \overset{H}{\underset{H}{\mid}} & \overset{H}{\underset{CN}{\mid}} \\ C & - C \end{array} \right]_n$$   in combination with other monomers

$(C_3H_3N)_n$          Mol. wt:  100 000-150 000

#### 1.3 Chemical and physical properties of typical fibres

(a) Description: Wool-like

(b) Softening-point: 235-255°C (acrylic); 150°C (modacrylic)

(c) Specific gravity: 1.17 (acrylic); 1.37 (modacrylic)

(d) Solubility: Soluble in warm dimethylformamide, dimethylacetamide, in some concentrated salt solutions, and in 80%
sulphuric acid solution;  insoluble in hydrochloric acid,
glacial acetic acid and cold 90% phenol solution (Anon., 1973)

(e) Stability: Acrylic fibres have been reported to cyclize to
new polymers at temperatures above 250°C instead of reverting
to the component monomers (US Department of Labor, 1978).
Products produced by pyrolysis at 300-900°C have been studied;
the main products at 300°C are aliphatic aldehydes (van Grimbergen
*et al.*, 1975).

(f) Reactivity: Resistant to chemicals, weak alkalis and common
organic solvents;  attacked by hot, strong, alkaline solutions
(Anon., 1973).

## 1.4  Technical products and impurities

Many different kinds of acrylic and modacrylic fibres and variants
are available throughout the world, and their exact composition is not
commonly known.  The US Federal Trade Commission has defined acrylic fibres
as 'any long chain synthetic polymer composed of at least 85% by weight of
acrylonitrile', and modacrylic fibres as 'containing less than 85% but at
least 35% by weight of acrylonitrile' (US Department of Labor, 1978).  In
acrylic fibres, the remainder is generally acrylates, methacrylates or
vinyl monomers.  In modacrylic fibres, the remainder consists of vinylidene
chloride, vinyl chloride, vinyl bromide and other vinyl monomers (see also
individual monographs, pp. 367, 377, 439).  Depending on the country,
these fibres are available as yarn, staple and tow.

A typical acrylic fibre contains 85-91% acrylonitrile, 7-8% of an
acrylate comonomer (e.g., methyl acrylate or methyl methacrylate) and 2-5%
of other comonomers and additives, such as dyeing aids, coloured pigments,
titanium dioxide (a delusterant), optical brighteners, heat stabilizers,
fire retardants and light stabilizers.  The modacrylic fibre produced in
the largest quantity is composed of 37% acrylonitrile, 40% vinylidene
chloride, 20% isopropylacrylamide and 3% methyl acrylate.

Modacrylic fibres may contain similar amounts and kinds of additives
as acrylic fibres.

The levels of residual, unreacted acrylonitrile in commercial acrylic
and modacrylic fibres have been reported to be generally less than 1 mg/kg
(ppm) (US Consumer Product Safety Commission, 1978).

## 2. Production, Use, Occurrence and Analysis

Reviews have been published on acrylic and modacrylic fibres (Davis & Shapiro, 1964; Kennedy, 1968).

### 2.1 Production and use

#### (a) Production

Development of acrylic fibres was started in Europe and the US in the late 1930's. The first modacrylic fibre was introduced in the US in 1948, and the first acrylic fibre was introduced in 1950. Japan began commercial production of acrylic and modacrylic fibres in 1957. The US Federal Trade Commission officially defined the composition of acrylic and modacrylic fibres in 1960 (Davis & Shapiro, 1964; Kennedy 1968).

Acrylic and modacrylic fibres are prepared by polymerizing acrylo-nitrile and comonomers in suspension or in solution. In suspension poly-merization, the monomers are suspended in water by agitation. When a catalyst is added, polymerization occurs and the polymer separates as water-insoluble beads. These polymer beads are dissolved in a spinning solvent which is then extruded into a spinning bath (wet spinning) or into a column of circulating air (dry spinning), forming the fibres. In solu-tion polymerization, the monomers are dissolved in an organic solvent (dimethylformamide or dimethylacetamide) or a concentrated aqueous solution of zinc chloride, sodium thiocyanate or nitric acid. An initiator such as azobisisobutyronitrile is added, polymerization occurs, and the polymer remains dissolved. This polymer solution can then go directly to the spinneret, where it is either dry spun or wet spun to form the fibres.

In 1976, five US companies produced a total of 282 million kg acrylic and modacrylic fibres, of which 93-94% were acrylic fibres (Anon., 1977c). US imports of acrylic and modacrylic fibres combined were 10 million kg in 1976; exports were 50 million kg.

In 1976, 18 countries in Europe produced a total of 896 million kg of acrylic and modacrylic fibres. The countries (and the number of produ-cers in each country) were: Austria (1), Belgium (1), Bulgaria (1) Eire (1), France (2), the Federal Republic of Germany (3), the German Democratic Republic (2), Greece (2), Hungary (1), Italy (5), The Netherlands (1), Poland (1), Portugal (1), Romania (1), Spain (2), Turkey (2), the UK (3) and Yugoslavia (1) (Anon., 1977c). The major producing countries were the Federal Republic of Germany, Italy and the UK.

Five countries in North and South America, excluding the US, produced 82 million kg of acrylic and modacrylic fibres in 1976: Argentina (1), Brazil (2), Canada (1), Mexico (3) and Peru (1) (Anon., 1977c).

In Japan, six companies produced 288 million kg of acrylic fibres and 1 made 21 million kg of modacrylic fibres in 1976; imports of these fibres were negligible, but exports amounted to 141 million kg.

Four other countries produced a total of 162 million kg acrylic and modacrylic fibres in 1976:  Taiwan (2), India (2), Israel (1) and the Republic of Korea (2) (Anon., 1977c).

Worldwide production of acrylic and modacrylic fibres in 1976 is estimated to have been 1700-1800 million kg.

(b) Use

Acrylic and modacrylic fibres are used in a variety of textile applications because of their wool-like texture, hydrophobic properties, ability to be dyed easily, excellent resistance to shrinkage and weathering, low weight, resilience and thermoplastic nature (which enables them to be crimped to produce a high-bulk yarn).  Modacrylic fibres have the additional property of flame retardancy, but their softening point is much lower than that of acrylic fibres, and this prevents their use in some applications.

A total of 286 million kg of acrylic and modacrylic fibres were used in the US in 1976 (US Consumer Product Safety Commission, 1978).  Of the 237 million kg acrylic fibres used in 1974, 65% (154 million kg) was used in clothing, 33.5% (80 million kg) in home furnishings, 0.2% (0.5 million kg) in industrial markets and 1.3% (3.3 million kg) in miscellaneous applications.

The clothing in which acrylic fibres are used includes sweaters, handcraft yarns, deep pile fabrics, single- (e.g., for simulated fur fabrics) and double-knit yard goods and woven fabrics.  The knitted yard goods are used in women's dresses, loungewear, trousers, coats and suits and in men's shirts, suits and trousers.  Woven fabrics are used in women's dresses.

Home furnishing applications include carpets and rugs, blankets, draperies, curtains, upholstery and bedspreads.

Industrial markets for acrylic fibres include filters for dry substances, frequently for air pollution control, in webbing, in dye nets, and as a graphite fibre precursor.

Miscellaneous applications include fibrefill batting for pillows, clothing and upholstered furniture;  protective fabrics;  felts;  non-woven fabrics;  sandbags and other bagging;  and hairpieces.

Of the 16 million kg of modacrylic fibres used in the US in 1974 69% (11 million kg) was used in clothing, 26% (4.2 million kg) in home furnishings, 3% (0.5 million kg) in industrial applications and 2% (0.3 million kg) in miscellaneous applications.

Most of the clothing applications of modacrylic fibres are in deep-pile fabrics used as simulated fur fabrics for coats and trim.  Because of their flame retardant properties, they are also used in nonflammable

children's sleepwear and nonflammable work clothes [For a description of
the possible carcinogenic risk from flame retardants, see IARC, 1979].

Home furnishing applications of modacrylic fibres include carpets and
rugs (the largest market), blankets, draperies, curtains, upholstery and
bedspreads.

Industrial markets for modacrylic fibres include paint roller covers,
filters for aqueous substances, webbing and chemical-resistant twine.
Miscellaneous uses include protective fabrics, felts and hairpieces.

Of the 168 million kg acrylic and modacrylic fibres used in Japan in
1976, 55% was in clothing, 44% in home furnishings and 1% in industrial
applications.

2.2  Occurrence

Acrylic and modacrylic fibres are not known to occur as natural
products.

2.3  Analysis

Pyrolysis-gas chromatography can be used to analyse vinyl chloride-
acrylonitrile copolymer (Tanaka et al., 1975).  Polyacrylonitrile and
acrylonitrile copolymers have been analysed qualitatively by infra-red
spectrophotometry and pyrolysis-gas chromatography (Alloing & Dandoy,
1967).

Polyacrylonitrile and modacrylic fibres can be also analysed by infra-
red spectrometry, saponification and micro-Kjeldahl methods (Minkwitz &
Zimmer, 1974).


3.  Biological Data Relevant to the Evaluation

of Carcinogenic Risk to Humans

3.1  Carcinogenicity studies in animals

No data were available to the Working Group.

3.2  Other relevant biological data

(a)  Experimental systems

Implantation of polyacrylonitrile (Orlon) into the peritoneal cavity
of 3 dogs resulted in intraintestinal adhesions and adhesions to the
omentum with fibroblastic and foreign body reactions (Usher & Wallace, 1958).

No data on the embryotoxicity, teratogenicity, metabolism or mutagenicity of these compounds were available to the Working Group.

(b) Human data

No data were available to the Working Group.

## 3.3 Case reports and epidemiological studies

No data were available to the Working Group.

## Acrylonitrile-butadiene-styrene copolymers

### 1. Chemical and Physical Data

### 1.1 Synonyms and trade names

Chem. Abstr. Services Reg. No.:  9003-56-9

Chem. Abstr. Name:  2-Propenenitrile polymer with 1,3-butadiene and ethenylbenzene

ABS;  ABS copolymer;  ABS plastic;  ABS (polymer);  ABS resin; ABS terpolymer;  acrylonitrile-1,3-butadiene-styrene copolymer; acrylonitrile-butadiene-styrene polymer;  acrylonitrile-1,3-butadiene-styrene polymer;  acrylonitrile-butadiene-styrene resin;  acrylo-nitrile-butadiene-styrene terpolymer;  acrylonitrile polymer with 1,3-butadiene and styrene;  acrylonitrile-styrene-butadiene resin; butadiene-acrylonitrile-styrene copolymer;  butadiene-acrylonitrile-styrene terpolymer;  butadiene-styrene-acrylonitrile copolymer; styrene-acrylonitrile-butadiene copolymer;  styrene-acrylonitrile-butadiene polymer;  styrene-acrylonitrile-butadiene resin;  styrene-acrylonitrile-butadiene terpolymer;  styrene-butadiene-acrylonitrile copolymer

ABS 60;  Absafil;  Absaglas;  Absasar;  Absinol;  Abson;  Abson 820X14; Abson 821;  Abson 69163;  Abson 89110;  Abson 89131;  Abson 89140; Abson 89151;  ABSROM;  AFCORYL;  Ameripol 1013;  Arradur;  B 32; Bakelite;  Blendex;  Blendex 101;  Blendex 111;  Blendex 211; Blendex 301;  Blendex 311;  Blendex 401;  Blendex 425;  Blendex 435; Blendex 101ABS;  Cevian V;  Cevian V 120;  Cevian V 200;  Cevian V 610; Cycolac;  Cycolac AM 1000;  Cycolac CIT 31336;  Cycolac DH 1000;

Cycolac E;  Cycolac EP 3510;  Cycolac EPB;  Cycolac GSE 1000;
Cycolac GSM;  Cycolac GT 4502;  Cycolac H;  Cycolac HE;  Cycolac HM;
Cycolac KA;  Cycolac L 1000;  Cycolac MS;  Cycolac T;  Cycolac T 1100;
Cycolac T 2098;  Cycolac TD;  Cycolac TD 1001;  Cycoloy;  Cycopac;
Cycovin;  Denka ABS-GR 2000;  Dow 213;  Dow 300;  Dow 440;  Dow 500;
DP 35;  Dralastic;  Dylgl;  E 1000;  EPA 3530;  EPB 3570;  Estyrene;
Formid;  Forsan;  Forsan 048;  Fortylene;  Hi-blen 202;  Hiblen B 202;
Hycar 1577;  Hycar 1877X8;  JRS-ABS;  JSR-ABS 100;  301K;  Kaneace
SE 60;  KJT;  Kralastic;  Kralastic 2997;  Kralastic 3100;  Kralastic
K 3141;  Kralastic K 3170;  Kralastic K 3282;  Kralastic MH;
Kralastic MM 1801;  Kralastic MV;  Kralastic SR 1801;  Kralastic SRB;
Kralon;  Kurarasutiku K 3119;  Krynac 900X1;  Lacqran;  Lastilac;
Litac;  Lorkaril;  Lorkaril JA;  Lorkaril JCA;  Lorkaril JTE;
Lorkaril JTF;  Lustran;  Lustran 220;  Lustran 240;  Lustran 461;
Lustran 610;  Lustran 640;  Lustran 710;  Lustran 740;  Lustran 762;
Lustran 1762;  Lustran ABS 262;  Lustran ABS 640;  Lustran I 710;
Lustropack;  Lustrum;  Marbon E 1000;  Marbon EPA 3530;  Marbon TP
2098;  Marmix 16123;  Monsanto 299;  Monsanto 440;  Naugatuck 3168;
Neocaril;  Norsoran;  Novodur;  Novodur H 7004;  Novodur P 25;
Novodur PH/AT;  Novodur PH-GV;  Novodur PK;  Novodur P 20M;  Novodur
PM;  Novodur PM 2C;  Novodur P 2T/038;  Novodur PVM;  Novodur PX;
Novodur PX 792;  PG 299;  Polysar;  Ravikral;  Restiran;  Rexene;
Ronafil DSM;  Ronfalin;  Royalite 20;  Sconater;  Sconater 442MA;
Shinko-Lac;  Sicoflex;  SNK;  SR 1594;  Sternite;  Stylac;
Stylac 200;  Stylac 301;  Stylac XA 6705;  Sumirois I;  Sz NP;
T 2908;  T 4500;  TD 1001;  Terluran;  Terluran 877 T;  Toyolac;
Toyolac 100;  Toyolac 400;  Toyolac 9000;  Toyolac T 100;  TP 2098;
Tufrex;  Tufrex 410;  Tufrex 761;  Tybrene;  Tybrene 27;  Tybrene
217;  Tybrene 500;  Ugikral;  Urtal;  Urtal 1223;  Vallade OB;
Volkaril;  Vulkide A

## 1.2  Structural and molecular formulae and molecular weight

$$\left[\begin{array}{cc} H & H \\ | & | \\ -C & -C- \\ | & | \\ H & CN \end{array}\right]_x \quad \text{in combination with} \quad \left[\begin{array}{cccc} H & H & H & H \\ | & | & | & | \\ -C & -C & =C & -C- \\ | & & & | \\ H & & & H \end{array}\right]_y \quad \text{and} \quad \left[\begin{array}{cc} H & H \\ | & | \\ -C & -C- \\ & | \\ & H \end{array}\right]_z$$

$(C_3H_3N)_x$                       $(C_4H_6)_y$                      $(C_8H_8)_z$

Mol. wt:  60 000-200 000

## 1.3  Chemical and physical properties of the copolymers

From Keskkula (1970), unless otherwise specified

(a) Description: Rigid, thermoplastic solid (Hawley, 1977)

(b) Softening-point: 100-108°C

(c) Specific gravity: 1.04-1.05

(d) Solubility: Insoluble in alcohols, aliphatic hydrocarbons and mineral and vegetable oils (Hawley, 1977)

(e) Stability: Combustible but slow burning (Hawley, 1977). The main products produced by pyrolysis at 300-900°C were aliphatic aldehydes and styrene (van Grimbergen *et al.*, 1975). In addition, one would expect to find all pyrolysis products of styrene-acrylonitrile (see p. 98).

(f) Reactivity: Attacked by nitric and sulphuric acids, and by aldehydes, ketones, esters and chlorinated hydrocarbons (Hawley, 1977); unaffected by water, inorganic salts and alkalis

## 1.4  Technical products and impurities

Acrylonitrile-butadiene-styrene copolymers are available in the US in a full range of moulding and extrusion grades, which have different processing characteristics and a range of physical properties in the finished product. These resins are not random terpolymers of acrylonitrile, butadiene and styrene as the name implies; rather, they are a blend of

two phases:  (1) graft polymers of acrylonitrile and styrene on a polybutadiene substrate, and (2) styrene-acrylonitrile copolymers, with the acrylonitrile content ranging from 20-35%.  Some acrylonitrile-butadiene-styrene
resins may also contain α-methylstyrene-acrylonitrile copolymers.  The
graft polymer portion is rubbery and contributes toughness, and the styrene-
acrylonitrile copolymer portion contributes rigidity and resistance to
chemicals and solvents.  A typical medium impact grade of acrylonitrile-
butadiene-styrene copolymer is derived from 57.4% styrene, 13.3% butadiene
and 29.3% acrylonitrile, and has a softening point of $108^{\circ}$C and a specific
gravity of 1.05.

Typical acrylonitrile-butadiene-styrene copolymers in Japan have a
specific gravity of 1.03-1.05 and a softening point of $91-96^{\circ}$C.

Two US commercial copolymer samples examined were found to contain
30 and 50 mg/kg (ppm) residual, unreacted acrylonitrile monomer (US Consumer
Product Safety Commission, 1978).

## 2.  Production, Use, Occurrence and Analysis

### 2.1  Production and use

#### (a)  Production

A plastic material made from acrylonitrile, butadiene and styrene was
first introduced in the US in the late 1940's.  The polymer was a physical
blend of a butadiene-acrylonitrile rubbery copolymer and a styrene-
acrylonitrile copolymer.  In the 1950's, the technique of grafting styrene
and acrylonitrile onto polybutadiene rubber was perfected, thus introducing
the acrylonitrile-butadiene-styrene copolymers in use today (Basdekis,
1964).  These copolymers were first produced commercially in Japan in 1964.

Acrylonitrile-butadiene-styrene copolymers are produced commercially
in the US by graft polymerization of acrylonitrile and styrene on a polybutadiene substrate in emulsion, suspension and bulk processes (Morneau
*et al.*, 1978).

In 1976, seven US companies produced a combined total of 420-450
million kg acrylonitrile-butadiene-styrene copolymers.  Exports were
14.5 million kg, and imports were 3.6 million kg.

In the same year, 290 million kg acrylonitrile-butadiene-styrene
copolymers were produced in western Europe.  Among the major producing
countries (with production in millions of kg) were:  the Federal Republic
of Germany (70), France (25), Italy (40), Spain (5) and the UK (35).
A total of 99.5 million kg acrylonitrile-butadiene-styrene copolymers were
imported in 1975 by the following countries (millions of kg): Austria (2),
Belgium and The Netherlands (4), Denmark (8.5), Eire (0.5), the Federal
Republic of Germany (18), Finland (2), France (17), Norway (2.5), Portugal

(0.5), Spain (5), Sweden (8.5), Switzerland (4) and the UK (13). A total
of 50 million kg were exported in 1976 and 133 million kg in 1975; those
countries who exported in 1975 (millions of kg) were: Belgium and The
Netherlands (78), the Federal Republic of Germany (30), France (6), Italy
(12) and the UK (7).

In Japan, ten companies produced a total of 232 million kg acrylonitrile-butadiene-styrene copolymers in 1976. Exports amounted to 39 million
kg, and there were no imports.

Other regions for which production and trade data (millions of kg) are
available for 1975 include: Andean countries - imports (3); Argentina -
production (4), imports (1); southeast Asia - imports (6); Australia -
production (6), imports (2); Brazil - production (0.5), imports (3.5);
Canada - production (29), imports (3); Mexico - production (3); and
Taiwan - imports (3.5).

Worldwide production of acrylonitrile-butadiene-styrene copolymers in
1976 is estimated to have been approximately 1000 million kg.

(b)  Use

The 476.7 million kg acrylonitrile-butadiene-styrene copolymers used
in the US in 1977 were in: piping (22%), automotive components (20%),
appliance components (15%), components of business machines, telephones
and electrical and electronic equipment (10%), pipe fittings (7%),
recreational vehicle components (7%) and other uses (19%).

Pipes and pipe fittings made of acrylonitrile-butadiene-styrene
copolymers are primarily used (75%) for drain, waste and vent piping. Most
of the balance is believed to be used in sewer main piping and house-sewer
connection piping, with smaller amounts used for electrical conduit and
industrial piping.

Acrylonitrile-butadiene-styrene copolymers are used for automotive
interior components such as instrument panels, consoles, ducts, door-post
covers and other smaller parts. Exterior parts include front radiator
grilles and headlight housings. In the 1978 model year, an average of
8 kg acrylonitrile-butadiene-styrene copolymers were used on a US-produced
passenger car.

Components of large appliances accounted for most (75%) of the acrylonitrile-butadiene-styrene copolymers used in appliances, especially door
liners and food compartments of household refrigerators. The remainder
was used for components of small appliances, such as fans and bases of
blenders.

Telephone components accounted for a large share (35%) of the acrylonitrile-butadiene-styrene copolymers used in electrical or electronic
applications. The remainder was used for housings of calculators and for

housings, covers, consoles and other components of business machines and other electrical and electronic equipment.

Snowmobile components represent the largest single use of acrylonitrile-butadiene-styrene copolymers in recreational equipment. Other uses include interior components and parts for campers and marine recreation applications (e.g., canoes and interiors of small and large boats).

Other uses of acrylonitrile-butadiene-styrene copolymers include packaging (margarine tubs); luggage and cases; toys and sporting goods; and furniture.

The use pattern for the 180 million kg acrylonitrile-butadiene-styrene copolymers used in western Europe in 1975 was as follows: 31% in appliances, 22% in automotive components, 13% in electrical/electronic applications, 7% in furniture, 5% in recreation equipment (including luggage and boats), 3% in piping and 19% in other unspecified applications.

Use of acrylonitrile-butadiene-styrene copolymers in Japan in 1976 was as follows: appliances (48%), automotive components (26%), houseware (22%), furniture (2%) and other unspecified uses (2%).

The US Food and Drug Administration permits the use of acrylonitrile-butadiene-styrene copolymer as an article or component of articles intended for use in contact with all foods, except those containing alcohol, provided that the copolymer meets the following specifications: (1) it consists of 84-89 parts by weight of a matrix polymer containing 73-78 parts by weight acrylonitrile and 22-27 parts by weight styrene, and of 11-16 parts by weight of a grafted rubber consisting of 8-13 parts butadiene/styrene elastomer, containing 72-77 parts by weight butadiene and 23-28 parts by weight styrene, and 3-8 parts by weight of a graft polymer having the same composition range as the matrix polymer; (2) nitrogen content of 16-18.5%; (3) the finished copolymer article contains no more than 11 mg/kg (ppm) residual acrylonitrile monomer; and (4) it meets the specified extractive limitations for food contact (US Food & Drug Administration, 1977b).

Since September 1977, acrylonitrile-butadiene-styrene copolymers are no longer permitted in the fabrication of beverage containers (US Food & Drug Administration, 1977a).

## 2.2  Occurrence

Acrylonitrile-butadiene-styrene copolymers are not known to occur as natural products.

## 2.3  Analysis

These copolymers have been analysed by pyrolysis, solubilization of volatile pyrolysis products in water, pH measurement and thin-layer chromatography of pyrolysis products (Braun & Nixdorf, 1972a).

Pyrolysis-gas chromatography has been used to identify acrylonitrile-butadiene-styrene copolymers (Takeuchi & Murase, 1967) and in 57 plastics, rubbers and related materials (Fischer, 1967), 37 commercial polymers (Okumoto & Takeuchi, 1972) and vinyl polymer binders used in paper coatings (Seves *et al.*, 1972). These resins have also been identified by pyrolysis-gas chromatography with additional identification of the pyrolysis products by ultra-violet spectrometry, colour-forming reactions and thin-layer chromatography (Braun & Nixdorf, 1972b).

Differential thermal analysis has been used to identify acrylonitrile-butadiene-styrene copolymers (Bosch, 1975; Karaenev *et al.*, 1974; Yamagami *et al.*, 1970).

## 3. Biological Data Relevant to the Evaluation of Carcinogenic Risk to Humans

No data were available to the Working Group.

## Styrene-acrylonitrile copolymers

### 1. Chemical and Physical Data

### 1.1 Synonyms and trade names

Chem. Abstr. Services Reg. No.: 9003-54-7

Chem. Abstr. Name: 2-Propenenitrile polymer with ethenylbenzene

Acrylonitrile polymer with styrene; acrylonitrile-styrene copolymer; acrylonitrile-styrene polymer; acrylonitrile-styrene resin; polystyrene-acrylonitrile; styrene-acrylonitrile polymer

Acrilafil; ACS; Afcolene; AS 61CL; Cevian N; Cevian NF; Denka AS-CY; Dialux; Dikaril; Estyrene AS; FN 20; FN 25; Kostil; Kostil 235; Kostil AN(ATX)2010; Kralac 1155; Litac; LNA 21-1000; Lorkaril; Luran; Luran 368R; Luran 378P; Lustran; Lustran 28; Lustran A; Lustran A 21; Lustran A 2121; Lustran LNA 21; Piccoflex; Polysan; Rexene 106; RMD 4500; Sahrekkusu; SAN-C; Sanrex; Sanrex SANC; Sanrex San-H; Sepian N 050; Sepian N 6000HL; SN 20; SN 20P; SN 25; SNP 2; SNP 20P; Terulan KR 2540; Thermocomp BF; Trolitul AN: Trolitul EN; Tyril; Tyril 760; Tyril 767; Tyril 780; Tyril 783; Tyril 860; Tyril 867

## 1.2  Structural and molecular formulae and molecular weight

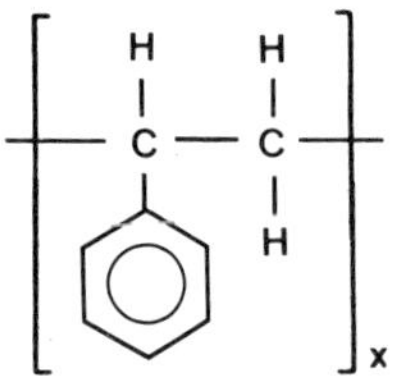

in combination with

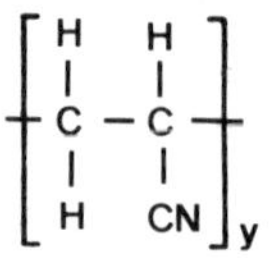

(65-80%)                                            (20-35%)

$(C_8H_8)_x$                                    $(C_3H_3N)_y$

Mol. wt:  100 000-400 000

## 1.3  Chemical and physical properties of the copolymers

From Lebovits (1964), unless otherwise specified

(a)  Description: Clear, colourless, thermoplastic solid

(b)  Softening point: $106°C$

(c)  Specific gravity: 1.06-1.08

(d)  Refractive index: $n_D$ 1.577-1.565

(e)  Solubility: Soluble in ketones; insoluble in aromatic compounds, although swelling occurs

(f)  Stability: Eleven compounds, including hydrogen cyanide, acetonitrile, propionitrile, acrylonitrile, toluene, styrene and ethylbenzene, have been identified in the products from pyrolysis under nitrogen at $500°C$ (Braun & Disselhoff, 1972).

(g)  Reactivity: Resistant to water, aqueous acids and alkalis, detergents and bleaches, gasoline and chlorinated hydrocarbons

## 1.4  Technical products and impurities

Styrene-acrylonitrile copolymers are available in the US in several moulding grades which have different processing characteristics and a range of physical properties in the finished product. They consist of a copolymer produced by copolymerizing 20-35 wt % acrylonitrile and 65-80% styrene. The residual, unreacted acrylonitrile content, as determined by gas chromatography, is 0.05-1.0 wt %. A typical styrene-acrylonitrile resin has a softening point of $110^{\circ}$C, a specific gravity of 1.08, a water absorption rate of 0.25% in 24 hours and a refractive index of 1.57 (Peng, 1978).

One US commercial resin sample examined was found to contain 15 mg/kg (ppm) residual, unreacted acrylonitrile monomer (US Consumer Product Safety Commission, 1978).

## 2. Production, Use, Occurrence and Analysis

### 2.1 Production and use

#### (a) Production

Commercial production of styrene-acrylonitrile copolymers in the US was first reported in 1947 (US Tariff Commission, 1947). They were first produced commercially in Japan in 1964.

Styrene-acrylonitrile copolymers are produced by emulsion, suspension and continuous mass polymerization processes. The continuous mass process has the advantage that there is no need for emulsifiers, suspending agents, salts or water (Peng, 1978).

Two US companies produced a combined total of approximately 50 million kg styrene-acrylonitrile copolymers in 1976. However, five other companies which produce acrylonitrile-butadiene-styrene copolymers can also produce styrene-acrylonitrile, which they use for blending in the production of acrylonitrile-butadiene-styrene copolymers. US exports of styrene-acrylonitrile copolymers amounted to 5.9 million kg in 1976; imports were less than 0.5 million kg.

Western European production of styrene-acrylonitrile copolymers in 1977 was 63 million kg.

In Japan, four companies produced a total of 63 million kg styrene-acrylonitrile copolymers in 1976. Exports amounted to 4 million kg; there were no imports.

Worldwide production of styrene-acrylonitrile copolymers in 1976 is estimated to have been 180 million kg.

#### (b) Use

In the US, styrene-acrylonitrile copolymers are special resins used principally for drinking tumblers and other houseware items, such as blender jars and covers, and some dishes and trays. Automotive applications include instrument panel windows. These resins are used for instrument lenses in general, as battery jars, for medical instruments and utensils, tape reels and covers and other items in the electronics field, and as a stiffening component in semi-rigid polyvinyl chloride sheet.

In Japan, styrene-acrylonitrile copolymers were used in 1976 as follows: production of acrylonitrile-butadiene-styrene copolymers, 40%; electrical/electronic applications, 25%; housewares, 23%; and automotive components, 12%.

In the US, styrene-acrylonitrile copolymer may be used as a component of packaging materials provided that, when it is used with non-alcoholic beverages, it: (1) has a minimum average molecular weight of 30 000; (2) consists of the copolymer produced by copolymerizing 66-72 parts by weight acrylonitrile and 23-34 parts by weight styrene; (3) has a nitrogen content of 17.4-19%; (4) the finished article contains no more than 80 mg/kg (ppm) residual acrylonitrile monomer; and (5) it meets the specified extractives limitations. When used in contact with other types of aqueous, fatty or dry food (excluding its use in bottles), the copolymer must meet the following specifications: (1) the minimum viscosity for a 10% solution at 25°C is 10 cP; (2) it consists of the copolymer produced by copolymerizing 45-65 parts by weight acrylonitrile and 35-55 parts by weight styrene; (3) it has a nitrogen content of 12.2-17.2%; (4) the finished article contains no more than 50 mg/kg (ppm) residual acrylonitrile monomer; and (5) it meets the specified extractives limitations. The Food and Drug Administration requires additional specific requirements for acrylonitrile copolymers, in general, when used in contact with food (US Food & Drug Administration, 1977b).

Since September 1977, styrene-acrylonitrile copolymers are not permitted in the fabrication of beverage containers (US Food & Drug Administration, 1977a).

## 2.2 Occurrence

Styrene-acrylonitrile copolymers are not known to occur as natural products.

## 2.3 Analysis

Simple tests for identifying 14 common polymers have been described, in which the polymers are floated on water, burned or fractured (Selerowicz, 1976).

Pyrolysis-gas chromatography has been used to determine styrene-acrylonitrile copolymers, alone (Braun & Disselhoff, 1972); in combination with mass spectrometry (Asahara *et al.*, 1969); in acrylic copolymers with infra-red spectral analysis (Alloing & Dandoy, 1967); in 57 plastics, rubbers and related materials (Fischer, 1967); in 37 commercial polymers (Okumoto & Takeuchi, 1972); and in synthetic resins, using ultra-violet spectrometry, colour-forming reactions and thin-layer chromatography for additional identification of the pyrolysis products (Braun & Nixdorf, 1972b).

Styrene-acrylonitrile copolymers have been identified by infra-red spectral analysis (Kimmer & Schmolke, 1972).

Styrene polymers, including styrene-acrylonitrile copolymers, have been identified using thin-layer chromatography of the pyrolysis products (Braun & Nixdorf, 1969).

### 3.  Biological Data Relevant to the Evaluation
### of Carcinogenic Risk to Humans

No data were available to the Working Group.

### 4.  Summary of Data Reported and Evaluation

### 4.1  Experimental data

Acrylonitrile was tested in two experiments in rats by oral administration and inhalation exposure. Although full results were not available, the data indicate that acrylonitrile is carcinogenic in rats, producing tumours of the forestomach, brain and Zymbal gland. Acrylonitrile is also embryotoxic, teratogenic and mutagenic.

No carcinogenicity data on acrylic and modacrylic fibres or on acrylonitrile-butadiene-styrene and styrene-acrylonitrile copolymers were available to the Working Group.

### 4.2  Human data

A preliminary epidemiological report on cancer incidence and mortality demonstrated that individuals who were exposed to acrylonitrile in certain areas of a textile fibres plant had an increased risk of cancer of the lung and of the large intestine. Exposure to acrylonitrile is known to occur in various occupational settings, and members of the general population may be exposed as a result of fumigant applications on tobacco and contact with food and other consumer goods contaminated by this compound.

No data relating to the carcinogenicity of acrylic or modacrylic fibres or acrylonitrile-butadiene-styrene and styrene-acrylonitrile copolymers in humans were available to the Working Group (see also monographs on styrene and styrene oxide, pp. 231 and 275).

### 4.3  Evaluation

Animal experiments involving oral administration and inhalation exposure have demonstrated that tumours are induced in the brain, forestomach and Zymbal gland in male and female rats. In a preliminary report, humans exposed to acrylonitrile in a synthetic fibres plant were found to be at a statistically increased risk of cancer, particularly of the lung and of the large intestine. This combined evidence from human and experimental data, in addition to the finding that acrylonitrile is mutagenic, indicates that, while confirmatory evidence in experimental animals and humans is desirable, acrylonitrile should be regarded as if it were carcinogenic to humans.

# 5. References

Ageeva, T.S. (1970)  The condition of the metabolism of mediating substances in workers producing acrylonitrile (Russ.).  Tr. Sarat. Med. Inst., 78, 10-13

Alloing, A. & Dandoy, J. (1967)  Examination of acrylic copolymers by various complementary methods (Fr.).  Ind. Chim. Belg., 32, 182-186 [Chem. Abstr., 70, 97204a].

Anon. (1972)  Fire Protection Guide on Hazardous Materials, 4th ed., Boston, Mass., National Fire Protection Association, pp. 49-32-49-33, 325M-19

Anon. (1973)  Chemical Technology: An Encyclopedic Treatment, Vol VI, Wood, paper, textiles, plastics and photographic materials, New York, Barnes & Noble, pp. 327-329

Anon. (1977a)  New plastic migration standards aligned in Europe, USA. European Chemical News, 18 March, p. 28

Anon. (1977b)  Safety Year Book, Amsterdam, Veiligheidsinstituut, p. 180

Anon. (1977c)  World man-made fiber survey. Textile Organon, 48, 75, 77, 85-99

Asahara, T., Seno, M. & Yatsugi, S. (1969)  Determination of pyrolysis product of copolymers by gas chromatography-mass spectrometry (Jap.) Seisan-Kenkyu, 21, 461, 466-467 [Chem. Abstr., 73, 131332q]

Basdekis, C.H. (1964)  ABS Plastics, New York, Reinhold, p. 2

Beneš, V. & Černá, V. (1959) Acrylonitrile: acute toxicity and mechanism of action (Ger.).  J. Hyg. Epidemiol. (Praha), 3, 106-116

Berck, B. (1960)  Retention of acrylonitrile and carbon tetrachloride by shelled walnuts fumigated with Acrylon.  J. agric. Food Chem., 8, 128-131

Berg, G.L., ed. (1977)  1977 Farm Chemicals Handbook, 63rd issue, Willoughby, Ohio, Meister Publishing Co., pp. D5, D50

Boklag, E.P. (1975)  Hygienic characteristics of working conditions in the production of acrylonitrile (Russ.).  Zdravookhr. Beloruss., 8, 41-44 [Chem. Abstr., 84, 94875y]

Bollini, M., Seves, A. & Focher, B. (1974)  Determination of free monomers in water emulsions of synthetic polymers or copolymers (Ital.). Ind. Carta, 12, 234-240 [Chem. Abstr., 81, 121672b]

Bondarev, G.I., Stasenkova, K.P. & Vissarionova, V.Y. (1976) Protective
    action of sulfur-containing compounds in poisoning with acrylic acid
    nitrile (Russ.). Vopr. Pitan., 4, 55-58

Bosch, K. (1975) Thermoanalytical identification of plastics (Ger.).
    Beitr. Gerichtl. Med., 33, 280-284 [Chem. Abstr., 84, 60332d]

Braun, D. & Disselhoff, R. (1972) Pyrolysis-gas-chromatographic analysis
    of acrylonitrile-styrene copolymers (Ger.). Angew. Makromol. Chem.,
    23, 103-115 [Chem. Abstr., 77, 88868n]

Braun, D. & Nixdorf, G. (1969) Identification of styrene- and α-methyl-
    styrene-containing polymers by thin-layer chromatography (Ger.).
    Gummi, Asbest Kunstst., 22, 183-184 [Chem. Abstr., 70, 972102z]

Braun, D. & Nixdorf, G. (1972a) Simple method of separation for the
    analysis of synthetic resins. III. Soluble polymers with basic
    reaction of the products of pyrolysis. Kunststoffe, 62, 268-271
    [Chem. Abstr., 77, 62339r]

Braun, D. & Nixdorf, G. (1972b) Separation of synthetic resins for
    analysis. 4. Soluble resins with neutral reaction of the pyrolysis
    products (Ger.). Kunststoffe, 62, 318-322

Brieger, H., Rieders, F. & Hodes, W.A. (1952) Acrylonitrile: spectro-
    photometric determination, acute toxicity, and mechanism of action.
    Arch. ind. Hyg., 6, 128-140

Czajkowska, T. (1971) Acrylonitrile metabolites excretion following a
    single dose (Pol.). Med. Pracy, 22, 381-385

Davis, C.W. & Shapiro, P. (1964) Acrylic fibers. In: Bikales, N.M., ed.,
    Encyclopedia of Polymer Science and Technology, Plastics, Resins,
    Rubbers, Fibers, Vol. 1, New York, Interscience, pp. 342-373

Dinu, V. (1975) Activity of glutathione peroxidase and catalase and the
    concentration of lipid peroxides in acute intoxication with acrylo-
    nitrile. Rev. Roum. Biochim., 12, 11-14

Dinu, V. & Klein, R. (1976) Catalase activity, glutathione and lactic
    acid levels in rats acutely intoxicated by acrylonitrile (Fr.).
    J. Pharmacol. (Paris), 7, 223-226

Eurocop-Cost (1976) A Comprehensive List of Polluting Substances which
    have been Identified In Various Fresh Waters, Effluent Discharges,
    Aquatic Animals and Plants, and Bottom Sediments, EUCO/MDU/73/76,
    XII/476/76, 2nd ed., Luxembourg, Commission of the European Communi-
    ties, p. 19

Fassett, D.W. (1963) Cyanides and nitriles. In: Patty, F.A., ed.,
    Industrial Hygiene and Toxicology, 2nd revised ed., Vol. II,
    Toxicology, New York, Interscience, pp. 2009-2012

Fedorchuk, S.Y. (1973) Functional state of the skin of female sewing-factory workers engaged in manufacturing products from textiles containing synthetic fibers (Russ.). Nauchno-Issled. Tr., Tsentr. Nauchno-Issled. Inst. Shveinoi Prom-sti., 24, 35-39 [Chem. Abstr., 83, 120317u]

Fischer, W.G. (1967) Pyrolytic gas-chromatography (Ger.). Glas-Instrum.-Tech., 11, 562, 567-570, 775-780, 1086-1088, 1091-1095 [Chem. Abstr., 68, 78636k]

Fugate, W.O. (1963) Acrylonitrile. In: Kirk, R.E. & Othmer, D.F., eds, Encyclopedia of Chemical Technology, 2nd ed., Vol. 1, New York, John Wiley & Sons, pp. 338-339

Gage, J.C., Strafford, N. & Truhaut, R. (1962) Methods for the Determination of Toxic Substances in Air - Acrylonitrile, Method 21, International Union of Pure and Applied Chemistry, London, Butterworths

Gardner, F.F. & Winnewisser, G. (1975) Detection of interstellar vinyl cyanide (acrylonitrile). Astrophys. J., 195, L127-L130 [Chem. Abstr., 82, 148236v]

Ghersin, Z., Stitzl, A. & Manea, R. (1969) Comparative study of titrimetric and colorimetric methods for determining acrylonitrile in waste waters (Rom.). Rev. Chim. (Bucharest), 20, 689-694 [Chem. Abstr., 72, 124853m]

Ghiringhelli, L. (1954) Acrylonitrile: toxicity and action (Ital.). Med. Lav., 45, 305-312

Grasselli, J.G. & Ritchey, W.M., eds (1975) CRC Atlas of Spectral Data and Physical Constants for Organic Compounds, 2nd ed., Vol. II, Cleveland, Ohio, Chemical Rubber Co., p. 102

van Grimbergen, M., Reybrouck, G. & van de Voorde, H. (1975) Air pollution due to the burning of thermoplastics. II (Ger.). Z. Bakteriol., Hyg., Abt. 1: Orig. B., 160, 139-147

Guerin, M.R., Olerich, G. & Horton, A.D. (1974) Routine gas chromatographic component profiling of cigarette smoke for the identification of biologically significant constituents. J. chromatogr. Sci., 12, 385-391

Gut, I., Nerudová, J., Kopecký, J. & Holeček, V. (1975) Acrylonitrile biotransformation in rats, mice, and Chinese hamsters as influenced by the route of administration and by phenobarbital, SKF 525-A, cysteine, dimercaprol, or thiosulfate. Arch. Toxicol., 33, 151-161

Hashimoto, K. & Kanai, R. (1965) Studies on the toxicology of acrylonitrile. Metabolism, mode of action and therapy. Ind. Health, 3, 30-46

Hawley, G.G., ed. (1977)  The Condensed Chemical Dictionary, 9th ed.,
    New York, Van Nostrand-Reinhold, p. 2

Heuser, S.G. & Scudamore, K.A. (1969)  Determination of fumigant residues
    in cereals and other foodstuffs:  a multi-detection scheme for gas
    chromatography of solvent extracts.  J. Sci. Food Agric., 20, 566-572

IARC (1978)  Directory of On-Going Research in Cancer Epidemiology, 1978,
    (IARC Scientific Publications No. 26), Lyon, p. 293 (Abstract No. 772)

IARC (1979)  IARC Monographs on the Carcinogenic Risk of Chemicals to
    Humans, 20, Some Halogenated Hydrocarbons (in press)

Jaeger, R.J., Conolly, R.B. & Murphy, S.D. (1974)  Toxicity and biochemical
    changes in rats after inhalation exposure to 1,1-dichloroethylene,
    bromobenzene, styrene, acrylonitrile or 2-chlorobutadiene (Abstract
    No. 16).  Toxicol. appl. Pharmacol., 29, 81

Karaenev, S., Mikhnev, B., Panaiotova, M. & Petkova, M. (1974)  Study of
    ABS (acrylonitrile-butadiene-styrene) copolymers by differential
    thermal analysis (Russ).  Plast. Massy, 1, 66-67 [Chem. Abstr., 81,
    26075a]

Kennedy, R.K. (1968)  Modacrylic fibers.  In:  Bikales, N.M., ed.,
    Encyclopedia of Polymer Science and Technology, Plastics, Resins,
    Rubbers, Fibers, Vol. 8, New York, Interscience, pp. 812-839

Keskkula, H. (1970)  Styrene polymers (plastics).  In:  Bikales, N.M., ed.,
    Encyclopedia of Polymer Science and Technology, Plastics, Resins,
    Rubbers, Fibers, Vol. 13, New York, Interscience, pp. 396, 408

Kimmer, W. & Schmolke, R. (1972)  Infrared-spectroscopic analysis of
    styrene-acrylonitrile copolymers and ABS (acrylonitrile-butadiene-
    styrene) (Ger.).  Plaste Kaut., 19, 260-262 [Chem. Abstr., 77,
    49259v]

Kleshcheva, M.S., Usacheva, V.T. & Pozharova, V.N. (1971)  Determination
    of residual monomers and non-polymerising impurities in polystyrene
    plastics by means of gas chromatography (Russ.).  Plast. Massy, 7,
    57-58

Knobloch, K., Szendzikowski, S., Czajkowska, T. & Krysiak, B. (1971)
    Experimental studies upon acute and subacute toxicity of acryloni-
    trile (Pol.).  Med. Pracy, 22, 257-269

Knobloch, K., Szendzikowski, S. & Czajkowska, T. (1972)  Experimental
    studies on chronic acrylonitrile toxicity (Pol.).  Med. Pracy, 23,
    243-257

Korzhova, I.T., Kleshcheva, M.S., Porodina, M.N., Korkhova, R.D.,
    Balandina, V.A. & Khokhlov, V.A. (1974) Gas-chromatographic deter-
    mination of toxic concentrations of styrene and acrylonitrile vapors
    during the synthesis of polystyrene plastics (Russ.). Plast. Massy,
    5, 67-69 [Chem. Abstr., 81, 110759j]

Kotova, V.N., Komarova, T.P. & El'tsefon, B.S. (1972) Effect of dodecyl-
    mercaptan, *tert*-butyl perbenzoate, and surfactants on the combined
    spectrophotometric determination of styrene and acrylonitrile in
    aqueous solutions (Russ.). Khim.-Farm. Zh., 6, 53-56 [Chem. Abstr.,
    77, 66247g]

Kroeller, E. (1970) Residual acrylonitrile determination in food (Ger.).
    Deut. Lebensm.-Rundsch., 66, 11-33 [Chem. Abstr., 72, 77505n]

Krynska, A. (1970) Method of determining acrylonitrile in air (Pol.).
    Pr. Cent. Inst. Ochr. Pr., 20, 303-310 [Chem. Abstr., 74, 90798w]

Lebovits, A. (1964) Acrylonitrile polymers. In: Bikales, N.M., ed.,
    Encyclopedia of Polymer Science and Technology, Plastics, Resins,
    Rubbers, Fibers, Vol. 1, New York, Interscience, pp. 428-431

Maltoni, C., Ciliberti, A. & Di Maio, V. (1977) Carcinogenicity bioassays
    on rats of acrylonitrile administered by inhalation and by ingestion.
    Med. Lav., 68, 401-411

Markelov, M.A. & Semenenko, E.I. (1976) Determination of microconcen-
    trations of substances migrating from polymer materials to water
    (Russ.). Plast. Massy, 1, 57-59 [Chem. Abstr., 84, 155747g]

Matsumura, Y. & Arito, H. (1975) Toxic volatile components of organic
    soil consolidating agents. Ind. Health, 13, 135-149 [Chem. Abstr.,
    84, 151310m]

de Meester, C., Poncelet, F., Roberfroid, M. & Mercier, M. (1978a)
    Mutagenic activity of acrylonitrile. A preliminary study.
    Arch. int. Physiol. Biochim., 86, 418-419

de Meester, C., Poncelet, F., Roberfroid, M. & Mercier, M. (1978b) Muta-
    genicity of acrylonitrile. Toxicology, 11, 19-27

Milvy, P. (1978) Letter to the editor. Mutat. Res., 57, 110-112

Milvy, P. & Wolff, M. (1977) Mutagenic studies with acrylonitrile.
    Mutat. Res., 48, 271-278

Minkwitz, D. & Zimmer, H. (1974) Analysis of polyacrylonitrile and moda-
    crylic fibers (Ger.). Melliand Textilber. Int., 55, 909-910
    [Chem. Abstr., 82, 18450z]

Morneau, G.A., Pavelich, W.A. & Roettger, L.G. (1978) ABS resins. In: Grayson, M., ed., Encyclopedia of Chemical Technology, 3rd ed., Vol. 1, New York, John Wiley and Sons, pp. 442-456

Musserskaya, A.N. & Boklag, E.P. (1976) Hygienic evaluation of ventilation in the modern production of acrylonitrile (Russ.). Zdravookhr. Beloruss., 1, 51-53 [Chem. Abstr., 85, 165783a]

National Institute for Occupational Safety and Health (1977a) Current Intelligence Bulletin: Acrylonitrile, July 1, Rockville, Md

National Institute for Occupational Safety and Health (1977b) National Institute for Occupational Safety and Health Manual of Analytical Methods, 2nd ed., Part II, Standards Completion Program Validated Methods, Vol. 3, Method No. S156, Washington DC, US Government Printing Office

National Institute for Occupational Safety and Health (1978) A Recommended Standard for Occupational Exposure to Acrylonitrile, DHEW (NIOSH) Publ. No. 78-116, Cincinnati, Ohio

Okumoto, T. & Takeuchi, T. (1972) Rapid characterization of polymeric materials by pyrolysis-gas chromatography (Jap.). Nippon Kagaku Kaishi, 1, 71-78 [Chem. Abstr., 76, 141459n]

Orusev, T. & Popovski, P. (1973) Symptoms of chronic occupational acrylonitrile poisoning (Macedonian). God. Zb. Med. Fak. Skopje, 19, 187-192

Orusev, T., Bauer, S. & Popovski, P. (1973) Occupational exposure to acrylonitrile in a plant for production of acrylic synthetic fibers (Macedonian). God. Zb. Med. Fak. Skopje, 19, 445-449 [Chem. Abstr., 81, 29030t]

Panova, R.V., Belova, R.A. & Lavrushina, T.S. (1969) Chromatographic determination of residual monomers in latexes (Russ.). Prom. Sin. Kauch., Nauch.- Tekh. Sb., 1, 21-23 [Chem. Abstr., 74, 43238d]

Parsons, J.S. & Mitzner, S. (1975) Gas chromatographic method for concentration and analysis of traces of industrial organic pollutants in environmental air and stacks. Environ. Sci. Technol., 9, 1053-1058

Patterson, R.M., Bornstein, M.I. & Garshick, E. (1976) Assessment of acrylonitrile as a potential air pollution problem, Vol. VI, US Environmental Protection Agency, Contract No. 68-02-1337, Task 8, Springfield, Va, National Technical Information Service, No. PB-258 358

Paulet, G. & Desnos, J. (1961) Acrylonitrile. Toxicity - mechanism of therapeutic action (Fr.). Arch. int. Pharmacodyn., 131, 54-83

Peng, F.M. (1978) Survey and styrene-acrylonitrile copolymers. In:
    Grayson, M., ed., Encyclopedia of Chemical Technology, 3rd ed.,
    Vol. 1, New York, John Wiley and Sons, pp. 427-442

Perry, R.H. & Chilton, C.H., eds (1973) Chemical Engineers' Handbook
    5th ed., New York, McGraw-Hill, p. 3-61

Petrova, L.I., Noskova, M.P., Balandina, V.A. & Guricheva, Z.G. (1972)
    Polarographic determination of acrylonitrile in aqueous extract of
    styrene-acrylonitrile copolymers (Russ.). Gig. i Sanit., 37, 62-65
    [Chem. Abstr., 76, 127898y]

Ponomarev, Y.P., Anufrieva, T.L. & Shkorbatova, T.L. (1974) Polarographic
    determination of acrylonitrile in waste waters using extraction (Russ.).
    Vodosnabzh., Kanaliz. Gidrotekh. Sooruzh., 17, 67-70 [Chem. Abstr.,
    82, 34803x]

Radimer, G.F., Davis, J.H. & Ackerman, A.B. (1974) Fumigant-induced toxic
    epidermal necrolysis. Arch. Dermatol., 110, 103-104

Reichle, A. & Tengler, H. (1968) Gas-chromatographic procedures for
    determining residual monomers in the polymer. Determination of
    acrylonitrile in polyacrylonitrile (Ger.). Plastverarbeiter, 19,
    921-924 [Chem. Abstr., 70, 97206c]

Roy, S.S. (1977) Titrimetric determination of residual monomers in
    styrene-acrylonitrile copolymers. Analyst, 102, 302-305

Russell, J.W. (1975) Analysis of air pollutants using sampling tubes and
    gas chromatography. Environ. Sci. Technol., 9, 1175-1178

Russkikh, A.A. (1972) Determination of acetone cyanohydrin and acrylo-
    nitrile in air (Russ.). In: Bezhaev, M.S., ed., Proceedings of the
    4th Conference of People Employed in Universities and Industrial
    Laboratories of South-East USSR on Physico-chemical Methods of
    Analytical Control of Industrial Products, Dagestan, USSR, State
    University, Vol. 3, p. 100 [Chem. Abstr., 81, 16301g]

Russkikh, A.A. (1973) Photometric determination of acrylonitrile and
    methacrylonitrile in air (Russ.). Zavod. Lab., 39, 5-6 [Chem. Abstr.,
    78, 101566e]

Sato, M., Ishizu, S. & Momotani, H. (1975) Determination of acrylonitrile,
    cyanide, and thiocyanate in blood and urine (Jap.). Sangyo Igaku, 17,
    99-105 [Chem. Abstr., 84, 100292z]

Schmoetzer, G. (1972) Determination of residual monomers in emulsion
    polymers (Ger.). Fresenius' Z. anal. Chem., 260, 10-24 [Chem. Abstr.,
    77, 127080w]

Scupakas, D. (1968) Industrial hygiene conditions during the reworking of plastics and problems of improving them (Russ). In: Yavnaist, E.Y., ed., Proceedings of the First Conference on Actual Problems of Industrial Hygiene and Occupational Pathology, 1967, Riga, Medical Institute, pp. 128-132 [Chem. Abstr., 72, 47094k]

Selerowicz, A. (1976) Simple methods for the identification of thermoplastics (Pol.). Mechanik, 49, 30-31 [Chem. Abstr., 85, 6079j]

Senatskommission zur Prüfung gesundheitsschädlicher Arbeitsstoffe (1977) Maximum concentrations in the workplace (Ger.), part 13, Bonn, Deutsche Forschungsgemeinschaft, p. 13

Seves, A., Croce, A. & Brizzi, P. (1972) Gas chromatography by pyrolysis for the identification of coating binders (Ital.). Ind. Carta, 10, 271-280 [Chem. Abstr., 77, 154171h]

Shackelford, W.M.. & Keith, L.H. (1976) Frequency of Organic Compounds Identified in Water, EPA-600/4-76-062, Athens, Ga, US Environmental Protection Agency, p. 55

Sokal, J.A. & Klyszejko-Stefanowicz, L. (1972) Nicotinamide-adenine dinucleotides in acute poisoning with some toxic agents (Pol.). Lodz. Tow. Nauk., Pr. Wydz., 3, 104 pp. [Chem. Abstr., 79, 62271d]

Stamova, N., Gincheva, N., Spasovskü, M., Bainova, A., Ivanova, S., Kurkchiev, S., Khristeva, V., Mukhtarova, M., Karadzhova, N. et al. (1976) Labor hygiene during the production of Bulana synthetic fibers (Bul.). Khig. Zdraveopaz., 19, 134-140 [Chem. Abstr., 86, 176464u]

Stefanescu, T. & Ursu, G. (1973) Method for acrylonitrile and acetonitrile determination in residual waters (Rom.). Mater. Plast. (Bucharest), 10, 330-334 [Chem. Abstr., 80, 40770j]

Steichen, R.J. (1976) Modified solution approach for the gas chromatographic determination of residual monomers by head-space analysis. Anal. Chem., 48, 1398-1402

Szabó, S. & Selye, H. (1971) Adrenal apoplexy and necrosis produced by acrylonitrile. Endokrinologie, 57, 405-408

Szabó, S., Bailey, K.A., Boor, P.J. & Jaeger, R.J. (1977) Acrylonitrile and tissue glutathione: differential effect of acute and chronic interactions. Biochem. biophys. Res. Comm., 79, 32-37

Takeuchi, T. & Murase, K. (1967) Investigation of ABS (acrylonitrile-butadiene-styrene) resins by pyrolysis gas chromatography (Jap.). Kogyo Kagaku Zasshi, 70, 454-460 [Chem. Abstr., 68, 74882q]

Tanaka, M., Nishimura, F. & Shono, T. (1975) Pyrolysis-gas chromatography of vinyl chloride-methyl methacrylate and vinyl chloride-acrylonitrile copolymers. Anal. chim. acta, 74, 119-124 [Chem. Abstr., 82, 86798u]

Tarkowski, S. (1968) Studies on acrylonitrile effect on some properties of cytochrome oxidase (Pol.). Med. Pracy, 19, 525-531

Taubinger, R.P. (1969) Direct determination of free acrylonitrile in aqueous copolymers latexes. I. Rapid potentiometric titration method. Analyst (Lond.), 94, 628-633 [Chem. Abstr., 71, 113873w]

Thiess, A.M. & Fleig, I. (1978) Analysis of chromosomes of workers exposed to acrylonitrile. Arch. Toxicol., 41, 149-152

Uhde, W.J. & Koehler, U. (1967) Testing of plastic articles. Determination of monomeric compounds in the volatile fraction of styrene polymers (Ger.). Z. Lebensm. Unters.-Forsch., 135, 135-140 [Chem. Abstr., 67, 117599b]

Union Carbide Corporation (1970) Toxicology Studies - Acrylonitrile, New York, Industrial Medicine and Toxicology Department

US Consumer Product Safety Commission (1978) Assessment of Acrylonitrile Contained in Consumer Products, Final Report, Contract No. CPSC-C-77-0009, Task No. 1014K, H.I.A./Economic Analysis, Washington DC

US Department of Commerce (1977a) US Imports for Consumption and General Imports, TSUSA Commodity by Country of Origin, FT 246/Annual 1976, Bureau of the Census, Washington DC, US Government Printing Office, p. 226

US Department of Commerce (1977b) US Exports, Schedule B Commodity Groupings, Schedule B Commodity by Country, FT410/December, Bureau of the Census, Washington DC, US Government Printing Office, p. 2-86

US Department of Labor (1978) Occupational exposure to acrylonitrile (vinyl cyanide). Proposed standard and notice of hearing. Fed. Regist., 43, 2586-2621

US Environmental Protection Agency (1977) Optional procedures for classification of pesticide uses by regulation. Fed. Regist., 42, 44170, 44178

US Food & Drug Administration (1977a) Acrylonitrile copolymers used to fabricate beverage containers; final decision. Fed. Regist., 42, 48528-48544, 61254

US Food & Drug Administration (1977b)  Substances for use only as components of adhesives.  US Code Fed. Regul., Title 21, parts 175.105, 175.300, 175.320, 176.170, 176.180, 177.1010, 177.1020, 177.1040, 177.1200, 177.2600, 178.3790, 180.22, pp. 438, 445, 452, 455, 465, 471-472, 482-483, 486, 488, 496, 501-504, 555, 557, 596, 609-611

Usher, F.C. & Wallace, S.A. (1958)  Tissue reaction to plastics.  A comparison of Nylon, Orlon, Dacron, Teflon, and Marlex.  Arch. Surg., 76, 997-999

US International Trade Commission (1977a)  Synthetic Organic Chemicals, US Production and Sales, 1976, USITC Publication 833, Washington DC, US Government Printing Office, pp. 300, 313

US International Trade Commission (1977b)  Synthetic Organic Chemicals, US Production and Sales, 1975, USITC Publication 804, Washington DC, US Government Printing Office, pp. 194, 205

US Occupational Safety and Health Administration (1976)  Occupational safety and health standards, subpart Z - toxic and hazardous substances.  US Code Fed. Regul., Title 29, Chapter XVII, Section 1910.1000, Washington DC, Bureau of National Affairs, p. 31:8302

US Tariff Commission (1941)  Synthetic Organic Chemicals, US Production and Sales, 1940, Report No. 148, Second Series, Washington DC, US Government Printing Office, p. 53

US Tariff Commission (1947)  Synthetic Organic Chemicals, US Production and Sales, 1947, Report No. 162, Second Series, Washington DC, US Government Printing Office, p. 119

Ustinovskaya, I.A., Kizilova, L.I., Gavrilina, L.Y., Malakhov, V.V. & Yashin, Y.I. (1977)  Gas-chromatographic analysis of products from the oxidative ammonolysis of propylene (Russ.).  Izv. Sib. Otd. Akad. Nauk SSSR, Ser. Khim. Nauk, 2, 115-118 [Chem. Abstr., 87, 77980y]

Vainio, H. & Mäkinen, A. (1977)  Styrene and acrylonitrile induced depression of hepatic nonprotein sulfhydryl content in various rodent species.  Res. Comm. chem. Path. Pharmacol., 17, 115-124

Venitt, S. (1978)  Letter to the editor.  Mutat. Res., 57, 107-109, 113

Venitt, S., Bushell, C.T. & Osborne, M. (1977)  Mutagenicity of acrylonitrile (cyanoethylene) in Escherichia coli.  Mutat. Res., 45, 283-288

Volkova, Z.A. & Bagdinov, Z.M. (1969)  Industrial hygiene problems in vulcanization processes of rubber production (Russ.).  Gig. i Sanit., 34, 33-40 [Chem. Abstr., 71, 128354b]

Weast, R.C., ed. (1976)  CRC Handbook of Chemistry and Physics, 57th ed., Cleveland, Ohio, Chemical Rubber Co., p. C-465

Wilson, R.H. (1944)  Health hazards encountered in the manufacture of synthetic rubber. J. Am. med. Assoc., 124, 701-703

Wilson, R.H., Hough, G.V. & McCormick, W.E. (1948)  Medical problems encountered in the manufacture of American-made rubber. Ind. Med., 17, 199-207

Windholz, M., ed. (1976)  The Merck Index, 9th ed., Rahway, NJ, Merck & Co., pp. 17-18

Wiśniewska-Knypl, J.M., Knobloch, K., Jablońska, J. & Ruta, U. (1970) Decrease of tissue respiration, activity of oxoglutarate dehydrogenase and level of sulfhydryl groups in acute acrylonitrile intoxication in rats (Pol.). Med. Pracy, 21, 543-549

Wronski, M. & Smal, Z. (1974)  Thiomercurimetric determination of acrylonitrile in water (Pol.). Chem. Anal. (Warsaw), 19, 633-638 [Chem. Abstr., 81, 175988c]

Wynder, E.L. & Hoffmann, D. (1967)  Tobacco and Tobacco Smoke. Studies in Experimental Carcinogenesis, New York, Academic Press, p. 450

Yamagami, M., Nakao, R., Fukumoto, T. & Tsurugi, J. (1970) Differential thermal analysis of ABS (acrylonitrile-butadiene-styrene) resins at higher temperatures (Jap.). Nippon Gomu Kyokaishi, 43, 647-651 [Chem. Abstr., 73, 99817p]

Zaytseva, N.A., Tolstobrova, S.A. & Il'in, D.T. (1972)  Chromatographic determination of unreacted monomers in emulsions of acrylic copolymers (Russ.). Soviet chem. Ind., 48, 298-299

Zotova, L.V. (1976)  Toxic effects of acrylonitrile on experimental animals following its absorption through the skin (Russ.). Gig. i Sanit., 10, 103-105

CAPROLACTAM and NYLON 6

Caprolactam

## 1.  Chemical and Physical Data

1.1  Synonyms and trade names

Chem. Abstr. Services Reg. No.:  105-60-2

Chem. Abstr. Name:  Hexahydro-2*H*-azepin-2-one

Aminocaproic lactam;  6-aminohexanoic acid cyclic lactam;
2-azacycloheptanone;  6-caprolactam;  ε-caprolactam;  Ω-caprolactam;
hexahydro-2-azepinone;  6-hexanelactam;  2-ketohexamethylenimine;
2-oxohexamethylenimine;  2-perhydroazepinone

1.2  Structural and molecular formulae and molecular weight

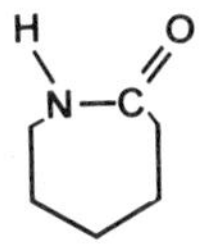

$C_6H_{11}NO$          Mol. wt:  113.2

1.3  Chemical and physical properties of the pure substance

(a)  Description:  White solid (Hawley, 1971)

(b)  Boiling-point:  139°C (12 mm) (Windholz, 1976a)

(c)  Melting-point:  69-71°C (Weast, 1976)

(d)  Refractive index:  $n_D^{40}$ 1.4935 (Hawley, 1971)

(e)  Spectroscopy data:  $\lambda_{max}$ 198 ($E_1^1$ = 686);  infra-red, Raman and
nuclear magnetic resonance spectral data have been tabulated
(Grasselli & Ritchey, 1975).

(f)  Solubility:  Soluble in water, ethanol, methanol, ether,
tetrahydrofurfuryl alcohol, dimethylformamide, chlorinated
hydrocarbons and cyclohexene (Windholz, 1976a)

(g)  Stability:  Hygroscopic (Behun, 1964)

(h)  Conversion factor:  1 ppm vapour in air = 4.6 mg/m$^3$

## 1.4  Technical products and impurities

Caprolactam is available in the US in molten and flake forms;  the
molten form accounts for 98-99% of the caprolactam that is shipped within
the country.  General specifications are as follows:  appearance, white
crystalline solid;  solidification point (dry basis), 69°C min;  and with
maximum impurities as follows:  moisture, 0.5%;  volatile bases, as
ammonia, 20 mg/kg (ppm);  filtrate ignition residue, 20 mg/kg (ppm);
cyclohexanone oxime, 10 mg/kg (ppm);  water insolubles, 10 mg/kg (ppm);
iron, 1 mg/kg (ppm);  free acid, 0.02 mEq/kg;  and free base, 0.2 mEq/kg.

Caprolactam is available commercially in Japan as a white powder with
a melting-point of 65-68°C and a boiling-point of 122-124°C (at 5 mm).

## 2.  Production, Use, Occurrence and Analysis

### 2.1  Production and use

#### (a)  Production

Caprolactam was first prepared by Gabriel & Maas in 1899 by melting
ε-amino-*n*-caprylic acid followed by vacuum distillation (Prager *et al*.,
1935;  Snider & Richardson, 1968).  In the US, all three manufacturers
(US International Trade Commission, 1977) use the 'conventional' process,
or modifications of it, to convert cyclohexanone to caprolactam:  the
cyclohexanone is reacted with hydroxylamine sulphate in the presence of
aqueous ammonia to form cyclohexanone oxime, which isomerizes with the
addition of fuming sulphuric acid to a crude caprolactam-sulphuric acid
mass.  This is rapidly neutralized and diluted to give caprolactam and
ammonium sulphate.  Various modifications are used to vary the quantities
of ammonium sulphate obtained as a coproduct of the reaction.  One US
company manufactures caprolactam by reacting a stream of cyclohexanone (in
the presence of toluene) with hydroxylamine phosphate oxime to give cyclohexanone oxime, which is converted to caprolactam by the same remaining
steps as in the conventional process.

In Italy, one manufacturer produces caprolactam from toluene by oxidation to benzoic acid followed by hydrogenation to cyclohexane carboxylic
acid;  this is reacted with nitrosylsulphuric acid in fuming sulphuric acid
in the presence of cyclohexane to produce caprolactam sulphate, which is
then neutralized to caprolactam.

One Japanese company produces caprolactam by the photochemical nitro-
sation of cyclohexane to give cyclohexanone oxime hydrochloride, which is
converted to caprolactam with fuming sulphuric acid.

Caprolactam has been produced commercially in the US since 1955 (Snider & Richardson, 1968). In 1976, three companies reported production of 354 million kg caprolactam (US International Trade Commission, 1977); 10.2 thousand kg were imported (US Department of Commerce, 1977a), from the Federal Republic of Germany (98% of total) and the UK; 13.1 million kg were exported, to Brazil (5.2% of total), Canada (47.9), Chile (0.6), Mexico (15.8) and Taiwan (30.5) (US Department of Commerce, 1977b).

An estimated 33 million kg caprolactam were produced in Mexico in 1975.

Total western European production in 1976 was 635 million kg, in the following countries (production in millions of kg): Benelux (320), the Federal Republic of Germany (150), Italy (140) and Spain (25). Exports from western Europe in that year were 320 million kg, and imports were 225 million kg. Annual caprolactam production in eastern Europe is greater than 484 million kg.

Caprolactam has been produced commercially in Japan since 1945. In 1976, four companies produced approximately 474 million kg caprolactam, and 107 million kg were exported.

About 28 million kg caprolactam were produced in the Republic of Korea in 1975.

Total annual caprolactam production capacity in the Middle East and Africa is estimated to be 25 million kg.

(b) Use

Caprolactam is used almost exclusively to produce polycaprolactam, more commonly known as nylon 6: in the US, 92.2% is used to produce nylon 6 fibres, 7.4% for nylon resins and films and about 0.4% for miscellaneous applications. For a detailed description on the uses of nylon 6 fibres, resins and films, see p. 123.

Miscellaneous applications for caprolactam are as a reactive additive for floor polishes and in special coatings, brush bristles and textile stiffeners.

In western Europe and Japan, 80-85% of caprolactam is used for nylon 6 fibres and 15-20% for nylon resins; in Europe, small quantities are used in engineering films.

The US Food and Drug Administration permits the use of caprolactam-ethylene-ethyl acrylate graft polymers as a component of side seam cements intended for use in contact with food (US Food & Drug Administration, 1977a).

The American Conference of Governmental Industrial Hygienists recommends that an employee's exposure to caprolactam not exceed an eight-hour
time-weighted average of 1 mg/m$^3$ for dust and approximately 20 mg/m$^3$
(5 ppm) for vapour in the workplace air during any eight-hour work shift
of a forty-hour work week (American Conference of Governmental Industrial
Hygienists, 1976).

## 2.2 Occurrence

Caprolactam is not known to occur as a natural product.

In a study of the suitability of using drinking-water supply pipes
made of nylon 6, the concentration of caprolactam in the water after 1.5
days at 40$^\circ$C was 1.06 mg/1 (ppm) (Sheftel & Sova, 1974).

Caprolactam has been reported to be present in trace amounts in the
waste waters from nylon 6 plants in Japan and Russia (Otsubo *et al.*, 1974;
Pevzner & Melent'eva, 1975). It has been detected in (1) finished
drinking-water in the US (Safe Drinking Water Committee, 1977; US Environmental Protection Agency, 1976); (2) effluent water from landfill leachate
in Delaware (Shackelford & Keith, 1976); and (3) the final effluent waste-
water from a dye manufacturing plant, at levels of 36-150 µg/1 (ppb)
(Games & Hites, 1977).

## 2.3 Analysis

Caprolactam has been determined in waste-water by gas chromatography-
mass spectrometry, with a limit of detection of about 1 µg/1 (ppb) (Games
& Hites, 1977); by polarography after conversion to aminocaproic acid
(Eremin & Kopylova, 1973); and by colorimetry after forming a dye with
*para*-nitroaniline, with a limit of detection of >0.4 mg/1 (ppm) (Baicheva,
1975). Colorimetry at 500 nm of the iron (III)-hydroxamic acid complex
has been used to determine caprolactam in air, with a limit of detection
of 50 µg/sample (Kurchatova, 1974), and in waste-water in the range of
15 mg/1 (ppm) (Otsubo *et al.*, 1974).

Caprolactam has been determined in technical grade nylon 6 by selective extraction with anhydrous trichloroethylene (Skwarski *et al.*, 1973).

Thin-layer chromatography has been used to determine caprolactam in
blood and tissue (Tsendrovskaya *et al.*, 1972).

### 3.  Biological Data Relevant to the Evaluation
### of Carcinogenic Risk to Humans

## 3.1  Carcinogenicity studies in animals[1]

No data were available to the Working Group.

## 3.2  Other relevant biological data

### (a)  Experimental systems

#### Acute toxicity

The $LD_{50}$ in mice by inhalation was 0.45 mg/1 (Lomonova, 1966);  by s.c. injection, 0.75 g/kg bw;  by i.p. injection, 0.58 g/kg bw;  and by i.v. injection, 0.48 g/kg bw;  the oral $LD_{100}$ was 1.2 g/kg bw (Hohensee, 1951).

Doses of 350-600 mg/kg bw administered intraperitoneally to rats produced toxic effects that included tremors, convulsions, chromodacryorrhoea (bloody eye discharge) and temperature depression.  I.v. injections of 100-300 mg/kg bw to rabbits produced tremors, convulsions, mydriasis (dilatation of the pupil) and opisthotonos (tetanic spasm) (Goldblatt *et al.*, 1954).

#### Embryotoxicity and teratogenicity

In rats, concentrations of 120-150 mg/m$^3$ caprolactam in air reduced fertility and caused death of embryos (Khadzhieva, 1969).

#### Metabolism

After its i.p. injection, caprolactam is excreted by rats partly unchanged and partly as ε-amino acid.  Rabbits metabolize caprolactam almost completely (Goldblatt *et al.*, 1954).

No data on the mutagenicity of this compound were available to the Working Group.

### (b)  Humans

Irritability, nervousness, loss of control and some confusion were reported to occur in workers exposed to caprolactam (Hohensee, 1951). Nervous system, genito-urinary tract and cardiovascular system disorders

---

[1]The Working Group was aware of a planned oral carcinogenicity study in rats and mice (Toxicology Information Program, 1976).

were observed in female workers exposed to caprolactam during the manufacture of nylon 6 (Petrov, 1975). Exposure to 5 mg/m$^3$ of the airborne
dust caused skin irritation in sensitive people. However, most people
had a response threshold at or near 46 mg/m$^3$ (10 ppm). Caprolactam
provoked skin irritation on direct contact, and the vapours irritated
eyes, nasal passages and (sometimes) skin (Fergusson & Wheeler, 1973).

### 3.3  Case reports and epidemiological studies

No data were available to the Working Group.

## Nylon 6

### 1.  Chemical and Physical Data

### 1.1  Synonyms and trade names

Chem. Abstr. Services Reg. No.:  25038-54-4

Chem. Abstr. Name:  Poly[imino(1-oxo-1,6-hexanediyl)]

6-Aminohexanoic acid homopolymer; caproamide polymer; caprolactam
oligomer; caprolactam polymer; ε-caprolactam polymer; hexahydro-
2$H$-azepin-2-one homopolymer; polyamide 6; poly(ε-aminocaproic
acid); polycaproamide; poly(ε-caproamide); polycaprolactam;
poly(ε-caprolactam); poly(iminocarbonylpentamethylene)

A 1030; A 1030NO; Akulon; Akulon M 2W; Alkamid; Amilan CM 1001;
Amilan CM 1011; Amilan CM 1031; Amilan CM 1001C; Amilan CM 1001G;
ATM 2 (nylon); Bonamid; Capran 80; Capran 77C; Caprolon B;
Caprolon V; Capron; Capron 8250; Capron 8252; Capron 8253;
Capron 8256; Capron B; Capron GR 8256; Capron GR 8257; Capron
GR 8258; Capron PK 4; Chemlon; CM 1001; CM 1011; CM 1031;
CM 1041; Danamid; Dull 704; Durethan BK; Durethan BK 30S;
Durethan BKV 30H; Durethan BKV 55H; Ertalon 6Sa; Extron 6N;
Grilon; Itamid; Itamid 250; Itamide 25; Itamide 35; Itamide 250;
Itamide 350; Itamide 250G; Itamide S; Kaprolit; Kaprolit B;
Kaprolon; Kaprolon B; Kapromin; Kapron; Kapron A; Kapron B;
KS 30P; Maranyl F 114; Maranyl F 124; Maranyl F 500; Metamid;
Miramid H 2; Miramid WM 55; Nylon A1035SF; Nylon CM 1031;

Nylon X 1051; Orgamide; Orgamid RMNOCD; P 6 (polyamide); PA 6; PA 6 (polymer); PK 4; PKA; Plaskin 8200; Plaskon 201; Plaskon 8201; Plaskon 8205; Plaskon 8207; Plaskon 8252; Plaskon 8202C; Plaskon 8201HS; Plaskon XP 607; Polyamide PK 4; Relon P; Renyl MV; SIPAS 60; Spencer 401; Spencer 601; Steelon; Stilon; Stylon; Tarlon X-A; Tarlon XB; Tarnamid T; Tarnamid T 2; Tarnamid T 27; TNK 2G5; Torayca N 6; UBE 1022B; Ultramid B 3; Ultramid B 4; Ultramid B 5; Ultramid BMK; Vidlon; Widlon; Zytel 211

## 1.2 Structural and molecular formulae and molecular weight

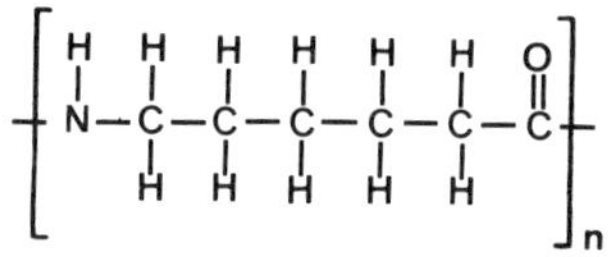

$$\left[ \begin{array}{c} \text{H} \quad \text{H} \quad \text{H} \quad \text{H} \quad \text{H} \quad \text{H} \quad \text{O} \\ | \quad | \quad | \quad | \quad | \quad | \quad \| \\ \text{N} - \text{C} - \text{C} - \text{C} - \text{C} - \text{C} - \text{C} \\ | \quad | \quad | \quad | \quad | \\ \text{H} \quad \text{H} \quad \text{H} \quad \text{H} \quad \text{H} \end{array} \right]_n$$

$(C_6H_{11}NO)_n$          Mol. wt: 14 000-20 000

## 1.3 Chemical and physical properties of the unoriented polymer

From Sweeny & Zimmerman (1969), unless otherwise specified

(a) Description: White, tough, translucent, crystalline solid

(b) Melting-point: 223°C; softens at 210°C

(c) Density: d 1.13

(d) Refractive index: n 1.530

(e) Solubility: Soluble in strong acids, phenol and cresol (Windholz, 1976b)

(f) Stability: Degrades on exposure to light; hydrolyses and degrades at elevated temperature (Windholz, 1976b). The products from pyrolysis at 400-500°C have been identified and include aliphatic aldehydes (van Grimbergen et al., 1975).

(g) Reactivity: Stable to aqueous alkalis but degrades rapidly in aqueous acids (Windholz, 1976b).

## 1.4 Technical products and impurities

Nylon 6 is available in the US as fibres and as resins for use in plastics. Nylon fibres are available as yarn, monofilaments and staple which can be blended with other fibres. Nylon resins are generally available as homopolymers, however, 5-10% co-reactants may be added in the final stage of polycondensation to improve specific performance properties. Blending additives may also be used but seldom exceed 10-15%. Reinforcement with glass fibres or minerals (30-40% by weight) is also common.

No detailed information on the possible presence of unreacted monomer in the polymer was available to the Working Group.

## 2. Production, Use, Occurrence and Analysis

### 2.1 Production and use

#### (a) Production

Nylon 6 was first obtained by Gabriel & Maas in 1899 by heating ε-aminocaproic acid. It was prepared by Schlack in 1938 by heating caprolactam with water (Swecny, 1968). Large-scale commercial production of nylon 6 was first begun in Germany in 1941 and in the US in 1955.

Nylon 6 resins are produced commercially using batch or continuous polymerization processes where molten caprolactam is reacted with controlled amounts of water to obtain α-aminocaproic acid, which condenses to nylon 6 resin as water and unreacted monomer are removed. The nylon 6 chips may then be spun into fibres.

In 1976, 35 US companies produced 296 million kg nylon 6 fibres, and eight companies produced 24 million kg nylon 6 resin for use in plastics (four of these companies produced regenerated nylon 6 resin from waste fibres). US imports of all types of nylon fibres in 1976, including nylon 6, were 30 million kg, and exports were 75 million kg. US imports of all types of nylon resins in 1975 were 1.4 million kg.

Total world production of all types of nylon fibres amounted to 2830 million kg in 1976, and production by various regions is estimated to have been as follows (millions of kg): North and South America, excluding the US (195), Europe (1142) and Asia, Oceania and Africa combined, excluding Japan (251) (Anon., 1977).

Those countries in North and South America, excluding the US, that produce nylon 6 fibre include (with number of producers): Argentina (8), Brazil (14), Canada (2), Chile (2), Colombia (3), Guatemala (1), Mexico (8), Peru (3), Uruguay (1) and Venezuela (5) (Anon., 1977).

In Europe, nylon 6 fibres are produced in the following countries (number of producers): Belgium (2), Bulgaria (1), Czechoslovakia (3), Denmark (1), Eire (2), the Federal Republic of Germany (5), France (4), the German Democratic Republic (3), Greece (2), Hungary (1), Italy (9), Malta (1), The Netherlands (1), Poland (1), Portugal (1), Romania (1), Spain (4), Sweden (1), Switzerland (2), Turkey (3), the UK (5) and Yugoslavia (2) (Anon., 1977).

Other countries which produce nylon 6 fibres include (number of producers): Australia (2), Bangladesh (1), Egypt (1), India (10), Indonesia (2), Iran (2), Israel (1), Kenya (1), New Zealand (1), Pakistan (3), Republic of Korea (4), Republic of the Philippines (2), Singapore (1), Sri Lanka (1), Taiwan (16) and Thailand (3) (Anon., 1977).

In 1975, seven Japanese companies produced an estimated 250 million kg of nylon 6 fibres; 75 million kg of all types of nylon fibres were exported.

Total world production of all types of nylon resins for use in plastics amounted to 340 million kg in 1976. An estimated 150 million kg nylon resins were produced in western Europe, with the Federal Republic of Germany contributing the largest amount (60-70 million kg). Two companies in the Federal Republic of Germany produce nylon 6 resins for use in plastics, and Italy, The Netherlands and Switzerland each have one nylon 6 resin-producing company.

In 1976, five Japanese companies produced 30 million kg of nylon 6 resins for use in plastics; 4 million kg of all types of nylon resins for use in plastics were exported.

(b)  Use

In 1976, 956 million kg nylon fibres were used in the US, with nylon 6/6 accounting for 62.2%; nylon 6, 30.5%; nylon waste, 5.2%; and other nylon fibres, 2.1%.

In 1976, use of all types of nylon fibres, including nylon 6, in the US was as follows: home furnishings (61%), clothing (18%), industrial uses (16%) and other applications (5%).

An estimated 627 million kg nylon fibres were used in home furnishing applications in the US in 1976, including use in carpets and rugs (94.4% of the total home furnishing use), upholstery (4.3%), blankets (0.5%), draperies and curtains (0.2%) and other home furnishings (0.6%).

Clothing applications used about 174 million kg, and included knit fabrics (55.8% of total), hosiery (23.9%) and woven fabrics (20.3%).

Industrial applications used about 155 million kg nylon fibres, for use in tire cord (69.5% of total industrial use), belting and hose (8.9%), cordage, i.e., rope, twine, etc. (7.8%), seat belts (4.5%), webbing and tapes (3.2%), other tire fabrics (2.7%) and other industrial applications (3.4%).

Miscellaneous applications for nylon fibres include protective and coated fabrics (18.2% of total miscellaneous use), sewing thread (14.0%), transportation upholstery (13.4%), nonwoven fabrics (12.1%), brushes (8.3%), fishnet and fishline (6.0%), felts (4.8%), fibrefill (4.4%) and other uses (18.8%).

Nylon 6 resins are used in engineering plastics (high-performance materials used as replacements for metal parts) which are used in injection moulding (43.5% of total nylon 6 use) and extrusion applications (56.5%). Injection moulding resins are used primarily to make components and parts for automobiles and lorries (21.7% of total use), but also for electrical and electronic (4.3%), industrial machinery (4.3%), hardware and furniture (4.3%), appliance (4.3%) and consumer (4.3%) applications. Extrusion resins are used for film, extrusion coating and tape (30.4% of total use), nontextile monofilament (4.3%), wire and cable (15.2%) and tubing (6.5%).

In Japan, all types of nylon fibres are used in industrial applications (57% of total use), clothing (30%) and home furnishing applications (13%). Nylon resins for use in plastics are used in electrical/electronics (20% of total nylon resin use), automotive (18%), building materials (9%), appliances (8%) and other uses (45%).

The US Food and Drug Administration permits the use of nylon 6 for processing, handling and packaging food provided that the resins have a specific gravity of $1.15\pm0.015$, a melting-point of 200-230°C, dissolve in 1 hour in boiling 4.2 N hydrochloric acid, and have maximum extractable fractions (expressed as weight percentage of resin) in water (1.0), in 95% ethanol (2.0), in ethyl acetate (1.0) and in benzene (1.0) (US Food & Drug Administration, 1977b).

## 2.2  Occurrence

Nylon 6 is not known to occur as a natural product.

## 2.3  Analysis

No information was available to the Working Group on methods for determining nylon 6 resins in foods or other parts of the environment.

Pyrolysis-gas chromatography has been used to identify 37 commercial polymers (Okumoto & Takeuchi, 1972) and polyamides, including nylon 6 (Kretzchmar & Gross, 1975). Pyrolysis followed by infra-red spectroscopy can be used to identify paint resins and polymers, including nylon 6 (Smalldon, 1969).

Thermal degradation, followed by mass spectral analysis, has been used to identify plastics and coating enamels, including nylon 6 (Murdoch & Rigby, 1973) and 10 commercial polymers (nylon type unspecified) (Zeman, 1972).

Infra-red spectral analysis may be used to identify microscopic samples of manmade fibres, including nylon (nylon type unspecified) (Fox & Schuetzman, 1968).

Nylon 6 can be identified by paper electrophoresis (Bauters, 1970), paper or thin-layer chromatography (Raven & Earland, 1970) and condensation with formaldehyde and polarography of the Schiff base obtained (Shtal *et al.*, 1968).

$^{13}$C-Nuclear magnetic resonance spectroscopy has been used to identify nylon fibres, including nylon 6 (Kirret *et al.*, 1974).

## 3. Biological Data Relevant to the Evaluation of Carcinogenic Risk to Humans

### 3.1 Carcinogenicity studies in animals

#### Intraperitoneal administration

Five films of polycaprolactam (nylon 6), of about 10 mm in diameter, were implanted intraperitoneally in each of 9 BD rats. Four out of 6 rats which survived for 360 days had local sarcomas (Druckrey & Schmähl, 1952).

### 3.2 Other relevant biological data

No data were available to the Working Group.

### 3.3 Case reports and epidemiological studies

No data were available to the Working Group.

## 4. Summary of Data Reported and Evaluation

### 4.1 Experimental data

No data on the carcinogenicity or mutagenicity of caprolactam were available to the Working Group.

Intraperitoneal implantation of nylon 6 in rats induced local sarcomas.

4.2  Human data

No case reports or epidemiological studies relating to the carcino-genicity of either caprolactam or its polymer were available to the Working Group.

The high levels of production of caprolactam and of nylon 6 indicate that occupationally exposed groups could be identified.  In addition, the widespread use of all types of nylon in consumer products (including textiles, home furnishings and tire cord) indicates exposure of the general population.

4.3  Evaluation

Data from only one experimental study with nylon 6, and the absence of both animal and human data on caprolactam, preclude a definite assessment of the carcinogenicity of caprolactam and of its polymer.  Because of the widespread exposure of humans, consideration should be given to the initiation of further animal and epidemiological studies (see also 'General Remarks on the Substances Considered', p. 35).

## 5. References

American Conference of Governmental Industrial Hygienists (1976) TLVs Threshold Limit Values for Chemical Substances in Workroom Air Adopted by ACGIH for 1976, Cincinnati, Ohio, p. 11

Anon. (1977) World man-made fiber survey. Textile Organon, 48, 75, 77

Baicheva, D. (1975) Development of a new method for determination of caprolactam in waste waters (Bulg.). Tr. Vodosnabdyavane, Kanaliz. Sanit. Tekh., 11, 91-104 [Chem. Abstr., 87, 43611p]

Bauters, M. (1970) Electrophoretic identification of nylons 66, 6 and 11 (Fr.). Bull. Inst. Text. Fr., 24, 7-12 [Chem. Abstr., 72, 133439h]

Behun, J.D. (1964) Amines. In: Bikales, N.M., ed., Encyclopedia of Polymer Science and Technology, Plastics, Resins, Rubbers, Fibers, Vol. 1, New York, Interscience, p. 870

Druckrey, H. & Schmähl, D. (1952) Carcinogenic action of plastic films (Ger.). Z. Naturforsch., 7, 353-356

Eremin, Y.G. & Kopylova, G.A. (1973) Polarographic determination of caprolactam in waste waters (Russ.). Zavod. Lab., 39, 1065-1066 [Chem. Abstr., 80, 87239h]

Ferguson, W.S. & Wheeler, D.D. (1973) Caprolactam vapor exposures. Am. ind. Hyg. Assoc. J., 34, 384-389

Fox, R.H. & Schuetzman, H.I. (1968) The infrared identification of microscopic samples of manmade fibers. J. Forensic Sci., 13, 397-406 [Chem. Abstr., 69, 78333e]

Games, L.M. & Hites, R.A. (1977) Composition, treatment efficiency, and environmental significance of dye manufacturing plant effluents. Anal. Chem., 49, 1433-1440

Goldblatt, M.W., Farquharson, M.E., Bennett, G. & Askew, B.M. (1954) ε-Caprolactam. Br. J. ind. Med., 11, 1-10

Grasselli, J.G. & Ritchey, W.M., eds (1975) CRC Atlas of Spectral Data and Physical Constants for Organic Compounds, 2nd ed., Vol. III, Cleveland, Ohio, Chemical Rubber Co., p. 444

van Grimbergen, M., Reybrouck, G. & van de Voorde, H. (1975) Air pollution due to the burning of thermoplastics. II (Ger.). Zbl. Bakt. Hyg., Abt. I. Orig. B, 160, 139-147

Hawley, G.G., ed. (1971)  The Condensed Chemical Dictionary, 8th ed.,
    New York, Van Nostrand-Reinhold, p. 164

Hohensee, F. (1951)  Pharmacologic and physiological action of ε-capro-
    lactam (Ger.). Faserforsch. Textiltech., 8, 299-303

Khadzhieva, E.D. (1969)  The effect of kaprolaktam on the reproduction of
    albino rats (Russ.). Gig. i Sanit., 34, 25-28

Kirret, O., Lippmaa, E. & Pehk, T. (1974)  Analysis of nylon fibers by
    carbon-13 NMR spectroscopy (Russ.). Eesti NSV Tead. Akad. Toim.,
    Keem., Geol., 23, 269-271 [Chem. Abstr., 82, 59605x]

Kretzschmar, H.J. & Gross, D. (1975)  Pyrolysis-gas chromatography of
    polyamides (Ger.). Kunststoffe, 65, 92-94 [Chem. Abstr., 83,
    132217z]

Kurchatova, G. (1974)  Determination of caprolactam in the air (Bulg.).
    Letopisi Khig.- Epidemiol. Sluzhba, 8, 203-206 [Chem. Abstr., 84,
    34781e]

Lomonova, G.V. (1966)  Toxicity of caprolactam (Russ.). Gig. Tr. Prof.
    Zabol., 10, 54-57

Murdoch, I.A. & Rigby, L.J. (1973)  Thermal volatilization analysis by
    mass spectrometry. Dyn. Mass Spectrom., 3, 255-264 [Chem. Abstr.,
    79, 137625h]

Okumoto, T. & Takeuchi, T. (1972)  Rapid characterization of polymeric
    materials by pyrolysis-gas chromatography (Jap.). Nippon Kagaku
    Kaishi, 1, 71-78 [Chem. Abstr., 76, 141459n]

Otsubo, T., Tajiri, H. & Shinpo, Y. (1974)  Spectrophotometric determin-
    ation of trace amounts of ε-caprolactam in waste water with iron(III)
    chloride (Jap.). Bunseki Kagaku, 23, 163-166 [Chem. Abstr., 81,
    41128p]

Petrov, N.V. (1975)  Health status of women working in the chemical fiber
    industry according to data of medical examinations (Russ.). Vrach.
    Delo, 10, 145-148

Pevzner, I.D. & Melent'eva, N.D. (1975)  Analysis of waste waters during
    production of polyamides (Russ.). Plast. Massy, 5, 67-68 [Chem.
    Abstr., 83, 102794t]

Prager, B., Jacobson, P. & Richter, F., eds (1935)  Beilsteins Handbuch
    der Organischen Chemie, 4th ed., Vol. 21, Syst. No. 3179, Berlin,
    Julius Springer, p. 240

Raven, D.J. & Earland, C. (1970)  Chromatographic identification of nylons. J. Soc. Dyers Colour., 86, 313 [Chem. Abstr., 73, 88289s]

Safe Drinking Water Committee (1977)  Drinking Water and Health, Washington DC, National Academy of Sciences, pp. 698-700, 798

Shackelford, W.M. & Keith, L.H. (1976)  Frequency of Organic Compounds Identified in Water, EPA-600/4-76-062, Athens, Ga, US Environmental Protection Agency, pp. 96-97

Sheftel, V.O. & Sova, R.E. (1974)  Sanitary-chemical study of the migration of a monomer from Kaprolon to water (Russ.). Gig. i Sanit., 6, 93-94 [Chem. Abstr., 81, 122046n]

Shtal, S.S., Dmitrieva, V.N. & Bezuglyi, V.D. (1968)  Qualitative identification of polyamides by a polarographic method (Russ.). Plast. Massy, 9, 61-63 [Chem. Abstr., 70, 5146g]

Skwarski, T., Laszkiewicz, B., Mikolajczyk, T. & Pryc, A. (1973)  Determination of composition of the technical product of the hydrolytic polymerization of caprolactam. II. Determination of caprolactam and its oligomers by the selective extraction method. Polimery, 18, 135-137 [Chem. Abstr., 79, 19145d]

Smalldon, K.W. (1969)  Identification of paint resins and other polymeric materials from the infrared spectra of their pyrolysis products. Forensic Sci. Soc. J., 9, 135-140 [Chem. Abstr., 72, 122996m]

Snider, O.E. & Richardson, R.J. (1968)  Polyamide fibers. In: Kirk, R.E. & Othmer, D.F., eds, Encyclopedia of Chemical Technology, 2nd ed., Vol. 16, New York, John Wiley and Sons, pp. 46-47

Sweeny, W. (1968)  Polyamides (general). In: Kirk, R.E. & Othmer, D.F., eds, Encyclopedia of Chemical Technology, 2nd ed., Vol. 16, New York, John Wiley and Sons, pp. 29-32

Sweeny, W. & Zimmerman, J. (1969)  Polyamides. In: Bikales, N.M., ed., Encyclopedia of Polymer Science and Technology, Plastics, Resins, Rubbers, Fibers, Vol. 10, New York, Interscience, pp. 557-559, 561, 568

Toxicology Information Program (1976)  Carcinogenesis bioassay of caprolactam. Tox-Tips, 1(5), 25

Tsendrovskaya, V.A., Kataeva, S.N. & Kofanov, V.I. (1972)  Determination of caprolactam in biological media by thin-layer chromatography (Russ.). Gig. i Sanit., 50, 83-84 [Chem. Abstr., 78, 24807e]

US Department of Commerce (1977a)  US Imports for Consumption and General Imports, TSUSA Commodity by Country of Origin, FT 246/Annual 1976, Bureau of the Census, Washington DC, US Government Printing Office, p. 218

US Department of Commerce (1977b)  US Exports, Schedule B Commodity Groupings, Schedule B Commodity by Country, FT410/December, Washington DC, US Government Printing Office, p. 2-84

US Environmental Protection Agency (1976)  Organic Compounds Identified in Drinking Water in the US, Health Effects Research Laboratory, Cincinnati, Ohio [quoted in Safe Drinking Water Committee (1977), p. 698]

US Food & Drug Administration (1977a)  Food and drugs. Resinous and polymeric coatings. US Code Fed. Regul., Title 21, part 175.300, p. 458

US Food & Drug Administration (1977b)  Food and drugs. Nylon resins. US Code Fed. Regul., Title 21, part 177.1500, p. 519

US International Trade Commission (1977)  Synthetic Organic Chemicals, US Production and Sales, 1976, USITC Publication 833, Washington DC, US Government Printing Office, pp. 299, 304

Weast, R.C., ed. (1976)  CRC Handbook of Chemistry and Physics, 57th ed., Cleveland, Ohio, Chemical Rubber Co., p. C-336

Windholz, M., ed. (1976a)  The Merck Index, 9th ed., Rahway, NJ, Merck & Co., p. 224

Windholz, M., ed. (1976b)  The Merck Index, 9th ed., Rahway, NJ, Merck & Co., p. 875

Zeman, A. (1972)  Identification of high polymers by thermal degradation in the mass spectrometer. In: Wiedemann, H.G., ed., Thermal Analysis, Proceedings of the International Conference, 3rd, 1971, Vol. 3, Basel, Switzerland, Birkhaeuser, pp. 219-227 [Chem. Abstr., 78, 148551m]

## CHLOROPRENE and POLYCHLOROPRENE

### Chloroprene

## 1. Chemical and Physical Data

### 1.1 Synonyms and trade names

Chem. Abstr. Services Reg. No.:  126-99-8

Chem. Abstr. Name:  2-Chloro-1,3-butadiene

2-Chlorobutadiene;  β-chloroprene

### 1.2 Structural and molecular formulae and molecular weight

$$\begin{array}{c} H\\ H \end{array}\!\!>\!\!C = \overset{\displaystyle H}{\underset{\displaystyle H}{C}} - \overset{\displaystyle Cl}{C} = C\!\!<\!\!\begin{array}{c} H\\ H \end{array}$$

$C_4H_5Cl$                    Mol. wt:  88.5

### 1.3 Chemical and physical properties of the pure substance

From Weast (1976), unless otherwise specified

(a)  Description:  Colourless, inflammable liquid (Hawley, 1971)

(b)  Boiling-point:  59.4°C

(c)  Density:  $d_4^{20}$ 0.9583;  vapour density, 3 (air = 1)
(Anon., 1972)

(d)  Refractive index:  $n_D^{20}$ 1.4583

(e)  Spectroscopy data:  $\lambda_{max}$ 223 nm ($E_1^1$ = 1595);  mass spectral
data have been tabulated (Grasselli & Ritchey, 1975).

(f)  Solubility:  Partially soluble in water;  soluble in ether,
acetone, benzene and most organic solvents

(g)  Volatility:  Vapour pressure is 300 mm at 32.8°C (Anon., 1975a).

(h)  Stability: Flash-point, $-20^{\circ}$C (Hawley, 1971); polymerizes on standing (Pollock & Stevens, 1965)

(i)  Conversion factor: 1 ppm in air = 3.6 mg/m$^3$ (Irish, 1963)

## 1.4  Technical products and impurities

Chloroprene available in the US has a minimum purity of 95% (Hawley, 1971). Inhibitors such as hydroquinone (see IARC, 1977) or phenothiazine are generally added when it is to be stored (Bauchwitz, 1964).

## 2.  Production, Use, Occurrence and Analysis

Two review articles have been published on chloroprene (Bauchwitz, 1964; National Institute for Occupational Safety and Health, 1977).

### 2.1  Production and use

(a)  Production

Chloroprene was first prepared in 1930 by the reaction of monovinyl-acetylene with hydrochloric acid in the presence of a metal halide (Bauchwitz, 1964; Carothers et al., 1931).

Until 1970, all chloroprene production in the US was based on dimerization of acetylene to monovinylacetylene and addition of hydrogen chloride. However, by 1972, all production was based on butadiene. Chloroprene is produced from butadiene in a two-step process: butadiene is first reacted with chlorine to form a mixture of dichlorobutene isomers, from which the 3,4-dichloro-1-butene isomer is isolated and then reacted with caustic soda to form chloroprene. The other isomer (1,4-dichloro-2-butene) formed during the first reaction step can either be isomerized to 3,4-dichloro-1-butene for additional chloroprene production or be used in the manufacture of adiponitrile. In Japan, 70% of chloroprene is based on acetylene, and 30% is based on butadiene.

Although the date of first US production of chloroprene itself is not known, its polymer (polychloroprene) was first introduced commercially in the US in 1932 (Hargreaves & Thompson, 1965), and separate commercial production of the polymer was first reported in 1943 (US Tariff Commission, 1945). In 1976, two US companies produced an estimated 164 million kg chloroprene.

Data on US imports and exports of chloroprene are not available, presumably because only its sole derivative, polychloroprene, is traded.

In 1977, 100 million kg chloroprene were made in western Europe in the following countries (1 producer each): the Federal Republic of Germany, France, The Netherlands and the UK (Ruebensaal, 1977).

Chloroprene has been produced commercially in Japan since 1962. In 1976, three companies produced a total of 80 million kg.

In 1975, chloroprene was also produced in the USSR and in the People's Republic of China (Ruebensaal, 1975).

Total world production of chloroprene in 1977 is estimated to have been 300 million kg.

(b) Use

Chloroprene is used almost exclusively, without isolation, in the production of polychloroprene elastomers. For a detailed description of the uses of the polymer, see p. 143.

The US Food and Drug Administration permits the use of chloroprene as a component of adhesives that are intended for use in food packaging (US Food & Drug Administration, 1977).

The US Occupational Safety and Health Administration's health standards for exposure to air contaminants require that an employee's exposure to chloroprene not exceed an eight-hour time-weighted average of 90 mg/m$^3$ (25 ppm) in the workplace air in any eight-hour work shift of a forty-hour work week (US Occupational Safety and Health Administration, 1976). In August 1977, the National Institute for Occupational Safety and Health recommended that occupational exposure to chloroprene be limited to a maximum concentration of 3.6 mg/m$^3$ (1 ppm) in air, determined as a ceiling concentration for a 15-minute period during a forty-hour work week (Anon., 1977; National Institute for Occupational Safety and Health, 1977).

Work environment hygiene standards (all in terms of eight-hour time-weighted averages) for chloroprene in air, as reported by Wincll (1975), are as follows: Czechoslovakia, 50 mg/m$^3$ (14 ppm); the Federal Republic of Germany, 90 mg/m$^3$ (25 ppm); the German Democratic Republic, 10 mg/m$^3$ (2.7 ppm); and Sweden, 90 mg/m$^3$ (25 ppm). The maximum acceptable ceiling concentration of chloroprene in the USSR is 2 mg/m$^3$ (0.54 ppm).

2.2  Occurrence

Chloroprene is not known to occur as a natural product.

Chloroprene has been detected as an impurity at levels of several ppm in commercial vinyl chloride in Italy (Sassu *et al.*, 1968) and in Japan (Kurosaki *et al.*, 1968), and in acrylonitrile in the USSR (Panina & Fain, 1968).

During 1973, at a US chloroprene polymerization plant, airborne concentrations of chloroprene were found to range from 50-5000 mg/m$^3$ (14-1420 ppm) in the make-up area, from 440-24 300 mg/m$^3$ (130-6760 ppm) in the reactor area, from 10-1500 mg/m$^3$ (6-440 ppm) in the monomer recovery area and from 400-900 mg/m$^3$ (113-252 ppm) in the latex area (Infante *et al.*, 1977). In 1977, mean airborne concentrations of chloroprene of up to 0.72 mg/m$^3$ (0.2 ppm) were reported in a roll building area in a metal fabricating plant where poly-chloroprene was applied extensively to metal cylinders prior to vulcani-zation; an individual who developed an angiosarcoma of the liver with no prior history of vinyl chloride exposure or thorotrast usage had worked in this area (Infante, 1977).

It has been estimated that approximately 2500-3000 workers in the US are currently exposed to chloroprene during its manufacture and polymeri-zation (Infante et al., 1977).

Workers in a Russian shoe factory were reportedly often exposed to chloroprene concentrations of 20-25 mg/m$^3$ (5.5-7 ppm) (Buyanov & Svishchev, 1973). Concentrations in the air inside a Russian polychloroprene rubber plant were found to be 14.5-53.4 mg/m$^3$ (4-14.8 ppm); 500 meters from the plant, the concentration was 0.2-1.57 mg/m$^3$ (0.05-0.43 ppm); and 7000 meters from the plant, the concentration was 0.12-0.38 mg/m$^3$ (0.03-0.1 ppm) (Mnatsakanyan et al., 1972). Near another Russian polychloroprene rubber plant, the chloroprene concentration in air in the immediate vici-nity was 28.45 mg/m$^3$ (7.9 ppm); 500 meters away, it was 0.727 mg/m$^3$ (0.2 ppm); and 7000 meters away, it was 0.199 mg/m$^3$ (0.05 ppm) (Apoyan et al., 1970).

Polychloroprene may contain 0.01-0.5% free chloroprene (National Institute for Occupational Safety and Health, 1977).

2.3  Analysis

A colorimetric method for determining chloroprene in the workplace air has been described in which the coloured complex of chloroprene with the para-nitrophenyldiazonium ion is determined spectrophotometrically (Babina, 1969).

Ultra-violet spectrophotometry at 222.6 nm after trapping in ethanol has been used to determine chloroprene in the air around a polychloroprene rubber plant (Apoyan et al., 1970).

Chloroprene and other unsaturated monomers have been removed from air by ethanolic mercuric acetate and analysed by paper chromatography; the sensitivity of the method for chloroprene was 3.0 µg (Kaznina, 1972).

Gas chromatography can be used to determine chloroprene: (1) in air in the presence of other monomers (Gizhlaryan et al., 1976; Sharpanova et al., 1972; Turusova & Khanina, 1975); (2) in air, with a sensitivity of 0.005 mg/m$^3$ (0.0014 ppm) (Sukiasyan et al., 1976); (3) as an impurity in acrylonitrile (Panina & Fain, 1968); (4) as an impurity in vinyl chloride at several mg/kg (ppm) (Sassu et al., 1968); and (5) as a resi-dual monomer in polychloroprene latexes, with a sensitivity of less than 0.002 wt % and a coefficient of variation of 3-10% (Bunyatyants et al., 1976).

Preparative gas chromatography was also used to separate impurities, including chloroprene, in vinyl chloride, which were then identified using infra-red spectrometry, mass spectrometry, elemental analyses and measurement of physical properties (Kurosaki *et al.*, 1968).

## 3.   Biological Data Relevant to the Evaluation
### of Carcinogenic Risk to Humans

### 3.1   Carcinogenicity studies in animals[1]

#### (a)   Oral administration

Rat:   A group of 100 random-bred albino rats received twice-weekly doses of 200 mg/kg bw chloroprene in sunflower oil by gavage for 25 weeks; 40 rats survived for 2 years.   No tumours were observed (Zil'fyan *et al.*, 1975, 1977) [The Working Group noted the incomplete reporting of the experiment].

#### (b)   Skin application

Mouse:   Three groups of random-bred albino mice received either (a) 50 twice-weekly skin applications of a 50% solution of chloroprene in benzene for 25 weeks, or (b) 50 twice-weekly skin applications of 0.1% 9,10-dimethyl-1,2-benzanthracene (DMBA) in benzene, or (c) 50 skin applications of the 50% chloroprene solution in benzene and 5 skin applications of a 0.01% DMBA solution in benzene.   Of 100 mice treated with 50% chloroprene, 58 survived 6 months, and 37 survivors were killed after 18 months; no tumours of the skin or other organs were reported.   Of 80 mice treated with 0.1% DMBA, 60 were still alive at the appearance of the first skin tumour (time unspecified), and 92% of these developed skin carcinomas. Of 80 mice treated with chloroprene and 0.01% DMBA, 42 survived for 6 months;   no skin or other tumours were reported (Zil'fyan *et al.*, 1975, 1977) [The Working Group noted the incomplete reporting of the experiment].

#### (c)   Inhalation and/or intratracheal administration

Rat:   Chloroprene was administered intratracheally to 100 random-bred albino rats in doses of 200 mg/kg bw five times at 20-day intervals.   Gross and microscopic pathological examination revealed no tumours in the lungs of animals that died or were killed 6 or 14 months after chloroprene administration (Zil'fyan *et al.*, 1977) [The Working Group noted the insufficient duration of the experiment].

---

[1]The Working Group was aware of studies in progress to investigate the carcinogenicity of chloroprene by oral administration to rats and by inhalation exposure in rats and hamsters (IARC, 1978;   Toxicology Information Program, 1976, 1977).

## (d)  Subcutaneous and/or intramuscular administration

Rat:  A group of 110 random-bred albino rats received 10 s.c. injections of 400 mg/kg bw chloroprene in sunflower oil;  88 rats survived 6
or more months.  Another group of 100 rats received 50 injections of 200
mg/kg bw, and 46 survived 6 months or more.  No local sarcomas were observed in either group within 2 years.  Among 60 rats injected with single
doses of 0.5 mg/animal DMBA, 50 survived to the appearance of the first
tumour (3.5 months), and 32 (64%) developed local sarcomas.  Following a
single injection of 0.5 mg/animal DMBA in the left flank and 50 s.c.
injections of 200 mg/kg bw chloroprene in the right flank, 42 rats were
still alive at the appearance of the first tumour (4 months), and 24 (57%)
developed local sarcomas (side not specified) (Zil'fyan *et al.*, 1975, 1977)
[The Working Group noted the incomplete reporting of the experiment].

## 3.2  Other relevant biological data

### (a)  Experimental systems

### Toxic effects

The oral $LD_{50}$ of chloroprene in rats is 251 mg/kg bw and in mice
260 mg/kg bw (Asmangulyan & Badalyan, 1971).  In Charles River male rats
the $LC_{50}$ for a 4-hour exposure was 8.2 $g/m^3$ (2280 ppm) (Clary *et al.*,
1978).

The dose that killed about 100% of animals after an 8-hour inhalation
exposure was approximately 7.5 $g/m^3$ (2000 ppm) in rabbits and from 15-20
$g/m^3$ (4000-5500 ppm) in rats.  Symptoms included inflammation of the mucous
membranes of the eyes and nose, followed by depression of the central
nervous system.  Death resulted from respiratory failure.  In mice, toxic
effects have been reported after 8 hours' exposure to levels of chloroprene as low as 40-500 $mg/m^3$ (12-130 ppm);  and 600 $mg/m^3$ (170 ppm) killed
100% of animals (von Oettingen *et al.*, 1936).

Repeated inhalation exposure of experimental animals to chloroprene
resulted in central nervous system depression (Asmangulyan & Badalyan,
1971;  Davtyan, 1972;  Nyström, 1948;  von Oettingen *et al.*, 1936), delayed
reversal of conditioned reflexes (Airapetyan & Matevonyan, 1973) and histological changes in brain tissue (Movsesyan *et al.*, 1964).

Chloroprene induces a number of biochemical alterations in various
species, including inhibition of liver detoxification mechanisms (Davtyan,
1972), decreased activity of hepatic enzymes and glycogen content in liver
(Gizhlaryan *et al.*, 1972; Martinyan, 1966; Mkhitaryan, 1959, 1960c;
Mkhitaryan & Astvatsatryan, 1959; Nikogosyan, 1959) and renal and splenic
damage (Asmangulyan & Badalyan, 1971;  von Oettingen *et al.*, 1936).  Hyper-
tropy and hyperfunction of the adrenals (Allaverdyan, 1970; Mkhitaryan
*et al.*, 1971) have also been observed.

In rats, repeated exposure to chloroprene by inhalation for 6 hours/
day on 5 days/week for 4 weeks resulted in slight growth depression and
behavioural effects with 1.4 $g/m^3$ (39 ppm) and loss of hair, growth retardation and morphological liver damage with 5.8 $g/m^3$ (160 ppm) and 22.5
$g/m^3$ (625 ppm). In hamsters, this exposure resulted in slight irritation
and restlessness with 1.4 $g/m^3$ (39 ppm), growth retardation, irritation
and liver damage with 5.8 $g/m^3$ (160 ppm) and death with 22.5 $g/m^3$ (625 ppm)
(Clary, 1977).

Repeated oral administration of 15 mg/kg bw chloroprene to rats
daily for 5 months produced no lethal effects (Asmangulyan & Badalyan,
1971). Acute and chronic effects have been noted following administration
of chloroprene to the skin of rats (von Oettingen *et al.*, 1936).

Chloroprene is more toxic to fasted rats with decreased hepatic
glutathione content than to fed rats (Jaeger *et al.*, 1975a,b).

A variety of immunological effects have resulted from chloroprene
exposure, including a decrease in the number of antibody-forming cells in
the spleen (Agakhanyan *et al.*, 1973) and enhancement of transplanted
tumour growth (Zil'fyan & Fichidzhyan, 1972).

### Embryotoxicity and teratogenicity

An embryotoxic effect was seen in pregnant rats that inhaled concentrations of chloroprene ranging from 0.13-53.4 $mg/m^3$ (0.035-15 ppm) (Melik-
Alaverdyan *et al.*, 1976; Mnatsakayan *et al.*, 1972; Salnikova & Fomenko,
1973, 1975). The highest embryotoxic effect was observed when 4 $mg/m^3$
(1.1 ppm) chloroprene were inhaled during the entire pregnancy, or inter-
mittently on days 1-2, 3-4 or 11-12, or given orally at a dose of 0.5
mg/kg bw/day for 14 days or on days 3-4 or 11-12. A teratogenic effect
(meningoencephaloceles) was seen when chloroprene was administered on days
5-6, 9-10, 11-12, 13-14 and 15-16 of gestation (Salnikova & Fomenko, 1975).

Neither embryotoxic nor teratological effects were reported by Culik
*et al.* (1976) after exposing pregnant rats to 90.5 $mg/m^3$ (25 ppm) chloroprene for 4 hours daily from day 1 to day 12 or from day 3 to day 20 of
gestation.

### Metabolism

When a mixture of chloroprene in air was passed through a mouse-liver
microsomal preparation, a volatile alkylating metabolite was formed, as
demonstrated by trapping with 4-(4-nitrobenzyl)pyridine (Barbin *et al.*,
1977; Bartsch *et al.*, 1978).

### Mutagenicity and other short-term tests

Chloroprene vapours induced reverse mutations in *Salmonella typhimurium*
TA100 and TA1530. Addition of a 9000 x *g* supernatant of liver from mice or

one human surgical specimen enhanced mutagenicity (Bartsch, 1976; Bartsch *et al*., 1975, 1976, 1979).

In *Drosophila melanogaster*, recessive lethal mutations were induced by feeding male flies 5.7 and 11.4 mM chloroprene for 3 days (Vogel, 1976).

As early as 1936, von Oettingen *et al*. (1936) observed that the reproduction of male mice and rats was affected after inhalation of chloroprene at concentrations of 42-540 mg/m$^3$ (12-150 ppm) for mice and 430-22,400 mg/m$^3$ (120-6000 ppm) for rats. Testicular atrophy, or reduction in the numbers and motility of sperm in rats with non-atrophied testes, occurred at an exposure level of 0.15 mg/m$^3$ (0.04 ppm) (Davtyan, 1972; Sanotskii, 1976). Spermatogenesis in C57BL/6 mice was affected after 2 months' exposure to 0.32 mg/m$^3$ (0.09 ppm) chloroprene (Sanotskii, 1976). A significant increase in embryotoxicity was observed in female rats fertilized by males exposed to 3.8 mg/m$^3$ (1 ppm) 4 hours daily for 48 days (Davtyan *et al*., 1973).

Chloroprene induced dominant lethal mutations and chromosome aberrations in bone-marrow cells of rats exposed to 0.14-3.6 mg/m$^3$ in air (0.04-1.0 ppm) (Davtyan, 1972; Davtyan *et al*., 1973; Sanotskii, 1976) and dominant lethal mutations in mice exposed to 1.85-3.5 mg/m$^3$ in air (0.5-1 ppm) (Sanotskii, 1976). Mixtures of chloroprene plus dodecylmercaptan plus ammonia (Bagramjan & Babajan, 1974), and chloroprene plus methyl methacrylate (Bagramjan & Babajan, 1974; Bagramjan *et al*., 1976) also induced chromosome aberrations in bone-marrow cells of rats.

(b)  Humans

The primary effects of acute exposure to high concentrations of chloroprene in air are central nervous system depression, injury to the lungs, liver and kidneys, irritation of skin and mucous membranes and respiratory difficulties (Irish, 1963; Nyström, 1948). Dermatitis and hair loss due to contact with chloroprene and its polymers have also been reported (Nyström, 1948; Ritter & Carter, 1948; Schwartz, 1945; Volkov, 1971).

Symptoms of chronic chloroprene exposure include headache, irritability, dizziness, insomnia, fatigue, respiratory irritation, cardiac palpitations, chest pain, gastrointestinal disorders, dermatitis, temporary loss of hair, conjunctivitis and corneal necrosis (Barskii *et al*., 1972; Lloyd *et al*., 1975; Nyström, 1948; Sax, 1975; Schwartz, 1945). Hepatomegaly, with a decrease in liver function tests, toxic hepatitis, dystrophy of the myocardium and changes in the nervous system (Orlova & Solov'eva, 1962), circulatory changes (Khachatryan & Oganesyan, 1974; Mirzabekyan & Nikogosyan, 1959), anaemia (Nyström, 1948), hypoglycaemia (Mkhitaryan, 1960a; Nikogosyan, 1958), altered enzyme activities (Mkhitaryan, 1960b; Mnatsakanyan & Mushegyan, 1964) and dysfunction of both the central and peripheral nervous systems, particularly the cholinergic branch (Gasparyan,

1965), have also been reported. A decrease in blood cholinesterase activity has also been seen in exposed workers (Gasparyan, 1965). Pathological
changes in the cardiovascular and nervous systems were observed in 44% of
patients with chronic chloroprene poisoning (Khachatryan & Oganesyan, 1974).

Inhalation of chloroprene causes pathomorphological changes in the
periodontium: periodontitis (49%), gingivitis (22%), erosion of teeth
(17%) and caries (5%) (Arevshatyan, 1972).

Low immunological reactivity was observed in 208 chloroprene workers
immunized with typhoid vaccine (Mikaelyan & Frangulyan, 1965).

Davtyan *et al.* (1973) cited cases of children born with physical
and mental defects to female workers in a polymerization area of a
chloroprene rubber factory.

A significant rise in the number of chromosome aberrations was
observed in blood cells from 18 workers exposed to an average chloroprene concentration of 18 mg/m$^3$ (5 ppm) for from 2 to more than 10 years.
A frequency of 4.7% chromosome aberrations and 3.7% gaps was found in the
treated group, as compared with 0.65 and 1.14%, respectively, in a control
group of 9 workers from a motor car plant. However, there was no relationship in the exposed group between exposure time and aberration frequency,
neither was there any evidence of numerical chromosome changes (Katosova,
1973).

Among 56 workers exposed to chloroprene, chloroprene latex or chloroprene rubber [the concentration of chloroprene in the air being about
6 mg/m$^3$ (1.6 ppm)] the incidence of chromosomal aberrations (mainly single
breaks and double fragments) in cultured peripheral blood lymphocytes was
2.78%, compared with 0.53 and 1.14% chromosome aberrations in two groups
of controls (Zhurkov *et al.*, 1977).

Fomenko & Katosova (1973) (reviewed by Sanotskii, 1976) reported an
increased frequency of chromosome aberrations in lymphocyte cultures from
28 female workers who were exposed for 1 to 20 years to 1-7 mg/m$^3$ (0.3-2
ppm) chloroprene.

A statistically significant increase in chromosome aberrations was
found in the lymphocytes of 5 workers in contact with 2-2.2 mg/m$^3$ (0.55-
0.6 ppm) chloroprene and 0.5-2 mg/m$^3$ (0.1-0.5 ppm) methyl methacrylate
in air. The incidences of chromatid breaks (single fragments) and chromosome breaks (fragment pairs) were found to be 16.8% and 16.9%, respectively
(Bagramjan *et al.*, 1976).

Functional disturbances in spermatogenesis and morphological abnormalities of sperm were observed among workers occupationally exposed to
chloroprene (Sanotskii, 1976).

A three-fold excess of spontaneous abortions has been reported in the wives of chloroprene workers (Sanotskii, 1976).

## 3.3  Case reports and epidemiological studies[1]

Khachatryan (1972a) reported a study of lung cancer risk in relation to industrial exposure to chloroprene based on 87 cases of lung cancer diagnosed in the oncology department of the greater industrial Yerevan region during the period 1956-1970. The frequency ratio of primary lung cancer among the 'control' groups compared with that of the chloroprene groups was reported to be:  2.67 times lower in persons working with chemicals unrelated to chloroprene, 6.3 times lower in workers in non-chemical industries and 17.5 times lower in workers in cultural and civic institutions [The limitations of this study include failure to distinguish prevalent from incident cases, failure to document completeness of case ascertainment among the exposure group, failure to adjust for effects of age and sex, failure to measure the extent of exposure and failure to control for the potential confounding effect of smoking or other non-chloroprene-related exposures].

Simultaneously with the lung cancer study, Khachatryan (1972b) investigated the risk of skin cancer in relation to industrial chloroprene exposure. The percentage of diagnosed skin cancers by exposure group was reported as follows:  Group 1 - never worked in industry, 0.12% (11 cases/ 8520 examined);  Group 2 - lengthy experience in non-chemical industries, 0.40% (35/8755);  Group 3 - lengthy exposure to chemicals unrelated to chloroprene, 0.66% (32/4780);  Group 4 - worked only in plants utilizing chloroprene derivatives, 1.6% (33/2250);  and Group 5 - extended work experience in chloroprene production only, 3.07% (21/684) [The limitations of the study are the same as those described above for the lung cancer study;  in addition, the absence of histological information on cell type is particularly important in this study of reported skin cancer].

Pell (1978) reported a study of cancer mortality among two cohorts of males engaged in the production and/or polymerization of chloroprene, one cohort consisting of 234 men first exposed between 1931-1948 and the other of 1576 men first exposed between 1942-1957. Both cohorts were followed until the end of 1974. Whereas the numbers of lung cancer deaths in each cohort (3 in the first and 16 in the second) were about those expected on the basis of US or company-wide rates, the risks of digestive cancer (19 *versus* 13.3) and of lymphatic and hematopoietic cancer (7 *versus* 4.5) were

---

[1]Khairullina (1973) (quoted by Sanotskii, 1976) referred to the appearance of tumours in female workers, but no anatomical or pathological information was given which would allow an epidemiological evaluation to be made.

slightly elevated in the second cohort when contrasted with company-wide experience (in the first cohort, 3 digestive cancers were observed, which differed very little from the number expected). There were 8 lung cancer cases (4 living and 4 deceased) among maintenance mechanics in the second cohort (1576 men), accounting for 40% of the lung cancers in the total study cohort, although only 17% of the total cohort was composed of maintenance mechanics. Infante *et al.* (1977) have commented on the significance of these observations in mechanics, since their tasks include replacement of leaking pipefittings, installation of equipment and general maintenance in the reactor areas - tasks which have a potentially high exposure to chloroprene. These authors also commented on the methodological shortcoming in the Pell (1978) study inherent in combining chloroprene monomer production workers and polymerization workers in the second cohort [The Pell (1978) study has the following limitations: (1) a possibility of ascertainment bias in the cohort restricted to active employees at inception of the study, since retired workers, disabled workers and former chloroprene workers were not uniformly included in the initial cohort; (2) no data on potential confounding variables such as smoking history and other occupational exposures; (3) no exposure information based on measurements of chemical concentration; (4) no data on cell types of the malignancies; (5) still incomplete follow-up of the second cohort for an adequate latent period; and (6) small number of person-years of exposure].

One case of liver angiosarcoma (pathologically confirmed) has been reported in a worker exposed to chloroprene who had no known occupational exposure to vinyl chloride or medical exposure to thorotrast (Infante, 1977).

Polychloroprene

1.   Chemical and Physical Data

1.1   Synonyms and trade names

Chem. Abstr. Services Reg. No.:   9010-98-4

Chem. Abstr. Name:   2-Chloro-1,3-butadiene homopolymer

Chlorobutadiene polymer;   2-chloro-1,3-butadiene polymer;   chloroprene polymer;   poly(2-chlorobutadiene);   poly(2-chloro-1,3-butadiene);   1,4-*cis*-poly(chloroprene);   polychloroprene;   *trans*-1,4-polychloroprene

Duprene;   GR-M;   Nairit;   Neoprene;   Perbunan C;   Plastifix PC;   Sovprene;   Svitpren

1.2  Structural and molecular formulae and molecular weight

$$\left[\begin{array}{c} Cl \\ \diagdown \\ C=C \\ \diagup \quad \diagdown \\ CH_2 \quad\quad H \end{array}\begin{array}{c} CH_2 \\ \diagup \\ \\ \\ \end{array}\right]_n$$

$(C_4H_5Cl)_n$          Mol. wt:  80 000–200 000

1.3  Chemical and physical properties of the rubber

From Windholz (1976), unless otherwise specified

(a)  Description:  White-to-amber, rubbery solid (Anon., 1975b)

(b)  Melting-point:  Softens at about 80°C

(c)  Refractive index:  $n_D$ 1.55–1.56

(d)  Spectroscopy data:  Infra-red spectral data have been tabulated for the latex form (Grasselli & Ritchey, 1975).

(e)  Solubility:  Insoluble in water;  swells in kerosene, benzene and acetone (Dean, 1973)

(f)  Stability:  Combustion of polychloroprene cables has been reported to produce hydrogen chloride and chlorine (Csonev, 1969).

1.4  Technical products and impurities

Over 35 commercial grades of polychloroprene elastomers are available in the US.  The two major categories are the solid and latex forms.  The solid form has a specific gravity of 1.23 and is generally available in white-to-amber chips.  Polychloroprene latex (an aqueous dispersion) is a milky-white liquid with a specific gravity of 1.08–1.15 and contains 41–60% solids, depending on the type (Anon., 1975b).  Polychloroprene elastomers are usually vulcanized with metallic oxides (a combination of magnesium and zinc oxide) and must contain antioxidants.  The different grades vary with the processing aids used;  these may include accelerators (dithiocarbamates and guanidines), lubricants (stearic acid, microcrystalline waxes and low-molecular-weight polyethylenes), tackifiers (hydrogenated rosin esters and coumarone-indene resins), fillers (clay and carbon black), plasticizers (petroleum oils), stabilizers (anionic, nonionic and amphoteric surfactants) and thickeners (natural and synthetic gums).  Various grades are blended to obtain specific properties (Hargreaves & Thompson, 1965).

No detailed information on the possible presence of unreacted monomer in the polymers was available to the Working Group.

## 2.  Production, Use, Occurrence and Analysis

### 2.1  Production and use

#### (a)  Production

Polychloroprene was first introduced in the US in 1932 (Hargreaves & Thompson, 1965), although commercial production was not reported separately until 1943 (US Tariff Commission, 1945).  Polychloroprene is produced commercially by the emulsion polymerization of chloroprene using free radical initiators.  The details of the polymerization vary, depending on the type of polychloroprene produced.  The process used to make general-purpose polychloroprene is representative of that used for producing both solid and latex forms:  chloroprene is emulsified in water with the sodium soap of rosin acids at $38^{\circ}$C and then polymerized at $40^{\circ}$C by the addition of potassium peroxydisulphate.  Sulphur may also be added.  The polychloroprene is then vulcanized with a metallic oxide and processed with various other aids, depending on its end use.

2-Mercaptoimidazoline (ethylene thiourea) is used in the production of vulcanized natural or synthetic (including polychloroprene) gaskets or other components (see IARC, 1974).

Two US companies produced about 165 million kg polychloroprene in 1976;  imports were 3.1 million kg and were from the following countries: the Federal Republic of Germany (60.7%), France (29.4%), Japan (2.7%), Romania (2.2%) and the UK (5.0%) (US Department of Commerce, 1977); exports were 46.2 million kg.

Production in western Europe in 1976 amounted to 85 million kg.  The major producers were the following (in millions of kg):  the Federal Republic of Germany (40), France (3) and the UK (20).  Exports from western Europe in 1976 were 25 million kg and imports 40 million kg. Total production in 1977 was 100 million kg.

Polychloroprene has been produced commercially in Japan since 1962. In 1976, three companies produced a total of 77 million kg;  imports were 1 million kg, and 41 million kg were exported.

Total world production of polychloroprene in 1977 is estimated to have been 300 million kg.

#### (b)  Use

In 1976, about 110 million kg polychloroprene were used in the US, as follows:  production of industrial and automotive rubber goods (63%), wire and cable applications (13%), construction applications (10%), adhesive applications (8%) and miscellaneous uses (6%).

Polychloroprene is used in a wide variety of industrial and automotive goods, including hose, tubing, belting, diaphragms, weather stripping, seals, gaskets and moulded and extruded goods. They are used in wire and cable jackets. Construction applications include highway joint seals, pipe gaskets, bridge mounts and expansion joints. They are also used in adhesive cements and coatings, mastics, caulks and sealants. Miscellaneous applications include: tire sidewalls; chemically blown cellular products; consumer products (shoes, sporting goods and house and garden products); coatings for fabrics, sheet goods and thread; binder or impregnant for fibres, nonwoven fabrics and cellulose or asbestos paper; and as an additive for the elasticization of concrete.

In Japan, polychloroprene is used for the manufacture of industrial goods (60%) and other applications, primarily adhesives (40%).

The US Food and Drug Administration permits the use of polychloroprene as a component of resinous and polymeric coatings and in rubber articles intended for use in contact with food (US Food and Drug Administration, 1977).

## 2.2 Occurrence

Polychloroprene is not known to occur as a natural product. No data on possible environmental exposure to the compound were available to the Working Group.

## 2.3 Analysis

Plastics and rubbers, including polychloroprene, have been identified using pyrolysis-gas chromatography (Braun & Canji, 1974; Feuerberg, 1967; Fischer, 1967; Okumoto & Takeuchi, 1972; Sugiki & Yamamoto, 1972; Ural'skii *et al.*, 1976) and differential scanning calorimetry (Sircar & Lamond, 1972).

## 3. Biological Data Relevant to the Evaluation
### of Carcinogenic Risk to Humans

No data were available to the Working Group.

## 4. Summary of Data Reported and Evaluation

### 4.1 Experimental data

Chloroprene was tested in rats by oral, subcutaneous and intratracheal administration and in mice by skin application. Although no carcinogenic effects were found, these studies were considered by the Working Group to be inadequate to allow an evaluation of the carcinogenicity of chloroprene in experimental animals.

Chloroprene is embryotoxic, teratogenic and mutagenic.

No data on the carcinogenicity of polychloroprene were available to the Working Group.

## 4.2  Human data

Production of chloroprene and polychloroprene is extensive and use of the polymer diffuse.  Occupational exposures during the polymerization process have been reported to be associated with a wide variety of organ and systemic toxicological effects.  In one study, an excess of lung and skin cancers was related to occupational exposure to chloroprene;  in another investigation, no excess of lung cancer or other types of cancer was reported among chloroprene workers.

One case report was available describing the occurrence of an angio-sarcoma of the liver in a worker exposed to chloroprene.

Data on cytogenetic effects and reproductive disturbances in workers exposed to chloroprene and in their wives suggest that chloroprene is mutagenic to humans.

No information on possible carcinogenic effects in persons exposed only to the polymer was available to the Working Group.

## 4.3  Evaluation

Reports of increased frequencies of lung and skin cancer in workers exposed to chloroprene raise the possibility that chloroprene is carcino-genic to humans.  These studies, however, have methodological deficiencies: in particular, failure to define epidemiological measures of cancer frequency.  The one negative epidemiological study available does not rule out the possibility that chloroprene is carcinogenic, since the period of follow-up of the cohort is still relatively short, because the signifi-cance of the study is limited by the low number of person-years of experi-ence, and information is lacking on the extent of exposure.

Despite the obvious limitations inherent in a single case report, attention is called to the reported association of liver angiosarcoma with chloroprene.

The epidemiological reports regarding cytogenetic effects and repro-ductive disturbances in workers exposed to chloroprene and in their wives are consistent with experimental evidence that chloroprene is mutagenic.

The inconclusive nature of both the epidemiological studies (and the single case report) and the available carcinogenicity studies in experimental animals preclude an evaluation of the potential carcinogenicity of chloroprene to humans. Intensified efforts should be made to obtain further experimental and epidemiological evidence with regard to chloroprene and cancer (see also 'General Remarks on the Substances Considered', p. 35).

# 5. References

Agakhanyan, A.G., Allaverdyan, A.G. & Panosyan, S.G. (1973)  Effect of chloroprene on antibody formation in rats (Russ.). Zh. eksp. klin. Med., 13, 28-30 [Chem. Abstr., 80, 104587q]

Airapetyan, A.A. & Matevonyan, M.S. (1973)  Effect of chloroprene poisoning on reflex behavior processes in rats (Russ.). Biol. Zh. Arm., 26, 11-18 [Chem. Abstr., 80, 78914x]

Allaverdyan, A.G. (1970)  Changes in adrenal glands during acute and chronic chloroprene poisoning (Russ.). Tr. Klin. Otd. Nauch.-Issled. Inst. Gig. Tr. Profzabol., 1, 150-157 [Chem. Abstr., 77, 71039v]

Anon. (1972)  Fire Protection Guide on Hazardous Materials, 4th ed., Boston, Mass., National Fire Protection Association, p. 325M-41

Anon. (1975a)  Properties and handling of chloroprene (CD). Intermediates Facts Sheet, Wilmington, Del., Elastomer Chemicals Department, E.I. Du Pont de Nemours & Co.

Anon. (1975b)  Du Pont Products Book, Wilmington, Del., E.I. Du Pont de Nemours & Co., pp. 133-135

Anon. (1977)  NIOSH recommends limit of 3.6 milligrams for chloroprene. Occupational Safety & Health Reporter, 18 August, pp. 366-367

Apoyan, K.K., Abeshyan, M.M., Gofmekler, V.A., Mnatsakanyan, A.V., Mutafyan, G.A., Pogosyan, U.G. & Tarverdyan, A.K. (1970)  Spectro-photometric method for determining chloroprene in the air (Russ.). Gig. i Sanit., 35, 61-64 [Chem. Abstr., 73, 133811u]

Arevshatyan, G.S. (1972)  Prophylactic care of the oral cavities of workers engaged in chloroprene production (Russ.). Biol. Zh. Arm., 25, 115-117 [Chem. Abstr., 78, 47442w]

Asmangulyan, T.A. & Badalyan, S.O. (1971)  Toxicity of chloroprene in an acute test during oral administration (Russ.). Tr. Erevan. Med. Inst., No. 15, Book 1, 461-465 [Chem. Abstr., 78, 67807x]

Babina, M.D. (1969)  Determination of volatile substances released into the air by footwear factories (Russ.). In: Murav'eva, S.I., ed., New Fields of Industrial Hygiene Chemistry, Moscow, Meditsina, pp. 227-232 [Chem. Abstr., 72, 24270a]

Bagramjan, S.B. & Babajan, E.A. (1974)  Cytogenetic study of the mutagenic activity of chemical substances isolated from Nairit latexes MKh and LNT-1 (Russ.). Biol. Zh. Arm., 27, 102-103

Bagramjan, S.B., Pogosjan, A.S., Babajan, E.A., Ovanesja, R.D. & Charjan, S.M. (1976) Mutagenic effect of small concentrations of volatile substances, emitted from polychloroprene latexes LNT-1 and MKH, during their combined uptake by the animal (Russ.). Biol. Zh. Arm., 29, 98-99

Barbin, A., Planche, G., Croisy, A., Malaveille, C. & Bartsch, H. (1977) Detection of electrophilic metabolites of halogenated olefins with 4-(4-nitrobenzyl)pyridine (NBP) or with Salmonella typhimurium (Abstract). In: 2nd International Conference on Environmental Mutagens, Edinburgh, July 1977, p. 59

Barskii, V.D., Marakushkina, V.K. & Meshakova, N.M. (1972) Hygienic evaluation of the working conditions and health of workers employed in the production of chloroprene rubber in eastern Siberia (Russ.). Nauch Tr., Irkutsk. Med. Inst., 115, 5-8 [Chem. Abstr., 80, 112119d]

Bartsch, H. (1976) Mutagenicity tests in chemical carcinogenesis. In: Rosenfeld, C. & Davis, W., eds, Environmental Pollution and Carcinogenic Risk (INSERM Symposia Series, Vol. 52; IARC Scientific Publications No. 13), Lyon, pp. 229-240

Bartsch, H., Malaveille, C., Montesano, R. & Tomatis, L. (1975) Tissue-mediated mutagenicity of vinylidene chloride and 2-chlorobutadiene in Salmonella typhimurium. Nature (Lond.), 255, 641-643

Bartsch, H., Malaveille, C., Barbin, A., Bresil, H., Tomatis, L. & Montesano, R. (1976) Mutagenicity and metabolism of vinyl chloride and related compounds. Environ. Health Perspect., 17, 193-198

Bartsch, H., Malaveille, C., Barbin, A. & Planche, G. (1979) Mutagenic and alkylating metabolites of haloethylenes, chlorobutadienes and dichlorobutenes produced by rodent or human liver tissues; evidence for oxirane formation by P450-linked microsomal mono-oxygenases. Arch. Toxicol. (in press)

Bauchwitz, P.S. (1964) Chloroprene. In: Kirk, R.E. & Othmer, D.F., eds, Encyclopedia of Chemical Technology, 2nd ed., Vol. 5, New York, John Wiley and Sons, pp. 215-231

Braun, D. & Canji, E. (1974) Simple pyrolysis-gas chromatographic analysis method for identification of elastomers (Ger.). Gummi, Asbest, Kunstst., 27, 272-275 [Chem. Abstr., 81, 122295t]

Bunyatyants, Z.V., Sukiasyan, A.G. & Gnusina, S.A. (1976) Chromatographic method for determining the residual monomer in chloroprene latexes (Russ.). Prom.-st. Sint. Kauch., 5, 13-15 [Chem. Abstr., 85, 193871w]

Buyanov, A.A. & Svishchev, G.A. (1973) Protection of the atmosphere from shoe-factory industrial emissions (Russ.). Izv. Vyssh. Ucheb. Zaved., Tekhnol. Legk. Prom., 3, 68-71 [Chem. Abstr., 79, 83006m]

Carothers, W.H., Williams, I., Collins, A.M. & Kirby, J.E. (1931) Acetylene polymers and their derivatives. II. A new synthetic rubber: chloroprene and its polymers. J. Am. chem. Soc., 53, 4203-4225

Clary, J.J. (1977) Toxicity of chloroprene, 1,3-dichlorobutene-2 and 1,4-dichlorobutene-2. Environ. Health Perspect., 21, 271-274

Clary, J.J., Feron, V.J. & Reuzel, P.G.J. (1978) Toxicity of β-chloroprene (2-chlorobutadiene-1,3): acute and subacute toxicity. Toxicol. appl. Pharmacol., 46, 375-384

Csonev, B. (1969) Data on the safety problems of plastics containing chlorine (Hung.). Banyasz. Kut. Intez., Kozlem., 13, 125-135 [Chem. Abstr., 72, 82688d]

Culik, R., Kelly, D.P. & Clary, J.J. (1976) β-Chloroprene (2-chlorobutadiene-1,3) embryotoxic and teratogenic studies in rats (Abstr. No. 194). Toxicol. appl. Pharmacol., 37, 172

Davtyan, R.M. (1972) Toxicological characteristics of the action of chloroprene on the reproductive function of male rats. In: Proceedings of the 2nd Conference on Toxicology and Hygiene of Petroleum Products, 1971, Yaroslavl, USSR, Medical Institute, pp. 95-97 [Chem. Abstr., 80, 91720a]

Davtyan, R.M., Fomenko, V.N. & Andreyeva, G.P. (1973) Question of the effect of chloroprene on the generative function of mammals (males) (Russ.). Toksikol. Nov. Prom. Khim. Veshchestv, 13, 58-62

Dean, J.A., ed. (1973) Lange's Handbook of Chemistry, 11th ed., New York, McGraw-Hill, p. 7-457

Feuerberg, H. (1967) Pyrolysis-gas chromatography of organic polymers (Ger.). Ind. Chim. Belge, Spec. No. 32, Pt. 1, 140-144 [Chem. Abstr., 70, 97208e]

Fischer, W.G. (1967) Pyrolytic gas-chromatography (Ger.). Glas-Instrum.-Tech., 11, 562, 567-570, 775-780, 1086-1088, 1091-1095 [Chem. Abstr., 68, 78636k]

Fomenko, V.N. & Katosova, L.D. (1973) The results of cytogenetic analysis of the peripheral blood in women workers in contact with chloroprene latex (Russ.). In: Proceedings of Occupational Gynecology and Obstetrics, Kazan, pp. 33-37 [quoted in Sanotskii, 1976]

Gasparyan, E.I. (1965)  Data on neuro-humoral shifts occurring under the effect of chloroprene (Russ.).  Gig. Tr. Prof. Zabol., 9, 19-24

Gizhlaryan, M.S., Khechumov, S.A. & Khechumova, R.M. (1972)  Comparative toxicity of chlorinated hydrocarbons from the production of chloro-prene rubber Nairit PNK (Russ.).  In:  Proceedings of the 2nd Conference on Toxicology and Hygiene of Petroleum Products, 1971, Yaroslavl, USSR, Medical Institute, pp. 91-94 [Chem. Abstr., 80, 67128t]

Gizhlaryan, M.S., Avetisyan, D.P. & Arystatova, M.S. (1976)  Gas-chromato-graphic determination of chloroorganic substances from Nairit PNK production in air during their joint presence (Russ.).  Gig. i Sanit., 1, 64-66 [Chem. Abstr., 85, 9794z]

Grasselli, J.G. & Ritchey, W.M., eds (1975)  CRC Atlas of Spectral Data and Physical Constants for Organic Compounds, 2nd ed., Cleveland, Ohio, Chemical Rubber Co., Vol. II, p. 565;  Vol. III, p. 671

Hargreaves, C.A. & Thompson, D.C. (1965)  2-Chlorobutadiene polymers.  In: Bikales, N.M., ed., Encyclopedia of Polymer Science and Technology, Plastics, Resins, Rubbers, Fibers, Vol. 3, New York, Interscience, pp. 705-730

Hawley, G.G., ed. (1971)  The Condensed Chemical Dictionary, 8th ed., New York, Van Nostrand-Reinhold, p. 206

IARC (1974)  IARC Monographs on the Evaluation of Carcinogenic Risk of Chemicals to Man, 7, Some Anti-thyroid and Related Substances, Nitrofurans and Industrial Chemicals, Lyon, pp. 45-50

IARC (1977)  IARC Monographs on the Evaluation of the Carcinogenic Risk of Chemicals to Man, 15, Some Fumigants, the Herbicides 2,4-D and 2,4,5-T, Chlorinated Dibenzodioxins and Miscellaneous Industrial Chemicals, Lyon, pp. 155-175

IARC (1978)  Information Bulletin on the Survey of Chemicals Being Tested for Carcinogenicity, No. 7, Lyon, pp. 67, 263, 275

Infante, P.F. (1977)  Carcinogenic and mutagenic risks associated with some halogenated olefins.  Environ. Health Perspect., 21, 251-254

Infante, P.F., Wagoner, J.K. & Young, R.J. (1977)  Chloroprene: observa-tions of carcinogenesis and mutagenesis.  In:  Hiatt, H.H., Watson, J.D. & Winsten, J.A., eds, Origins of Human Cancer, Book A, Cold Spring Harbor, N.Y., Cold Spring Harbor Laboratory, pp. 205-217

Irish, D. (1963)  Aliphatic halogenated hydrocarbons.  In: Patty, F.A., ed., Industrial Hygiene and Toxicology, Vol. II, New York, Interscience, pp. 1319-1321

Jaeger, R.J., Conolly, R.B. & Murphy, S.D. (1975a)  Short-term inhalation
    toxicity of halogenated hydrocarbons.  Effects on fasting rats.
    Arch. environ. Health, 30, 26-31

Jaeger, R.J., Conolly, R.B., Reynolds, E.S. & Murphy, S.D. (1975b)  Bio-
    chemical toxicology of unsaturated halogenated monomers.  Environ.
    Health Perspect., 11, 121-128

Katosova, L.D. (1973)  Cytogenetic analysis of peripheral blood of workers
    engaged in the production of chloroprene (Russ.).  Gig. Tr. Prof.
    Zabol., 17, 30-32

Kaznina, N.I. (1972)  Determination of unsaturated compounds in the air by
    mercury salt addition (Russ.).  Gig. i Sanit., 37, 63-66 [Chem. Abstr.,
    77, 92364n]

Khachatryan, E.A. (1972a)  The occurrence of lung cancer among people
    working with chloroprene (Russ.).  Vop. Onkol., 18, 85-86

Khachatryan, E.A. (1972b)  The role of chloroprene compounds in the process
    of skin neoplasm formation (Russ.).  Gig. Tr. Prof. Zabol., 16, 54-55

Khachatryan, M.R. & Oganesyan, G.L. (1974)  Changes in the nervous and
    cardiovascular system of shoe industry workers having contact with
    Nairit cements in the Masis Company (Russ.).  Zh. eksp. klin. Med.,
    14, 85-89 [Chem. Abstr., 82, 63862w]

Khairullina, A.S. (1973)  The incidence of gynaecological disease among
    women workers employed in the production of articles made of Nairite
    latex (Russ.).  In: Proceedings of Occupational Gynecology and
    Obstetrics, Kazan, pp. 83-89 [quoted in Sanotskii, 1976]

Kurosaki, M., Taima, S., Hatta, T. & Nakamura, A. (1968)  Identification
    of high-boiling materials as by-products in vinyl chloride manufacture
    (Jap.).  Kogyo Kagaku Zasshi, 71, 488-491 [Chem. Abstr., 69, 56857b]

Lloyd, J.W., Decoufle, P. & Moore, R.M., Jr (1975)  Background information
    on chloroprene.  J. occup. Med., 17, 263-265

Martinyan, G.V. (1966)  Effect of chloroprene and hyposulfite on transaminase
    activity (Armen.).  Biol. Zh. Armenii, 19, 36-41 [Chem. Abstr., 66,
    1230v]

Melik-Alaverdyan, N.O., Kagramanyan, R.G. & Kalantarova, E.G. (1976)  Repro-
    ductive function and sex maturation in rats of 3 generations born to
    mothers with chloroprene poisoning (Russ.).  Zh. eksp. klin. Med., 16,
    54-59

Mikaelyan, V.G. & Frangulyan, L.A. (1965)  Effect of chloroprene on immuno-
    logic reactivity of organism in persons vaccinated against typhoid
    fever (Russ.).  Tr. Erevan. Med. Inst., Min. Zdravookhr. Arm. SSR,
    14, 239-244 [Chem. Abstr.. 66. 58658z]

Mirzabekyan, G.I. & Nikogosyan, S.V. (1959)  Effect of 2-chloro-1,3-butadiene on the quantity of vitamin C in blood, urine, and internal organs of animals (Russ.).  Gig. Tr. Prof. Zabol., 3, 15-20

Mkhitaryan, V.G. (1959)  The effect of chloroprene on liver and brain respiration (Russ.).  Vop. Biokhim. Akad. Nauk Armyan SSR, 1, 135-147 [Chem. Abstr., 55, 27663b]

Mkhitaryan, V.G. (1960a)  Effect of chloroprene on the protein, cholesterol, and glucose contents in blood of laborers. VIII. (Russ.). Izvest. Akad. Nauk Armyan SSR, Biol. Nauk, 13, 65-74 [Chem. Abstr., 55, 16806d]

Mkhitaryan, V.G. (1960b)  Action of chloroprene on metabolism. VI. Biochemical changes in blood of laborers under chronic influence of chloroprene (Russ.).  Izvest. Akad. Nauk Armyan SSR, Biol. Nauk, 13, 27-39 [Chem. Abstr., 55, 76631]

Mkhitaryan, V.G. (1960c)  Effect of chloroprene on adenosinotriphosphatase activity in the organs of rats. IX. (Russ.).  Trudy Erevansk. Med. Inst., 11, 41-47 [Chem. Abstr., 56, 10508b]

Mkhitaryan, V.G. & Astvatsatryan, S.A. (1959)  The influence of 2-chloro-1,3-butadiene (chloroprene) on the phosphatase activity of the organs of white rats. V. (Russ.).  Izvest. Akad. Nauk Armyan SSR, Biol. Nauk, 12, 13-20 [Chem. Abstr., 53, 20505e]

Mkhitaryan, V.G., Chilingaryan, L. & Stepanyan, L.A. (1971)  Reaction of adrenal glands to chronic chloroprene poisoning (Russ.).  Tr. Erevan. Med. Inst., 15 (1), 275-283 [Chem. Abstr., 78, 53628c]

Mnatsakanyan, A.V. & Mushegyan, A.V. (1964)  On the effect of low chloroprene concentrations on the porphyrin metabolism in children (Russ.). Gig. i Sanit., 29, 83-84

Mnatsakanyan, A.V., Pogosyan, U.G., Apoyan, K.K., Gofmekler, V.A. & Kanayan, A.S. (1972)  Embryotoxic action of emissions of the chloroprene synthetic rubber industry using as material for study the progeny (first generation) of white rats (Russ.).  Tr. Er. Gos. Inst. Usoversh. Vrachei, 5, 155-158 [Chem. Abstr., 80, 112115z]

Movsesyan, T.B., Mnatsakanyan, A.V. & Galstyan, O.K. (1964)  Pathomorphology of brain elements of white rats with chloroprene poisoning (Russ.). Izv. Akad. Nauk Armyan SSR, Biol. Nauk, 17, 51-58 [Chem. Abstr., 62, 9684b]

National Institute for Occupational Safety and Health (1977)  Criteria for a Recommended Standard - Occupational Exposure to Chloroprene, DHEW (NIOSH) Publ. No. 77-210, Washington DC, US Government Printing Office

Nikogosyan, S.V. (1958) Influence of 2-chlorobutadiene on blood sugar level in man and in experimental animals (Armen.). Izvest. Akad. Nauk Armyan SSR, Biol. Nauk, 11, 61-64 [Chem. Abstr., 52, 18909g]

Nikogosyan, S.V. (1959) The effect of 2-chlorobutadiene-1,3 on the glycogen content of liver and the concentration of pyrogallic acid in the blood of experimental animals (Russ.). Gig. i Sanit., 24, 32-34

Nyström, A.E. (1948) Health hazards in the chloroprene rubber industry and their prevention. A clinical and experimental study with special reference to chloroprene as well as oxidation and polymerization products thereof. Acta med. scand., 132, Suppl. 219, 1-125

von Oettingen, W.F., Hueper, W.C., Deichmann-Gruebler, W. & Wiley, F.H. (1936) 2-Chloro-butadiene (chloroprene): its toxicity and pathology and the mechanism of its action. J. ind. Hyg. Toxicol., 18, 240-270

Okumoto, T. & Takeuchi, T. (1972) Rapid characterization of polymeric materials by pyrolysis-gas chromatography (Jap.). Nippon Kagaku Kaishi, 1, 71-78 [Chem. Abstr., 76, 141459n]

Orlova, A.A. & Solov'eva, E.A. (1962) Clinical picture of chronic exposure to various chemicals used in synthetic rubber (Russ.). Tr. Voronezhsk. Med. Inst., 47, 86-87

Panina, L.A. & Fain, B.S. (1968) Chromatographic determination of impurities in acrylonitrile (Russ.). Zavod. Lab., 34, 283 [Chem. Abstr., 69, 32851u]

Pell, S. (1978) Mortality of workers exposed to chloroprene. J. occup. Med., 20, 21-29

Pollock, J.R.A. & Stevens, R., eds (1965) Dictionary of Organic Compounds, 4th ed., Vol. 2, New York, Oxford University Press, p. 681

Ritter, W.L. & Carter, A.S. (1948) Hair loss in neoprene manufacture. J. ind. Hyg. Toxicol., 30, 192-195

Ruebensaal, C.F. (1975) The Rubber Industry Statistical Report and Changing Markets and Manufacturing Patterns in the Synthetic Rubber Industry, New York, International Institute of Synthetic Rubber Producers, pp. 2, 4, 11, 13, 19, 23, 26, 30, 34, 35

Ruebensaal, C.F. (1977) The Rubber Industry Statistical Report and Changing Markets and Manufacturing Patterns in the Synthetic Rubber Industry, New York, International Institute of Synthetic Rubber Producers, pp. 11, 13, 16, 19

Salnikova, L.S. & Fomenko, V.N. (1973) Experimental investigation of the influence produced by chloroprene on the embryogenesis (Russ.). Gig. Tr. Prof. Zabol., 17, 23-26

Salnikova, L.S. & Fomenko, V.N. (1975) Comparative characterization of the embryotropic effect produced by chloroprene, depending upon the mode of its action with different routes of entrance (Russ.). Gig. Tr. Prof. Zabol., 19, 30-33

Sanotskii, I.V. (1976) Aspects of the toxicology of chloroprene: immediate and long-term effects. Environ. Health Perspect., 17, 85-93

Sassu, G.M., Zilio-Grandi, F. & Conte, A. (1968) Gas chromatographic determination of impurities in vinyl chloride. J. Chromatogr., 34, 394-398

Sax, N.I. (1975) Dangerous Properties of Industrial Materials, 4th ed., New York, Van Nostrand-Reinhold, p. 553

Schwartz, L. (1945) Skin hazards in the manufacture and processing of synthetic rubber. J. Am. med. Assoc., 127, 389-391

Sharpanova, I.K., Taradai, E.P., Styskin, E.L. & Chikishev, Y.G. (1972) Determination of monomers in air by gas-adsorption chromatography with temperature programming (Russ.). Kauch. Rezina, 31, 48-50 [Chem. Abstr., 78, 7402b]

Sircar, A.K. & Lamond, T.G. (1972) Identification of elastomers by thermal analysis. Rubber Chem. Technol., 45, 329-345 [Chem. Abstr., 77, 49773h]

Sugiki, S. & Yamamoto, K. (1972) Simple quantitative analytical method for three-component blended rubbers of NR-SBR-BR [neoprene rubber-styrene-butadiene rubber-butadiene rubber] by pyrolysis gas chromatography using radio-frequency induction heating apparatus (Jap.). Nippon Gomu Kyokaishi, 45, 299-303 [Chem. Abstr., 77, 6861t]

Sukiasyan, A.G., Geodakyan, K.T., Khzanyan, G.S. & Berudzhanyan, O.S. (1976) Method for the determination of chloroprene in the air (Russ.). Arm. Khim. Zh., 29, 728-730 [Chem. Abstr., 86, 95113b]

Toxicology Information Program (1976) A long-term inhalation study of beta-chloroprene to rats. Tox-Tips, 3, 4

Toxicology Information Program (1977) Chronic inhalation of beta-chloroprene in hamsters. Tox-Tips, 13, 31

Turusova, K.N. & Khanina, V.K. (1975) Chromatographic determination of chloroprene in the air (Russ.). Gig. i Sanit., 7, 81-82

Ural'skii, M.L., Gorelik, R.A., Malyshev, A.I. & Bukanov, A.M. (1976) Pyrolytic gas chromatographic analysis of chloroprene rubbers in rubber vulcanizates (Russ.). Kauch. Rezina, 8, 57-59 [Chem. Abstr., 85, 161537a]

US Department of Commerce (1977) US Imports for Consumption and General Imports. TSUSA Commodity by Country of Origin, FT 246/Annual 1976, Bureau of the Census, Washington DC, US Government Printing Office, p. 235

US Food and Drug Administration (1977) Food and drugs. US Code Fed. Regul., Title 21, parts 175.105, 175.300, 177.2600, pp. 438, 440, 452, 456, 555

US Occupational Safety and Health Administration (1976) Occupational safety and health standards subpart Z - toxic and hazardous substances. US Code Fed. Regul., Title 29, Chapter XVII, Section 1910.1000, p. 31:8302

US Tariff Commission (1945) Synthetic Organic Chemicals, US Production and Sales, 1941-43, Report No. 153, Second Series, Washington DC, US Government Printing Office, p. 59

Vogel, E. (1976) Mutagenicity of carcinogens in Drosophila as function of genotype-controlled metabolism. In: de Serres, F.J., Fouts, J.R., Bend, J.R. & Philpot, R.M., eds, In vitro Metabolic Activation in Mutagenesis Testing, Amsterdam, Elsevier North Holland Biomedical Press, pp. 63-79

Volkov, Z.A. (1971) Hygienic problems in the industrial use of chloroprene and divinylstyrene latexes (Russ.). In: Problems of Synthesis and Properties of Latex, pp. 23-25 [Chem. Abstr., 78, 47439a]

Weast, R.C., ed. (1976) CRC Handbook of Chemistry and Physics, 57th ed., Cleveland, Ohio, Chemical Rubber Co., p. C-216

Windholz, M., ed. (1976) The Merck Index, 9th ed., Rahway, NJ, Merck & Co., p. 840

Winell, M. (1975) An international comparison of hygienic standards for chemicals in the work environment. Ambio, 4, 34-36

Zhurkov, V.S., Fichidzhjan, B.S., Batikjan, H.G., Arutjunjan, R.M. & Zil'fjan, V.N. (1977) Cytogenetic examination of persons contacting with chloroprene under industrial conditions. Tsitol. Genet., 11, 210-212

Zil'fyan, V.N. & Fichidzhyan, B.S. (1972)  Effect of chloroprene on develop-
    ment of Crocker's murine sarcoma.  In:  Proceedings of a Scientific
    Conference Devoted to the 50 Years of the Universities of USSR and
    to the 25 Years of the Armenian Institute of Roentgenology and Onco-
    logy, 1972, Yerevan, USSR, Armenian Institute of Roentgenology and
    Oncology, pp. 105-106 [Chem. Abstr., 81, 22099p]

Zil'fyan, V.N., Fichidzhyan, B.S. & Pogosova, A.M. (1975)  Results of
    testing chloroprene for carcinogenicity (Russ.).  Zh. eksp. klin.
    Med., 15, 54-57

Zil'fyan, V.N., Fichidzhyan, B.S., Garibyan, D.K. & Pogosova, A.M. (1977)
    Experimental study of chloroprene for carcinogenicity (Russ.).
    Vop. Onkol., 23, 61-65

ETHYLENE and POLYETHYLENE

Ethylene

## 1.  Chemical and Physical Data

1.1  Synonyms and trade names

Chem. Abstr. Services Reg. No.:  74-85-1

Chem. Abstr. Name:  Ethene

Acetene;  bicarburetted hydrogen;  olefiant gas

Elayl

1.2  Structural and molecular formulae and molecular weight

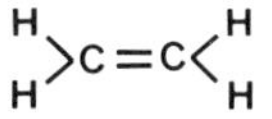

$$\begin{matrix} H \\ H \end{matrix} \Big\rangle C = C \Big\langle \begin{matrix} H \\ H \end{matrix}$$

$C_2H_4$                  Mol. wt:  28.0

1.3  Chemical and physical properties of the pure substance

From Weast (1976), unless otherwise specified

(a)  Description:  Colourless gas (Windholz, 1976)

(b)  Boiling-point:  $-103.7°C$

(c)  Melting-point:  $-169.2°C$ (freezing-point, $-181°C$)

(d)  Density:  $d_4^{-10}$ 0.384

(e)  Refractive index:  $n_D^{100}$ 1.363

(f)  Spectroscopy data:  $\lambda_{max}^{gas}$ 161.5 nm ($E_1^1$ = 3110);  166 nm
($E_1^1$ = 2253);  174 nm ($E_1^1$ = 1789);  infra-red, nuclear
magnetic resonance and mass spectral data have been tabulated
(Grasselli & Ritchey, 1975).

(g) <u>Solubility</u>: Insoluble in water; slightly soluble in ethanol, acetone and benzene; soluble in ether

(h) <u>Volatility</u>: Vapour pressure is 38 000 mm at 8.9°C (Perry & Chilton, 1973).

(i) <u>Stability</u>: Polymerizes at high pressures (Pollock & Stevens, 1965); inflammable limits in air, 3.1% and 32% (Anon., 1972)

(j) <u>Reactivity</u>: Reacts vigorously with oxidizing materials; explodes spontaneously in sunlight with chlorine (Anon., 1972)

(k) <u>Conversion factor</u>: 1 ppm in air = 1.15 mg/m$^3$

## 1.4 Technical products and impurities

In the US, high-purity ethylene has the following typical specifications: ethylene, 99.9 mol %; ethane, 0.1 mol %; methane, nil; propylene and heavier, 40 ppm by vol (46 mg/m$^3$); carbon dioxide, 5 ppm by vol (5.75 mg/m$^3$); carbon monoxide, <3 ppm by vol (3.45 mg/m$^3$); sulphur, 3 ppm by wt (mg/kg); hydrogen, <3 ppm by wt (mg/kg); acetylene, 2 ppm by wt (mg/kg); water, <1 ppm by wt (mg/kg); and oxygen, <1 ppm by wt (mg/kg).

Typical specifications for commercial ethylene produced in western Europe are as follows: ethylene, 99.9%; impurities (ppm max) - methane (200), ethane (200), propylene (10), C$_4$+ (10), carbon dioxide (5), hydrogen (5), methanol (5), dichloropropane (5), chlorine (3), acetylene (2), oxygen (2), total sulphur, mainly hydrogen sulphide (2), water (2) and carbon monoxide (1) (Hahn *et al.*, 1975).

Typical specifications for ethylene produced in Japan are as follows: ethylene, 99.8% min; acetylene, <50 ppm; carbon dioxide <50 ppm; carbon monoxide, <10 ppm; hydrogen sulphide, <5 ppm; and oxygen, <5 ppm.

## 2. Production, Use, Occurrence and Analysis

## 2.1 Production and use

### (a) Production

Ethylene was prepared by Deimann in 1795 by treating ethanol with concentrated sulphuric acid (Prager *et al.*, 1918). Most ethylene is produced commercially by the steam cracking of natural gas liquids (ethane, propane, butane) or heavy liquid feedstocks (naphtha, field condensate, gas oil, raffinate). It is also recovered from petroleum refinery off-gases, principally from catalytic cracking operations. In 1976, about 67% of all ethylene produced in the US was from steam cracking of natural gas liquids,

24% from heavy liquid feedstocks, and 9% was recovered from refinery off-gases.  Outside the US, over 90% of ethylene production is based on naphtha feedstock.  In India and Peru, ethylene is produced by dehydration of ethanol produced from fermentation wastes.  One Japanese plant produces ethylene by direct crude oil cracking.

Commercial production of ethylene in the US was first reported in 1922 (US Tariff Commission, 1923).  In 1976, 29 US companies reported production of 10 200 million kg ethylene (US International Trade Commission, 1977).  Exports were 20 million kg and were sent to the following countries (per cent of total):  Canada (61), Colombia (9), Mexico and other countries (2), Spain (20) and Venezuela (8) (US Department of Commerce, 1977a).  Imports in 1976 were 9 million kg, predominantly from Canada.

Total western Europe production in 1976 amounted to 10 385 million kg.  Among the major producers were the following countries (in millions of kg);  Austria (105), Denmark (40), the Federal Republic of Germany (2,785), Finland (125), France (1690), Greece (15), Italy (1445), Spain (280), Sweden (320), Switzerland (25) and the UK (1255).  Imports into western Europe in 1976 were 312 million kg.

Ethylene was first produced commercially in Japan in 1958;  15 companies manufacture it currently.

Production of ethylene in 1976 by the major producing regions is estimated to have been as follows:  North America, 10 930 million kg;  western Europe, 10 355;  Japan, 3805;  eastern Europe, at least 1890;  South America, 605;  and other countries, 880.

(b)  Use

In 1976, 85% of total US ethylene production was used directly for the manufacture of four chemicals:  polyethylene (42% of total ethylene consumption), ethylene oxide (19%), ethylene dichloride (15%) and ethylbenzene (9%).  Other derivatives, in order of decreasing ethylene use, include ethylene oligomerization products, ethanol, acetaldehyde, vinyl acetate, ethyl chloride, ethylene-propylene elastomers, propionaldehyde, and ethylene dibromide.  Miscellaneous applications include its use as a comonomer in some types of polypropylene and in ethylene-vinyl acetate copolymers, and for the production of a number of other chemicals such as vinyl toluene, aluminium alkyls, ethyl anilines, diethyl sulphate, 1,4-hexadiene and ethyl bromide.  Less than 0.5 million kg ethylene are used annually to ripen fruits and vegetables.

Low-density polyethylene (LDPE) and high-density polyethylene (HDPE) are both ethylene homopolymers, but their properties and applications vary significantly.  For a detailed description of their uses, see p. 170.

Most ethylene oxide is used to produce ethylene glycol, which is used primarily in anti-freeze formulations and in polyester fibre manufacture.

Additional major derivatives of ethylene oxide include nonionic surfactants; di-, tri-, and polyethylene glycols; glycol ethers; and ethanolamines.

Over 80% of ethylene dichloride is used to produce vinyl chloride monomer. For a detailed description of the uses of vinyl chloride, see monograph, p. 377. Ethylene dichloride is also used to produce chlorinated solvents (trichloroethylene, perchloroethylene and 1,1,1-trichloroethane), vinylidene chloride (see monograph, p. 439) and ethylene-amines. It is also used as a lead scavenger in leaded gasolines.

Ethylbenzene is used almost exclusively for styrene production; less than 1% is used in other applications such as miscellaneous solvent uses. For a detailed description of the uses of styrene, see monograph, p. 231.

Use of ethylene in western Europe in 1977 was as follows: LDPE (39%), ethylene dichloride (17%), HDPE (14%), ethylene oxide (13%), ethylbenzene (7%) and other uses, e.g., acetaldehyde, ethanol and vinyl acetate (10%).

Use of ethylene in Japan in 1976 was as follows: LDPE (27%), ethylene dichloride (16%), ethylene oxide (14%), HDPE (13%), acetaldehyde (11%), ethylbenzene (9%) and other uses (10%).

## 2.2  Occurrence

### (a)  Natural sources

Ethylene is produced by all plant tissues in significant amounts and acts as an endogenous plant growth regulator. Its role in plant growth, flower production and fruit ripening has been reviewed (Pratt & Goeschl, 1969). It has been found to be evolved from germinating seeds of bean, corn, cotton and pea plants (Vančura & Stotzky, 1976), from fading morning glory flowers (Kende & Hanson, 1976) and from ripening avocadoes (Adato *et al.*, 1976). It is produced by soil micro-organisms, including fungi (Lynch, 1974) and bacteria (Primrose, 1976; Smith, 1976).

Ethylene has been detected in marsh gas in the Atlantic coastal plain (Swain, 1975) and in gases desorbed from coal samples (Kim & Douglas, 1973).

### (b)  Air

In the UK, ethylene concentrations in the air of a rural area over a two-year period varied from 0.53-11.5 $\mu g/m^3$ (0.46-10 ppb), with a mean of 2.64 $\mu g/m^3$ (2.3 ppb) (Cox *et al.*, 1976). Ethylene concentrations in the air near Delft, The Netherlands, averaged 18 $\mu g/m^3$ (15.5 ppb) (Bos *et al.*, 1977). In South Africa, ethylene was detected in the air of three large cities (Louw *et al.*, 1977). In the US, ethylene concentrations in the air varied from 29-88 $\mu g/m^3$ (25-77 ppb) in downtown Los Angeles, from 21-24 $\mu g/m^3$ (18-21 ppb) in Azusa, California (Altshuller *et al.*, 1971), from 5.8-37 $\mu g/m^3$ (5-32 ppb) in Pasadena, California (Menzies & Shumate, 1976), from 805 $\mu g/m^3$ (700 ppb) in the centre of Washington DC to 45 $\mu g/m^3$ (39 ppb) in an outlying area (Abeles & Heggestad, 1973), and from 7 $\mu g/m^3$ (6.1 ppb) to 8.2 $mg/m^3$ (7100 ppb) in the Houston, Texas area (Gordon & Meeks, 1977).

Ethylene has been determined in the expired air of 2/8 human subjects at a rate of 0.91 and 120 $\mu g$/hour (Conkle *et al.*, 1975).

### (c) Water

The concentration and probable sources of hydrocarbons, including ethylene, in the marine environment have been reviewed (McAuliffe, 1976). Concentrations of ethylene have been measured in the Gulf of Mexico (1.7-35.0 nl/1), the Caribbean Sea (2.2-12.0 nl/1), the Atlantic Ocean (0.7-30.0 nl/1), and the Pacific Ocean (2.0-11.0 nl/1) (Lamontagne *et al.*, 1975; Swinnerton & Lamontagne, 1974).

### (d) Combustion and pyrolysis products

The combustion products of burning white pine wood were found to contain 57.5 $mg/m^3$ (50 ppm) ethylene (O'Mara, 1974).

Exhaust gases from jet engines operated at simulated high-altitude supersonic flight conditions were found to contain ethylene at concentrations ranging from 0.16-420 $mg/m^3$ (0.14 to 365.7 ppm) (Katzman & Libby, 1975). A diesel-powered passenger car was found to emit ethylene in its exhaust at a rate of 0.0349 g/mile (21.7 mg/km) when burning a commercial diesel fuel and 0.0280 g/mile (17.4 mg/km) when burning a standard US Environmental Protection Agency smoke test fuel (Braddock & Bradow, 1975).

Ethylene has been found in gaseous products from the pyrolysis of rice hulls at a concentration of 3.6 vol % (Brodowski *et al.*, 1976) and in gaseous products from pyrolysis of solid municipal waste at concentrations ranging from 0.04-3.42 vol % (Jerman & Carpenter, 1968).

## 2.3 Analysis

Methods used for the analysis of ethylene have been reviewed (Forrester, 1969).

An assay method intended for medicinal use involves gas chromatography and a thermal conductivity detector (Carson, 1972). Methods of detecting unsaturated hydrocarbons, including ethylene, in air have been described in which the chemiluminescence of a reaction of the olefins with ozone (Quickert *et al.*, 1975), or with active nitrogen (Baity *et al.*, 1974) is measured.

A portable instrument for determining trace gases, including ethylene, in industrial atmospheres uses a photoionization technique and has a limit of detection of 0.115 $mg/m^3$ (0.1 ppm) (Driscoll & Spaziani, 1975).

Infra-red spectrophotometry has been used to detect ethylene in gaseous mixtures, with a limit of detection of 50 µg (Rochkind, 1967), in flue gases from gas-fired appliances, with an accuracy of 0.15 mg/m³ (0.1 ppm) (DeWerth, 1971), and in ambient air, with a limit of detection of 0.3 µg/m³ (0.2 ppb) (Gordon & Meeks, 1977). Absorption of infra-red radiation from a laser source has been used to detect ethylene in gaseous mixtures, with a limit of detection of 0.3 µg/m³ (0.2 ppb) (Kreuzer et al., 1972), and in ambient air (Menzies & Shumate, 1976).

Ethylene has been determined in the atmosphere by trapping in methanolic mercuric acetate, isolation of the reaction product by thin-layer chromatography and quantification by atomic absorption. The method has a limit of detection of 0.15 mg/m³ (0.1 ppm) (Jennen et al., 1975).

Ethylene has been determined in air at the ppb level by enriching the samples in a temperature gradient tube prior to gas chromatographic analysis with flame-ionization detection (Kaiser, 1973).

The Intersociety Committee, composed of ten organizations, has published a method of analysis for atmospheric hydrocarbons, including ethylene, using gas chromatography and oxygen-hydrogen flame-ionization detection, with a limit of detection of 11.5 µg/m³ (10 ppb) ethylene (Intersociety Committee, 1972). Gas chromatographic methods using various means of detection have also been used for the analysis of ethylene in: (1) mixtures of medicinal gases (Finkelson, 1973); (2) ambient air, with a limit of detection of 0.57 µg/m³ (0.5 ppb) (Westberg et al., 1974); (3) ambient air using cryogenic temperature programming (Giannovario et al., 1976); (4) air, with a limit of detection of 0.015 µg/m³ (0.01 ppb) (De Greef et al., 1976); (5) fresh-water, at the ppb level (Shultz et al., 1976); (6) sea-water, in concentrations as low as $2 \times 10^{-12}$ mol of gas ($5 \times 10^{-11}$ g) (Swinnerton & Linnenbom, 1967); (7) gases evolved from fruit, with a limit of detection of 0.1 or 30 ppb (0.1 or 34 µg/m³) (Galliard & Grey, 1969; Galliard et al., 1968); (8) gases evolved or utilized by micro-organisms, with a limit of detection of $5 \times 10^{-12}$ g (Herbert & Holding, 1972); (9) exhaust gases and stack gases (Lamb et al., 1973); and (10) gaseous products from pyrolysis of solid municipal waste (Jerman & Carpenter 1968).

Automatic monitoring systems using gas chromatography for determining hydrocarbons, including ethylene, in air have limits of detection of 1.15 mg/m³ (1 ppm) (Villalobos & Chapman, 1971) and 3-5.75 µg/m³ (2-5 ppb) (Jeltes & Burghardt, 1972).

Gas chromatography combined with mass spectrometry has been used to determine ethylene in gaseous mixtures and in hydrocarbon oils, with a limit of detection of 0.58 mg/m³ (0.5 ppm) (Leigh & Lynaugh, 1974). Gas chromatography combined with addition of standard mixtures, removal of selected compounds on diatomite, infra-red spectrometry and mass spectrometry has been used to separate and determine volatile organic compounds, including ethylene, in city air (Louw et al., 1977).

## 3.   Biological Data Relevant to the Evaluation

## of Carcinogenic Risk to Humans

### 3.1  Carcinogenicity studies in animals[1]

No data were available to the Working Group.

### 3.2  Other relevant biological data

#### (a)  Experimental systems

#### Toxic effects

Ethylene inhaled at a dose of 11.5 g/m$^3$ (10 000 ppm) for 4 hours is acutely hepatotoxic in rats pretreated with the polychlorinated biphenyl Aroclor 1254 given orally at a dose of 300 µmol/kg bw once daily for 3 days.   It is not acutely toxic without such pretreatment.   Inhibition of epoxy hydratase in fasted rats increases the acute hepatotoxic effect of inhaled ethylene (Conolly & Jaeger, 1977;   Conolly *et al.*, 1977).

#### Absorption, distribution, excretion and metabolism

Male CBA mice exposed to air containing 19.6 mg/m$^3$ (17 ppm) $^{14}$C-labelled ethylene metabolized the ethylene to ethylene oxide, which binds to cellular proteins (IARC, 1976).   A relatively small fraction of the radioactivity was incorporated in various tissues or was excreted in the urine, where 3% was identified as hydroxyethylcysteine.   Treatment with higher doses of ethylene allowed the identification of *S*-(2-hydroxyethyl)-cysteine by gas chromatography-mass spectrometry (Ehrenberg *et al.*, 1977).

No data on the embryotoxicity or mutagenicity of this compound were available to the Working Group.

#### (b)  Humans

In working atmospheres, high concentrations of ethylene can cause asphyxia by lowering the oxygen concentration (Gerarde, 1963).

### 3.3  Case reports and epidemiological studies

No data were available to the Working Group.

------------

[1]The Working Group was aware of a study in progress to investigate the carcinogenicity of ethylene in rats by inhalation exposure (Toxicology Information Program, 1977).

## Low-density and high-density polyethylenes

### 1. Chemical and Physical Data

### 1.1 Synonyms and trade names

Chem. Abstr. Services Reg. No.: 9002-88-4

Chem. Abstr. Name: Ethene homopolymer

Ethene polymer; ethylene homopolymer; ethylene polymer; polythene
AC 8; AC 8 (polymer); AC 394; AC 680; AC 1220; AC GA: ACP 6;
A 60-20R; A 60-70R; Acroart; Agilene; Alathon 14; Alathon 15;
Alathon 1560; Alathon 6600; Alathon 7026; Alathon 7040; Alathon
7050; Alathon 7140; Alathon 7511; Alathon 5B; Alathon 71XHN;
Alcowax 6; Aldyl A; Alithon 7050; Alkathene; Alkathene 17/04/00;
Alkathene 22 300; Alkathene 200; Alkathene ARN 60; Alkathene
WJG 11; Alkathene WNG 14; Alkathene XDG 33; Alkathene XJK 25;
Allied PE 617; Alphex FIT 221; Ambythene; Amoco 610A4; Bakelite
DFD 3300; Bakelite DHDA 4080; Bakelite DYNH; Bareco Polywax 2000;
Bareco Wax C 7500; Bicolene C; BPE-I; Bralen KB 2-11; Bralen RB
03-23; Bulen A; Bulen A 30; Carlona 58-030; Carlona 900; Carlona
18020 FA; Carlona PXB; Chemplex 3006; CIPE; Coathylene HA 1671;
Courlene-X3; CPE; CPE 16; CPE 25; Cryopolythene; Cry-O-Vac L;
Daisolac; Daplen; Daplen 1810 H; DFD 0173; DFD 0188; DFD 2005;
DFD 6005; DFD 6032; DFD 6040; DFDJ 5505; DGNB 3825; Diothene;
Dixopak; DMDJ 4309; DMDJ 5140; DMDJ 7008; DQDA 1868; DQWA 0355;
DXM 100; Dylan; Dylan super; Dylan WPD 205; DYNH; DYNK 2; Eltex;
Eltex 6037; Eltex A 1050; Epolene C; Epolene C 10; Epolene C 11;
Epolene E; Epolene E 10; Epolene E 12; Epolene N; Etherin;
Etherol; 23F203; Fabritone PE; FB 217; Fertene; Flamolin MF
15711; Flothene; FM 510; Fortiflex 6015; Fortiflex A 60/500;
FP 4; 2100 GP; Grex; Grex PP 60-002; Grisolen; HFDB 4201;
Hi-fax; Hi-fax 1900; Hi-fax 4401; Hi-fax 4601; Hizex; Hizex 5000;
Hizex 5100; Hizex 3000B; Hizex 3300F; Hizex 7000F; Hizex 7300F;
Hizex 1091J; Hizex 1291J; Hizex 1300J; Hizex 2100J; Hizex 2200J;

Hizex 2100LP;  Hizex 5100LP;  Hizex 6100P;  Hizex 3000S;  Hizex 3300S;

Hizex 5000S;  Hi-Zex 7000F;  Hoechst PA 190;  Hoechst Wax PA 520;

Hostalen;  Hostalen GD 620;  Hostalen GD 6250;  Hostalen GF 4760;

Hostalen GF 5750;  Hostalen GM 5010;  Hostalen GUR;  Hostalen HDPE;

Irax;  Irrathene R;  Lacqten 1020;  LD 400;  LD 600;  LDPE 4;  Lupolen;

Lupolen 4261A;  Lupolen 6042D;  Lupolen 1010H;  Lupolen 1800H;

Lupolen 1810H;  Lupolen 6011H;  Lupolen KR 1032;  Lupolen KR 1051;

Lupolen KR 1257;  Lupolen 6011L;  Lupolen L 6041D;  Lupolen N;

Lupolen 1800S;  Manolene 6050;  Marlex 9;  Marlex 50;  Marlex 60;

Marlex 960;  Marlex 6003;  Marlex 6009;  Marlex 6015;  Marlex 6050;

Marlex 6060;  Marlex EHM 6001;  Marlex M 309;  Marlex TR 704;

Marlex TR 880;  Marlex TR 885;  Marlex TR 906;  Microthene;

Microthene 510;  Microthene 704;  Microthene 710;  Microthene F;

Microthene FN 500;  Microthene FN 510;  Microthene MN 754-18;

Mirason 9;  Mirason 16;  Mirason M 15;  Mirason M 50;  Mirason M 68;

Mirason Neo 23H;  Mirathen;  Mirathen 1313;  Mirathen 1350;  Moplen

RO-QG 6015;  Neopolen;  Neopolen 30N;  Neozex 45150;  Neozex 4010B;

Nopol (polymer);  Novatec JUO 80;  Novatec JVO 80;  NVC 9025;

Okiten G 23;  Orizon;  Orizon 805;  6020P;  PA 130;  PA 190;  PA 520;

PA 560;  PAD 522;  P 2010B;  PE 512;  PE 617;  PEN 100;  PEP 211;

PES 100;  PES 200;  Petrothene;  Petrothene LB 861;  Petrothene LC

731;  Petrothene LC 941;  Petrothene NA 219;  Petrothene NA 227;

Petrothene XL 6301;  P 4007EU;  P 4070L;  Planium;  Plaskon PP 60-002;

Plastazote X 1016;  Plastronga;  Plastylene MA 2003;  Plastylene MA

7007;  Politen;  Politen I 020;  Poly-Em 12;  Poly-Em 40;  Poly-Em 41;

Polyethylene AS;  Polymist A12;  Polymul CS 81;  Polysion N 22;

Polywax 1000;  Porolen;  P 2070P;  PPE 2;  Procene UF 1.5;  Profax

A 60-008;  P 2020T;  P 2050T;  P 4007T;  PTs 2;  PVP 8T;  Py 100;

RCH 1000;  Repoc;  Rigidex;  Rigidex 35;  Rigidex 50;  Rigidex type 2;

Ropol;  Ropothene OB.03-110;  Sanwax 161P;  Sclair 59;  Sclair 2911;

Sclair 19A;  Sclair 96A;  Sclair 59C;  Sclair 79d;  Sclair 11K;

Sclair 19X6;  SDP 640;  Sholex 5003;  Sholex 5100;  Sholex 6000;

Sholex 6002;  Sholex F 171;  Sholex F 6050C;  Sholex F 6080C;

Sholex 4250HM; Sholex L 131; Sholex S 6008; Sholex Super; Sholex XMO 314; Socarex; SRM 1475; SRM 1476; Staflen E 650; Stamylan 900; Stamylan 1000; Stamylan 1700; Stamylan 8200; Stamylan 8400; Sumikathene; Sumikathene F 101-1; Sumikathene F 210-3; Sumikathene F 702; Sumikathene G 201; Sumikathene G 202; Sumikathene G 701; Sumikathene G 801; Sumikathene G 806; Sumikathene Hard 2052; Sunwax 151; Super dylan; Suprathen; Suprathen C 100; Takathene; Takathene P 3; Takathene P 12; Telcotene; Telecothene; Tenaplas; Tenite 800; Tenite 1811; Tenite 2910; Tenite 2918; Tenite 3300; Tenite 3340; Trovidur PE; Tyrin; Tyvek; Unifos Dyob S; Unifos EFD 0118; Valeron; Valspex 155-53; Velustral KPA; Vestolen; Vestolen A 616; Vestolen A 6016; Wax LE; WJG 11; WNF 15; WVG 23; XL 335-1; XL 1246; XNM 68; XO 440; Yukalon EH 30; Yukalon HE 60; Yukalon K 3212; Yukalon LK 30; Yukalon MS 30; Yukalon PS 30; Yukalon YK 30; ZF 36

1.2  Structural and molecular formuale and molecular weight

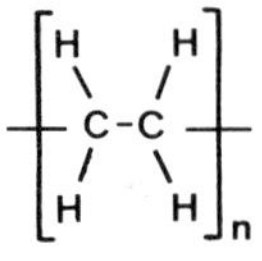

$$\left[\begin{array}{c} \underset{H}{\overset{H}{\diagdown}} \phantom{x} \underset{H}{\overset{H}{\diagup}} \\ C\text{-}C \\ \underset{H}{\overset{}{\diagup}} \phantom{x} \underset{H}{\overset{}{\diagdown}} \end{array}\right]_{n}$$

$(C_2H_4)_n$                    Mol. wt:  100 000-500 000

1.3  Chemical and physical properties of the polymers

From Raff (1967)

Low-density polymer

(a)  Description:  Translucent solid

(b)  Melting-point:  108-126°C (crystalline)

(c)  Density:  0.910-0.925

(d)  Refractive index:  $n_D^{24}$ 1.51

(e)  Spectroscopy data:  Infra-red spectra of polyethylene are reported.

(f)  Stability: Darkens on exposure to sunlight; acrolein and
     formaldehyde have been identified in the vapours from heated
     polyethylene (Høvding, 1969).

(g)  Reactivity: Resistant to water and dilute aqueous acids and
     alkalis; fuming sulphuric and nitric acids and other oxidizing
     agents attack it slowly.

## High-density polymer

(a)  Description: Opaque solid

(b)  Melting-point: 126-136°C (crystalline)

(c)  Density: 0.941-0.965

(d)  Refractive index: $n_D^{25}$ 1.54

(e)  Spectroscopy data: Infra-red spectra of polyethylene are
     reported.

(f)  Stability: Yellows on exposure to sunlight

(g)  Reactivity: Resistant to water and dilute aqueous acids and
     alkalis; fuming sulphuric and nitric acids and other oxidizing
     agents attack it slowly.

## 1.4  Technical products and impurities

### Low-density polyethylene

Most low-density polyethylene (LDPE) resins available in the US are
ethylene homopolymers with a molecular weight of 100 000-500 000 and a
crystallinity of about 50%. Copolymer resins are also available; those
containing vinyl acetate are the most important commercially. Impurities
in LDPE resins result mainly from the decomposition of the peroxide catalysts used in the polymerization process; however, information about their
composition is not available.

### High-density polyethylene

Most high-density polyethylene (HDPE) resins available in the US
are ethylene homopolymers with a molecular weight of several hundred
thousand and a crystallinity of 75-80%. Copolymers containing relatively
small amounts of 1-hexene and 1-butene or propylene are also available and
have densities in the range of 0.950-0.959 g/cm³. HDPE resins are typically

supplied as pellets containing small quantities of additives that improve their processing properties.  Ash content varies with the manufacturing process used, and unspecified organic and inorganic impurities are also commonly present.

No detailed information on the possible presence of unreacted monomer in the polymers was available to the Working Group.

## 2.  Production, Use, Occurrence and Analysis

### 2.1  Production and use

#### (a)  Production

A low-molecular-weight polyethylene was first obtained by von Pechman in 1898 by the decomposition of an ethereal solution of diazomethane on standing.  A solid, high-molecular-weight polyethylene was first prepared in England in 1933 (Raff, 1967).  Commercial production of polyethylene in the US was first reported in 1941 (US Tariff Commission, 1945).

#### Low-density polyethylene

LDPE resins are generally produced commercially by high-pressure processes, at 1020-3500 atmospheres.  Two types of reactors are used: a continuous-flow, stirred autoclave and a tubular reactor.  Generally, pure ethylene is charged into the reactor, and no solvent is used.  The reactor effluent is flashed, and unreacted monomer is recycled.  The liquid polymer is solidified by cooling and is put through a pelletizing extruder. Among the predominant initiators used for the production of LDPE resins are decanoyl peroxide and the following *t*-butyl esters:  peroxypivalate, peroctoate, peroxyneodecanoate, perbenzoate and peroxyacetate.

In 1976, 14 US companies reported the production of 2 573 million kg LDPE resins (US International Trade Commission, 1977).  Exports amounted to 235 million kg in that year and went to the following countries (% of total):  Belgium (5.5), Brazil (6.9), Canada (19.4), Colombia (3.1), Hong Kong (8.7), Mexico (7.2), The Netherlands (3.6), the Republic of Korea (3.0), Singapore (2.9), Thailand (3.1), the UK (3.1), Venezuela (3.3) and more than 40 other countries (30.2) (US Department of Commerce, 1977a). US imports in 1976 amounted to 6.7 million kg and were from the following countries (% of total):  Canada (36%), the Federal Republic of Germany (31%), France (13%), Japan (9%), The Netherlands (9%) and eight other countries (2%) (US Department of Commerce, 1977b).

Total western European production in 1976 amounted to 3 805 million kg in the following countries (production in millions of kg):  Austria (95), Belgium (225), Denmark (40), the Federal Republic of Germany (745), Finland (125), France (680), Italy (640), The Netherlands (480), Spain (240), Sweden (150) and the UK (385).  Exports from western Europe in 1976 were 385 million kg.  Annual LDPE resin production capacity in eastern Europe in 1976 was more than 729 million kg.

LDPE resins have been produced commercially in Japan since 1958. In 1976, eleven companies produced 957 million kg LDPE resins; 205 million kg were exported, and 1 million kg were imported.

In 1974, production of LDPE resins in Canada amounted to about 128 million kg and in Mexico, 89 million kg.

High-density polyethylene

HDPE resins are typically produced by low-pressure processes, at 1–200 atmospheres. Generally, the ethylene is dissolved in organic solvents in which a solid catalyst is suspended, and the polymer forms a slurry. A new vapour-phase process which uses no solvent has been developed in the US and in the Federal Republic of Germany.

One type of solid catalyst widely used in the production of HDPE resin is based on chromic oxide. Ziegler catalysts (mixtures of aluminium alkyls and titanium chlorides prepared under special conditions) are also used commercially.

In 1976, 14 US producers reported the production of 1 415 million kg HDPE resins (US International Trade Commission, 1977). Exports in that year amounted to 157 million kg and went to the following countries (% of total): Brazil (6.7), Canada (20.2), Colombia (4.0), Hong Kong (3.3), Mexico (22.0), Thailand (3.0), Turkey (3.8), Venezuela (4.5) and more than 45 other countries (32.5) (US Department of Commerce, 1977a). US imports in 1976 amounted to 7.4 million kg and were from the following countries (% of total): Canada (38), the Federal Republic of Germany (25), Italy (14), Japan (13), the UK (8) and eight other countries (2) (US Department of Commerce, 1977b).

Total western European production in 1976 amounted to 1 430 million kg, in the following countries (production in millions of kg): Belgium (90), the Federal Republic of Germany (690), France (225), Italy (170), The Netherlands (70), Spain (70), Sweden (50) and the UK (65). Exports from western Europe in that year were 225 million kg. Annual production capacity for HDPE resins in eastern Europe in 1975 is estimated to have been 155 million kg.

HDPE resins have been produced commercially in Japan since 1958. In 1976, eleven companies produced 436 million kg HDPE resins; 133 million kg were exported.

Production of HDPE resins in Canada in 1974 amounted to 87 million kg.

Total world production of HDPE resins in 1977 is estimated to have been approximately 4000 million kg.

(b)  Use

Compared to LDPE resins, HDPE resins have greater toughness and stiffness, superior mechanical strength and higher service temperature limits.

Low-density polyethylene

In 1976, use of for LDPE in the US was as follows:  for the production of film (65%), for injection moulding (15%), for extrusion coating (9%), for electrical wire and cable insulation (7%) and for miscellaneous applications (4%).

Over 60% of the LDPE film produced in the US is used for packaging, with 22% used for food and 38% for non-food applications.  It is used to package baked goods, fruits and vegetables, sweets, frozen food, meat and poultry, soft-drink cases, butter and lard, noodles and other dry foods, dried vegetables, snack foods and cereals.  Non-food packaging applications include industrial liners and shipping sacks, pallet shrink film and other shrink wrap, soft goods and garment bags, and other non-food wraps.  Non-packaging applications for LDPE film include rubbish bags, various uses in construction and in agriculture, sandwich bags, disposables (e.g., nappies) and other miscellaneous household and industrial uses.

Products made from LDPE injection moulding resin include housewares, lids, toys and novelties and other miscellaneous articles.

LDPE resin in extrusion coating is used primarily in packaging (89%), to coat paperboard, paper, foil, film and other substrates, for both food and non-food applications.  It is also used as insulation for communication wire (60%) and power cable (40%).

In 1977, use of LDPE resin in western Europe was as follows:  film, 70% (heavy-duty sacks, 11%;  agricultural, 10%;  shrink film, 8%;  carrier bags, 7%;  rubbish bags, 6%;  laminates, 3%;  and other, 25%);  injection moulding, 11%;  extrusion coating, 7%;  wire and cable, 6%;  and others, 6%.  LDPE end-uses in western Europe were as follows:  packaging (61.2%), agriculture (7.2%), household (6.4%), construction (5.1%), toys (3.4%), engineering and transport (3.3%), electrical/electronics (3.0%), furnishing (0.3%) and others (10.1%).

The 1976 Japanese use pattern for LDPE resin was as follows:  film and sheet (55%), extrusion coating (14%), wire and cable (9%), injection moulding (6%), blow moulding (3%), pipe (1%), fibre and other uses (12%).

High-density polyethylene

HDPE resin was used in the US in 1976 as follows:  blow moulding (39%), injection moulding (35%), piping and tubing (13%), film (4%) and other applications (9%).

HDPE resins are used to produce blow-moulded containers, including bottles for household chemicals, dairy bottles and shipping and other containers (e.g., for antifreeze). Injection moulding applications include food containers; shipping pails; houseware; crates, trays and bottle cases; closures (e.g., for aerosol tins); toys; and other uses, including rubbish containers, horticulture, furniture and automotive applications.

HDPE resins are used in corrugated tubing for underground drainage and for pressure pipes and pipe fittings for distribution of natural gas.

HDPE film is used for heavy-duty shipping bags and in food packaging.

Other applications for HDPE resins include wire and cable, other extruded products and sheet.

Use of HDPE in western Europe in 1974 was for blow moulding (47%), injection moulding (37%) and extrusion (16%). HDPE end-uses in western Europe were packaging (61.3%), household (8.1%), toys (5.9%), engineering and transport (5.4%), construction (4.5%), agriculture (0.9%), electrical/electronics (0.7%), furnishing (0.2%) and others (13%).

The 1976 Japanese use pattern for HDPE resins was in injection moulding (32%), blow moulding (22%), tape (12%), film (11%), fibre (9%), piping (2%) and others (12%).

### Low- and high-density polymers

In 1975, 1.6 million kg polyethylene were used in Europe in plastic biomaterials for medical applications; 1.5 million kg were used in the US. Polyethylene is used extensively in facial reconstruction, oral surgery, in the replacement of ossicles in the ear, in joint prostheses (as an ultra-high-molecular-weight/high density grade), e.g., as the acetabular component in hip-joint replacements, in numerous exoprostheses, in surgical drapes and in intrauterine devices (Halpern & Karo, 1977).

The US Food and Drug Administration permits the use of polyethylene as a synthetic masticatory substance in chewing-gum base (mol. wt: 2000-21 000) and as a roughage replacement in feedlot rations for finishing slaughter cattle. Polyethylene may also be used as an article or component of articles intended for use in contact with food, e.g., food packaging materials (US Food and Drug Administration, 1977).

## 2.2 Occurrence

Polyethylene is not known to occur as a natural product.

## 2.3 Analysis

A review of methods for determining the level of polyethylene in tallow has been published (Mordret *et al.*, 1976).

A fast and simple way of identifying 15 packaging films, including polyethylene, has been described, in which the films were treated with ten different solvents and the solubility and physical appearance of the film at room temperature and at the boiling-points of the solvents were noted (Van Gieson, 1969).

The colours of polymers, including polyethylene, and of their nitrated derivatives in various solvents have been used for their identification (El-Kodsi & Schurz, 1973).

Spectrophotometric techniques in the ultra-violet, visible and infrared spectra can be used to identify polyethylene in paper coatings (Luciani & Corradini, 1971). Infra-red spectroscopy has been used to determine polyethylene in softeners for textiles (McCall *et al.*, 1970).

Various polymers, including polyethylene, have been identified by pyrolysing the polymer and identifying the pyrolysis products by: (1) polarography of bromo or nitro derivatives of the degraded polymers (Dmitrieva *et al.*, 1971); (2) thin-layer chromatography (Pastuska, 1969); (3) a combination of ultra-violet analysis, colour-forming reactions and thin-layer chromatography (Braun & Nixdorf, 1972); (4) mass spectrometry (Zeman, 1973); and (5) gas chromatography (Feuerberg, 1967; Iglauer & Bentley, 1974; Northmore, 1972; Okumoto & Takeuchi, 1972; Willmott, 1969).

## 3.  Biological Data Relevant to the Evaluation
### of Carcinogenic Risk to Humans

### 3.1  Carcinogenicity studies in animals

#### (a)  Subcutaneous and/or intramuscular administration

Mouse: Albino mice (Paris strain) were given s.c. implants of a pure polyethylene film without plasticizer; 3/28 survivors developed local sarcomas (Oppenheimer *et al.*, 1952). Among albino (Longacre) mice given s.c. implants of a pure, plain film (15 mm diameter and 0.02 mm thick), 3/29 survivors developed malignant tumours at the site of implantation (Oppenheimer *et al.*, 1955).

Two groups of 1-3-month-old BALB/cAn mice, one of 42 males and 45 females and one of 41 males and 32 females, received s.c. implants of commercial polyethylene discs (20 mm diameter and 0.38 mm thick) with either a smooth or roughened surface. The first sarcoma at the site of implantation was seen after $7\frac{1}{2}$ months, at which time the numbers of survivors in the two groups were 71 and 60 mice. The total number of sarcomas after 13 months was 35 in the mice given smooth discs and 7 in mice given roughened discs (Bates & Klein, 1966).

Rat: A commercial polyethylene film, 0.002 mm thick, was implanted in 98 Wistar rats; 10/80 survivors developed sarcomas, the first tumour appearing after 392 days. In rats given a pure polyethylene film without plasticizer, 5/40 survivors developed local sarcomas. No local sarcomas developed in 5 rats given implants of surgical cotton (Oppenheimer *et al.*, 1952).

Among 50 Wistar and 50 Hisaw rats of both sexes that received implants of pure polyethylene film without plasticizer in the abdominal wall and over the skull, 8/63 developed fibrosarcomas after 434 or more days (2 associated with cranial and 6 with abdominal implants). No such tumours occurred among 28 Hisaw controls subjected to sham operations (Bering *et al.*, 1955).

In Wistar rats given s.c. implants of polyethylene film 15 mm in diameter and of varying thicknesses and physical status, the following incidences of malignant tumours were found at the site of implantation:

| Polyethylene type | Thickness (mm) | Effective number of rats | Number (%) of tumours |
|---|---|---|---|
| Plain commercial film | 0.05 | 80 | 10 (12.5%) |
| Plain pure film | 0.02 | 55 | 11 (20%) |
| Perforated pure film | 0.02 | 41 | 6 (14.6%) |
| Textile pure film | 0.15 | 40 | 1 (2.5%) |
| Plain film - high mol. wt | 0.07 | 34 | 3 (8.8%) |
| Powder | - | 42 | 0 (0%) |

The minimum latent period was shorter with the plain films than with the perforated film or the textile (385 and 392 days *versus* 407 and 497 days, respectively) (Oppenheimer *et al.*, 1955).

Glass cover-slips, 18 mm in diameter, were implanted subcutaneously into the left and right flanks of 90 Wistar rats. Four months later, in a group of 27 of these rats, polyethylene powder was inserted against the cover-slip on the right side and glass powder against that on the left side. Five and six sarcomas developed, respectively, with mean latent periods of 570 and 547 days. In another group of 27 rats, the glass cover-slips were removed after 4 months and polyethylene powder was implanted into the empty pocket in one side and glass powder into the other; one sarcoma occurred on the side containing polyethylene and none on that containing glass powder. In 25 rats, the glass cover-slip on the right side was removed after 4 months, and no sarcomas developed; whereas 6 sarcomas occurred on the left side in association with the glass cover-slip left *in situ*, with a mean latent period of 503 days (Oppenheimer *et al.*, 1961).

Fifty five albino rats were given implants of polyethylene film
(10 mm diameter) into the left abdominal s.c. tissue and of polyethylene
mesh (10 mm diameter) on the right side.  After 18-24 months, 4 sarcomas
were found at 45 sites at which films had been implanted, and 1 at 52
sites at which mesh had been implanted (Shulman *et al.*, 1963).

Intrauterine contraceptive devices were made from polyethylene with or
without barium sulphate and implanted subcutaneously into 142 Wistar rats.
Sarcomas associated with the implant developed in 25-70% of the animals
after 9 months.  No sarcomas developed in rats given implants of stainless
steel (Southam & Babcock, 1966) [The Working Group noted the incomplete
reporting of the experiment].

Two groups of 20 male CB stock rats received s.c. implants of a
segment of polyethylene (620 mg) or a gelatin capsule containing 530 mg of
the shredded plastic.  Two groups of controls received either a sham operation or empty gelatin capsules.  All survivors were killed after 93 weeks.
Six sarcomas and 1 squamous-cell carcinoma developed at the implantation
sites in 7 rats treated with the solid implants;  5 sarcomas occurred in
rats given the capsules containing shredded polyethylene.  No implantation-
site tumours occurred in controls (Carter & Roe, 1969).

High-density polyethylene discs, 18 mm diameter and 0.14 mm thick,
were inserted subcutaneously in the abdominal region of male Wistar rats.
One group of 22 rats received the discs bilaterally, and another group of
120 rats received the polyethylene disc on one side and a glass disc on the
other.  Surviving animals were killed after 39 months.  Only 55 rats with
either bilateral or a single polyethylene disc were subjected to pathological examination.  Five fibrosarcomas were found at the site of implantation
of polyethylene discs between 347 and 644 days after implantation, but no
tumours were associated with the glass discs.  In 54 effective rats implanted with plastic discs (polymethylmethacrylate, polyethylene or epoxy casting resin) on one side of the abdomen and with glass discs on the other
that did not develop a fibrosarcoma associated with the plastic, 5 were
found to have fibrosarcomas associated with the glass disc.  The latent
period of tumour induction ranged from 204-662 days (Lavorgna *et al.*, 1972).

Hamster:  Of 50 hamsters given s.c. implants (squares of 20 mm each
side) of polyethylene film, two survived more than 442 days;  both developed
tumours at the site of implantation, which were diagnosed as a malignant
mesenchymal tumour and a fibrosarcoma, after 442 and 457 days, respectively
(Bering & Handler, 1957).

(b)  Intraperitoneal administration

Rat:  Four groups of 30 3-month-old female Bethesda black rats received
i.p. implants of polyethylene in the form of a cube (3.5 x 3.5 x 3 mm), disc
(12 mm diameter), rolled film (10 x 1.75 cm) or powder (65 mg) and were
observed for up to 24 months.  Sarcomas associated with the implant were
found in 6/25 rats implanted with the rolled-up strips of film, in 0/25 rats

implanted with the cubes and in 1/22 rats implanted with the discs. In rats implanted with polyethylene powder, multicystic foreign-body granulomas of the serosal surface of the liver, kidney, spleen and anterior abdominal wall were observed (Hueper, 1961).

Implantation of polyethylene rods (10 x 2 x 2 mm) and powder into the peritoneal cavity of 20 and 19 Wistar rats of both sexes, respectively, produced no local tumours; 11 and 5 rats in the two groups survived up to 800 days (Simmers *et al.*, 1963).

Particles of polyethylene less than 3 mm in greatest dimension and weighing 1.5 g were implanted intraperitoneally into 38 male and 36 female Bethesda black rats. Within 2 years, 24 male rats developed i.p. fibrosarcomas and 5 other (unspecified) tumours, and 19 female animals developed i.p. fibrosarcomas and one another (unspecified) tumour. The incidence of tumours in control male rats was 4/37 and that in female controls 7/37 (Autian *et al.*, 1975) [The Working Group noted the incomplete reporting of histological findings].

(c) Other experimental systems

Combined subcutaneous and intraperitoneal implantation: Polyethylene films were implanted subcutaneously and intraperitoneally in 23 BD rats; among the 14 rats still alive at the time of appearance of the first tumour (15 months), 8 developed s.c. sarcomas and 1 developed an i.p. fibroma (Druckrey & Schmähl, 1954).

Intrauterine implantation: Among 102 female Wistar rats that received intrauterine insertions of a 10 mm portion of a polyethylene intrauterine contraceptive device, 5 developed epidermoid carcinomas and 1 a sarcoma of the uterus within 2 years; all animals that had epidermoid carcinomas also had pyometra, which is associated with squamous metaplasia. The first tumour appeared at 20 months, at which time 49 animals were still alive. Among 406 controls, 3 squamous-cell and 1 adenocarcinoma of the uterus were observed; among 106 rats given inserts of stainless steel, 6 epidermoid carcinomas and 1 sarcoma of the uterus developed (Corfman & Richart, 1967).

3.2 Other relevant biological data

(a) Experimental systems

I.p. implantation of polyethylene film balls into 4 rats killed after 11 days, 38 days, 3 months and 4 months, resulted in the formation of a fibrous capsule in which little or no inflammatory reaction occurred; however, foreign-body giant cells were seen in some places where the surface of the ball was not absolutely smooth. Such cells were also seen at the edges of small pieces of film implanted intraperitoneally. Implantation of polyethylene mesh into rabbits produced proliferation of connective tissue within the mesh but no inflammatory reaction between 3 and 24 months (Bing, 1955).

Implantation of 10 g polyethylene (Marlex 50) pellets into the peritoneal cavity of dogs produced a mild inflammatory reaction and no adhesions
within 7 days (Usher & Wallace, 1958).

In rats given s.c. implants of $[-CH_2-{}^{14}CH_2-]$-polyethylene, radioactivity was excreted in the urine only after 26 weeks. No radioactivity was
found in the urine after removal of the films (Oppenheimer *et al.*, 1955).

No data on the embryotoxicity, teratogenicity or mutagenicity of
this compound were available to the Working Group.

(b)  Humans

No data were available to the Working Group.

Dermatitis resulting from heat-sealing of polyethylene bags was attri-
buted to formaldehyde and acrolein (Høvding, 1969).

3.3  Case reports and epidemiological studies

In 209 consecutive endometrial biopsies from women who attended a
contraceptive clinic, Ober *et al.* (1968) found two cases of endometrial
squamous metaplasia and one of atypical glandular hyperplasia among users
of polyethylene intrauterine contraceptive devices for periods ranging from
1 day to 105 months. They reported one well-differentiated adenocarcinoma
of the endometrium in a woman who had had a polyethylene device for 4 years
9 months.

Lane *et al.* (1974) reported that follow-up biopsies of 9 women with
squamous metaplasia who used a polyethylene device failed to disclose
persistence or progression of the metaplasia [The Working Group noted that
this series was based on small numbers with a short follow-up period, and
that no techniques were used which would permit differentiation of mechanical from chemical effects].


4.  Summary of Data Reported and Evaluation

4.1  Experimental data

No data on the carcinogenicity or mutagenicity of ethylene were
available to the Working Group.

Polyethylene was tested by subcutaneous implantation in rats and mice,
by intraperitoneal implantation in rats, using discs, films, rods, fragments
and powder, and by intrauterine insertion in rats of polyethylene devices.
Subcutaneous implantation of all forms except the powder resulted in local
sarcomas, the incidences of which varied with the size and form of the
implants. The results obtained following intrauterine implantation of
polyethylene devices could not be used to evaluate the carcinogenicity of
polyethylene.

## 4.2  Human data

The massive production of ethylene and polyethylene and the general use of the polymer over the past several decades indicate that exposure of workers and the general population is common.  In addition, medical use (e.g., for intrauterine contraceptive devices) has been extensive. No epidemiological studies relating to the carcinogenicity of these compounds were available to the Working Group.

## 4.3  Evaluation

No information was available to the Working Group for evaluating the possible carcinogenic effects of ethylene in humans;  and the available data on polyethylene do not permit an evaluation of its potential carcinogenicity.  Experimental carcinogenicity studies on the monomer are recommended.

The results of animal implantation experiments using polyethylene and the limitations of the data from humans indicate the need for further epidemiological studies of persons receiving implants or insertions of devices made from the polymer (see also 'General Remarks on the Substances Considered', p. 35).

## 5. References

Abeles, F.B. & Heggestad, H.E. (1973) Ethylene: an urban air pollutant. J. Air Pollut. Control Assoc., 23, 517-521

Adalo, I., Gazit, S. & Blumenfeld, A. (1976) Relationship between changes in abscisic acid and ethylene production during ripening of avocado fruits. Aust. J. Plant Physiol., 3, 555-558

Altshuller, A.P., Lonneman, W.A., Sutterfield, F.D. & Kopczynski, S.L. (1971) Hydrocarbon composition of the atmosphere of the Los Angeles basin - 1967. Environ. Sci. Technol., 5, 1009-1016

Anon. (1972) Fire Protection Guide on Hazardous Materials, 4th ed., Boston, Mass., National Fire Protection Association, pp. 49-116-49-117

Autian, J., Singh, A.R., Turner, J.E., Hung, G.W.C., Nunez, L.J. & Lawrence, W.H. (1975) Carcinogenesis from polyurethans. Cancer Res., 35, 1591-1596

Baity, F.W., McClenny, W.A. & Bell, J.P. (1974) Detection of hydrocarbons by chemiluminescence with active nitrogen at 388 nm. In: Preprints of Papers presented at the 167th National Meeting, Los Angeles, Ca, Vol. 14, Washington DC, American Chemical Society, Division of Environmental Chemistry, pp. 310-312

Bates, R.R. & Klein, M. (1966) Importance of a smooth surface in carcinogenesis by plastic film. J. natl Cancer Inst., 37, 145-151

Bering, E.A., Jr & Handler, A.H. (1957) The production of tumors in hamsters by implantation of polyethylene film. Cancer, 10, 414-415

Bering, E.A., Jr, McLaurin, R.L., Lloyd, J.B. & Ingraham, F.D. (1955) The production of tumors in rats by the implantation of pure polyethylene. Cancer Res., 15, 300-301

Bing, J. (1955) The tissue reaction to implanted plastics. Acta path. microbiol. scand., 105, Suppl., 16-26

Bos, R., Guicherit, R. & Hoogeveen, A. (1977) Distribution of some hydrocarbons in ambient air near Delft and the influence on the formation of secondary air pollutants. Sci. total Environ., 7, 269-281

Braddock, J.N. & Bradow, R.L. (1975) Emissions Patterns of Diesel-powered Passenger Cars, Paper no. 750682, Warrendale, Pa, Society of Automotive Engineers, Inc.

Braun, D. & Nixdorf, G. (1972)  A simple method of separation for analysis of plastics.  4.  Soluble plastics with neutral reaction of pyrolysis products (Ger.).  Kunststoffe, 62, 318-322

Brodowski, P.T., Wilson, N.B. & Scott, W.J. (1976)  Chromatographic analysis of gaseous products from pyrolysis of organic wastes with a single column.  Anal. Chem., 48, 1812-1813

Carson, N.A. (1972)  Assay of NF ethylene by gas chromatography.  J. Assoc. off. anal. Chem., 55, 1067-1069

Carter, R.L. & Roe, F.J.C. (1969)  Induction of sarcomas in rats by solid and fragmented polyethylene:  experimental observations and clinical implications.  Br. J. Cancer, 23, 401-407

Conkle, J.P., Camp. B.J. & Welch, B.E. (1975)  Trace composition of human respiratory gas.  Arch. environ. Health, 30, 290-295

Conolly, R.B. & Jaeger, R.J. (1977)  Acute hepatotoxicity of ethylene and halogenated ethylenes after PCB pretreatment.  Environ. Health Perspect., 21, 131-135

Conolly, R.B., Jaeger, R.J. & Szabo, S. (1977)  Acute hepatotoxicity of ethylene, vinyl fluoride, vinyl chloride, and vinyl bromide after Aroclor 1254 pretreatment (Abstract No. 36).  Toxicol. appl. Pharmacol., 41, 146

Corfman, P.A. & Richart, R.M. (1967)  Induction in rats of uterine epidermoid carcinomas by plastic and stainless steel intrauterine devices.  Am. J. Obstet. Gynecol., 98, 987-991

Cox, R.A., Derwent, R.G. & Sandalls, F.J. (1976)  Some Air Pollution Measurements Made at Harwell, Oxfordshire, During 1973-1975, AERE-R 8324, Harwell, UK, Atomic Energy Research Establishment, Environmental and Medical Sciences Division

De Greef, J., De Proft, M. & De Winter, F. (1976)  Gas chromatographic determination of ethylene in large air volumes at the fractional parts-per-billion level.  Anal. Chem., 48, 38-41

DeWerth, D.W. (1971)  Infrared spectrophotometric measurement of air pollutants in the flue gases of gas-fired appliances.  In: White, J.W., ed., Proceedings of the 1st Conference on Natural Gas Research Technology, Chicago, Ill., Institute of Gas Technology, pp. 27-46 [Chem. Abstr., 80, 99659h]

Dmitrieva, V.N., Shtal, S.S., Kovalev, I.P., Kononenko, L.V. & Bezuglyi, V.D. (1971)  Identification of polyolefins by a polarographic method (Russ.).  Zavod. Lab., 37, 154-156 [Chem. Abstr., 74, 126310x]

Driscoll, J.N. & Spaziani, F.F. (1975)  Trace gas analysis by photoionization.  Anal. Instrum., 13, 111-114

Druckrey, H. & Schmähl, D. (1954)  Carcinogenicity of polyethylene films in rats (Ger.).  Z. Krebsforch., 96, 529-530

Ehrenberg, L., Osterman-Golkar, S., Segerbäck, D., Svensson, K. & Calleman, C.J. (1977)  Evaluation of genetic risks of alkylating agents.  III.  Alkylation of haemoglobin after metabolic conversion of ethene to ethene oxide *in vivo*.  Mutat. Res., 45, 175-184

El-Kodsi, G. & Schurz, J. (1973)  Chemical characterization of high polymers. I.  Nitration and subsequent reactions (Ger.).  Papier (Darmstadt), 27, 253-255 [Chem. Abstr., 79, 54022h]

Feuerberg, H. (1967)  Pyrolysis-gas chromatography of organic polymers (Ger.).  Ind. Chim. Belge, Spec. No. 32, Pt. 1, 140-144 [Chem. Abstr., 70, 97208e]

Finkelson, M.J. (1973)  Gas-solid chromatographic determination of oxygen, nitrogen, carbon dioxide, ethylene, and nitrous oxide at ambient temperature.  J. Assoc. off. anal. Chem., 56, 119-123

Forrester, C. (1969)  Analysis of ethylene.  In:  Miller, S.A., ed., Ethylene and Its Industrial Derivatives, London, Ernest Benn Ltd, pp. 319-334

Galliard, T. & Grey, T.C. (1969)  A rapid method for the determination of ethylene in the presence of other volatile natural products. J. Chromatogr., 41, 442-445

Galliard, T., Rhodes, M.J.C., Wooltorton, L.S.C. & Hulme, A.C. (1968) Metabolic changes in excised fruit tissue.  III.  The development of ethylene biosynthesis during the ageing of disks of apple peel. Phytochemistry, 7, 1465-1470

Gerarde, H.W. (1963)  The aliphatic (open chain, acyclic) hydrocarbons. In:  Patty, F.A., ed., Industrial Hygiene and Toxicology, Vol. II, New York, Interscience, p. 1204

Giannovario, J.A., Grob, R.L. & Rulon, P.W. (1976)  Analysis of trace pollutants in the air by means of cryogenic gas chromatography. J. Chromatogr., 121, 285-294

Gordon, S.J. & Meeks, S.A. (1977)  A study of gaseous pollutants in the Houston, Texas area.  Am. Inst. chem. Eng. Symp. Ser., 73, 84-94

Grasselli, J.G. & Ritchey, W.M., eds (1975)  CRC Atlas of Spectral Data and Physical Constants for Organic Compounds, 2nd ed., Vol. III, Cleveland, Ohio, Chemical Rubber Co., p. 278

Hahn, A., Chaptal, A. & Sialelli, J. (1975)  Why olefin specs have changed. Hydrocarbon Processing, February, pp. 89-92

Halpern, B.D. & Karo, W. (1977) Medical applications. In: Bikales, N.M., ed., Encyclopedia of Polymer Science and Technology, Plastics, Resins, Rubbers, Fibers, Suppl. Vol. 2, New York, Interscience, pp. 369, 379, 387, 388

Herbert, R.A. & Holding, A.J. (1972) Rapid separation and estimation of gases produced or utilized by micro-organisms. J. chromatogr. Sci., 10, 174-175

Høvding, G. (1969) Occupational dermatitis from pyrolysis products of polythene. Acta derm.-venereol., 49, 147-149

Hueper, W.C. (1961) Carcinogenic studies on water-insoluble polymers. Pathol. Microbiol., 24, 77-106

IARC (1976) IARC Monographs on the Evaluation of the Carcinogenic Risk of Chemicals to Man, 11, Cadmium, Nickel, Some Epoxides, Miscellaneous Industrial Chemicals and General Considerations on Volatile Anaesthetics, Lyon, pp. 157-167

Iglauer, N. & Bentley, F.F. (1974) Pyrolysis GLC for the rapid identification of organic polymers. J. chromatogr. Sci., 12, 23-33

Intersociety Committee (1972) Tentative method of analysis for $C_1$ through $C_5$ atmospheric hydrocarbons. In: Methods of Air Sampling and Analysis, Washington DC, American Public Health Association, pp. 131-138

Jeltes, R. & Burghardt, E. (1972) Automatic gas chromatographic measurement of $C_1$-$C_5$ hydrocarbons in air. Atmos. Environ., 6, 793-805

Jennen, A., Alaerts, G. & Ronsmans, G. (1975) Determination of ethylene in the atmosphere (Fr.). Analusis, 3, 427-429 [Chem. Abstr., 84, 34819y]

Jerman, R.I. & Carpenter, L.R. (1968) Gas chromatographic analysis of gaseous products from the pyrolysis of solid municipal waste. J. Gas Chromatogr., 6, 298-301

Kaiser, R.E. (1973) Enriching volatile compounds by a temperature gradient tube. Anal. Chem., 45, 965-967

Katzman, H. & Libby, W.F. (1975) Hydrocarbon emissions from jet engines operated at simulated high-altitude supersonic flight conditions. Atmos. Environ., 9, 839-842

Kende, H. & Hanson, A.D. (1976) Relationship between ethylene evolution and senescence in morning-glory flower tissue. Plant Physiol., 57, 523-527

Kim, A.G. & Douglas, L.J. (1973)  Gases desorbed from five coals of low gas content. Report of Investigations 7768, Washington DC, Bureau of Mines

Kreuzer, L.B., Kenyon, N.D. & Patel, C.K.N. (1972)  Air pollution: sensitive detection of ten pollutant gases by carbon monoxide and carbon dioxide lasers. Science, 177, 347-349

Lamb, A., Larson, K.A. & Tollefson, E.L. (1973)  A gas chromatographic method for exhaust gas analysis. J. Air Pollut. Control Assoc., 23, 200-202

Lamontagne, R.A., Smith, W.D. & Swinnerton, J.W. (1975)  $C_1-C_3$ hydrocarbons and chlorophyll $a$ concentrations in the equatorial Pacific Ocean. In: Gibb, T.R.P., ed., Analytical Methods in Oceanography, Advances in Chemistry Series 147, Washington DC, American Chemical Society, pp. 163-171

Lane, M.E., Dacalos, E., Sobrero, A.J. & Ober, W.B. (1974)  Squamous metaplasia of the endometrium in women with an intrauterine contraceptive device:  follow-up study. Am. J. Obstet. Gynecol., 119, 693-697

Lavorgna, J.J., Burstein, N.A., Schiller, A.L. & Harris, W.H. (1972)  The carcinogenesis of plastics used in orthopedic surgery. An assessment of the incidence in rats and the possible relevance to man. Clin. Orthop. rel. Res., 88, 223-227

Leigh, D. & Lynaugh, N. (1974)  Qualitative and quantitative analysis of dissolved gas by gas chromatography-mass spectrometry. In: West, A.R., ed., Advances in Mass Spectrometry, Vol. 6, Barking, Essex, Applied Science Publishers Ltd, pp. 463-470

Louw, C.W., Richards, J.F. & Faure, P.K. (1977)  The determination of volatile organic compounds in city air by gas chromatography combined with standard addition, selective subtraction, infrared spectrometry and mass spectrometry. Atmos. Environ., 11, 703-717

Luciani, M. & Corradini, T. (1971)  Spectrophotometric and chromatographic analysis of paper coatings (Ital.). Cellul. Carta, 22, 19-35 [Chem. Abstr., 76, 73969b]

Lynch, J.M. (1974)  The Formation of Ethylene by Soil Micro-organisms. In: Letcombe Laboratory Annual Report, Letcombe, Oxon., UK, Agricultural Research Council, pp. 88-95

McAuliffe, C.D. (1976)  Surveillance of the marine environment for hydrocarbons. Marine Sci. Commun., 2, 13-42

McCall, E.R., Morris, N.M., Tripp, V.W. & O'Connor, R.T. (1970)  Identi-
    fying softeners and fabric additives by infrared spectroscopy.
    Text. Chem. Color., 2, 105-116 [Chem. Abstr., 72, 134016e]

Menzies, R.T. & Shumate, M.S. (1976)  Remote measurements of ambient air
    pollutants with a bistatic laser system.  Appl. Optics, 15, 2080-2084

Mordret, F., Bloch, C. & Le Barbanchon, N. (1976)  Comparison of some
    methods for polyethylene determination in tallow (Fr.).  Rev. fr.
    Corps gras, 23, 213-222 [Chem. Abstr., 85, 65158g]

Northmore, B.R. (1972)  Characterization of polyolefins using a Curie-
    point pyrolyzer and gas chromatography.  Br. Polymer J., 4, 511-525
    [Chem. Abstr., 79, 5810e]

Ober, W.B., Sobrero, A.J., Kurman, R. & Gold, S. (1968)  Endometrial
    morphology and polyethylene intrauterine devices.  A study of 200
    endometrial biopsies.  Obstet. Gynecol., 32, 782-793

Okumoto, T. & Takeuchi, T. (1972)  Rapid characterization of polymeric
    materials by pyrolysis-gas chromatography (Jap.).  Nippon Kagaku
    Kaishi, No. 1, 71-78 [Chem. Abstr., 76, 141459n]

O'Mara, M.M. (1974)  The combustion products from synthetic and natural
    products.  Part 1:  Wood.  J. Fire Flammability, 5, 34-53

Oppenheimer, B.S., Oppenheimer, E.T. & Stout, A.P. (1952)  Sarcomas
    induced in rodents by embedding various plastic films.  Proc. Soc.
    exp. Biol. (N.Y.), 79, 366-369

Oppenheimer, B.S., Oppenheimer, E.T., Danishefsky, I., Stout, A.P. &
    Eirich, F.R. (1955)  Further studies of polymers as carcinogenic
    agents in animals.  Cancer Res., 15, 333-340

Oppenheimer, E.T., Willhite, M., Danishefsky, I. & Stout, A.P. (1961)
    Observations on the effects of powdered polymer in the carcinogenic
    process.  Cancer Res., 21, 132-134

Pastuska, G. (1969)  Pyrolysis thin-layer chromatography of high polymers
    (Ger.).  Gummi, Asbest, Kunstst., 22, 718-721 [Chem. Abstr., 71,
    92108h]

Perry, R.H. & Chilton, C.H., eds (1973)  Chemical Engineers' Handbook,
    5th ed., New York, McGraw-Hill, p. 3-62

Pollock, J.R.A. & Stevens, R., eds (1965)  Dictionary of Organic Compounds,
    4th ed., Vol. 3, New York, Oxford University Press, pp. 1377-1378

Prager, B., Jacobson, P., Schmidt, P. & Stern, D., eds (1918) Beilsteins Handbuch der Organischen Chemie, 4th ed., Vol. 1, Syst. No. 11, Berlin, Springer, p. 180

Pratt, H.K. & Goeschl, J.D. (1969) Physiological roles of ethylene in plants. In: Machlis, L., ed., Annual Review of Plant Physiology, Palo Alto, California, Annual Reviews Inc., pp. 541-584

Primrose, S.B. (1976) Formation of ethylene by Escherichia coli. J. gen. Microbiol., 95, 159-165

Quickert, N., Findlay, W.J. & Monkman, J.L. (1975) Modification of a chemiluminescent ozone monitor for the measurement of gaseous unsaturated hydrocarbons. Sci. total Environ., 3, 323-328

Raff, R.A.V. (1967) Ethylene polymers. In: Bikales, N.M., ed., Encyclopedia of Polymer Science and Technology, Plastics, Resins, Rubbers, Fibers, Vol. 6, New York, Interscience, pp. 275-277, 292-293, 299-300, 304, 332

Rochkind, M.M. (1967) Infrared analysis of multicomponent gas mixtures. Anal. Chem., 39, 567-574

Shulman, J., Wiznitzer, T. & Neuman, Z. (1963) A comparative study of sarcoma formation by implanted polyethylene film and mesh in white rats. Br. J. Plast. Surg., 16, 336-340

Shultz, D.J., Pankow, J.F., Tai, D.Y., Stephens, D.W. & Rathbun, R.E. (1976) Determination, storage, and preservation of low molecular weight hydrocarbon gases in aqueous solution. J. Res. US Geol. Surv., 4, 247-251

Simmers, M.H., Agnew, W.F. & Pudenz, R.H. (1963) Effects of plastic polymers within the rat's peritoneal cavity. Bol. Inst. Estud. Med. Biol. Méx., 21, 1-13

Smith, A.M. (1976) Ethylene production by bacteria in reduced microsites in soil and some implications to agriculture. Soil Biol. Biochem., 8, 293-298

Southam, C.M. & Babcock, V.I. (1966) Induction of subcutaneous tumors in rats by plastic loops and spirals. Am. J. Obstet. Gynecol., 96, 134-140

Swain, F.M. (1975) Marsh Gas from the Atlantic Coastal Plain, AD-A010 236, Springfield, Va, National Technical Information Service

Swinnerton, J.W. & Lamontagne, R.A. (1974) Oceanic distribution of low-molecular-weight hydrocarbons. Baseline measurements. Environ. Sci. Technol., 8, 657-663

Swinnerton, J.W. & Linnenbom, V.J. (1967) Determination of the $C_1$ to $C_4$ hydrocarbons in sea water by gas chromatography. J. Gas Chromatogr., 5, 570-572

Toxicology Information Program (1977) Inhalation study of ethylene gas. Tox-Tips, 13, 3

US Department of Commerce (1977a) US Exports, Schedule B Commodity Groupings, Schedule B Commodity by Country, FT410/December, Bureau of the Census, Washington DC, US Government Printing Office, pp. 2-80, 2-120, 2-121

US Department of Commerce (1977b) US Imports for Consumption and General Imports, TSUSA Commodity by Country of Origin, FT 246/Annual 1976, Bureau of the Census, Washington DC, US Government Printing Office, p. 234

US Food and Drug Administration (1977) Food and drugs. US Code Fed. Regul., Title 21, parts 172.615, 175.105, 175.300, 176.200, 177.1200, 177.1520, 177.2600, 573.780, pp. 384-385, 438, 445, 452, 456, 482, 490-491, 504, 506, 520-526, 555, 557

Usher, F.C. & Wallace, S.A. (1958) Tissue reaction to plastics. A comparison of Nylon, Orlon, Dacron, Teflon and Marlex. Arch. Surg., 76, 997-999

US International Trade Commission (1977) Synthetic Organic Chemicals, US Production and Sales, 1976, USITC Publication 833, Washington DC, US Government Printing Office, pp. 27, 31, 182, 186

US Tariff Commission (1923) Census of Dyes and other Synthetic Organic Chemicals, 1922, Tariff Information Series - No. 31, Washington DC, US Government Printing Office, p. 113

US Tariff Commission (1945) Synthetic Organic Chemicals, US Production and Sales, 1941-43, Report No. 153, Second Series, Washington DC, US Government Printing Office, p. 116

Vančura, V. & Stotzky, G. (1976) Gaseous and volatile exudates from germinating seeds and seedlings. Can. J. Bot., 54, 518-532

Van Gieson, P. (1969) Here's a quick, easy way to identify films. Package Eng., 14, 76-77 [Chem. Abstr., 71, 71274u]

Villalobos, R. & Chapman, R.L. (1971) A gas chromatographic method for automatic monitoring of pollutants in ambient air. Instrum. Soc. Am. Transactions, 10, 356-362

Weast, R.C., ed. (1976) CRC Handbook of Chemistry and Physics, 57th ed., Cleveland, Ohio, Chemical Rubber Co., p. C-298

Westberg, H.H., Rasmussen, R.A. & Holdren, M. (1974)  Gas chromatographic analysis of ambient air for light hydrocarbons using a chemically bonded stationary phase.  Anal. Chem., 46, 1852-1854

Willmott, F.W. (1969)  Pyrolysis-gas chromatography of polyolefins. J. chromatogr. Sci., 7, 101-108 [Chem. Abstr., 70, 78403y]

Windholz, M., ed. (1976)  The Merck Index, 9th ed., Rahway, NJ, Merck & Co., p. 498

Zeman, A. (1973)  Identification of some commercially available polymers by thermal degradation in a mass spectrometer (Ger.).  Angew. makromol. Chem., 31, 1-24

METHYL METHACRYLATE and
POLYMETHYL METHACRYLATE

Methyl methacrylate

## 1. Chemical and Physical Data

### 1.1 Synonyms and trade names

Chem. Abstr. Services Reg. No.: 80-62-6

Chem. Abstr. Name: 2-Methyl-2-propenoic acid methyl ester

Methacrylic acid methyl ester; methylmethacrylate; methyl 2-methylpropenoate; methyl 2-methyl-2-propenoate; MME

Pegalan

### 1.2 Structural and molecular formulae and molecular weight

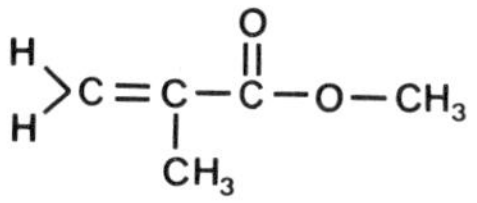

$$\begin{array}{c} H \\ H \end{array}\!\!\!\!>\!C = C - \overset{\overset{\displaystyle O}{\|}}{C} - O - CH_3 \\ \hspace{2.2cm} | \\ \hspace{2.2cm} CH_3$$

$C_5H_8O_2$                    Mol. wt: 100.1

### 1.3 Chemical and physical properties of the pure substance

From Weast (1976), unless otherwise specified

(a) Description: Colourless liquid (Hawley, 1971)

(b) Boiling-point: 100-101$^\circ$C; 24$^\circ$C (32 mm)

(c) Melting-point: -48$^\circ$C

(d) Density: $d_4^{20}$ 0.9440

(e) Refractive index: $n_D^{20}$ 1.4142

(f) Spectroscopy data: $\lambda_{max}$ 231 nm ($E_1^1$ = 10); infra-red, Raman, nuclear magnetic resonance and mass spectral data have been tabulated (Grasselli & Ritchey, 1975).

(g)  Solubility:  Sparingly soluble in water and ethylene glycol;
     miscible in ethanol, ether and acetone

(h)  Volatility:  Vapour pressure is 40 mm at 25.5°C (Perry & Chilton,
     1973).

(i)  Stability:  Flash-point (open cup), 10°C (Anon., 1972);  poly-
     merizes on exposure to light or heat in presence of oxygen
     (Pollock & Stevens, 1965)

(j)  Conversion factor:  1 ppm in air = 4.1 mg/m$^3$

## 1.4  Technical products and impurities

Methyl methacrylate available commercially in the US has the following typical specifications:  methyl methacrylate, 99.8% min;  methacrylic
acid, 0.003% max;  water, 0.03% max;  it may contain a small amount of
hydroquinone (see IARC, 1977) and its monomethyl ether as inhibitors.

In Japan, commercial methyl methacrylate has a minimum purity of
99.6%, contains a maximum of 0.05% water, and has a specific gravity of
0.942-0.946 (20°C/4°C).

## 2.  Production, Use, Occurrence and Analysis

### 2.1  Production and use

(a)  Production

Methyl methacrylate was first prepared by the addition of hydrochloric
acid to a mixture of methyl α-amino-isobutyrate hydrochloride and sodium
nitrite (Barker & Skinner, 1924).  All US and Japanese production of methyl
methacrylate is based on the cyanhydrin process, in which acetone and
hydrogen cyanide are reacted to produce acetone cyanhydrin, which is
treated with concentrated sulphuric acid.  Without being isolated, the
resulting methacrylamide sulphate is reacted directly with methanol to
form crude methyl methacrylate, which is purified by distillation.

Commercial production of methyl methacrylate in the US was first
reported in 1937 (US Tariff Commission, 1938).  In 1975, three US companies
produced 248 million kg (US International Trade Commission, 1977).

US imports of methyl methacrylate are estimated to have been approximately 4.5 million kg in 1975.  In 1976, 22.8 million kg methyl methacrylate
were exported from the US to the following countries (per cent of total):
Argentina (5.0), Australia (6.6), Canada (19.9), Chile (2.9), Colombia (3.7),

the Federal Republic of Germany (2.4), Mexico (13.2), The Netherlands (2.5), New Zealand (2.3), Peru (2.8), Taiwan (13.3), the UK (9.5), Venezuela (5.4) and at least 12 other countries (10.5) (US Department of Commerce, 1977).

Production of methyl methacrylate in western Europe in 1976 was 220 million kg.

This compound has been produced commercially in Japan for more than thirty years. In 1975, seven companies produced 114 million kg, exports were 19 million kg and imports were negligible.

(b) Use

Approximately 75% of all US methyl methacrylate production is used captively by its manufacturers for the production of acrylic polymers based on homopolymers of methacrylate esters or on copolymers with acrylic esters. An estimated US use pattern for methyl methacrylate in 1975 is as follows: for the production of acrylic sheet and acrylic moulding and extrusion powders (60%), in surface coating resins (22%), in emulsion polymers (8%) and in other applications (10%).

Methyl methacrylate is mainly used to produce its homopolymer, polymethyl methacrylate, the major constituent of acrylic sheet and acrylic moulding and extrusions powders. For a detailed description of the uses of polymethyl methacrylate, see p. 198.

It is also used to produce copolymers (with ethyl acrylate, $n$-butyl acrylate and other acrylic esters) which are the major part of the coating binder used in acrylic surface coatings. In 1975, latex accounted for approximately two-thirds of the methyl methacrylate used to make surface coating resins, and lacquer accounted for almost all of the remainder (a small amount was used in enamels). Approximately 55% of the methyl methacrylate used for latex coatings was in exterior latex house paints; an additional 30% was used in interior gloss and semi-gloss paints; and 10% in interior flat wall and ceiling paints. The largest single end use for acrylic lacquer resins was in top-coats for new cars; however, because of environmental restrictions, this use has been decreased.

Methyl methacrylate copolymers are also used in the manufacture of emulsion polymers, which have the following applications (% of methyl methacrylate used): floor polishes (52%); textile backcoatings, adhesives, finishes, binders, dirt-release agents and thickeners (21%); paper coatings and paper pulp strengtheners (15%); sealants (6%); leather base coatings and finishes (4%); and others (2%).

Other uses of methyl methacrylate are in modification of unsaturated polyester resins (5% of total US methyl methacrylate consumption), production of higher methacrylates (1%), acrylic fibres (1%) and miscellaneous applications (3%). It is used in unsaturated polyester resins to replace part of the styrene to improve the weatherability of fibreglass-reinforced plastics. It is also used to produce higher methacrylates (e.g., ethyl, n-butyl, and 2-ethylhexyl methacrylate) by transesterfication. One US company uses methyl methacrylate (at a level of 8% by weight of the polymer) in the production of acrylic fibres. The miscellaneous uses include acrylic film, inks, radiation-polymerized impregnants for wood, solvent-based adhesives and binders, and as an impact modifier of polyvinyl chloride.

Western European use of methyl methacrylate in 1976 was in the production of polymethyl methacrylate (80%), paints (9.5%), acrylic emulsions (3%), polvyinyl chloride modifiers (3%), fibres (2%) and unsaturated polyester resins (0.5%).

In Japan, methyl methacrylate is used to produce polymethyl methacrylate (55% of total use) and methyl methacrylate copolymers with ethyl and butyl methacrylate (45%).

The US Food and Drug Administration permits the use of methyl methacrylate polymers and copolymers as components of the following products when they are intended for use in contact with food: (1) rigid, semi-rigid and modified acrylic and vinyl plastics (at a maximum level of 5 wt % of the total polymer); (2) waxed paper and paperboard packaging; (3) adhesives; (4) polyolefin films; (5) resinous and polymeric coatings; and (6) as cross-linking agents in polyester resins. The amounts present may not exceed that which is reasonably required to produce the intended effect (US Food and Drug Administration, 1977).

The US Occupational Safety and Health Administration's health standards for exposure to air contaminants require that an employee's exposure to methyl methacrylate not exceed an eight-hour time-weighted average of 410 mg/m$^3$ (100 ppm) in the workplace air in any eight-hour work shift of a forty-hour work week (US Occupational Safety and Health Administration, 1976).

2.2  Occurrence

Methyl methacrylate is not known to occur as a natural product.

(a)  Air

Total emissions of methyl methacrylate to the ambient air in the US in 1974 were estimated by the US Environmental Protection Agency to be 3.6 million kg. The sources and amounts were: methyl methacrylate production, 1.7 million kg; end-product manufacture, 1.7 million kg; and bulk storage, 0.2 million kg (Patterson et al., 1976).

In one study in Europe, emissions of methyl methacrylate to the ambient air were estimated to range from 139-563 g/hour during the drying of paints based on acrylic resins. The concentrations of methyl methacrylate in the air exhaust stack were estimated to range from 20-81 mg/m$^3$ (5-20 ppm) (Schulz & Günther, 1972).

Methyl methacrylate has been detected in studies in the USSR at levels of 0.004-0.29 mg/m$^3$ (0.001-0.075 ppm) in the atmosphere above surfaces freshly painted with commercial acrylic latexes (Kravchenko & Chemer, 1977) and in the atmosphere of an experimental plastic dwelling (Ekimova *et al.*, 1969).

Methyl methacrylate has been detected as a gaseous product of the combustion of polymethyl methacrylate (Forestier, 1975).

(b)  Water

Methyl methacrylate has been detected:  (1) in US river water (Shackelford & Keith, 1976);  (2) in finished drinking-water at levels of less than 1.0 µg/l (ppb) (US Environmental Protection Agency, 1975);  and (3) in commercial, deionized, charcoal-filtered, finished drinking-water in New Orleans (Dowty *et al.*, 1975).

(c)  Occupational exposure

The US National Institute for Occupational Safety and Health estimated in 1974 that 30 000 workers in the US had been exposed to methyl methacrylate.  In a study of exposure at five plants manufacturing polymethyl methacrylate sheet, the mean eight-hour time-weighted average exposure ranged from 16-3C0 mg/m$^3$ (4-88 ppm), and the highest exposure for workers examined medically was 100-200 mg/m$^3$ (25-50 ppm) (Cromer & Kronoveter, 1976).

(d)  Other

Residual methyl methacrylate in five commercial acrylic bone cements has been reported to migrate into a prepared tissue medium.  The highest concentrations of methyl methacrylate (0.7-5.1 wt %) were detected in the fatty components of bone marrow (Willert *et al.*, 1973)  Residual methyl methacrylate has also been detected in commercial polystyrene plastics at a concentration of 36 mg/kg (ppm) (Kleshcheva *et al.*, 1969a).

2.3  Analysis

Gas chromatography has been used to determine residual methyl methacrylate:  (1) after migration from medical polymers into aqueous solutions (Markelov & Semenenko, 1976);  (2) in latexes, acrylates and polymers (Lazaris & Kalmykova, 1972);  (3) in aqueous emulsions of synthetic polymers and copolymers (Bollini *et al.*, 1975);  (4) in emulsions of acrylic copolymers used in paints and varnishes, with a limit of detection of 10 or 200 mg/kg (ppm), depending on the method used (Zaytseva *et al.*, 1972);  (5) in styrene copolymers, at levels of 36 mg/kg (ppm), with a relative error of ± 10% (Kleshcheva *et al.*, 1969a), and with a limit of detection of 10 mg/kg (ppm) (Kleshcheva *et al.*, 1971);  and (6) in three commercial latexes (Panova *et al.*, 1969).  Methyl methacrylate has also been determined by gas chromatography with flame-ionization detection in waste-water (Kleshcheva et al., 1969b) and in tissue samples surrounding bone cement (Willert et al., 1973). It has been determined in drinking-water by gas chromatography with mass spectrometry (Dowty et al., 1975).

The retention characteristics of methyl methacrylate have been reported for six gas chromatographic stationary phases of varying polarity (Ashes & Haken, 1971).

Methyl methacrylate can be determined by polarography in effluent waters from polymer production, in the concentration range of 0.2-5 mg/l (ppm) (Dmitrieva et al., 1975); in plant sewage from the production of plastics stabilizers (Meshkova & Dmitrieva, 1974); and in waste-water (after prior extraction), with an error of ± 4-7% (Ponomarev et al., 1974). Methyl methacrylate can also be determined polarographically in prepared mixtures of acrylic acids and esters, in the concentration range of 0.16-1.51 g/l, with a relative error of ± 2.06% (Bezuglyi et al., 1970); in the air of industrial facilities (Dmitrieva & Kotok, 1976); and in ambient air, after concentration using silica gel (Dmitrieva et al., 1976). Polarographic methods are reported to be more specific and sensitive than colorimetric methods for determining methyl methacrylate (Dmitrieva & Kotok, 1976; Dmitrieva et al., 1976).

Methyl methacrylate has been determined spectrophotometrically at 350 nm after formation of the iodine chloride derivative, with a limit of detection of 0.5 mg/l (Rapaport & Ledovskikh, 1972), and after treatment with potassium permanganate, with a limit of detection of 3 mg/kg (ppm) (Patterson et al., 1976). Residual monomers, including methyl methacrylate, have been determined in emulsion polymers after separation by gel chromatography and measurement by ultra-violet spectrophotometry at 200 nm (Schmötzer, 1972).

Proton magnetic resonance spectral analysis (with an accuracy of ± 2%) and infra-red spectrometry have been used to identify and determine residual methyl methacrylate in commercial acrylic bone cement used in joint replacement surgery and dentistry (Sheinin et al., 1976); nuclear magnetic resonance spectroscopy was used to identify methyl methacrylate in an investigation of 24 brands of restorative resins (Asmussen, 1975).

## 3. Biological Data Relevant to the Evaluation of Carcinogenic Risk to Humans

### 3.1 Carcinogenicity studies in animals

#### (a) Oral administration

Rat: Groups of 25 male and 25 female Wistar rats were administered 0, 6, 60 or 2000 mg/l (ppm) methyl methacrylate in their drinking-water for 2 years; no treatment-related tumours were found (Borzelleca *et al.*, 1964) [The Working Group noted that insufficient details on survival and pathological examination were given].

## (b) Skin application

Rat: Ten Wistar rats were painted on the back of the neck with methyl methacrylate 3 times a week for 4 months and then kept for lifespan. No local tumours were observed (Oppenheimer *et al.*, 1955) [The Working Group noted that the study was inadequate due to the insufficient number of animals at risk and the short duration of treatment].

## 3.2 Other relevant biological data

### (a) Experimental systems

#### Toxic effects

In mice, the $LD_{50}$ of methyl methacrylate by i.p. injection is 1.2 ml/kg bw (1.13 g/kg bw) (Autian, 1975). The oral $LD_{50}$ in rats is 8.4 ml/kg bw (7.8 g/kg bw), and the lowest lethal oral concentration in rabbits is 7 ml/kg bw (6.6 g/kg bw) (Deichmann, 1941).

A concentration of 15 mg/l of the monomer in air proved lethal to all rabbits, guinea-pigs and rats tested within a 5-hour period of exposure. Rats were the most sensitive and guinea-pigs the least sensitive (Deichmann, 1941). No deaths occurred when doses of 40 ml/kg bw (38 g/kg bw) were applied to the skin of rabbits (Spealman *et al.*, 1945).

Degenerative changes in the liver were observed in guinea-pigs exposed to 39 mg/l methyl methacrylate vapours for 3 hours daily for 15 days (Spealman *et al.*, 1945).

Liquid methyl methacrylate (0.1 ml/animal) injected subcutaneously into guinea-pigs induced local necrosis and local inflammation (Mohr, 1958).

Homsy *et al.* (1972) reported a characteristic fall in blood pressure within 50 seconds after an i.v. injection of methyl methacrylate monomer in dogs. At a dose of 1.25 g/l saline, death occurred due to respiratory arrest.

Exposure of mice to 164 mg/l in air for 14 min increased the sleeping time induced by sodium pentobarbital from 90 to 250 min (Lawrence & Autian, 1972).

#### Embrytoxicity and teratogenicity

Three groups of pregnant Sprague-Dawley rats were treated intraperitoneally with doses of 0.13, 0.27 and 0.44 ml/kg bw (0.1, 0.2 and 0.4 g/kg bw) on days 5, 10 and 15 of gestation; 24 to 59 foetuses per group were checked. Significantly reduced foetal body weights were observed in all 3 groups; and a significantly greater number of 'haematomas' were seen at various sites in animals given the two higher doses. None of the three doses induced skeletal defects (Autian, 1975; Singh *et al.*, 1972a,b).

### Metabolism

In rats, up to 88% of a single dose of 5.7 mg/kg bw methyl($^{14}$C)methacrylate is expired as $^{14}CO_2$ in 10 days, irrespective of the route of administration and of the specific labelling of the propylene residue of the molecule. Small amounts of $^{14}$C-methylmalonate, $^{14}$C-succinate and, possibly, $^{14}$C-β-hydroxyisobutyrate and 2-formylpropionate were excreted (Bratt & Hathway, 1977).

In groups of 25 male and 25 female rats administered 0, 6, 60 and 2000 mg/l (ppm) methyl methacrylate orally in drinking-water for a period of 2 years, weight gain was decreased during the first few weeks in animals of both sexes given the highest dose. Haematological effects and urine concentrations of protein and reducing agents did not differ materially from those of control animals. In animals given the highest dose level, there was an increase in kidney:body-weight ratios in female but not in male rats (Borzelleca *et al.*, 1964).

### Mutagenicity and other short-term tests

White rats were exposed by inhalation to methyl methacrylate (0.74 mg/m$^3$; 0.18 ppm) and chloroprene (0.54 mg/m$^3$; 0.15 ppm). Chromosome aberrations were found in up to 8% of bone-marrow cells in animals killed at 1, 4 and 75 days after exposure, compared with 3.5% in controls (Bagramjan *et al.*, 1976).

An increased frequency of chromosome aberrations was found in bone-marrow cells of male rats exposed for 4 months to a mixture of chloroprene (2.8 mg/m$^3$; 0.78 ppm) and methyl methacrylate (4.0 mg/m$^3$; 1 ppm) (Bagramjan & Babajan, 1974).

### (b) Humans

One report on 152 workers exposed to 2-200 mg/m$^3$ (0.5-50 ppm) methyl methacrylate states that 119 complained of headaches, 45 noted pain in the extremities, 32 showed excessive fatigue, 32 had sleep disturbance, 30 had loss of memory and 25 showed irritability. A majority of the workers has been employed for 10 or more years (Blagodatin *et al.*, 1970).

A more recent report described a study of 91 exposed and 43 nonexposed workers at five plants manufacturing polymethyl methacrylate sheets. Their exposure to methyl methacrylate varied from 16-200 mg/m$^3$ (4-49 ppm), based on a mean eight-hour, time-weighted average exposure. No detectable acute toxic signs or symptoms were recorded (Cromer & Kronoveter, 1976).

Direct skin contact with methyl methacrylate has been found to cause allergic responses (Fisher, 1954; Pegum & Medhurst, 1971; Shellow, 1954; Spealman *et al.*, 1945).

Five workers in contact with chloroprene (2-2.2 mg/m$^3$; 0.56-0.61 ppm) and methyl methacrylate (0.5-2 mg/m$^3$; 0.1-0.5 ppm) were found to have a statistically significant increase in chromosome aberrations in their lymphocytes. The incidences of chromatid breaks (single fragments) and chromosome breaks (fragment pairs) were found to be 16.8% and 16.9%, respectively (Bagramjan *et al.*, 1976).

### 3.3 Case reports and epidemiological studies

No data were available to the Working Group.


Polymethyl methacrylate

## 1. Chemical and Physical Data

### 1.1 Synonyms and trade names

Chem. Abstr. Services Reg. No.: 9011-14-7

Chem. Abstr. Name: 2-Methyl-2-propenoic acid methyl ester homopolymer

Methacrylic acid methyl ester polymers; methyl methacrylate homo-polymer; methyl methacrylate polymer; methyl methacrylate resin; poly(methyl methacrylate)

Acronal S 320 D; Acrylite; Acryloid A-15; Acrypet; Acrypet M 001; Acrypet V; Acrypet VH; Acrysol ASE; Akuripetto VH; Altulor M 70; A 21LV; AO 120; CMW Bone Cement; Crinothene; Degalan LP 59/03; Degalan S 85; Delpet 50M; Delpet 60N; Delpet 80N; Diakon; Diakon LO 951; Diakon MG; Diakon MG 101; Disapol M; DV 400; Elvacite 2008; Elvacite 2009; Elvacite 2010; Elvacite 2021; Elvacite 2041; Elvacite 6011; Elvacite 6012; K 120 N; Kallocryl K; Kallodent 222; Kallodent clear; Kaneace PA 20; Korad; LPT; LPT 1; LSO-M; LSO-M 4B; Lucite; Lucite 30; Lucite 47; Lucite 120; Lucite 129; Lucite 130; Lucite 140; Lucite 147; Lucite 180; Metaplex NO: Metaplex 4002T; MH 101-2; 50N; 50N (polymer); Organic glass E 2; Osteobond; Osteobond Surgical Bone Cement;

Palacos;  Palacos R;  Paraglas;  Parapet 60N;  Paraplex P 543;

Paraplex P 681;  Perspex;  Plex 8572F;  Plex 8572-F;  Plexiglas;

Plexigum M 920;  PMMA;  PMMA-A;  Pontalite;  Repairsin;  Resarit 4000;

Rhoplex B 85;  Riston;  Romacryl;  Shinkolite;  SO 95;  SO 120;

SO 140;  SOL;  SOL 90;  SOL 95;  ST 1;  ST 1 (polymer);  Stellon pink;

Sumipex B-LG;  Sumipex B-MH;  Sumipex-B MHD;  Sumipex LG;  Sumipex LO;

Sumipex MHO;  Superacryl AE;  Superacryl O;  Surgical Simplex;

Surgical Simplex P;  Tensol 7;  Torex G;  Vedril;  Vedril 5;

Vedril 8

## 1.2  Structural and molecular formulae and molecular weight

$$\left[ \begin{array}{cc} H & \overset{\displaystyle O}{\underset{\displaystyle |}{\overset{\displaystyle \|}{C}}} - O - CH_3 \\ | & | \\ -C - C - \\ | & | \\ H & CH_3 \end{array} \right]_n$$

$(C_5H_8O_2)_n$           Mol. wt:  100 000-200 000

## 1.3  Chemical and physical properties of the polymer

From Luskin & Myers (1964), unless otherwise specified

(a)  Description:  Water-white, transparent solid (Hawley, 1977)

(b)  Glass-transition temperature:  $105^\circ C$

(c)  Density:  1.188 (at $30^\circ C$), 1.179 (at $25^\circ C$) (conventional);
     1.22 (at $30^\circ C$), 1.206 (at $25^\circ C$) (isotactic)

(d)  Refractive index:  $n_D^{25}$ 1.489-1.491

(e)  Spectroscopy data:  Infra-red spectral data have been tabulated.

(f)  Solubility:  Insoluble in water;  moderately soluble in
     2-butanone, ethanol, ethyl acetate, $n$-butanol, 2-ethylhexanol,
     2-methoxyethanol, dimethyl formamide, nitromethane, ethylene
     dichloride and toluene

(g)  Stability:  Resistant to light and outdoor exposure weathering;
     extremely resistant to alkaline saponification and relatively

unaffected by inorganic and organic acids. Evolves gaseous methyl methacrylate on combustion (Forestier, 1975). The products of pyrolysis at approximately 580°C in air include mainly $C$-oxides, carbonyl compounds and methyl methacrylate (Hagen, 1968).

## 1.4  Technical products and impurities

Polymethyl methacrylate is the major constituent of thermoplastic acrylic resins (small amounts of methacrylic acid and acrylic monomers, e.g., $n$-butyl acrylate, may also be used as comonomers) available in the US as moulding pellets, in cast stock shapes (such as sheet, rod, tube and block), as fine powders, as films and as light-conducting filament. Acrylic resins modified for improved impact resistance are also available in moulding pellets and cast sheet for applications which require a high degree of toughness (Gambino, 1975).

No detailed information on the possible presence of unreacted monomer in the polymer was available to the Working Group.

## 2.  Production, Use, Occurrence and Analysis

## 2.1  Production and use

### (a)  Production

Acrylic resins were first developed in Germany in 1927 and were first produced commercially in the US in the early 1930's. Acrylic resins based on polymethyl methacrylate are produced by bulk and by suspension polymerization processes, in which polymerization is initiated with organic peroxides or azo compounds (Kine & Novak, 1978).

No data were available on the amount of polymethyl methacrylate produced in the US. An estimated 100 million kg methyl methacrylate were used in 1975 to produce polymethyl methacrylate-based acrylic resins for sheet, moulding and extrusion powders (including modified acrylics); the three companies which produce methyl methacrylate also produce polymethyl methacrylate. No data on US imports or exports of polymethyl methacrylate were available.

Western European production of polymethyl methacrylate in 1976 is estimated to have been 160 million kg.

Polymethyl methacrylate has been produced commercially in Japan since 1946. In 1975, four companies produced approximately 32.6 million kg, and exports amounted to 10 million kg.

(b)  Use

Polymethyl methacrylate is used primarily as the main constituent of acrylic sheet and acrylic moulding and extrusion powders.

Although advertising signs and displays are the largest end use for acrylic sheet, accounting for about 30%, this use is increasing only slowly.  Glazing, the second largest end use for acrylic sheet, is one of its fastest growing uses;  glazing uses include aircraft windshields and canopies, drive-in teller windows, enclosures for swimming-pools and sports arenas, greenhouse glazing, ice-hockey rink guards, inspection windows, marine-craft windshields, skylights, taxi partitions, telephone and toll booths, and decorative and break-resistant windows.  Other uses for acrylic sheet include plumbing and bath fixtures, lighting fixtures, building panels and miscellaneous uses.

Acrylic moulding and extrusion powders are used primarily in automotive applications for tail-light lenses, control dials and knobs, light and instrument covers, medallions, nameplates and wheel discs.  Other uses include appliance parts (e.g., dials and knobs, nameplates and window panels), brush backs, tap knobs, furniture parts, highway markers, housewares, jewellery, lenses and lighting fixtures.

An estimated 1000 kg acrylic resins, primarily polymethyl methacrylate, are used each year in the US and Europe as plastic biomaterials in the following applications:  bone replacements in unstressed situations; corneal implants, hard contact lenses and intraocular lenses;  and bone cements to fill bone defects, stabilize fractures and secure implants to bones (Halpern & Karo, 1977a).  Polymethyl methacrylate is also used in dentistry to make dentures, fillings and tooth replica implants (Halpern & Karo, 1977b).

In western Europe, polymethyl methacrylate is used in approximately equal quantities as moulding pellets and cast stock shapes.  Uses are varied and include transport cushioning, lighting, profiles, signs, construction and sanitary ware.

2.2  Occurrence

Polymethyl methacrylate is not known to occur as a natural product.

2.3  Analysis

Simple tests have been described to identify and analyse major plastics, including polymethyl methacrylate (Gaponenko, 1973), and to identify transparent materials, including polymethyl methacrylate, in which the materials were floated on water, machined, dissolved in solvents or burned (Dunn & Sansom, 1968).

A review has been published on the use of pyrolysis-gas chromatography in combination with differential thermal analysis, thermogravimetry and mass spectrometry to determine polymethyl methacrylate (Audebert, 1968). Pyrolysis-gas chromatography has been used to identify polymeric materials, including polymethyl methacrylate, among: (1) 37 commercial polymers (Okumuto & Takeuchi, 1972); (2) adhesives used in building, in combination with thermogravimetric and differential thermal analysis (Rona, 1971); (3) plastics and rubbers (Fischer, 1967); (4) vinyl polymers, with a limit of detection of 5-10 µg per sample (McCormick, 1969); and (5) synthetic binders used for paper coatings, with subsequent analysis by infra-red vapour spectroscopy (Luciani *et al.*, 1972).

Polymethyl methacrylate has been identified by pyrolysis followed by ultra-violet spectrophotometry, colour-forming reactions and thin-layer chromatography of the pyrolysis products (Braun & Nixdorf, 1972). It has also been identified by alkali-fusion degradation, followed by analysis using gas chromatography (Frankoski & Siggia, 1972), and has been distinguished from other acrylic copolymers and homopolymers by Curie point pyrolysis followed by gas chromatographic analysis (Haken & McKay, 1973).

Polymethyl methacrylate used as a paper coating has been identified by spectrophotometric analysis in the visible, ultra-violet and infra-red regions and also by liquid and gas chromatography (Luciani & Corradini, 1971).

Differential thermal analysis has been used to identify twelve groups of plastics, including polymethyl methacrylate, by their characteristic thermograms (Bosch, 1975).

## 3. Biological Data Relevant to the Evaluation
## of Carcinogenic Risk to Humans

### 3.1 Carcinogenicity studies in animals

### (a) Subcutaneous and/or intramuscular administration

Mouse: A group of 50 6-week-old Harlan albino Swiss mice received s.c. implants into the lateral abdominal wall of 10 x 10 x 0.2 mm methyl methacrylate (MMA) films, prepared by polymerizing commercially obtained monomer liquid (containing 1.0 mg/kg hydroquinone, see IARC, 1977) and polymer powder (containing cadmium oxide pigments, see IARC, 1976) similar to that used in making dentures. The first fibrosarcoma at the implantation site was found in mice given MMA films 257 days after the operation, when 20 of the 50 original mice were still alive; 4 additional fibrosarcomas developed at 405, 438, 454 and 469 days after the implantation. Fifty control mice received s.c. implants of cellophane films; 1 fibrosarcoma at the implantation site was found 400 days after the operation among the 7 mice still alive at that time (Laskin *et al.*, 1954).

Two groups of 50 6-week-old Harlan albino Swiss mice received s.c. implants into the lateral abdominal wall of 10 x 10 x 0.20-0.25 mm films of cold- or heat-cured polymerized MMA. An equal number of control mice of the same age, sex and strain were implanted with cellophane films of identical size and 0.1 mm thickness. Animals were observed weekly for 420 days. At this time, when 22, 13 and 25 mice, respectively, were still alive, one mammary carcinoma, considered to be 'spontaneous', was found near a heat-cured MMA film implant. The study ended after 575 days, when surviving animals were 2 mice that received heat-cured MMA film, 10 that received cold-cured MMA film and 5 in the control group. Histopathology revealed no neoplastic foci at the site of implantation (Kydd & Sreebny, 1960).

Groups of 7-8-week-old female Swiss albino mice were treated given s.c. implants into the left flank of various polyMMA films that were either unlabelled or had $^{14}$C- or $^{3}$H-labels (sites unspecified), and were observed for up to 100 weeks: one group of mice received implants of unlabelled polyMMA film (0.5 mm thick) of varying sizes (15 x 15 mm, 12 x 12 mm, 6 x 6 mm or 6 x 12 mm); a second group received $^{14}$C-labelled film of the same thickness and sizes; and a third group received implants of $^{3}$H-labelled film (12 x 12 x 0.5 mm). The incidences of sarcomas at the site of implantation ranged from 6.6-26% in mice implanted with unlabelled film. In mice implanted with the $^{14}$C-labelled film, the incidences of sarcomas were higher, 50% (5/10) and 31% (10/32), for the 15 x 15 mm and 12 x 12 mm films, respectively, compared with the incidence in mice implanted with the unlabelled films of the same size, 16% (3/18) and 26% (10/38). However, the increase is not statistically significant. The incidence of sarcomas in mice given the $^{3}$H-labelled film was 22% (5/22) (Tomatis, 1966).

Rat: PolyMMA (Surgical Simplex P), cut into discs 18 mm in diameter and 0.14 mm thick, was inserted subcutaneously in the abdominal region of male Wistar rats. One group of 22 rats received the discs bilaterally, and another group of 25 rats received the polyMMA disc on one side and a glass disc on the other. Surviving animals were killed after 39 months. Only 22 rats with either bilateral or a single polyMMA disc were subjected to pathological examination. Two fibrosarcomas were found at the site of implantation of polyMMA discs between 349 and 471 days after implantation, but no tumours were associated with the glass discs. In 54 effective rats implanted with plastic discs (polyMMA, polyethylene or epoxy casting resin) on one side of the abdomen and with glass discs on the other that did not develop a fibrosarcoma associated with the plastic, 5 were found to have fibrosarcomas associated with the glass discs (Lavorgna et al., 1972).

Wistar rats were given s.c. implants of 15 x 15 mm square and 0.14 mm thick films of polyMMA. Twenty of 25 implanted rats were still alive at the time of appearance of the first tumour; these developed 4 sarcomas at the site of implantation (20%) within a latent period ranging from 581 to 685 days. Of the 50 surviving control rats implanted with glass coverslips, one developed a fibrosarcoma that appeared 659 days after implantation. Results from an experiment still underway at the time of reporting indicated that 11/25 rats implanted with purified polyMMA (instead of commercial grade) developed s.c. sarcomas. In this group, the first tumour developed at 447 days (Oppenheimer *et al.*, 1953, 1955) [The Working Group noted that the age and sex of implanted animals were not reported].

A group of 153 female Chester Beatty rats, 3-months of age, were implanted intramuscularly with polyMMA discs. Each animal received one large disc (18 mm diameter and 1.5 mm thick) in the left thigh and one medium (12 mm diameter) and one small (4 mm diameter) disc in the right thigh. Thirty-four tumours, all spindle-cell sarcomas, were observed in association with the largest discs within a latent period of 150-807 days; 7 animals had metastases to the lungs and/or mesentery. Sarcomas associated with the medium-sized discs were found in 17/142 rats still alive at the minimum latent period (297 days); 5 animals had metastases to the lungs and mesentery. No tumours were found in association with the smallest discs. The 51 sarcomas observed occurred in a total of 46 rats (Stinson, 1964).

Thirty-four female Wistar rats, 9-12-weeks of age, were given s.c. implants of polyMMA (Plexiglas) rings 24 mm in diameter with a hole of 21.5 mm; one fibroblastic sarcoma was detected in 1 rat after 112 weeks of observation (Zajdela, 1966).

Guinea-pig: Eight-six female Hartley guinea-pigs, 4-6-months old, were given i.m. implants of 3 polyMMA discs 1.5 mm thick but of different diameters (18, 12 and 4 mm). Three animals were killed at 6, 12, 18, 24 and 30 months after implantation to examine the tissue reactions around the discs; the remaining guinea-pigs were observed throughout their lifespan. No tumours were detected, even though some animals were still alive 48 months after the implantation (Stinson, 1964) [The Working Group noted that the effective number of animals at risk was not given].

(b) Intraperitoneal administration

Rat: Two groups of 25 male and 25 female rats (strain unspecified), aged 3-4 months, were given i.p. implants of either glass or polyMMA discs of about 20 mm in diameter, while 50 sham-operated animals served as controls. No tumours were found after 21 months in the glass-implanted group (21 survivors at 11 months). In the polyMMA implanted group, 20 rats survived 11 months, and 2 sarcomas were observed around the implant (at 13 and 14 months after implantation), one of which metastasized to the omentum and peritoneal cavity; a third tumour in the peritoneal cavity found at 20 months did not arise from the capsule enveloping the disc. One lipoma was observed at 11 months in the 23 sham-operated animals alive at that time (Brunner, 1959).

(c) Other experimental systems

Combined subcutaneous and intraperitoneal implantation: Outbred rats of both sexes (100-170 g weight) were implanted intraperitoneally with 5 discs and subcutaneously with 2 discs of polyMMA (16 x 0.2-0.4 mm). At 6 months, 27 sham-operated rats and 13 treated animals were still alive; these animals were observed up to 23 months, when all surviving animals were killed. Of treated animals, 1 developed a sarcoma near an i.p. implant, 1 developed a s.c. sarcoma (metastasizing to the lung), and 2 others developed (unspecified) tumours (Klärner, 1962) [The Working Group noted that neither the initial number of implanted animals nor the time of tumour appearance was given].

Six groups of 10 male and 10 female rats (strain unspecified) were given implants of polyMMA discs (17 mm in diameter and 1-2 mm thick); each rat received 5 discs intraperitoneally into the abdominal wall and 2 subcutaneously under the dorsal skin. The polyMMA discs contained 0, 2, 5, 10, 25 and 50% fibrin (to produce increasing roughness of the disc surface). Another control group consisted of 30 sham-operated animals. The numbers of animals at risk at the time of appearance of the first tumour were 20, 13, 15, 18, 14 and 13, respectively, in the implanted groups, and 15 in the control group; all animals were killed 17 months after the implantation. The numbers of sarcomas were 2 (10%), 5 (38%), 2 (13%), 3 (17%), 4 (29%) and 1 (8%) in the implanted groups. No tumours developed in the sham-operated rats. In all, 13 i.p. and 4 s.c. tumours were observed; the first tumour appeared after 9 months. Tumour development was not found to be related to fibrin concentration (Brunner, 1959).

Cheek-pouch implantation: Sixty-eight 1-2-month-old Syrian golden hamsters of both sexes were given implants into one cheek pouch of polyMMA rods (15 mm long and 9.5 mm diameter). The animals were allowed to live their lifespan or were killed when moribund. No implantation site tumours were observed (Dunham & Herrold, 1962).

3.2  Other relevant biological data

(a) Experimental systems

In mice given s.c. implants of $^{14}$C- and $^3$H-labelled polyMMA, radioactivity in the urine increased until the 7th-8th week after implantation of the films and decreased sharply thereafter. Very low levels of radioactivity were detected in saline in which labelled implants were immersed (Tomatis, 1966).

No data on the toxicity, teratogenicity, embryotoxicity, metabolism or mutagenicity of this compound were available to the Working Group.

(b) Humans

Nearly immediate hypotension and cardiac arrest have been reported in elderly patients who received hip prostheses in which methyl methacrylate cement was used to anchor the prosthesis to bone. Death due to embolism occurred in some of these cases (Cadle *et al.*, 1972; Cohen & Smith, 1971; Fowler, 1972; Kepes *et al.*, 1972; Kim & Ritter, 1972; Phillips *et al.*, 1971; Powell *et al.*, 1970).

## 3.3 Case reports and epidemiological studies

No data were available to the Working Group.

## 4. Summary of Data Reported and Evaluation

### 4.1 Experimental data

Methyl methacrylate was tested by oral administration and by skin application in rats. These studies were considered inadequate by the Working Group for an evaluation of the carcinogenicity of this compound. No data on the mutagenicity of methyl methacrylate alone were available to the Working Group.

Polymethyl methacrylate, when implanted intramuscularly, subcutaneously or intraperitoneally as discs, produced local sarcomas in rats. In mice, subcutaneous implantation of polymethyl methacrylate films also resulted in local sarcomas. Intramuscular implantation of polymethyl methacrylate in guinea-pigs and implantation into the cheek pouch in hamsters produced no implantation site tumours.

### 4.2 Human data

No case reports or epidemiological studies relating to the carcinogenicity of methyl methacrylate or polymethyl methacrylate were available to the Working Group. The wide use of both materials, including major industrial and specialized medical products, particularly in surface coatings, indicates human exposure. This has been documented in two studies that relate to the toxicity of these substances.

### 4.3 Evaluation

The data available to the Working Group do not permit an evaluation of the carcinogenicity to humans of methyl methacrylate or polymethyl methacrylate. However, the results of available animal experiments, together with evidence both of occupational exposure by inhalation and of exposure by implantation arising from medical applications, indicate the need for experimental and epidemiological studies (see also, 'General Remarks on the Substances Considered', p. 35).

## 5. References

Anon. (1972)  Fire Protection Guide on Hazardous Materials, 4th ed., Boston, Mass., National Fire Protection Association, p. 49-159

Ashes, J.R. & Haken, J.K. (1971)  The retention behaviour of isomeric butenoic acid esters on stationary phases of varying polar character. J. Chromatogr., 62, 39-45

Asmussen, E. (1975)  NMR-analysis of monomers in restorative resins. Acta odont. scand., 33, 129-134

Audebert, R. (1968)  Pyrolytic and gas phase chromatographic study of polymers (Fr.). Ann. Chim. (Paris), 3, 49-66 [Chem. Abstr., 68, 96403m]

Autian, J. (1975)  Structure-toxicity relationships of acrylic monomers. Environ. Health Perspect., 11, 141-152

Bagramjan, S.B. & Babajan, E.A. (1974)  Cytogenetic study of the mutagenic activity of chemical substances isolated from Nairit latexes MKh and LNT-1 (Russ.). Biol. Zh. Arm., 27, 102-103

Bagramjan, S.B., Pogosjan, A.S., Babajan, E.A., Ovanesjan, R.D. & Charjan, S.M. (1976)  Mutagenic effect of small concentrations of volatile substances, emitted from polychloroprene latexes LNT-1 and MKH, during their combined uptake by the animal (Russ.). Biol. Zh. Arm., 29, 98-99

Barker, A.L. & Skinner, G.S. (1924)  Deaminization of esters of alanine and of aminoisobutyric acid. J. Am. chem. Soc., 46, 403-414

Bezuglyi, V.D., Voskresenskaya, I.B., Dmitrieva, V.N. & Alekseeva, T.A. (1970)  Separate determination of methacrylic acid and acrylic and methacrylic esters in a mixture (Russ.). Zavod. Lab., 36, 1040-1042

Blagodatin, V.M., Golova, I.A., Blagodatkina, N.K., Rumyantseva, E.P., Goryacheva, L.A., Alieva, N.K. & Gronsberg, E.S. (1970)  Issues of industrial hygiene and occupational pathology in the manufacture of organic glass (Russ.). Gig. Tr. Prof. Zabol., 14, 11-14

Bollini, M., Seves, A. & Focher, B. (1975)  Determination of free monomers in aqueous emulsions of synthetic polymers and copolymers (Ital.). Textilia, 51, 25-28 [Chem. Abstr., 83, 60039t]

Borzelleca, J.F., Larson, P.S., Hennigar, G.R., Jr, Huf, E.G., Crawford, E.M. & Blackwell Smith, R., Jr (1964)  Studies on the chronic oral toxicity of monomeric ethyl acrylate and methyl methacrylate. Toxicol. appl. Pharmacol., 6, 29-36

Bosch, K. (1975)  Thermoanalytical identification of plastics (Ger.).
    Beitr. Gerichtl. Med., 33, 280-284 [Chem. Abstr., 82, 60332d]

Bratt, H. & Hathway, D.E. (1977)  Fate of methyl methacrylate in rats.
    Br. J. Cancer, 36, 114-119

Braun, D. & Nixdorf, G. (1972)  Separation of synthetic resin for analy-
    sis.  4.  Soluble resins with neutral reaction of the pyrolysis
    products (Ger.).  Kunststoffe, 62, 318-322

Brunner, H. (1959)  Experimental formation of tumours by implantation of
    polymethyl methacrylate in rats (Ger.).  Arzneimittelforsch., 9,
    396-399

Cadle, D., James, M.L., Ling, R.S.M., Piper, R.F., Pryer, D.L. &
    Wilmshurst, C.C. (1972)  Cardiovascular responses after methyl-
    methacrylic cement.  Br. med. J., iv, 107-108

Cohen, C.A. & Smith, T.C. (1971)  The intraoperative hazard of acrylic
    bone cement:  report of a case.  Anesthesiology, 35, 547-549

Cromer, J. & Kronoveter, K. (1976)  A Study of Methyl Methacrylate
    Exposures and Employee Health, US Department of Health, Education,
    and Welfare, National Institute for Occupational Safety and Health,
    Cincinnati, Ohio, Publication No. DHEW (NIOSH) 77-119, Washington DC,
    US Government Printing Office, pp. 1-43

Deichmann, W. (1941)  Toxicity of methyl, ethyl and $n$-butyl methacrylate.
    J. ind. Hyg. Toxicol., 23, 343-351

Dmitrieva, V.N. & Kotok, L.A. (1976)  Polarographic determination of
    methyl methacrylate and styrene in the air of industrial facilities
    (Russ.).  Gig. i Sanit., 4, 59-61 [Chem. Abstr., 85, 181617e]

Dmitrieva, V.N., Meshkova, O.V. & Bezuglyi, V.D. (1975)  Determination
    of low contents of organic impurities in effluents from polymer
    production (Russ.).  Zh. anal. Khim., 30, 1406-1409

Dmitrieva, V.N., Kotok, L.A. & Stepanova, N.S. (1976)  Polarographic
    determination of methyl methacrylate in the atmosphere (Russ.).
    Gig. i Sanit., 12, 73-74 [Chem. Abstr., 86, 176125j]

Dowty, B.J., Carlisle, D.R. & Laseter, J.L. (1975)  New Orleans drinking
    water sources tested by gas chromatography-mass spectrometry.  Occur-
    rence and origin of aromatics and halogenated aliphatic hydrocarbons.
    Environ. Sci. Technol., 9, 762-765

Dunham, L.J. & Herrold, K.M. (1962)  Failure to produce tumors in the
    hamster cheek pouch by exposure to ingredients of betel quid;
    histopathologic changes in the pouch and other organs by exposure
    to known carcinogens.  J. natl Cancer Inst., 29, 1047-1067

Dunn, P. & Sansom, G.F. (1968)  Identification of transparent materials
     for safety applications.  Australas. Eng., February, 37-38 [Chem.
     Abstr., 72, 91039v]

Ekimova, N.I., Mikhailova, A.A. & Lifshits, L.I. (1969)  Sanitary-chemical
     studies in an experimental plastic dwelling (Russ.).  Gig. Primen.
     Polim. Mater. Izdelii Nikh, 1, 131-135 [Chem. Abstr., 75, 52461u]

Fischer, W.G. (1967)  Pyrolytic gas-chromatography (Ger.).  Glas-Instrum.-
     Tech., 11, 562, 567-570, 775-780, 1086-1088, 1091-1095 [Chem. Abstr.,
     68, 78636k]

Fisher, A.A. (1954)  Allergic sensitization of the skin and oral mucosa
     to acrylic denture materials.  J. Am. med. Assoc., 156, 238-242

Forestier, M. (1975)  Combustion products of synthetic materials (Fr.).
     Rev. Tech. Feu, 16, 24-26 [Chem. Abstr., 84, 136391v]

Fowler, A.W. (1972)  Methylmethacrylic cement and fat embolism.  Br. med.
     J., iv, 108

Frankoski, S.P. & Siggia, S. (1972)  Analysis of carboxylic esters using
     alkali fusion reaction gas chromatography.  Anal. Chem., 44, 507-511

Gambino, H.J., Jr (1975)  Acrylic.  In: Agranoff, J., ed., 1975-1976
     Modern Plastics Encyclopedia, Vol. 52, No. 10A, New York, McGraw-Hill,
     pp. 8, 10, 12

Gaponenko, I.M. (1973)  Simple analysis and identification of major
     plastics (Russ.).  In:  Ivanyutin, M.I., ed., Organic Reagents,
     Analytical Chemistry, Metal Corrosion, Smolensk, Smolensk State
     Pedagogic Institute, pp. 71-75 [Chem. Abstr., 83, 60146a]

Grasselli, J.G. & Ritchey, W.M., eds (1975)  CRC Atlas of Spectral Data
     and Physical Constants for Organic Compounds, 2nd ed., Vol. IV,
     Cleveland, Ohio, Chemical Rubber Co., p. 317

Hagen, E. (1968)  Composition of pyrolysis gases of plastics (Ger.).
     Plaste Kaut., 15, 711-713 [Chem. Abstr., 70, 4829v]

Haken, J.K. & McKay, T.R. (1973)  Quantitative pyrolysis gas chromatography
     of some acrylic copolymers and homopolymers.  Anal. Chem., 45,
     1251-1257

Halpern, B.D. & Karo, W. (1977a)  Medical applications.  In:  Bikales, N.M.,
     ed., Encyclopedia of Polymer Science and Technology, Plastics, Resins,
     Rubbers, Fibers, Suppl. Vol. 2, New York, Interscience, pp. 369,
     379-381, 385

Halpern, B.D. & Karo, W. (1977b) Dental applications. In: Bikales, N.M., ed., Encyclopedia of Polymer Science and Technology, Plastics, Resins, Rubbers, Fibers, Suppl. Vol. 2, New York, Interscience, pp. 206-217

Hawley, G.G., ed. (1971) The Condensed Chemical Dictionary, 8th ed., New York, Van Nostrand-Reinhold, p. 578

Hawley, G.G., ed. (1977) The Condensed Chemical Dictionary, 9th ed., New York, Van Nostrand-Reinhold, pp. 14, 523

Homsy, C.A., Tullos, H.S., Anderson, M.S., Diferrante, N.M. & King, J.W. (1972) Some physiological aspects of prosthesis stabilization with acrylic polymer. Clin. Orthop. rel. Res., 83, 317-328

IARC (1976) IARC Monographs on the Evaluation of Carcinogenic Risk of Chemicals to Man, 11, Cadmium, Nickel, Some Epoxides, Miscellaneous Industrial Chemicals and General Considerations on Volatile Anaesthetics, Lyon, pp. 39-74

IARC (1977) IARC Monographs on the Evaluation of the Carcinogenic Risk of Chemicals to Man, 15, Some Fumigants, the Herbicides 2,4-D and 2,4,5-T, Chlorinated Dibenzodioxins and Miscellaneous Industrial Chemicals, Lyon, pp. 155-175

Kepes, E.R., Underwood, P.S. & Becsey, L. (1972) Intraoperative death associated with acrylic bone cement. Report of two cases. J. Am. med. Assoc., 222, 576-577

Kim, K.C. & Ritter, M.A. (1972) Hypotension associated with methyl methacrylate in total hip arthroplasties. Clin. Orthop. rel. Res., 88, 154-160

Kine, B.B. & Novak, R.W. (1978) Acrylic ester polymers. In: Grayson, M., ed., Encyclopedia of Chemical Technology, 3rd ed., Vol. 1, New York, John Wiley and Sons, pp. 386-408

Klärner, P. (1962) Production of sarcomas by foreign bodies made of polymethacrylates and additives (Ger.). Z. Krebsforsch., 65, 99-100

Kleshcheva, M.S., Balandina, V.A., Usacheva, V.T. & Koroleva, L.B. (1969a) Determination of the residual monomer content in some polystyrene plastics by gas chromatography (Russ.). Vysokomol. Soedin., Ser. A, 11, 2595-2597 [Chem. Abstr., 72, 55912r]

Kleshcheva, M.S., Korzhova, I.T. & Pozharova, V.N. (1969b) Analysis of waste waters for methacrylic acid and methyl methacrylate levels (Russ.). Gazov. Khromatogr., 10, 94-96 [Chem. Abstr., 73, 80311x]

Kleshcheva, M.S., Usacheva, V.T. & Pozharova, V.N. (1971) Determination of residual monomers and non-polymerising impurities in polystyrene plastics by means of gas chromatography (Russ.). Plast. Massy, 7, 57-58

Kravchenko, T.I. & Chemer, G.A. (1977) Migration of acrylic and methacrylic acid esters from acrylate latexes (Russ.). Gig. i Sanit., 1, 100-102

Kydd, W.L. & Sreebny, L.M. (1960) Potential oncogenic properties of high polymers in mice. J. natl Cancer Inst., 25, 749-751

Laskin, D.M., Robinson, I.B. & Weinmann, J.P. (1954) Experimental production of sarcomas by methyl methacrylate implants. Proc. Soc. exp. Biol. (N.Y.), 87, 329-332

Lavorgna, J.J., Burstein, N.A., Schiller, A.L. & Harris, W.H. (1972) The carcinogenesis of plastics used in orthopedic surgery. An assessment of the incidence in rats and the possible relevance to man. Clin. Orthop. rel. Res., 88, 223-227

Lawrence, W.H. & Autian, J. (1972) Possible toxic effects from inhalation of dental ingredients by alteration of drug biologic half-life. J. dent. Res., 51, 878

Lazaris, L.Y. & Kalmykova, T.A. (1972) Determination of residual monomers and solvents in latexes, ether acrylates, and polymers (Russ.). Nov. Sorbenty Khromatogr., 18, 92-95 [Chem. Abstr., 80, 96391d]

Luciani, M. & Corradini, T. (1971) Spectrophotometric and chromatographic analysis of paper coatings (Ital.). Cellul. Carta, 22, 19-35 [Chem. Abstr., 76, 73969b]

Luciani, M., Corradini, T. & Fiorucci, P. (1972) Identification of synthetic binders for paper coatings by gas chromatographic analysis of their pyrolysis products (Ital.). Cellul. Carta, 23, 7-20 [Chem. Abstr., 78, 161105p]

Luskin, L.S. & Myers, R.J. (1964) Acrylic ester polymers. In: Bikales, N.M., ed., Encyclopedia of Polymer Science and Technology, Plastics, Resins, Rubbers, Fibers, Vol. 1, New York, Interscience, pp. 291-293, 299-305

Markelov, M.A. & Semenenko, E.I. (1976) Determination of microconcentrations of substances migrating from polymer materials to water (Russ.). Plast. Massy, 1, 57-59 [Chem. Abstr., 84, 155747g]

McCormick, H. (1969) Quantitative aspects of pyrolysis/gas-liquid chromatography of some vinyl polymers. J. Chromatogr., 40, 1-15

Meshkova, O.V. & Dmitrieva, V.N. (1974) Extraction polarographic determination of styrene and methylmethacrylate in plant sewage (Russ.). Zavod. Lab., 40, 28-29

Mohr, H.-J. (1958) Pathologic anatomy and causal genesis of tissue changes due to autopolymerizing methacrylate (Ger.). Z. ges. exp. Med., 130, 41-69

Okumoto, T. & Takeuchi, T. (1972) Rapid characterization of polymeric materials by pyrolysis-gas chromatography (Jap.). Nippon Kagaku Kaishi, 1, 71-78 [Chem. Abstr., 76, 141459n]

Oppenheimer, B.S., Oppenheimer, E.T., Stout, A.P. & Danishefsky, I. (1953) Malignant tumors resulting from embedding plastics in rodents. Science, 118, 305-306

Oppenheimer, B.S., Oppenheimer, E.T., Danishefsky, I., Stout, A.P. & Eirich, F.R. (1955) Further studies of polymers as carcinogenic agents in animals. Cancer Res., 15, 333-340

Panova, R.V., Belova, R.A. & Lavrushina, T.S. (1969) Chromatographic determination of residual monomers in latexes (Russ.). Prom. Sin. Kauch., Nauch.-Tekh. Sb., 1, 21-23 [Chem. Abstr., 74, 43238d]

Patterson, R.M., Bornstein, M.I. & Garshick, E. (1976) Assessment of Methyl Methacrylate as a Potential Air Pollution Problem, Vol. IX, US Environmental Protection Agency, Research Triangle Park, N.C., Contract No. 68-02-1337, Task 8, Springfield, Va, National Technical Information Service, No. PB-258361

Pegum, J.S. & Medhurst, F.A. (1971) Contact dermatitis from penetration of rubber gloves by acrylic monomer. Br. med. J., ii, 141-143

Perry, R.H. & Chilton, C.H., eds (1973) Chemical Engineers' Handbook, 5th ed., New York, McGraw-Hill, p. 3-57

Phillips, H., Cole, P.V. & Lettin, A.W.F. (1971) Cardiovascular effects of implanted acrylic bone cement. Br. med. J., iii, 460-461

Pollock, J.R.A. & Stevens, R., eds (1965) Dictionary of Organic Compounds, 4th ed., Vol. 4, New York, Oxford University Press, p. 2239

Ponomarev, Y.P., Meshkova, O.V., Ryzhova, L.I. & Dmitrieva, V.N. (1974) Determination of styrene and methyl methacrylate in waste water by polarography with the use of extraction (Russ.). In: Shkorbatova, T.L., ed., Physico-Chemical Methods of Purification and Analysis of Waste Waters from Industrial Plants, Moscow, Research Institute of Water Supply and Wastes, Hydrotechnic Engineering and Hydrogeology, pp. 99-104 [Chem. Abstr., 86, 21536v]

Powell, J.N., McGrath, P.J., Lahiri, S.K. & Hill, P. (1970)  Cardiac arrest associated with bone cement. Br. med. J., iii, 326

Rapaport, L.I. & Ledovskikh, N.G. (1972)  Iodochlorimetric determination of trace quantities of acrylamide and methyl methacrylate (Russ.). Gig. i Sanit., 37, 74-77 [Chem. Abstr., 77, 20051k]

Rona, A. (1971)  Instrumental investigation of adhesives used in the building industry. In: Symposium on Synthetic Resins in Building Construction, Paper RILEM (Reunion Int. Lab. Essais Rech. Mater. Constr.) 1967, Vol. 2, pp. 464-471 [Chem. Abstr., 76, 100475w]

Schmötzer, G. (1972)  Determination of residual monomers in emulsion polymers (Ger.). Fresenius' Z. anal. Chem., 260, 10-24

Schulz, H. & Günther, R. (1972)  Paint processing and prevention of air pollution - Investigations concerning organic substances from paint binders appearing in the drying air during paint drying in continuous ovens. Staub-Reinhalt. Luft, 32, 1-11

Shackelford, W.M. & Keith, L.H. (1976)  Frequency of Organic Compounds Identified in Water, EPA-600/4-76-062, Athens, Ga, US Enviromental Protection Agency, p. 153

Sheinin, E.B., Benson, W.R. & Brannon, W.L. (1976)  Determination of methyl methacrylate in surgical acrylic cement. J. pharm. Sci., 65, 280-283

Shellow, H. (1954)  Sensitization to acrylic denture materials. J. Am. med. Assoc., 156, 1527

Singh, A.R., Lawrence, W.H. & Autian, J. (1972a)  Embryonic-fetal toxicity and teratogenic effects of a group of methacrylate esters in rats. J. dent. Res., 51, 1632-1638

Singh, A.R., Lawrence, W.H. & Autian, J. (1972b)  Embryo-fetal toxicity and teratogenic effects of a group of methacrylate esters in rats (Abstract No. 106). Toxicol. appl. Pharmacol., 22, 314-315

Spealman, C.R., Main, R.J., Haag, H.B. & Larson, P.S. (1945)  Monomeric methyl methacrylate. Studies on toxicity. Ind. Med., 14, 292-298

Stinson, N.E. (1964)  The tissue reaction induced in rats and guinea-pigs by polymethylmethacrylate (acrylic) and stainless steel (18/8/Mo). Br. J. exp. Pathol., 45, 21-29

Tomatis, L. (1966)  Subcutaneous carcinogenesis by $^{14}$C and $^{3}$H labelled polymethylmethacrylate films. Tumori, 52, 165-172

US Department of Commerce (1977)  US Exports, Schedule B Commodity Groupings, Schedule B Commodity by Country, FT410/December, Bureau of the Census, Washington DC, US Government Printing Office, p. 2-84

US Environmental Protection Agency (1975) Preliminary Assessment of Suspected Carcinogens in Drinking Water, Report to Congress, Washington DC, p. II-5

US Food and Drug Administration (1977) Food and drugs. US Code Fed. Regul., Title 21, parts 175.105, 175.300, 175.320, 177.1010, 177.2420, 178.3790, 181.30, pp. 438, 445, 452, 456, 465, 496, 548-549, 596, 615

US International Trade Commission (1977) Synthetic Organic Chemicals, US Production and Sales, 1975, USITC Publication 804, Washington DC, US Government Printing Office, pp. 198, 219

US Occupational Safety and Health Administration (1976) Occupational safety and health standards, subpart Z - toxic and hazardous substances. US Code Fed. Regul., Title 29, Chapter XVII, Section 1910.1000, p. 31:8303

US Tariff Commission (1938) Dyes and Other Synthetic Organic Chemicals in the US, 1937, Report No. 132, Second Series, Washington DC, US Government Printing Office, p. 52

Weast, R.C., ed. (1976) CRC Handbook of Chemistry and Physics, 57th ed., Cleveland, Ohio, Chemical Rubber Co., p. C-465

Willert, H.-G., Frech, H.-A. & Bechtel, A. (1973) Measurements of the quantity of monomer leaching out of acrylic bone cement into the surrounding tissues during the process of polymerization. Am. chem. Soc., Div. Org. Coat. Plast. Chem., 33, 370-370g

Zajdela, F. (1966) Production of subcutaneous sarcomas in the rat by cellulose membranes of known porosity (Fr.). Bull. Cancer, 53, 401-408

Zaytseva, N.A., Tolstobrova, S.A. & Il'in, D.T. (1972) Chromatographic determination of unreacted monomers in emulsions of acrylic copolymers (Russ.). Khim. Prom. (Moscow), 48, 351-352 [Translation in Sov. chem. Ind. (1972), 48, 298]

## PROPYLENE and POLYPROPYLENE

## Propylene

### 1. Chemical and Physical Data

#### 1.1 Synonyms and trade names

Chem. Abstr. Services Reg. No.: 115-07-1

Chem. Abstr. Name: 1-Propene

Methylethene; methylethylene; propene; 1-propylene

#### 1.2 Structural and molecular formulae and molecular weight

$$\begin{array}{c} H \\ H \end{array}\!\!>\!C=C\!<\!\!\begin{array}{c} CH_3 \\ H \end{array}$$

$C_3H_6$                Mol. wt: 42.1

#### 1.3 Chemical and physical properties of the pure substance

From Weast (1976), unless otherwise specified

(a) Description: Colourless gas (Davis & Beach, 1968)

(b) Boiling-point: $-47.4^{\circ}C$

(c) Melting-point: $-185.25^{\circ}C$

(d) Density: $d_4^{20}$ 0.5193 (liquid at saturation pressure); vapour density, 1.5 (air = 1) (Anon., 1972)

(e) Refractive index: $n_D^{-70}$ 1.3567

(f) Spectroscopy data: Infra-red and mass spectral data have been tabulated (Grasselli & Ritchey, 1975).

(g) Solubility: Soluble in water (44.6 ml/100 ml), ethanol (1250 ml/100 ml) and acetic acid (524.5 ml/100 ml) (Davis & Beach, 1968)

(h) Volatility: Vapour pressure is 7600 mm at 19.8°C (Perry &
     Chilton, 1973).

(i) Stability: Inflammable limits, 2 and 11.1% (Anon., 1972);
     polymerizes only at elevated temperature and pressure in the
     presence of a catalyst (Davis & Beach, 1968)

(j) Reactivity: Reacts violently with oxidizing agents (Davis &
     Beach, 1968)

(k) Conversion factor: 1 ppm in air = 1.72 mg/m$^3$

## 1.4  Technical products and impurities

Propylene is generally available in the US as a chemical grade and as
a polymerization grade. Chemical grade propylene has a minimum purity of
92%. The polymerization grade typically contains 99.9% by vol propylene,
with the following impurities: propane, 285.5 mg/m$^3$ (166 ppm); ethane,
25.8 mg/m$^3$ (15 ppm); total extraneous unsaturates, <17.2 mg/m$^3$ (<10 ppm);
water, <10 mg/kg (ppm); butenes and heavier, 8.6 mg/m$^3$ (5 ppm); oxygen,
<5 mg/kg (ppm); propadiene, 3.4 mg/m$^3$ (2 ppm); ethylene, 1.7 mg/m$^3$ (1
ppm); acetylene, <1.7 mg/m$^3$ (1 ppm); methylacetylene, <1.7 mg/m$^3$ (<1
ppm); carbon monoxide, <1.7 mg/m$^3$ (<1 ppm); carbon dioxide, <1.7 mg/m$^3$
(<1 ppm); hydrogen, <1 mg/kg (ppm); and sulphur, 0.04 mg/kg (ppm).

Propylene is available in western Europe as a 92% pure chemical
grade and as a 99.8% pure polymerization grade. Polymerization grade
propylene typically contains the following impurities (ppm max):
saturates (200), butylene (20), ethylene (20), methylacetylene (10),
oxygen (10), butadiene (5), propadiene (5), carbon monoxide (5), carbon
dioxide (5), water (5), hydrogen (5) and methanol (5).

In Japan, propylene is available with the following specifications:
propylene content, 90.0 mol % min; C$_4$, 1.0 mol % max; ethane and ethylene,
1.0 mol % max; butadiene, 0.3 mol % max; methylacetylene, 0.3 mol % max;
propadiene, 0.3 mol % max; sulphur, 30 ppm max; hydrogen sulphide, 10 ppm
max; oxygen, 10 ppm max; and water, 10 ppm max.

## 2.  Production, Use, Occurrence and Analysis

## 2.1  Production and use

### (a)  Production

Propylene was prepared in 1851 by Reynolds by the pyrolysis of amyl
alcohol or a wide variety of other organic compounds (Prager et al., 1918).
Most propylene is produced commercially as a by-product of either ethylene

manufacture or refinery operations.  Refinery off-gases, principally from
catalytic cracking, contain substantial quantities of propylene that can
be used either in gasoline manufacture or for chemical manufacture (often
after further purification).  Most ethylene plants based on steam cracking
of natural gas liquids, naphtha and gas oil produce recoverable quantities
of propylene as a by-product.  The amount varies from 90-318 g propylene
per kg ethylene, depending on the feedstock and reaction conditions.

Propylene is believed to have been produced commercially in the US
for over 50 years;  however, production has only been reported for about
35 years (US Tariff Commission, 1945).  In 1976, 33 companies reported
production of 4550 million kg for use in chemicals (US International Trade
Commission, 1977).  An additional 5000 million kg were produced for use in
gasoline manufacture and other fuel applications.  Exports of propylene in
1976 amounted to 13.5 million kg and were sent to the following countries
(per cent of total):  Canada (4), Mexico (16), Republic of Korea (78) and
other countries (2) (US Department of Commerce, 1977).

Total western Europe production of propylene in 1976 for use in chemicals amounted to 5625 million kg, in the following eight countries (production in millions of kg):  Austria (75), Benelux (1150), Denmark (25), the
Federal Republic of Germany (1545), France (875), Italy (880), Spain (150),
Sweden (160) and the UK (765).  Exports from western Europe in that year
were 200 million kg.  Annual propylene production in eastern Europe is
estimated to be more than 1100 million kg.

Propylene has been produced commercially in Japan since 1963.  In 1976,
fifteen companies produced about 2635 million kg, and 24 million kg were
exported.

Propylene is also produced in the following countries (1975 production
estimates in millions of kg):  Argentina (8), Australia (65), Brazil (86),
Canada (199), Mexico (93) and Republic of Korea (58).  Annual propylene
production capacity in the Middle East and Africa is less than 200 million
kg.

Total worldwide production of propylene for use in chemicals in 1976
is estimated to have been 15 000 million kg.

(b)  Use

The amount of propylene used chemically in the US in 1976 is estimated
on the basis of derivatives production data to have been 5325 million kg.
Of this, 69% was used directly for the production of four chemicals:  polypropylene (25%), acrylonitrile (16%), isopropyl alcohol (14%) and propylene
oxide (14%).  Other derivatives, in order of decreasing propylene uses,
include butyraldehydes, cumene, dodecene, nonene, allyl chloride, acrylic
acid, ethylene-propylene elastomers, heptenes and acrolein.  Miscellaneous
applications include polymerization to low-molecular-weight homopolymers
used as lubricating oil additives;  uses as a comonomer in special polyvinyl

chloride resins; and use in hydroquinone and aluminium alkyl manufacture. For a detailed description of the uses of other chemical derivatives of propylene, see polypropylene, p. 222 and monographs on acrylonitrile, p. 73, acrylic acid, p. 47 and acrolein, p. 479. Monographs have already been published on isopropyl alcohol (IARC, 1977) and propylene oxide (IARC, 1976).

The pattern of chemical uses of propylene in western Europe in 1977 was as follows: acrylonitrile (23%), polypropylene (21%), butyraldehydes (17%), propylene oxide (13%), cumene (10%), isopropyl alcohol (7%) and other uses, e.g., heptenes, allyl chloride, ethylene propylene copolymers (9%).

Use of propylene in Japan in 1976 was in polypropylene (35%), acrylonitrile (33%), butyraldehyde (9%), propylene oxide (7%), cumene (6%), acetone (3%), isopropyl alcohol (2%) and others (5%).

## 2.2  Occurrence

### (a)  Natural sources

Propylene has been found in the gaseous metabolites released by germinating beans, corn, cotton and pea seeds (Vančura & Stotzky, 1976).

It has been detected in the gases desorbed from coal samples (Kim & Douglas, 1973).

### (b)  Air

In Japan, air concentrations of propylene in an industrial area near a petrochemical plant were 17-170 $\mu g/m^3$ (10-100 ppb) (Inoue et al., 1975).

In the UK, propylene concentrations in the air of a rural area over a two-year period varied from 0.17-8.2 $\mu g/m^3$ (0.10-4.8 ppb), with a mean of 1.19 $\mu g/m^3$ (0.7 ppb) (Cox et al., 1976).

The propylene concentration in the air in Delft, The Netherlands was found to vary with wind direction and time of day, the highest value (14 $\mu g/m^3$; 8 ppb) occurring in the early morning with a southerly wind (Bos et al., 1977).

Propylene has been detected in the air near a ship channel in Houston, Texas, USA and in downtown Phoenix, Arizona (Westberg et al., 1974), and determined at levels ranging from 12-448 $\mu g/m^3$ (7-260 ppb) in the air of a suburban community of Philadelphia near several industrial complexes (Giannovario et al., 1976). The centres of Los Angeles and Azusa, California, had average propylene concentrations in the air of 18 and 6.9 $\mu g/m^3$ (10.5 and 4 ppb), respectively (Altshuller et al., 1971). Propylene concentrations in Los Angeles air decreased from 0.070 ppm (as carbon) in 1963-1965, before vehicle exhaust controls had been put into effect, to 0.049 ppm (as carbon) in 1973 (Leonard et al., 1976).

(c)  Water

The concentration and probable sources of hydrocarbons, including propylene, in the marine environment have been reviewed (McAuliffe, 1976). Concentrations of propylene have been measured in the Gulf of Mexico (0.1-16 nl/l), the Caribbean Sea (0.2-5.8 nl/l), the Atlantic Ocean (trace - 11.0 nl/l) and the Pacific Ocean (0.6-3.6 nl/l) (Lamontagne et al., 1975;  Swinnerton & Lamontagne, 1974).

(d)  Combustion products

The combustion products of burning white pinewood were found to contain 86 mg/m$^3$ (50 ppm) propylene (O'Mara, 1974).

Exhaust gases from a jet engine operated at simulated high-altitude supersonic flight conditions were found to contain propylene at concentrations ranging from 223-245 mg/m$^3$ (129.6-143.4 ppm) (Katzman & Libby, 1975).  A diesel-powered passenger car was found to emit propylene in its exhaust at a rate of 0.0207 g/mile (12.9 mg/km) when burning a commercial diesel fuel and 0.0094 g/mile (5.8 mg/km) when burning a standard US Environmental Protection Agency smoke test fuel (Braddock & Bradow, 1975).

2.3  Analysis

Methods of detecting unsaturated hydrocarbons, including propylene, in air have been described in which the chemiluminescence of a reaction of the hydrocarbon with ozone (Quickert et al., 1975), or with active nitrogen (Baity et al., 1974), is measured.

Infra-red spectrophotometry of cryogenically-cooled gaseous mixtures can be used to detect propylene, with a limit of detection of 1.7 µmol or 100 ppm (Rochkind, 1967).  Absorption of infra-red radiation from a laser source can be used to detect propylene in gaseous mixtures, with a limit of detection of 5.2 µg/m$^3$ (3 ppb) (Kreuzer et al., 1972).

The Intersociety Committee, composed of ten organizations, has published a method of analysis for atmospheric hydrocarbons, including propylene, using gas chromatography and oxygen-hydrogen flame ionization detection, with a limit of detection of 0.17 µg/m$^3$ (0.1 ppb) propylene (Intersociety Committee, 1972).  Gas chromatographic methods using various means of detection have also been used for the separation and identification of propylene in:  (1) sea-water, with a limit of detection of $2 \times 10^{-12}$ mol of gas ($8.4 \times 10^{-11}$ g) (Swinnerton & Linnenbom, 1967);  (2) prepared gaseous hydrocarbon mixtures (Di Corcia & Samperi, 1975);  (3) a mixture of light hydrocarbons and permanent gases such as carbon monoxide, nitrogen and oxygen (Sarkar & Haselden, 1975);  (4) exhaust gases and stack gases (Lamb et al., 1973);  (5) ambient air, using a chemically-bonded stationary phase, with a limit of detection of 0.86 µg/m$^3$ (0.5 ppb) (Westberg et al., 1974);  (6) ambient air, using cryogenic temperature programming (Giannovario et al., 1976);  and (7) air, using an automated system, with a limit of detection of 3.4-8.6 µg/m$^3$ (2-5 ppb) (Jeltes & Burghardt, 1972).

Gas chromatography combined with mass spectrometry has been used to determine propylene in gaseous mixtures and in hydrocarbon oils, with a limit of detection of approximately 0.1 ppm (Leigh & Lynaugh, 1974).

## 3.  Biological Data Relevant to the Evaluation
## of Carcinogenic Risk to Humans[1]

No data were available to the Working Group.

## Polypropylene

### 1.  Chemical and Physical Data

### 1.1  Synonyms and trade names

Chem. Abstr. Services Reg. No.:  9003-07-0

Chem. Abstr. Name:  1-Propene homopolymer

Atactic polypropylene;  isotactic polypropylene;  paisley polymer; polypropene;  propene polymers;  propylene polymer;  syndiotactic polypropylene

Admer PB 02;  Amco;  Amerfil;  Amoco 1010;  Ampol C 60;  AT 36; Avisun;  Avisun 101;  Avisun 12-270A;  Avisun 12-407A;  Azdel; Beamette;  Bicolene P;  Carlona K 571;  Carlona KM 61;  Carlona P; Carlona PM 61 naturel;  Carlona PPLZ 074;  CD 419;  Celgard 2500; Celgard 3501;  Celgard KKX 2;  Celgard 2400W;  Chisso 5078;  Chisso Polypro 1014;  Clysar;  Coathylene PF 0548;  Courlene PY;  CPP 25S; D 151;  Daplen AD;  Daplen APP;  Daplen AS 50;  Daplen AT 10; Daplen ATK 92;  Daplen DM 55U;  Dexon E 117;  DLP;  DS 8620; Eastobond L 8080-270A;  Eastobond M 3;  Eastobond M 5;  Eastobond M 5H; Elpon;  El Rexene PP 115;  EM 490;  Enjay CD 392;  Enjay CD 460; Enjay CD 490;  Enjay E 11S;  Enjay E 117;  Epolene M 5H;  Epolene M 5K;

---

[1]The Working Group was aware of studies in progress to assess the carcinogenicity of propylene in mice and rats by inhalation exposure (Toxicology Information Program, 1976).

Epolene M 5W; Escon 622; Escon CD 44A; Escon EX 375; F 080PP; Gerfil; GPCD 398; Hercoflat 135; Hercotuf 110A; Hercotuf PB 681; Hercules 6523; Herculon; HF 20; HO 50; Hostalen N 1060; Hostalen PP; Hostalen PPH 1050; Hostalen PPN; Hostalen PPN 1060; Hostalen PPN 1075 F; Hostalen PPN 1076 F; Hostalen PPR 1042; Hostalen PPT VP 7090A; Hostalen PP-U; Huls P 6500; ICI 543; J 400; J 700; JGD 1800; JMD 4500; K 300; Lambeth; Lanco Wax PP 1362D; Lupareen; LYM 42; Marlex 9400; Marlex HGH 050-01; Maurylene; Meraklon; MFR 4; MH 4; Mitsui Polypro B 220; MM2A; Moplen; Moplen AD 50N; Moplen AS 50; Moplen Q 51C; Moplen T 30G; Mosten; Noblen; Noblen BC 8; Noblen D 101; Noblen D 501; Noblen EBG; Noblen FA 3; Noblen FL; Noblen FL 4; Noblen FL 6314; Noblen FP; Noblen FS 101; Noblen FS 2011; Noblen H; Noblen H 101; Noblen H 501; Noblen HS; Noblen JHHG; Noblen JK-M; Noblen MA 4; Noblen MH 6; Noblen MM 2A; Noblen S 50; Noblen S 101; Noblen SHG; Noblen 2VH501; Noblen W 101; Noblen W 501; Noblen W 502; Noblen WF 464; Novamont 2030; Novolen; Novolen KR 1300P; Novolen 1300ZX; Oletac 100; P 6500; Paisley 750; Pellon 2505; Pellon 2506; Pellon FT 2140; Pistac CC; Pistac L; Polypro 1014; Polypro B 220; Polypro G 400P; Polypro J 600; Polypro J 400P; Poprolin; PP 1; PP 1 (polymer); PP 2: PP 4; PP 1151; PPSD 30; PR 144; Profax; Profax 6301; Profax 6401; Profax 6423; Profax 6501; Profax 6523; Profax 6601; Profax 6723; Profax 6823; Profax 6523F; Profax PCO 72; Propathene; Propathene 22/44; Propathene 101/24; Propathene 112/00/Grey 9897; Propathene GSE 108; Propathene GSE 180; Propathene GWE 21; Propathene GW 522 M; Propathene GW 601M; Propathene GY 702M; Propathene HF 20; Propathene HW 70GR; Propathene HWM 25; Propathene LWF 31; Propathene LY 542M; Propathene O; Propathene PXC 3830; Propathene PXC 4515; Propathene PXC 8639; Propathene PXC 9617; Propolin; Propophane; PS 2011; PXC 3391; PXC 8639; Rexall 413S; 413S; SD 5220; Shell 5520; Shoallomer; Shoallomer FA 120; Shoallomer Fa 530; Shoallomer MA 210; TA 3; Tatren 141; Tatren EB 111; Tenite 423; Tenite 4231; Tenite 423DF; Tenite P 7673-079F; Trespaphan; Trespaphan CEA; Trespaphan

N 12;  Tuff-Lite;  Ulstron;  USI 11-4-0047;  Vestolen 5200;  Vestolen
P 5500;  Viscol 350P;  Viscol 550P;  Viscol 660 P;  W 101;  WEX 1242

## 1.2  Structural and molecular formulae and molecular weight

$$\left[\begin{array}{cc} \overset{\displaystyle H}{\underset{\displaystyle CH_3}{\overset{|}{\underset{|}{C}}}} & \overset{\displaystyle H}{\underset{\displaystyle H}{\overset{|}{\underset{|}{C}}}} \end{array}\right]_n \quad (n> 1000)$$

$(C_3H_6)_n$                         Mol. wt:  >40 000

## 1.3  Chemical and physical properties of the polymer

From Windholz (1976), unless otherwise specified

(a)  Description:  Transparent, colourless-to-yellow solid (Weast,
     1976)

(b)  Melting-point:  Softens at about $155^{\circ}C$, melts at about $165^{\circ}C$

(c)  Density:  0.90-0.92

(d)  Refractive index:  $n_D$ 1.49 (Weast, 1976)

(e)  Spectroscopy data:  Isotactic polypropylene has infra-red
     bands at 1154 and 973 $cm^{-1}$ (Repka, 1967).

(f)  Solubility:  Insoluble in cold organic solvents, although
     swelling occurs;  soluble in hot carbon tetrachloride and hot
     chloroform (Repka, 1967)

(g)  Stability:  Must be stabilized to prevent decomposition in
     sunlight.  Heating in the presence of air or oxygen produces
     carbon dioxide, carbon monoxide, hydrogen, $C_1$-$C_5$ saturated
     aliphatic hydrocarbons and polycyclic aromatic hydrocarbons
     (Le Moan & Chaigneau, 1971).  $C_6$-$C_{18}$ Hydrocarbons and methyl
     alkyl ketones have also been identified (Mitera et al., 1976).

(h)  Reactivity:  Resistant to acids and alkalis;  attacked by
     strong oxidizing agents (e.g., hydrogen peroxide)

## 1.4   Technical products and impurities

Polypropylene can be obtained in three different forms:  isotactic
(all methyl groups are aligned on the same side of the polymer chain),
syndiotactic (the methyl groups alternate regularly from one side of the
polymer chain to the other) and atactic (the methyl groups are arranged
randomly on the chain).  Generally, only the isotactic form of polypropylene is of commercial importance, although most commercial resins contain
about 70% of isotactic and crystalline polymer, 20-30% of isotactic and
amorphous polymer and 5-10% which is atactic and amorphous.

Polypropylene is available in various grades, some of which are copolymers made with low levels of ethylene.  For some uses, resins may be
blended with rubber modifiers or formulated with additives, such as anti-
oxidants  (phenolic oxidation inhibitors, such as 2,6-di-*tert*-butylphenol,
and a hydroperoxide decomposer, e.g., dilauryl-3,3'-thiodipropionate),
ultra-violet stabilizers (hydroxybenzophenone derivatives, hydroxyphenyl-
benzotriazole or phenyl salicylate), pigments, antistatic agents, flame
retardants, nucleating agents (mono-, di- or polycarboxylic acids or their
metal salts) and reinforcing materials (glass fibre and talc).

Residues from the catalysts used in the manufacturing process (titanium
trichloride and aluminium alkyls) remaining in polypropylene cannot exceed
100 mg/kg (ppm) without affecting the quality of the polymer.

In the US, polypropylene which is intended for use in contact with food
must consist of basic polymers, manufactured by the catalytic polymerization
of propylene, with a density of 0.880-0.913;  a melting-point of $160^{\circ}$-$180^{\circ}$C;
6.4 wt % max extractable fraction in $n$-hexane at reflux temperature;  and
9.8 wt % max soluble fraction in xylene at $25^{\circ}$C.  Noncrystalline polypropylene, used to plasticize polyethylene and polypropylene which comes into
contact with food, must also comply with certain required specifications
(US Food and Drug Administration, 1977).

No detailed information on the possible presence of unreacted monomer
in the polymers was available to the Working Group.


## 2.   Production, Use, Occurrence and Analysis

### 2.1  Production and use

#### (a)   Production

A propylene polymerization process, which utilized heterogeneous solid
catalysts and resulted in linear crystalline polypropylene, or isotactic
polypropylene, was first reported in 1955 (Natta *et al.*, 1955).  Commercial
processes for making polypropylene vary; however, the most widely used is
the slurry process.  In this process, the catalyst system is mixed with
propylene and a hydrocarbon diluent (e.g., cyclohexane or $n$-heptane) in the

reactor. After polymerization, the reaction mixture enters a flash tank where unreacted propylene is removed and recycled. The mixture can then be purified by extraction of low-molecular-weight and atactic fractions and then washed with methanol or isopropanol to remove most of the catalyst residues. Alternatively, the mixture leaving the flash tank may enter another reactor for copolymerization with ethylene. The polypropylene resin is then dried and pelletized, during which time additives may be added. Other processes that are used include the solution process (propylene is dissolved in a high-boiling hydrocarbon and polymerization is carried out in solution in high-pressure reactors) and the gas-phase process (in which polymer purification steps are not needed).

Commercial production of polypropylene in the US was first reported in 1958 (US Tariff Commission, 1959). In 1976, ten companies produced 1196 million kg of polypropylene resins, and 178 million kg were exported to the following countries (per cent of total): Brazil (11), Canada (27), France (4), Mexico (18), The Netherlands (5) and the remainder to the Federal Republic of Germany, the Republic of the Phillipines and others (35) (US Department of Commerce, 1977).

Total western Europe production in 1976 was 965 million kg. Among the major producers were the following countries (production in millions of kg): Austria (70), the Federal Republic of Germany (240), France (75), Italy (250), The Netherlands (60), Spain (30) and the UK (235). Exports from western Europe in that year were 380 million kg, and imports 215 million kg. Eastern Europe has an estimated polypropylene production capacity of 285 million kg per year.

Polypropylene has been produced commercially in Japan since 1963. In 1976, ten Japanese companies produced a total of 669 million kg, and 114 million kg were exported.

Worldwide production of polypropylene in 1976 is estimated to have been as much as 3500 million kg.

(b) Use

The pattern of use of polypropylene in the US in 1976 is estimated to have been as follows: injection moulding (48%), fibres (31%), film (8%) and other uses (13%).

Injection moulding applications are in automobile parts, in consumer products, in bottle caps and other closures for containers, in medical products such as disposable hypodermic syringes, in appliances and in many other miscellaneous products.

Polypropylene fibres and filaments are used in carpet backing, carpet face, ropes and cordage, industrial sacking and upholstery fabrics.

Polypropylene film, which is processed by stretching to orient the polymeric chains parallel to the plane of the film, is used for packaging (sometimes laminated to cellophane) of cigarettes, snack food, pet food and other similar products; to laminate restaurant menus; and as dielectric material for capacitors. Unoriented polypropylene film is used primarily to package textiles.

Extruded polypropylene is used for wire and cable insulation and for drinking straws. Blow-moulded polypropylene is mainly used to make bottles for syrups, fruit juices and household chemicals.

In 1975, an estimated 700 thousand kg polypropylene were used in Europe and the same amount in the US in plastic biomaterials for medical applications. Polypropylene is used extensively in surgical applications, as a solid in aortic valves, as a tissue-strengthening mesh (e.g., in hernia cases), as a suture material and to replace finger joints where hinge action is required (Halpern & Karo, 1977).

The use pattern for polypropylene in western Europe in 1976 was as follows: injection moulding (44%), fibres (36%) and other, e.g., film (20%).

The use pattern in Japan in 1976 was as follows: injection moulding (43%), film (25%), fibres (16%), blow moulding (4%) and other (12%).

The US Food and Drug Administration permits the use of polypropylene as a laminate with cellophane, as a component of adhesives and in resinous and polymeric coatings intended for use in contact with food, when it conforms to certain specifications (described above in section 1.4) (US Food and Drug Administration, 1977).

## 2.2  Occurrence

Polypropylene is not known to occur as a natural product.

The content of airborne polymer particulate (2-5 μ) in polypropylene production plants has been reported to vary from 5-40 mg/m$^3$ (Shvedchenko, 1969).

## 2.3  Analysis

No information was available to the Working Group on methods for determining polypropylene residues in foods or elsewhere in the environment.

Simple tests, such as floating, fracturing or burning, have been described for 14 polymers, including polypropylene (Selerowicz, 1976).

Procedures for the chemical characterization of polypropylenes involve flow rate measurements, spectroscopic analysis of chloroform-soluble material, residue on ignition and spectrographic analysis of residues after ignition (Trent *et al.*, 1972).

Differential thermal analysis has also been used to identify various plastics, including polypropylene (Bosch, 1975).

A fast and simple way of identifying fifteen packaging films, including polypropylene, is to treat them with ten different solvents, and to observe the solubility and physical appearance of the film at room temperature and at the boiling points of the solvents (Van Gieson, 1969).

Various polymers, including polypropylene, have been identified by pyrolysing the polymer and identifying the pyrolysis products by: (1) polarography of the bromo and nitro derivatives of the degraded polymer (Dmitrieva *et al.*, 1971); (2) a combination of ultra-violet analysis, colour-forming reactions and thin-layer chromatography (Braun & Nixdorf, 1972); (3) mass spectrometry (Zeman, 1973); and (4) gas chromatography (Audebert, 1968; Fischer, 1967; Iglauer & Bentley, 1974; Okumoto & Takeuchi, 1972; Willmott, 1969).

## 3. Biological Data Relevant to the Evaluation of Carcinogenic Risk to Humans

### 3.1 Carcinogenicity studies in animals

#### Subcutaneous and/or intramuscular administration

Rat: S.c. implantation of 8 polypropylene discs (20 mm diameter and 2 mm thick) to 70 E3 rats (sex not specified) produced a total of 55 local fibrosarcomas, the first appearing after 7 months. The experiment was terminated after 14 months, when 35 animals were still alive. In another group of 60 rats, which received a total of 480 implants, the discs were removed 8 months after the implantation. Two fibrosarcomas were observed at the 9th month, and 32 further local tumours were detected during the following 5 months. The experiment was terminated at 14 months, when 41 animals were still alive (Vollmar & Ott, 1961) [The Working Group noted that no controls were included in these experiments].

A combination of disc implantation (a total of 536 implants) and X-irradiation (3 x 200 rads, 2-3 weeks after implantation) to 67 rats (sex and age not specified) led to reduced survival. When the experiment was terminated after 14 months, a total of 34 local tumours had been found, and 18 animals were still alive. After implantation of a total of 560 samples of polypropylene powder to 70 rats, the first local fibrosarcoma was found 11 months later. When the experiment was terminated after 14 months, 4 rats had developed local sarcomas and 35 were still alive (Vollmar & Ott, 1961) [The Working Group noted that no controls were included in these experiments].

## 3.2 Other relevant biological data

No data were available to the Working Group.

## 3.3 Case reports and epidemiological studies

No data were available to the Working Group.

## 4. Summary of Data Reported and Evaluation

### 4.1 Experimental data

No data on the carcinogenicity or mutagenicity of propylene were available to the Working Group.

Polypropylene was tested in one experiment in rats by subcutaneous implantation of discs or powder; local sarcomas were induced at the site of implantation.

### 4.2 Human data

The massive production of both propylene and polypropylene and the general use of the polymer over the past several decades indicate that exposure of both workers and the general population is common. No epidemiological studies or case reports relating to the carcinogenicity of these compounds were available to the Working Group.

### 4.3 Evaluation

No information was available to the Working Group for evaluating the possible carcinogenic effects of propylene in humans; and the available data on polypropylene do not permit an evaluation of its carcinogenicity. The results of animal implantation experiments, however, indicate a need for experimental and epidemiological studies (see also 'General Remarks on the Substances Considered', p. 35).

## 5. References

Altshuller, A.P., Lonneman, W.A., Sutterfield, F.D. & Kopczynski, S.L.
(1971)  Hydrocarbon composition of the atmosphere of the Los Angeles
Basin-1967.  Environ. Sci. Technol., 5, 1009-1016

Anon. (1972)  Fire Protection Guide on Hazardous Materials, 4th ed.,
Boston, Mass., National Fire Protection Association, pp. 325M-122,
49-193-49-194

Audebert, R. (1968)  Study of polymers by pyrolysis and gas chromtography
(Fr.).  Ann. Chim., 3, 49-66

Baity, F.W., McClenny, W.A. & Bell, J.P. (1974)  Detection of hydrocarbons
by chemiluminescence with active nitrogen at 388 nm.  In:  Preprints of
Papers Presented at the 167th National Meeting, Los Angeles, Ca,
Vol. 14, Washington DC, American Chemical Society, Division of
Environmental Chemistry, pp. 310-312

Bos, R., Guicherit, R. & Hoogeveen, A. (1977)  Distribution of some hydrocarbons in ambient air near Delft and the influence on the formation
of secondary air pollutants.  Sci. total Environ., 7, 269-281

Bosch, K. (1975)  Thermoanalytical identification of plastics (Ger.).
Beitr. Gerichtl. Med., 33, 280-284 [Chem. Abstr., 84, 60332d]

Braddock, J.N. & Bradow, R.L. (1975)  Emissions Patterns of Diesel-powered
Passenger Cars, Paper No. 750682, Warrendale, Pa, Society of Automotive Engineers, Inc.

Braun, D. & Nixdorf, G. (1972)  Separation of synthetic resins for analysis.
4.  Soluble resins with neutral reaction of the pyrolysis products
(Ger.).  Kunststoffe, 62, 318-322

Cox, R.A., Derwent, R.G. & Sandalls, F.J. (1976)  Some Air Pollution
Measurements Made at Harwell, Oxfordshire during 1973-1975,
AERE-R 8324, Harwell, UK, Atomic Energy Research Establishment,
Environmental and Medical Sciences Division

Davis, W.H. & Beach, L.K. (1968)  Propylene.  In:  Kirk, R.E. & Othmer, D.F.,
eds, Encyclopedia of Chemical Technology, 2nd ed., Vol. 16, New York,
John Wiley and Sons, pp. 579, 581, 591

Di Corcia, A. & Samperi, R. (1975)  Rapid separation of $C_4$ hydrocarbons at
$50°C$ by modified gas-solid chromatography.  Anal. Chem., 47, 1853-1854

Dmitrieva, V.N., Shtal, S.S., Kovalev, I.P., Kononenko, L.V. & Bezuglyi, V.D.
(1971)  Identification of polyolefins by a polarographic method (Russ.).
Zavod. Lab., 37, 154-156 [Chem. Abstr., 74, 126310x]

Fischer, W.G. (1967) Pyrolytic gas-chromatography (Ger.). Glas-Instrum.-
    Tech., 11, 562, 567-570, 775-780, 1086-1088, 1091-1095 [Chem. Abstr.,
    68, 78636k]

Giannovario, J.A., Grob, R.L. & Rulon, P.W. (1976) Analysis of trace
    pollutants in the air by means of cryogenic gas chromatography.
    J. Chromatogr., 121, 285-294

Grasselli, J.G. & Ritchey, W.M., eds (1975) CRC Atlas of Spectral Data
    and Physical Constants for Organic Compounds, 2nd ed., Vol. IV,
    Cleveland, Ohio, Chemical Rubber Co., p. 298

Halpern, B.D. & Karo, W. (1977) Medical applications. In: Bikales, N.M.,
    ed., Encyclopedia of Polymer Science and Technology, Plastics, Resins,
    Rubbers, Fibers, Suppl. Vol. 2, New York, Interscience, pp. 369, 387-388

IARC (1976) IARC Monographs on the Evaluation of Carcinogenic Risk of
    Chemicals to Man, 11, Cadmium, Nickel, Some Expoxides, Miscellaneous
    Industrial Chemicals and General Considerations on Volatile Anaesthetics,
    Lyon, pp. 191-199

IARC (1977) IARC Monographs on the Evaluation of the Carcinogenic Risk of
    Chemicals to Man, 15, Some Fumigants, the Herbicides 2,4-D and 2,4,5-T,
    Chlorinated Dibenzodioxins and Miscellaneous Industrial Chemicals,
    Lyon, pp. 223-243

Iglauer, N. & Bentley, F.F. (1974) Pyrolysis GLC for the rapid identifi-
    cation of organic polymers. J. chromatogr. Sci., 12, 23-33

Inoue, K., Oka, K., Taguchi, K., Tajima, N., Tsujino, Y., Nishikawa, Y.,
    Hatanaka, H. & Yoshimura, K. (1975) Concentrations of ambient light
    hydrocarbons in Sakai seaside industrial and suburban areas (Jap.).
    Taiki Osen Kenkyu, 10, 121-134 [Chem. Abstr., 84, 94853q]

Intersociety Committee (1972) Tentative method of analysis for $C_1$ through
    $C_5$ atmospheric hydrocarbons. In: Methods of Air Sampling and Analysis,
    Washington DC, American Public Health Association, pp. 131-138

Jeltes, R. & Burghardt, E. (1972) Automatic gas chromatographic measurement
    of $C_1$-$C_5$ hydrocarbons in air. Atmos. Environ., 6, 793-805

Katzman, H. & Libby, W.F. (1975) Hydrocarbon emissions from jet engines
    operated at simulated high-altitude supersonic flight conditions.
    Atmos. Environ., 9, 839-842

Kim, A.G. & Douglas, L.J. (1973) Gases Desorbed from Five Coals of Low
    Gas Content: Report of Investigations 7768, Washington DC, Bureau of
    Mines

Kreuzer, L.B., Kenyon, N.D. & Patel, C.K.N. (1972)  Air pollution:  sensi-
    tive detection of ten pollutant gases by carbon monoxide and carbon
    dioxide lasers.  Science, 177, 347-349

Lamb, A., Larson, K.A. & Tollefson, E.L. (1973)  A gas chromatographic
    method for exhaust gas analysis.  J. Air Pollut. Control Assoc., 23,
    200-202

Lamontagne, R.A., Smith, W.D. & Swinnerton, J.W. (1975)  $C_1$-$C_3$ hydrocarbons
    and chlorophyll $a$ concentrations in the equatorial Pacific Ocean.  In:
    Gibb, T.R.P., ed., Analytical Methods in Oceanography, Advances in
    Chemistry Series 147, Washington DC, American Chemical Society,
    pp. 163-171

Leigh, D. & Lynaugh, N. (1974)  Qualitative and quantitative analysis of
    dissolved gas by gas chromatography-mass spectrometry.  In:
    West, A.R., ed., Advances in Mass Spectrometry, Vol. 6, Barking,
    Essex, Applied Sciences Publisher Ltd, pp. 463-470

Le Moan, G. & Chaigneau, M. (1971)  Pyrolysis of plastics.  V.  Poly-
    propylene (Fr.).  Ann. Pharm. Fr., 29, 259-262 [Chem. Abstr., 75,
    64532f]

Leonard, M.J., Fisher, E.L., Brunelle, M.F. & Dickinson, J.E. (1976)
    Effects of the motor vehicle control program on hydrocarbon concen-
    trations in the central Los Angeles atmosphere.  J. Air Pollut. Control
    Assoc., 26, 359-363

McAuliffe, C.D. (1976)  Surveillance of the marine environment for hydro-
    carbons.  Marine Sci. Commun., 2, 13-42

Mitera, J., Michal, J., Kubat, J. & Kubelka, V. (1976)  Analysis of
    thermooxidation products of polypropylene and polyethylene by gas
    chromatography/mass spectrometry.  Fresenius' Z. anal. Chem., 281,
    23-27 [Chem. Abstr., 85, 160933q]

Natta, G., Pino, P., Corradini, P., Danusso, F., Mantica, E., Mazzanti, G.
    & Moraglio, G. (1955)  Crystalline high polymers of $\alpha$-olefins.
    J. Am. chem. Soc., 77, 1708-1710

Okumoto, T. & Takeuchi, T. (1972)  Rapid characterization of polymeric
    materials by pyrolysis-gas chromatography (Jap.).  Nippon Kagaku
    Kaishi, 1, 71-78 [Chem. Abstr., 76, 141459n]

O'Mara, M.M. (1974)  The combustion products from synthetic and natural
    products - Part 1:  Wood.  J. Fire Flammability, 5, 34-53

Perry, R.H. & Chilton, C.H., eds (1973)  Chemical Engineers' Handbook,
    5th ed., New York, McGraw-Hill, p. 3-62

Prager, B., Jacobson, P., Schmidt, P. & Stern, D., eds (1918) Beilsteins Handbuch der Organischen Chemie, 4th ed., Vol. 1, Syst. No. 11, Berlin, Springer, p. 196

Quickert, N., Findlay, W.J. & Monkman, J.L. (1975) Modification of a chemiluminescent ozone monitor for the measurement of gaseous unsaturated hydrocarbons. Sci. total Environ., 3, 323-328

Repka, B.C., Jr (1967) Olefin polymers - polypropylene. In: Kirk, R.E. & Othmer, D.F., eds, Encyclopedia of Chemical Technology, 2nd ed., Vol. 14, New York, John Wiley and Sons, pp. 282-309

Rochkind, M.M. (1967) Infrared analysis of multicomponent gas mixtures. Anal. Chem., 39, 567-574

Sarkar, M.K. & Haselden, G.G. (1975) Separation of a mixture of permanent gases and light hydrocarbons by sub-ambient temperature programming of a single Porapak Q column. J. Chromatogr., 104, 425-428

Selerowicz, A. (1976) Simple methods for the identification of thermo-plastics. Mechanik, 49, 30-31

Shvedchenko, V.S. (1969) Hygienic characteristics of working conditions in polypropylene production (Russ.). In: Proceedings of the Hygienic Problems in Industrial Production of Polymeric Materials, Moscow, Scientific Research Institute of Hygiene, pp. 5-9 [Chem. Abstr., 75, 132652x]

Swinnerton, J.W. & Lamontagne, R.A. (1974) Oceanic distribution of low-molecular-weight hydrocarbons. Baseline measurements. Environ. Sci. Technol., 8, 657-663

Swinnerton, J.W. & Linnenbom, V.J. (1967) Determination of the $C_1$ to $C_4$ hydrocarbons in sea water by gas chromatography. J. Gas Chromatogr., 5, 570-572

Toxicology Information Program (1976) Carcinogenesis bioassay of propylene. Tox-Tips, 1(7), 13

Trent, D.M., Rinehart, R.W. & Ball, E. (1972) Chemical characterization of polypropylenes. Soc. Plastics Engineers, Technical Papers, Part I, 18, 378-391

US Department of Commerce (1977) US Exports, Schedule B Commodity Groupings, Schedule B Commodity by Country, FT410/December, Bureau of the Census, Washington DC, US Government Printing Office, pp. 2-80, 2-123

US Food and Drug Administration (1977) Food and drugs. US Code Fed. Regul., Title 21, parts 175.105, 175.300, 177.1200, 177.1520, pp. 438, 446, 452, 456, 504, 506, 520-526

US International Trade Commission (1977) Synthetic Organic Chemicals, US
    Production and Sales, 1976, USITC Publication 833, Washington DC,
    US Government Printing Office, pp. 27, 31

US Tariff Commission (1945) Synthetic Organic Chemicals, US Production
    and Sales, 1941-43, Report No. 153, Second Series, Washington DC,
    US Government Printing Office, p. 129

US Tariff Commission (1959) Synthetic Organic Chemicals, US Production
    and Sales, 1958, Report No. 205, Second Series, Washington DC,
    US Government Printing Office, p. 119

Vančura, V. & Stotzky, G. (1976) Gaseous and volatile exudates from
    germinating seeds and seedlings. Can. J. Bot., 54, 518-532

Van Gieson, P. (1969) Here's a quick, easy way to identify films.
    Package Eng., 14, 76-77 [Chem. Abstr., 71, 71274u]

Vollmar, J. & Ott, G. (1961) Experimental tumour formation by surgical
    plastics (Ger.). Langenbecks Arch. Klin. Chir., 298, 729-736

Weast, R.C., ed. (1976) CRC Handbook of Chemistry and Physics, 57th ed.,
    Cleveland, Ohio, Chemical Rubber Co., pp. C-463, C-794

Westberg, H.H., Rasmussen, R.A. & Holdren, M. (1974) Gas chromatographic
    analysis of ambient air for light hydrocarbons using a chemically
    bonded stationary phase. Anal. Chem., 46, 1852-1854

Willmott, F.W. (1969) Pyrolysis-gas chromatography of polyolefins.
    J. chromatogr. Sci., 7, 101-108

Windholz, M., ed. (1976) The Merck Index, 9th ed., Rahway, NJ, Merck &
    Co., pp. 985, 1016-1017

Zeman, A. (1973) Identification of some commercially available polymers
    by thermal degradation in a mass spectrometer (Ger.). Angew. Makromol.
    Chem., 31, 1-24

& Moran, 1975). In mid-1977, one major US company began using a process in which styrene was produced as a coproduct with propylene oxide. Ethylbenzene is first oxidized to ethylbenzene peroxide, which is reacted with propylene to yield propylene oxide and α-methylphenyl carbinol. The α-methylphenyl carbinol is then dehydrated to styrene. This process is also used in Japan and Spain.

Commercial production of styrene in the US was first reported in 1938 (US Tariff Commission, 1939). Thirteen US companies reported production of 2124 million kg styrene in 1975 (US International Trade Commission, 1977a) and of 2864 million kg in 1976 (US International Trade Commission, 1977b). US imports of styrene were 11.2 million kg in 1976, 99.9% of which came from Canada (US Department of Commerce, 1977a). The US exported over 432 million kg in 1976 to the following countries (per cent of total): Australia (6.0), Belgium (7.4), Brazil (15.6), France (2.0), Hong Kong (6.0), Italy (3.8), Mexico (6.1), The Netherlands (33), Republic of Korea (2.3), Spain (3.9), Taiwan (4.2), Venezuela (3.2), and at least 10 other countries (6.5) (US Department of Commerce, 1977b).

Canadian production of styrene in 1974 was 146 million kg, and Mexico produced 30 million kg.

Total western Europe production in 1976 amounted to 2340 million kg; among the major producers were the following countries (production in millions of kg): the Federal Republic of Germany (860), France (270), Italy (325), Spain (60) and the UK (340). Exports from western Europe in that year were 310 million kg, and imports were 400 million kg. Eight European countries that do not manufacture styrene imported the following quantities (millions of kg) in 1975: Austria (8), Denmark (1), Finland (16), Greece (4), Norway (4), Portugal (2), Sweden (20) and Switzerland (4).

Styrene has been produced commercially in Japan since 1959. In 1976, nine companies produced about 1090 million kg styrene; imports amounted to 13 million kg and exports were 58 million kg.

Three companies in India are believed to manufacture styrene; and the following countries are believed to have at least one styrene manufacturer: Argentina, Australia, Brazil, Bulgaria, Czechoslovakia, the German Democratic Republic, the People's Republic of China, Poland, Rumania, The Republic of South Africa, the USSR and Yugoslavia.

Worldwide production of styrene in 1977 is estimated to have been 7000 million kg.

(b) Use

About 87% of the styrene used in the US in 1976 was in the production of plastics and resins: polystyrene resins, 61%; acrylonitrile-butadiene-styrene terpolymer (ABS) and styrene-acrylonitrile copolymer (SAN) resins,

11%; styrene-butadiene copolymer resins, 8%; and unsaturated polyesters, 7%. About 11% was used to make styrene-butadiene rubber (SBR), and the remaining 2% was used in miscellaneous applications.

For detailed descriptions of the uses of these polymers, see polystyrene, p. 248, ABS and SAN copolymers, pp. 95 and 99, and styrene-butadiene copolymers (including SBR), p. 255.

Glass fibre-reinforced, unsaturated polyester resins made from styrene are used primarily in construction materials and boats. Styrene is also used in the synthesis of the styrene-divinylbenzene copolymers, which are used as a matrix for ion-exchange resins, and in the production of styrenated oils and styrene oxide (for information on the uses of styrene oxide, see monograph, p. 275).

In western Europe, 71% of the styrene used in 1974 was in plastics and resins (polystyrene resins, 63%; ABS and SAN resins, 8%); production of SBR and lattices used 11%, and the remaining 18% was used in miscellaneous applications (e.g., ethylene-propylene copolymers).

In 1976, the Japanese use pattern for styrene was as follows: polystyrene (65%), SBR (13%), ABS (12%), unsaturated polyesters (6%) and other applications (4%).

Worldwide, an estimated 62% of the styrene produced in 1974 was used in the manufacture of polystyrene (including expandable polystyrene); 13% in ABS and SAN resins; 17% in SBR; and 8% in other applications.

The US Food and Drug Administration permits the use of styrene: (1) as a synthetic flavouring substance and adjuvant; (2) as a cross-linking agent in polyester resins; and (3) in rubber articles (5 wt % max), when they are intended for use in contact with food. Styrene copolymers with acrylic or methacrylic monomers may be used in semi-rigid and rigid acrylic- and vinyl chloride-based plastics; and certain styrene copolymers (e.g., those with maleic anhydride) may be used in paper and paperboard coatings that are intended for use in contact with food. Additional styrene copolymers permitted in products in contact with food include styrene-divinyl-benzene cross-linked resins, styrene-maleic anhydride copolymers and styrene-methyl methacrylate copolymers used in plastics. The amounts present may not exceed those reasonably required to produce the intended effect (US Food and Drug Administration, 1977).

The US Occupational Safety and Health Administration's health standards for exposure to air contaminants require that an employee's exposure to styrene not exceed an eight-hour time-weighted average of 100 ppm (420 mg/m$^3$) in the workplace air in any eight-hour workshift of a forty-hour work week. During any work shift, an employee's exposure to styrene may not exceed a ceiling concentration limit of 200 ppm (840 mg/m$^3$), except for a time period of five minutes in any three-hour period when the concentration may be as high as 600 ppm (2500 mg/m$^3$) (US Occupational Safety and Health Administration, 1976).

Work environment hygiene standards (all in terms of eight-hour time-weighted averages) reported by Winell (1975), for styrene are as follows: Czechoslovakia, 200 mg/m$^3$ (47.5 ppm); the Federal Republic of Germany, 420 mg/m$^3$ (100 ppm); the German Democratic Republic, 200 mg/m$^3$ (47.5 ppm); and Sweden 210 mg/m$^3$ (50 ppm). In the USSR, the maximum allowable concentration (MAC) of styrene is 5 mg/m$^3$ (1.2 ppm); the organoleptic limit for styrene in drinking-water is 0.1 mg/l (Stöfen, 1973).

## 2.2 Occurrence

Styrene is not known to occur as a natural product.

### (a) Styrene-derived polymers

Styrene was one of eleven products formed when styrene-acrylonitrile copolymer was pyrolysed under nitrogen at 500°C (Braun & Disselhoff, 1972).

### (b) Air

Styrene has been detected in the ambient air: (1) at a level of 0.2 ppb (0.84 µg/m$^3$) in Nagoya, Japan (Hoshika, 1977); (2) at a concentration of 0.1 ppb (0.4 µg/m$^3$), with a maximum of 0.7 ppb (2.9 µg/m$^3$), in Delft, The Netherlands (Bos *et al.*, 1977); (3) in the streets of Leningrad, USSR (Ioffe *et al.*, 1977); and (4) in Tuscaloosa and in a national forest in Alabama (Holzer *et al.*, 1977).

### (c) Water

Styrene has been detected at a concentration of 1 µg/l (ppb) in the Scheldt River in The Netherlands, in the Kanawha River in West Virginia (Eurocop-Cost, 1976) and in effluent discharged from petroleum-refining (31 µg/l), chemical (30 µg/l), rubber (2.6-3 µg/l) and textile manufacturing plants in the US (Eurocop-Cost, 1976; Shackelford & Keith, 1976).

Styrene has also been detected in finished drinking-water in the US at concentrations of less than 1 µg/l (Safe Drinking Water Committee, 1977; US Environmental Protection Agency, 1975), and specifically in commercial, charcoal-filtered drinking-water in New Orleans, Louisiana (Dowty *et al.*, 1975).

### (d) Occupational exposure

Styrene has been detected in the workplace air in concentrations of 0.8-570 mg/m$^3$ (0.2-136 ppm) during the fabrication of glass-reinforced, plastic pipe joints (National Institute for Occupational Safety and Health, 1977a); and of 105-605 mg/m$^3$ (25-144 ppm) (time-weighted average), during the production of plastic boat components (National Institute for Occupational Safety and Health, 1977b). It has been detected in workplace atmospheres during (1) the curing of tires, in the US, in concentrations of 256-613 µg/m$^3$ (61-146 ppb) (Rappaport, 1975); (2) the production from polymeric materials of articles used in machine construction, in the USSR (Martynenko, 1973); and (3) the production of fibre-reinforced laminated plastics, in Czechoslovakia (Cakrtova & Vanecek, 1974).

Styrene has been detected in concentrations of 0.1-1.2 µg/g (ppb) in the subcutaneous fat tissue of styrene polymerization workers in the US (Wolff et al., 1977).

(e)    Food

Styrene was tentatively identified in a commercial hickory-wood smoke flavour (Hruza et al., 1974) and in food and water stored in a refrigerator with a plastic interior (Akhlyustina et al., 1973).

It has been found in yogurt packaged in polystyrene containers, at concentrations of 2.5-34.6 µg/kg (Withey, 1976). The content of styrene in the yogurt increased during the time between packaging and sampling: 20.4 µg/kg were found after 5 days, and 77.6 µg/kg after 56 days. In other products, 59.2 µg/kg were found in butter-fat cream after 24 days, 9.3 µg/kg in cottage cheese after 27 days, 17.2 µg/kg in homogenized milk after 19 days and 22.7 µg/kg in honey after 120 days (Withey & Collins, 1978).

(f)    Other

Six aromatic hydrocarbons, including styrene, were detected in the sidestream smoke of American-blend cigarettes (Jermini et al., 1976). Styrene has been detected in concentrations of 18.0 µg/cigarette in the smoke of American domestic, filter blend cigarettes (Baggett et al., 1974).

2.3  Analysis

The International Union of Pure and Applied Chemistry has adopted a colorimetric method for determining styrene in air, with a limit of detection of 840 mg/m$^3$ (200 ppm) (Gage et al., 1962). It can also be determined in air by collection on charcoal, extraction with carbon disulphide and gas chromatography, with an 85-90% average efficiency in the range of 210-840 mg/m$^3$ (50-200 ppm) (Burnett, 1976). In another study, dimethylformamide was used for the extraction, with similar efficiency (Kalliokoski & Pfäffli, 1975). Concentrations of 1.7 µg/m$^3$ to 1.7 mg/m$^3$ (0.4 ppb to 0.4 ppm) styrene in ambient air can be determined by collection on charcoal, heat desorption and gas chromatographic analysis (Parkes et al., 1976). It has been identified by gas chromatography-mass spectrometry in volatile gases released during rubber vulcanization, in the 0.42 mg/m$^3$ (0.1 ppm) range (Rappaport, 1975; Rappaport & Fraser, 1976). Gas chromatography with electron-capture detection was used on one sample of urban air to determine styrene as its dibromide derivative at a level of 0.8 µg/m$^3$ (0.2 ppb); the limit of detection was about 0.01 ng per sample, about 500 times more sensitive than flame-ionization detection (Hoshika, 1977).

Gas chromatography can be used to determine styrene in waste-waters in concentrations of 4.5-63 μg/l (ppb) (Pakhomova & Berendeeva, 1974), and lower levels have been measured after extraction with freon and concentration of the sample in a Kuderna-Danish apparatus (Austern *et al.*, 1975).

Residual styrene in styrene polymers can be determined by gas chromatography: (1) by a headspace method, with a limit of detection of 1 mg/kg (ppm) (Steichen, 1976); (2) with a limit of detection of 10 mg/kg (ppm) (Kleshcheva *et al.*, 1971): (3) in concentrations of 0.03-1.0% (Swiatecka & Zowall, 1975); and (4) with a limit of detection of 1 mg/kg (ppm) after extraction in water vapour and concentration in a suitable solvent (Zizin *et al.*, 1974). Gas chromatography can also be used to determine styrene migrating from medical polymers to water (Markelov & Semenenko, 1976) and from packaging materials to foods (Davies, 1974). Gas chromatography with flame-ionization detection and mass spectrometry has been used to study factors that affect the transfer of styrene from polystyrene containers to milk, which increases with temperature and storage time (Yamashita *et al.*, 1976). This same method has been used to determine styrene and related hydrocarbons in the subcutaneous fat of workers in a styrene polymerization plant; the limit of detection was 50 μg/kg (ppb) (Wolff *et al.*, 1977).

Thin-layer chromatography has been used to determine styrene as a residual starting material in the laboratory preparation of the antibiotics, synthomycin and levomycetin; the limit of detection was 100 μg per sample (Dolgopolov & Lishcheta, 1971).

Benzene extraction followed by polarography has been used to determine styrene in sewage from a plant producing plastic stabilizers (Meshkova & Dmitrieva, 1974) and in industrial effluent from polymer production, in the concentration range of 0.2-5.0 mg/l (ppm) (Dmitrieva *et al.*, 1975).

Raman spectral analysis has been used to determine residual styrene in commercial styrene-butadiene latexes at concentrations in the range of 0.6-12.4 wt %. The Raman results agree with those obtained by high-pressure liquid chromatography within 0.25% (Wancheck & Wolfram, 1976).

Ultra-violet spectrophotometric methods using absorption at 247 or 245 nm have been used to determine styrene in polymers and copolymers, with a limit of detection of 0.01-0.02 mg/l (Petrova *et al.*, 1974), and in biological fluids of experimental animals, with a limit of detection of 1000 ng per sample (Murav'eva & Smolyar, 1974).

Styrene has also been determined in benzene extracts of 9 samples of styrene-acrylonitrile copolymers by titrimetry using bromination (Roy, 1977).

3.  Biological Data Relevant to the Evaluation

of Carcinogenic Risk to Humans

## 3.1  Carcinogenicity studies in animals[1]

### Pre- and postnatal exposure

Mouse:  Twenty-nine pregnant $O_{20}$ mice were each given a single treatment of 1350 mg/kg bw styrene (99% pure) dissolved in olive oil by stomach
tube on the 17th day of gestation.  A control group of pregnant animals
received olive oil alone.  Neonatal mortality of the offspring was 43%,
compared with 22% in those of olive-oil treated controls.  The same amount
of styrene was then administered weekly by stomach tube to 45 male and 39
female progeny from weaning up to 16 weeks of age, at which time the treatment was stopped because of high mortality (64% alive at 20 weeks).  The
experiment was terminated at 100 weeks when all the animals had died.  No
differences in tumour incidences were found between mothers treated with
styrene and those given olive oil.  In the progeny, which received weekly
treatments, lung tumours (adenomas and adenocarcinomas) were found in
20/23 males and 32/32 females, compared with 8/19 and 14/21 olive oil-
treated controls ($P<0.01$, $P<0.01$) and 34/53 and 25/47 untreated controls
($P>0.05$, $P<0.001$).  No differences in tumour incidences at sites other than
lung were seen in the progeny, as compared with styrene-treated or olive-oil
or untreated controls (Ponomarkov & Tomatis, 1979).

Fifteen pregnant C57 black mice were each given a single treatment of
300 mg/kg bw styrene dissolved in olive oil by stomach tube on the 17th
day of gestation.  A control group of pregnant animals received olive oil
alone.  Neonatal mortality of the offspring was 37%.  The same amount of
styrene was then given weekly by stomach tube to 27 male and 27 female
progeny from weaning up to 120 weeks of age, at which time the survivors,
15 males and 12 females, were killed.  In mothers treated with single doses
of styrene, lymphomas were observed in 10/12 animals, compared with 3/5
olive-oil treated controls.  In male progeny treated weekly, liver tumours
(hepatocellular carcinomas) were found in 3/24 animals, compared with 1/12
olive-oil treated and 1/47 untreated controls (both hepatocellular adenomas)
($P>0.05$).  The incidences of tumours at other sites, both in mothers and
progeny, were no different from those in olive-oil or untreated controls
(Ponomarkov & Tomatis, 1979).

---

[1]The Working Group was aware of studies in progress to assess the
carcinogenicity of styrene by oral administration in mice and rats and by
inhalation exposure in rats (IARC, 1978a).

Rat: Twenty-one female BDIV rats were each given a single treatment of 1350 mg/kg bw styrene dissolved in olive oil by stomach tube on the 17th day of gestation, A control group of pregnant rats received olive oil alone. Neonatal mortality of the offspring was 10%. Subsequently, doses of 500 mg/kg bw were administered weekly by stomach tube to 73 male and 71 female progeny from weaning up to 120 weeks of age, at which time the survivors, 8 males and 20 females, were killed. Although 3 stomach tumours (adenoma, fibrosarcoma, carcinosarcoma) and 1 hepatocellular adenoma were seen in styrene-treated animals, the total tumour incidences in styrene-treated rats and controls were not statistically different (Ponomarkov & Tomatis, 1979).

## 3.2  Other relevant biological data

### (a)  Experimental systems

The toxicity and metabolism of styrene have been reviewed (Leibman, 1975).

### Toxic effects

The oral $LD_{50}$ of styrene in rats is approximately 5.0 g/kg bw (Union Carbide Corporation, 1957; Wolf et al., 1956); the $LD_{50}$ by i.p. injection is 2-3 g/kg bw (Ohtsuji & Ikeda, 1971).

The $LC_{50}$ concentration in mice for a 2-hour exposure was 21 g/m$^3$ (5000 ppm), and that for a 4-hour exposure in rats, 11.8 g/m$^3$ (2800 ppm) (Shugaev, 1969). Exposure of rats and guinea-pigs to styrene vapours in air at a level of 10-12 g/m$^3$ (approximately 2600 ppm) for 8 hours produced toxic effects; this concentration was toxic to 100% of rats after 21 hours' exposure. Exposure to 46 g/m$^3$ (11 000 ppm) for 30-60 min was acutely toxic (Spencer et al., 1942). Exposure to 16.8 g/m$^3$ (4000 ppm) killed 2/6 rabbits after 4 hours (Union Carbide Corporation, 1957).

When rats, guinea-pigs, rabbits and monkeys were exposed to styrene at concentration of 5.6-6.3 g/m$^3$ (1300 ppm) for 8 hours daily on 5 days a week for 6 months, 10% of guinea-pigs died of pulmonary irritation within a few days, and there was a slight increase in the weight of the liver and kidney of rats. Haematological parameters were not altered (Spencer et al., 1942).

Acute deaths in rats and guinea-pigs were due to injury of the central nervous system; delayed deaths were due to pneumonia, following initial lung irritation, and the lungs showing congestion, haemorrhage, oedema and exudation. The kidneys and liver also exhibited congestion (Spencer et al., 1942; Wilson et al., 1948).

Exposure of rats by inhalation to 1.3 mg/1 styrene (300 ppm) for 2-11 weeks for 6 hours daily on 6 days per week caused a marked accumulation of styrene in brain and perinephric fat. From the 9th week onwards, increased activity of lysosomal acid proteinase in brain was detected (Savolainen & Pfäffli, 1977).

I.p. administration of 150-1000 mg/kg bw styrene to mice, rats, hamsters and guinea-pigs caused a depression of the hepatic nonprotein sulphydryl content. Mouse was the most sensitive and rat the most resistant species (Vainio & Mäkinen, 1977).

In rats, daily i.p. administration of 3 or 6 doses of 500 mg/kg bw styrene doubled the activities of microsomal *para*-nitroanisole *O*-demethylase, epoxide hydratase and UDP glucuronosyl transferase (Parkki *et al.*, 1976).

Fourteen hours after single i.p. injections of 10, 100 or 500 mg/kg bw styrene to rats, the Michaëlis-Menten rate constants of benzo($a$)pyrene hydroxylase and aldrin epoxidase of liver microsomes were significantly reduced as compared with control animals; that of styrene oxide hydratase was reduced 6 hours after injection. The catalytic properties of styrene oxide synthetase were not modified (Lambotte-Vandepaer *et al.*, 1978).

I.p. doses of 2-3 g/kg bw styrene caused hepatic necrosis in hamsters, as observed by increased serum alanine aminotransferase activity and histological examination. The acute lethality was increased by pretreatment with phenobarbital (Parkki *et al.*, 1979).

### Embryotoxicity and teratogenicity

Doses of styrene ranging from 46-90 mg/kg egg injected into the yolk sac of fresh, fertile chicken eggs had no toxic effect (McLaughlin *et al.*, 1963, 1964). When injected on the fourth day of incubation, it had an $LD_{50}$ of 40 µmol/embryo; malformations were found in up to 20% of treated embryos, depending on dose and time of injection (Vainio *et al.*, 1977). Doses of 1.5-5 mg/m$^3$ (350-1100 ppm) inhaled by rats during the whole of pregnancy had an embryotoxic effect (Ragule, 1974).

### Absorption, distribution and excretion

The blood of rats was essentially cleared of radioactivity within 24 hours after s.c. injection of ($\beta$-$^{14}$C)styrene in arachis oil, and about 85% had been excreted. Most of the radioactivity was excreted *via* the urine, but about 12% of the $\beta$-carbon was oxidized to $CO_2$. About 3% of styrene was exhaled unchanged from the lungs (Danishefsky & Willhite, 1954).

Three to six hours after i.p. injection of $^{14}$C-styrene to rats, the levels of radioactivity in liver, brain, kidney and duodenum were higher than those in blood, lungs and spinal cord (Savolainen & Vainio, 1977).

### Metabolism

Styrene is converted metabolically to styrene oxide (see monograph, p. 275) (Leibman & Ortiz, 1969). Both styrene and styrene oxide are metabolized in the liver and in a number of extrahepatic tissues, such as kidney, intestine, lung and skin (Leibman & Ortiz, 1968; Ryan *et al.*, 1976).

The metabolism of styrene oxide proceeds *via* styrene glycol to mandelic acid, phenylglyoxylic acid and finally hippuric acid. 4-Vinylphenol and 1- or 2-phenylethanol have also been reported. Styrene oxide forms conjugates with glutathione, leading to the excretion of *N*-acetyl-*S*-(2-hydroxyphenylethyl)-L-cysteine (hydroxyphenylethyl mercapturic acid), and many of the other metabolites are excreted as glucuronides (Leibman, 1975).

Styrene metabolism was stimulated by phenobarbital (Ohtsuji & Ikeda, 1971) and suppressed by coadministration of toluene (Ikeda *et al.*, 1972). SKF 525-A (2-diethylaminoethyl 2,2-diphenyl propylacetate), a potent inhibitor of hepatic cytochrome P-450-linked oxidation (Gillette, 1963), depressed the metabolism of styrene. When SKF 525-A was given intraperitoneally to rats immediately before the styrene injection, the amount of urinary metabolites excreted during the first 2 hours was 50% of that excreted by animals given styrene alone (Ohtsuji & Ikeda, 1971).

### Mutagenicity and other short-term tests

Styrene induced reverse mutations in *Salmonella typhimurium* TA1535 and TA100 in the presence of a 9000 x *g* supernatant of liver of rats pretreated with Clophen C or Aroclor 1254; it was not mutagenic to TA1537, TA1538 or TA98 (de Meester *et al.*, 1977; Vainio *et al.*, 1976). Styrene was not mutagenic in a spot test with various strains of *S. typhimurium* without metabolic activation (Milvy & Garro, 1976).

It did not induce forward mutations in the yeast *Schizosaccharomyces pombe*, even in the presence of mouse-liver microsomes. In the host-mediated assay, using male Swiss albino mice, 1000 mg/kg styrene increased gene conversion frequency in *Saccharomyces cerevisiae* strain D4 (Loprieno *et al.*, 1976).

Styrene did not increase the frequency of mutation to 8-azaguanine resistance in cultured V79 Chinese hamster cells in the absence of metabolic activation (Loprieno *et al.*, 1976).

When male rats were exposed by inhalation to 1.3 g/m$^3$ (300 ppm) styrene in air for 2-11 weeks for 6 hours/day on 5 days/week, an increase in the frequency of chromosomal aberrations in bone-marrow cells (8-12% in the exposed group, 1-6% in the controls) was observed between 9 and 11 weeks (Meretoja *et al.*, 1978).

### (b)  Humans

Toxic effects of styrene in humans are compiled in Table 1. Neurological and psychological disturbances are among the most frequent observed effects.

Central nervous malformations were reported in 2 infants whose mothers were exposed occupationally to styrene polyester resin and organic peroxides. A third case has been reported in which the mother was exposed at home during pregnancy to the same compounds (Holmberg, 1977).

Table 1

Toxic effects of styrene in humans

| Reference | Number examined | Process | Estimated dose[1] | Effects |
|---|---|---|---|---|
| Barsotti et al., 1952 | 41 | Monomer manufacture, polymerization | 24–196 ppm x 1.5 yr | Slight leucopenia, relative lymphocytosis, irritation, decreased night vision |
| Bardoděj et al., 1960 | 58 | Resin | 50 ppm x 2 yr | Fatigue and sleepiness increased |
| Zielhuis, 1961 | 50 | Resin | Unknown x 2 yr | Decrease in γ-globulin, irritation, drowsiness |
| Katz, 1962 | 526 | Rubber | ≈20 ppm x 2 yr | Hepatomegaly (30%), splenomegaly (6%), increased bilirubin (35%), leucopenia (30%), reticulocytosis (59%) |
| Klimková-Deutschová, 1962 | 35 | Resin | 40–130 ppm x 1.9 yr | Sleepiness |
| Orlova & Solov'eva, 1962 | – | Rubber | – | Hepatomegaly (35%), mildly pronounced leucopenia, lymphocytosis, tendency to thrombocytopenia and reticulocytosis |
| Pratt-Johnson, 1964 | 1 | Resin | Unknown x 5 yr | Retrobulbar neuritis, reverting after one year |
| Ermolova et al., 1965 | 400 | Rubber | Unknown x 5–10 yr | Toxic hepatitis, leucopenia, lymphocytosis, monocytosis and reticulocytosis, increased irritability of autonomic nervous system |
| Šímko et al., 1966 | 101 males, 27 females | Resin | 170 ppm x 1.8 yr (mean) | Skin diseases; neurasthenic syndrome in one third of those exposed longer than 3 years |
| Hülzl et al., 1967 | 55 | Resin | 50–100 ppm x unstated | Weltmann reaction prolonged (48%), headache, fatigue, sleepiness |
| Araki et al., 1971 | 1 | Resin | Unknown x 14 yr | Skin atrophy, neurogenic muscular atrophy, anxiety reactions, abnormal electromyogram |
| Chmielewski et al., 1973 | 101 | Resin | 100–500 ppm x unknown | Higher glucose tolerance |
| Klimková-Deutschová et al., 1973 | 105 | Resin | Unknown | Headache, sleepiness, peripheral neuropathy, deteriorating EEG |

| Reference | Number | Material | Exposure | Effects |
|---|---|---|---|---|
| Oltramare et al., 1974 | 9 | Resin | 10-560 ppm x 1-8 yr | Lymphocytosis, conjunctivitis |
| Hrubá et al., 1975 | 122 | Resin | Unknown x 0.2-6 yr | Pseudoneurasthenic symptoms (headache, sleep disorders, increased fatigue), EEG abnormalities |
| Axelson, 1976 | 17 | Resin | <150 and >150 ppm x unstated | Increased reaction times in workers exposed to >150 ppm |
| Chmielewski & Renke, 1976 | 101 21 | Resin Resin | 100-300 ppm x 1 yr 300 ppm x 10 yr | Lengthening of the coagulation time, reduced prothrombin ratio, reduction in the number of platelets |
| Dolmierski et al., 1976 | 61 | Resin | 70 ppm x 1-10 yr | Pathological EEGs in 35 cases; moderate encephalopathy in 6 |
| Lindström et al., 1976 | 98 | Resin | 50-100 ppm x 0.5-14 yr | Disturbances in visuomotor accuracy and psychomotor performance |
| Lorimer et al., 1976a,b | 494 | Production of polystyrene | 60-100 ppm x 0.1-20 yr | Significant differences between the high and low exposure groups with regard to history of prenarcotic symptoms, acute lower respiratory symptoms, prevalence of $FEV_1/FVC < 75\%$, and elevated GGTP |
| Seppäläinen & Härkönen, 1976 | 96 | Resin | 50-100 ppm x 0.5-14 yr | Abnormal EEGs (24%), more in high-exposure group |
| Bergman & Lindberg, 1977 | 81 | Resin | <20 and >20 ppm x unknown | Impaired memory, lower haemoglobin concentration |
| Härkönen, 1977 Härkönen et al., 1978[2] | 98 | Resin | 50-100 ppm x 0.5-14 yr | Symptoms of fatigue, difficulties in concentration, symptoms of irritation, decrements in both visuomotor accuracy and psychomotor performance at >55 ppm |
| Lilis et al., 1978 | 494 | Styrene and polystyrene production | Unknown x 7->20 yr | Prenarcotic symptoms, distal hypoesthesia of the lower extremities, reduced radial and peroneal nerve conduction velocity |

[1] Conversion factor: 1 ppm in air = 4.2 $mg/m^3$
[2] For relationship between mandelic acid concentration in urine and concentration of styrene inhalated, see Fig. 5 in Härkönen et al., 1978

Styrene vapours are absorbed through the lungs (60-90%) (Åstrand, 1975; Bardodej & Bardodejova, 1970; Fiserova-Bergerova & Teisinger, 1965); the percutaneous absorption of styrene during exposure to concentrations up to 2.5 g/m$^3$ (600 ppm) in air is insignificant (about 2%) as compared with the respective pulmonary absorption (Riihimäki & Pfäffli, 1979). The percutaneous absorption of liquid styrene through the skin of the hand is 9-15 mg/cm$^2$/hr, and that of aqueous solutions (66-269 mg/l) is 40-180 µg/cm$^2$/hr (Dutkiewicz & Tyras, 1968).

Styrene is soluble in blood and has been found in fat tissue (van Rees, 1974). It was found in s.c. fat samples from 13/17 workers for as long as 3 days after the most recent occupational exposure to more than 4.2 mg/m$^3$ (1 ppm) styrene in air (Wolff, 1976; Wolff et al., 1977). It is rapidly depleted in the breath following exposure to 420 mg/m$^3$ (100 ppm) in air (Åstrand et al., 1974; Stewart et al., 1968).

The major urinary metabolites of styrene are mandelic acid and phenylglyoxylic acid (Bardodej & Bardodejova, 1966, 1970; Ohtsuji & Ikeda, 1970; Vrba et al., 1967), and these have therefore been proposed as indices of exposure to styrene (Buchet et al., 1974; Engström et al., 1974; Götell et al., 1972; Härkönen et al., 1974; Ikeda et al., 1974; Ohtsuji & Ikeda, 1970; Slob, 1973).

Ten men aged 20-41 years and exposed occupationally to styrene showed an increase in the rate of chromosomal aberrations in cultured lymphocytes from peripheral blood (11-26% compared with 3% or less among 5 non-exposed controls). In addition to an increase in chromosomal type breaks, decondensation of chromatin and increased numbers of micronucleii and nuclear bridges were also observed (Meretoja et al., 1977).

3.3 Case reports and epidemiological studies[1,2]

Lilis & Nicholson (1976) investigated the cancer mortality of workers in a chemical plant producing styrene monomers. These workers had a multiplicity of exposures to styrene, to benzene and, to a limited extent, to butadiene. The finding of 3 leukemias and 2 lymphomas among 104 deaths was considered by the authors to indicate the need for further study [The Working Group noted that the population at risk was not clearly defined and no analyses using a comparison population were undertaken].

---

[1]Subsequent to the finalization of this monograph by the Working Group in February 1978, the Secretariat became aware of more recent results of this study (Nicholson et al., 1979).

[2]The Working Group was aware of a mortality study in progress on workers exposed to styrene-based products (IARC, 1978b).

## Polystyrene

### 1.  Chemical and Physical Data

#### 1.1  Synonyms and trade names

Chem. Abstr. Services Reg. No.:  9003-53-6

Chem. Abstr. Name:  Ethenylbenzene homopolymer

Atactic polystyrene;  oligostyrene;  polystyrene latex;  polystyrol;
styrene polymers;  vinylbenzene polymer

3A;  A 3-80;  Afcolene;  Afcolene 666;  Afcolene S 100;  Bactolatex;
Bakelite SMD 3500;  BASF III;  BDH 29-790;  Bextrene XL 750;
Bicolastic A 75;  Bicolene H;  Bio-Beads S-X 2;  BP-KLP;  BSB-S 40;
BSB-S-E;  Bustren;  Bustren K 500;  Bustren K 525-19;  Bustren U 825;
Bustren U 825Ell;  Bustren Y 825;  Bustren Y 3532;  Cadco 0115;
Carinex GP;  Carinex HR;  Carinex HRM;  Carinex SB 59;  Carinex SB 61;
Carinex SL 273;  Carinex TGX/MF;  Copal Z;  Cosden 550;  Cosden 945E;
Denka QP3;  Diarex 43G;  Diarex HF 55;  Diarex HF 55-247;  Diarex HF
77;  Diarex HS 77;  Diarex HT 88;  Diarex HT 90;  Diarex HT 190;
Diarex HT 500;  Diarex HT 88A;  Diarex YH 476;  Dorvon;  Dorvon FR
100;  Dow 360;  Dow 456;  Dow 665;  Dow 860;  Dow 1683;  Dow MX 5514;
Dow MX 5516;  Dylark 250;  Dylene;  Dylene 8;  Dylene 9;  Dylene 8G;
Dylite F 40;  Dylite F 40L;  686E;  Edistir RB;  Esbrite;  Esbrite 2;
Esbrite 4;  Esbrite 4-62;  Esbrite 8;  Esbrite G 10;  Esbrite G-P 2;
Esbrite 500HM;  Esbrite LBL;  Escorez 7404;  Estyrene 4-62;  Estyrene
G 15;  Estyrene G 20;  Estyrene G-P 4;  Estyrene H 61;  Estyrene 500SH;
FC-MY 5450;  FG 834;  Foster Grant 834;  Gedex;  454H;  HF 10;  HF 55;
HF 77;  HH 102;  HHI 11;  Hi-Styrol;  Hostyren N;  Hostyren N 4000;
Hostyren N 7001;  Hostyren N 4000V;  Hostyren S;  HT 88;  HT 91-1;
HT 88A;  HT-F 76;  IT 40;  K 525;  KB (polymer);  KM;  KM (polymer);
Koplen 2;  KR 2537;  Krasten 1.4;  Krasten 052;  Krasten SB;  Lacqren
506;  Lacqren 550;  LS 061A;  LS 1028E;  Lustrex;  Lustrex H 77;
Lustrex HF 77;  Lustrex HH 101;  Lustrex HT 88;  MX 4500;  MX 5514;
MX 5516;  MX 5517-02;  168N15;  NaPSt;  NBS 706;  N 4000V;  Owispol GF;

Pelaspan 333; Pelaspan ESP 109s; Piccolastic; Piccolastic A; Piccolastic A 5; Piccolastic A 25; Piccolastic A 50; Piccolastic A 75; Piccolastic C 125; Piccolastic D; Piccolastic D-100; Piccolastic D 125; Piccolastic D 150; Piccolastic E 75; Piccolastic E 100; Piccolastic E 200; Polyco 220NS; Polyflex; Polystrol D; Polystyrene BW; Printel's; PRX 1195; PS 1; PS 2; PS 2 (polymer); PS 5 (polymer): PS 200; PS 209; PS-B; PSB-C; PSB-S; PSB-S 40; PSB-S-E; PS 454H: PSV-L; PSV-L 1; PSV-L 2; PSV-L 1S; PY 2763; R 3; R 3612; Rexolite 1422; Rhodolne; S 173; SB 475K; SD 188; Shell 300; SMD 3500; SPS 600; SRM 705; SRM 706; ST 90; Sternite 30; Sternite ST 30VL; ST 30UL; Styrafoil; Styragel; Styrex C; Styrocell PM; Styrofan 2D; Styroflex; Styrofoam; Styrolux; Styron; Styron 470; Styron 475; Styron 492; Styron 666; Styron 678; Styron 679; Styron 683; Styron 685; Styron 686; Styron 690; Styron 69021; Styron 440A; Styron 475D; Styron GP; Styron 666K27; Styron PS 3; Styron T 679; Styron 666U; Styron 666V; Styropian; Styropian FH 105; Styropol HT 500; Styropol IBE; Styropol JQ 300; Styropol KA; Styropor; TC 3-30; TGD 5161; TMDE 6500; Toporex 500; Toporex 550-02; Toporex 830; Toporex 850-51; Toporex 855-51; Trolitul; Trycite 1000; 825TV; 825TV-PS; 475U; 666U; U625; Ubatol U 2001; UCC 6863; UP 1; UP 2; UP 27; UPM; UPM 703; UPM 508L; Vestolen P 5232G; Vestyron; Vestyron 114-12; Vestyron 512; Vestyron MB; Vestyron N; Vinamul N 710; Vinamul N 7700; Vinyl Products R 3612; X 600

## 1.2 Structural and molecular formulae and molecular weight

$(C_8H_8)_n$                    Mol. wt:  10 000-1 000 000

1.3  Chemical and physical properties of the polymer

(a)  Description:  Transparent, hard solid (Hawley, 1971)

(b)  Melting-point:  240°C (Rudd, 1970)

(c)  Density:  1.04-1.065 (amorphous);  1.111 (crystalline) (Rudd, 1970)

(d)  Refractive index:  $n_D^{20}$ 1.591 (Boyer, 1970)

(e)  Spectroscopy data:  $\lambda_{max}$ 260, 215, 194, 80 nm;  infra-red, Raman and nuclear magnetic resonance spectra have been tabulated (Boyer, 1970).

(f)  Solubility:  Soluble in many organic solvents, including ethyl-benzene, methyl isobutyl ketone, tetrahydrofuran, benzene, toluene, methylene chloride and pyridine (Boyer & Keskkula, 1970)

(g)  Stability:  Yellows on exposure to light (Hawley, 1971)

(h)  Reactivity:  Attacked by hydrocarbon solvents but resists acids, alkalis and alcohols (Hawley, 1971)

1.4  Technical products and impurities

Polystyrene is available in the US in a variety of grades, but the three major types are:  (1) crystalline or straight polystyrene (37% of total polystyrene available in the US);  (2) impact-modified grades, which typically contain about 5% polybutadiene elastomer (51%);  and (3) expandable beads which contain a small amount of $n$-pentane entrapped in each globule (12%).  Straight and impact-modified polystyrene resins are usually supplied in granular form and may be sold in coloured form with, typically, 5-20% organic and/or inorganic pigments added.  Impurities of less than 1%, originating from styrene monomer production and storage and from catalysts and diluents, are likely to be present, but their composition is not commonly known.  No detailed information of the possible presence of unreacted monomer in the polymer was available to the Working Group.

One type of polystyrene resin available in Japan has the following properties:  specific gravity, 1.05;  tensile strength, 4.1-4.6 kg/mm$^2$; impact resistance, <2 kg cm/cm;  and Vicat softening point, 88-96.

## 2.  Production, Use, Occurrence and Analysis

### 2.1  Production and use

#### (a)  Production

Gelatinous polystyrene was first observed in 1839 by Simon after allowing styrene to stand in air.  Solid polystyrene was first prepared in 1845 by Blyth and Hoffmann by heating styrene in air (Platt, 1970).  Polystyrene resins are typically produced by a modified mass polymerization process in a continuous manner.  The liquid styrene monomer is diluted with a relatively small amount of a diluent, e.g., 5-15% of ethylbenzene (in some cases more diluent is used, and the process may then be called a solution process). The heated mixture of styrene, solvent and initiator is reacted at 120-160°C. Unreacted monomer and solvent are removed after polymerization is complete.

Polystyrene has been produced commercially in the US for over forty years (US Tariff Commission, 1938).  In 1976, 17 US companies produced 1453 million kg polystyrene (49% straight polystyrene and 51% impact-modified polystyrene).  US imports, amounting to 4.4 million kg in 1976, were from Canada (4%), Japan (94%) and nine other countries (2%) (US Department of Commerce, 1977a).  Exports were 81.7 million kg and went to the following countries (% of total):  Canada (16), Hong Kong (49), Iran (2), Taiwan (4), Thailand (2), the UK (2) and over 40 other countries (25) (US Department of Commerce, 1977b).

Total western Europe production in 1976 amounted to 1700 million kg; the major producers were the following (production in millions of kg): Belgium (190), the Federal Republic of Germany (470), Finland (20), France (280), Greece (10), Italy (260), The Netherlands (150), Norway (5), Spain (85), Sweden (10), Switzerland (2) and the UK (215).  Exports from western Europe in that year were 490 million kg, and imports 330 million kg.

Polystyrene production in 1975 in other countries was as follows (millions of kg):  Argentina (24), Australia (23), Brazil (48), Canada (68), Mexico (38), Republic of Korea (14) and Taiwan (18).

It has been produced commercially in Japan since 1964.  In 1976, eleven companies produced a total of 582 million kg;  exports amounted to 61 million kg, and imports to 2 million kg.

Worldwide production of polystyrene in 1976 is estimated to have been approximately 4200 million kg.

#### (b)  Use

Use of polystyrene resins in the US in 1977 was as follows:  packaging (35%);  toys, sporting goods and recreational articles (1%), housewares, furnishings and consumer products (10%), appliances and TV cabinets (9%), disposable serviceware and flatware (8%), construction (7%), electrical

and electronic parts (6%), miscellaneous chemical and industrial moulding (4%), furniture (2%) and other uses (8%).

The major use of polystyrene is in packaging: it is used to produce
a variety of containers, including cups, lids, trays, cartons, bottles,
boxes, vials, jars and tubs; sheet and film for wrapping; and loose fill
for packing. Toys, games and hobby kits are made from polystyrene resins.
Houseware, furniture and consumer product applications for polystyrene
include items such as handles on kitchen utensils, soap dishes, salt and
pepper shakers, watering cans, picture and mirror frames, room dividers,
toilet seats, planters and picnic coolers. Major appliance applications
are refrigerator doorliners, trays and covers; as housing for room air
containers and small appliances (e.g., blenders, mixers, clocks, hairdryers);
and for knobs and consoles of home laundry appliances. A variety of disposable dinnerware, cutlery, cocktail glasses and picnicware are produced
from polystyrene resins for use by hospitals, airlines, schools, fast-food
outlets and hotels.

Construction applications for polystyrene resins include insulation
board, shower doors and partitions, moulded shutters, cupboard doors, architectural trim mouldings, drainpipes and tubing. Electrical and electronic
parts made from polystyrene include calculators, tape reels, reel covers
and cassettes. Miscellaneous commercial and industrial moulding applications for polystyrene include 'egg-crate' light diffusers, other lighting
fixtures, display fixtures, coat hangers for the retail trade and knobs.
Furniture made from polystyrene resins includes one-piece tables, lamp
tables, cabinets, shelf units and components such as chair legs, arms and
backs. Other applications for polystyrene include medical, dental and other
laboratory articles, combs and brushes, eyeglasses, signs, office and school
supplies, novelties and other miscellaneous products.

In 1975, an estimated 300 thousand kg polystyrene were used in Europe
and 700 thousand kg in the US in plastic materials for medical applications.
Polystyrene is widely used as an ion-exchange resin to remove sodium, potassium, bile acids from body fluids and to lower serum cholesterol. It is
also used as a component of acrylic bone cements (Halpern & Karo, 1977).

The 1977 western Europe use pattern for polystyrene was as follows:
packaging (48%), appliances (10%), housewares (9%), refrigerators (85%),
furniture (6%), toys (4%) and other uses (15%).

Use in Japan in 1976 was in packaging (34%), electrical and electronic
appliances and television/radio, combined (36%) and housewares, toys and
other uses, combined (30%).

The US Food and Drug Administration permits the use of polystyrene
and rubber-modified polystyrene (impact-modified) as components of articles
intended for use in contact with food. The polystyrene used may not contain
more than 1 wt % residual styrene monomer (for rubber-modified polystyrene,
0.5 wt % max residual styrene) when determined by the prescribed method
(US Food and Drug Administration, 1977).

2.2 <u>Occurrence</u>

Polystyrene is not known to occur as a natural product.

It has been detected in the surface water of the Mediterranean Sea
(Polikarpov & Benzhitskii, 1975) and in US municipal waste at a level of
20 wt % of all plastics present (Jensen *et al.*, 1974).

2.3 <u>Analysis</u>

No information was available to the Working Group on methods for determining polystyrene residues in foods or other parts of the environment.

Simple tests have been described for identifying 14 thermoplastics in
which the polymers were burned, fractured or floated on water (Selerowicz,
1976). Thirty-seven commercial polymers, including polystyrene, have been
identified by temperature-programmed pyrolysis-gas chromatography (Okumoto
& Takeuchi, 1972).

Pyrolysis-gas chromatography has also been used to identify polystyrene in paper coating binders (Seves *et al.*, 1972) and to determine vinyl
polymers, including polystyrene (Haken & Ho, 1976; McCormick, 1969).
Pyrolysis coupled to gas chromatography and infra-red spectrophotometry in
the vapour phase has been used to identify synthetic binders, including
polystyrene, in commercial paper coatings (Luciani *et al.*, 1972). It has
also been identified in paper coatings by spectrophotometric techniques
in the visible, ultra-violet and infra-red regions and by liquid and gas
chromatography (Luciani & Corradini, 1971), and in paper products by extraction with chloroform followed by ultra-violet spectrophotometry at 250 and
260 nm of the extract (Spagnolo, 1974).

Synthetic resins, including polystyrene, have been identified by sub-
jecting the pyrolysis products to a combination of ultra-violet spectrophotometry, colour-forming reactions and thin-layer chromatography (Braun
& Nixdorf, 1972). Ten polymers have been determined quantitatively by
infra-red spectrophotometry, gas chromatography and colorimetric tube
measurement (Morimoto *et al.*, 1976). Adhesive resins used in the building
industry have been identified by pyrolysis-gas chromatography, thermogravimetry, differential thermogravimetry and differential thermal analysis
(Rona, 1971).

Pyrolysis and mass spectrometric analysis of the pyrolysis products
have been used to determine unknown polymeric material and industrial
adhesives, including polystyrene (Ryska, 1974), and to identify 10 commercial polymers, including polystyrene (Zeman, 1972).

### 3. Biological Data Relevant to the Evaluation
### of Carcinogenic Risk to Humans

## 3.1 Carcinogenicity studies in animals[1]

### Subcutaneous and/or intramuscular administration

Rat:  In Wistar rats given s.c. implants of polystyrene of different physical forms, the following incidences of sarcomas were observed at the site of implantation (Nothdurft, 1956):

| Form | Effective no. of rats | No. (%) of rats bearing tumours |
|------|------|------|
| Smooth discs (17 mm ⌀) | 47 | 37 (78.7) |
| Perforated discs | 51 | 25 (49.0) |
| Rods, spheres, fibres | 40 | 15 (37.5) |
| Powder | Unstated | 0 (0) |

These findings were subsequently confirmed by Oppenheimer *et al.*, 1958).

Discs (1.45 cm diameter x 0.026 mm thick) and perforated discs (central hole, 6 mm) of polystyrene were implanted subcutaneously into Wistar rats from three different sources (IC, E, Glaxo).  Differences were found in the incidence of local sarcomas (8-48%) according to source (Wistar E being the most sensitive), but no appreciable differences were found between those with perforated and those with unperforated discs (Rivière *et al.*, 1960).

## 3.2 Other relevant biological data

### (a) Experimental systems

In rats implanted subcutaneously with polystyrene discs, increased mucopolysaccharide synthesis in the adjacent tissue occurred within the first 4 months (Danishefsky *et al.*, 1959).

No data on the toxicity, embryotoxicity, teratogenicity or mutagenicity of this compound were available to the Working Group.

---

[1]The Working Group was aware of a study in progress to assess the carcinogenicity of polystyrene fibres implanted intraperitoneally into rats (IARC, 1978a).

(b) Humans

No data were available to the Working Group.

3.3  Case reports and epidemiological studies

No data were available to the Working Group


Styrene-butadiene copolymers

1.  Chemical and Physical Data

1.1  Synonyms and trade names

Chem. Abstr. Services Reg. No.:  9003-55-8

Chem. Abstr. Name:  Ethenylbenzene polymer with 1,3-butadiene

1,3-Butadiene-styrene copolymer;  butadiene-styrene polymer;  1,3-
butadiene-styrene polymer;  butadiene-styrene resin;  polybutadiene-
polystyrene copolymer;  SBS;  SBS (block polymer);  SBS copolymer;
styrene-1,3-butadiene copolymer;  styrene-butadiene polymer;  styrene
polymer with 1,3-butadiene

620;  8000A;  Afcolac B 101;  BASF 661;  Butakon 85-71;  Diarex 600;
Dienol S;  Dow 209;  Dow 234;  Dow 460;  Dow 620;  Dow 680;  Dow 816;
Dow Latex 612;  Dowtex TL 612;  DST 50;  DST 75;  Duranit;  Duranit
40;  Edistir RB 268;  Goodrite 1800X73;  Histyrene S 6F;  Hycar LX
407;  K 55E;  KRO 1;  KRO 2;  Litex CA;  Lytron 5202;  Marbon 8000A;
Marbon 9200;  Nipol 407;  Pharos 100.1;  Pliolite 151;  Pliolite 160;
Pliolite 491;  Pliolite 55B;  Pliolite S5;  Pliolite S 50;  Pliolite
S 5A;  Pliolite S 5D;  Polyco 2410;  Polyco 2415;  PS-SU2;  SD 345
(polymer);  SD 354;  S6F Histyrene resin;  SKS 85;  Soil stabilizer
661;  Solprene 300;  Solprene 303;  Synpol 1500;  Thermoplastic 125;
TR 201;  UP 1E;  Vestyron HI

## 1.2  Structural and molecular formulae

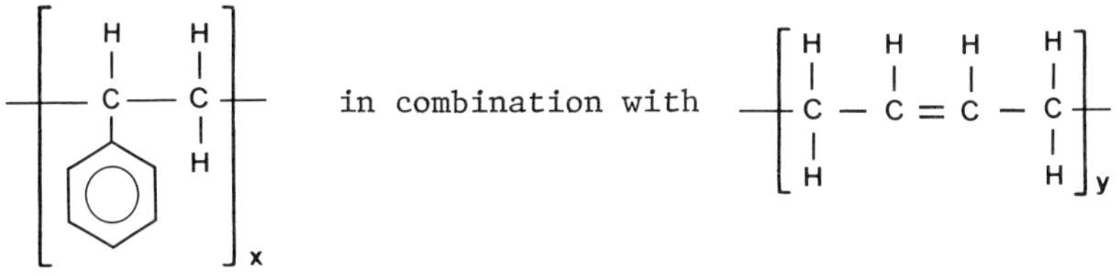

$(C_8H_8)_x - (C_4H_6)_y$

## 1.3  Chemical and physical properties of the unvulcanized rubber

From Brandrup & Immergut (1966)

(a)  Description:  Amorphous solid

(b)  Melting-point:  -59 to -64°C (glass-transition temperature)

(c)  Density:  d 0.933

(d)  Refractive index:  $n_D$ 1.5345

## 1.4  Technical products and impurities

Three basic types of styrene-butadiene copolymers are available in the US:  (1) styrene-butadiene elastomers (commonly called SBR, or styrene-butadiene rubber);  (2) styrene block copolymers with butadiene;  and (3) styrene-butadiene copolymer latexes.

SBR is available in dry and latex form.  Dry SBR made by emulsion poly-merization contains about 23-25% styrene units and 75-77% butadiene units on a polymer basis;  when made by solution polymerization the composition varies, but typical grades contain about 10-25% styrene units and 75-90% butadiene units.  A typical recipe for SBR made by cold emulsion polymeriza-tion is as follows (parts per 100 monomer):  butadiene (70), styrene (30), water (180), fatty acid soap (2.25), disproportionated rosin soap (2.25), potassium chloride (0.3), potassium hydroxide (0.3), *tert*-dodecyl mercaptan (0.23), sodium formaldehyde β-naphthalene sulphonate (0.04), sodium formalde-hyde sulphoxylate (0.04), *para*-methane hydroperoxide (0.04), tetrasodium ethylenediaminetetraacetate (0.025) and ferrous sulphate heptahydrate (0.013).  A typical recipe for SBR made by hot emulsion polymerization is as follows (parts per 100 monomer):  butadiene (75), styrene (25), water (180), fatty acid or rosin soap (5), *n*-dodecyl mercaptan (0.5) and potas-sium persulphate (0.3).

Recipes for SBR made by solution polymerization vary greatly and depend upon the properties desired. SBR is vulcanized (typically 1.5-2.0 parts sulphur per 100 parts of polymer are used), and accelerators, anti-oxidants, activators, fillers (e.g., carbon black), and softeners may be used, depending on the desired properties of the finished rubber. SBR is also extended with aromatic and naphthenic oils to improve handling and processing; the average oil content of SBR in 1976 was 28.0%. SBR latexes contain less than 45% styrene units (typically 23-25%) and are available with different solids content: high (60-68% solids), medium (55%) and low (30-45%).

Styrene block copolymers (see glossary, p. 36) with butadiene are available, with a styrene content of 25-50% (the most widely used grades contain 30% styrene units). They are usually compounded with fillers, extender oils and sometimes other polymers (e.g., polyindene or polysty-rene).

Styrene-butadiene copolymer latexes (distinct from SBR latex) contain 54-80% styrene units and 20-46% butadiene units. They generally have a resin content of 50%, and most are carboxylated with acids such as maleic, fumaric, acrylic or methacrylic acids.

In Japan, SBR generally contains 23.5% styrene units.

No detailed information on the possible presence of unreacted monomer in the polymers was available to the Working Group.

## 2. Production, Use, Occurrence and Analysis

### 2.1 Production and use

#### (a) Production

The first styrene-butadiene copolymer produced by emulsion polymeri-zation was patented in 1933 by Bock and Tschunker (Saltman, 1965). SBR is produced commercially by three processes: (1) cold emulsion polymeri-zation (85% of total US production); (2) hot emulsion polymerization (5%); and (3) solution polymerization (10%). Using the typical recipe cited in section 1.4 for the cold polymerization process, the ingredients are reacted at 5°C for about 6-7 hours until 60-65% conversion is achieved; the reaction is stopped by adding a short-stopping agent, and unconverted butadiene and styrene are removed; a stabilizer is added, and the emulsion is coagulated after any desired carbon black or oil has been added. If latex is the desired product, all steps after monomer removal are omitted. Hot polymerization processes are similar, except that the reaction tempera-ture is about 50°C and the reaction is stopped after 12 hours with about 70-75% conversion. In a typical solution polymerization, styrene and buta-diene are copolymerized in a hexane or cyclohexane solution in the presence of a small amount of $n$-butyllithium at 50°C; 98% conversion is achieved after 4 hours, and the reaction is stopped by adding a fatty acid deactivator followed by addition of a stabilizer;  solvent residues are removed when the elastomer is coagulated.

Styrene block copolymers with butadiene are typically produced by anionic solution polymerization with *sec*-butyllithium or *n*-butyllithium in a solvent such as cyclohexane, isopentane, *n*-hexane or mixtures.  The styrene is homopolymerized, followed by addition of the butadiene, and then more styrene is added.  The polymer is coagulated from the solution with water.  Styrene-butadiene copolymer latexes are produced by emulsion polymerization.

Styrene-butadiene rubber (SBR) was first produced commercially in the US in 1942, although pilot plants were in operation as early as 1938.  In 1976, nine companies produced 1191 million kg dry SBR, and ten companies produced 141 million kg SBR latex.  The corresponding net production of dry and latex forms (excluding weight of oils) amounted to 1072 million kg. US imports of SBR in that year were 41.8 million kg and exports 89.2 million kg (72% dry SBR and 28% SBR latex).  Two other companies produced 25 million kg styrene block copolymers (including copolymers with butadiene, isoprene and ethylene/butylene);  and 16 companies produced 61 million kg styrene-butadiene copolymer latex in the same year.

Total western Europe production in 1976 amounted to 1075 million kg. The major producers were the following countries (production in millions of kg):  Austria (5), the Federal Republic of Germany (195), Finland (2), France (185), Italy (155), Spain (70), Sweden (10) and the UK (190). Exports from western Europe in that year were 206 million kg and imports 186 million kg.  Production in other countries in 1975 was as follows (millions of kg):  Argentina (37), Australia (26), Brazil (96), Canada (91), Mexico (45) and Republic of Korea (24).

In Japan, SBR was first produced in 1950;  in 1976, nine companies produced 558 million kg, and exports were 139 million kg.

(b)  Use

The 1976 US use pattern for SBR was as follows:  in the production of tires and tire products, 65% (passenger car tires, 44%;  truck and bus tires, 10%;  tread rubber, 7%;  and other tires, 4%);  mechanical goods (non-automotive), 17%;  latex applications, 10%;  automotive applications, 6%;  and miscellaneous applications, 2%.  SBR is also used in appliance parts, wire and cable insulation, hoses, gaskets, seals, footwear, coated fabrics and sheeting, conveyor belts and moulded and extruded goods.  Latex applications for SBR include foam backing of carpets, paper saturation, dipped goods, adhesives and moulded foam applications.  Other automotive uses for SBR include hose, body and chassis parts, bumpers, weather strips, door and window seals, mats, etc.  Miscellaneous applications for SBR include its use as an impact modifier in plastics (e.g., polystyrene) and in the production of some ABS resins.

Styrene block copolymers (including copolymer with butadiene) were used in the US in 1976 in injection-moulded footwear (57%), for other injection moulding and extrusion applications (24%) and in adhesives (19%). Styrene block copolymers with butadiene are used to make soles for footwear designed for casual, recreational and sporting uses as well as for unit soles (sole and heel combined) for inexpensive shoes. Other injection moulding and extrusion applications include electrical wire and cable, related electrical components or parts, miscellaneous industrial applications, toys and housewares. Styrene block copolymers with butadiene are used as solvent cements in pressure-sensitive and contact adhesives, and as hot-melt adhesives for pressure-sensitive tapes, labels and case sealing.

Styrene-butadiene copolymer latexes are used primarily in carpet and upholstery backcoatings and as paper coatings. Other applications include use as a binder for asbestos felt base of vinyl floor tile, as a cement additive, as a nonwoven binder and as a component of latex paints.

In western Europe, SBR is used primarily for the production of tires (68% of total consumption).

Use of SBR in Japan in 1976 was in automotive applications (including tires), 56%; industrial goods, 8%; footwear, 7%; and other uses, 29%.

The US Food and Drug Administration permits the use of styrene-butadiene copolymers as components of rubber articles intended for repeated use in contact with food and for the preparation of textiles and textile fibres intended for use in contact with food. Styrene block copolymers with 1,3-butadiene are permitted for use in adhesives intended for use in contact with food and as articles or components of articles intended for use in contact with food, provided that the maximum extractable fraction in water is 0.025 mg/in$^2$ (0.003 mg/cm$^2$) of surface at reflux temperature for 30 min on a 0.075 inch (0.19 cm) thick sample, and that in 50% ethanol is 0.005 mg/in$^2$ (0.008 mg/cm$^2$) of surface at 65°C for 2 hours on a 0.075 inch (0.19 cm) thick sample (US Food and Drug Administration, 1977).

An estimated 10 000 workers in the US are potentially exposed to styrene-butadiene copolymers (Anon., 1976).

2.2 Occurrence

Styrene-butadiene copolymers are not known to occur as natural products.

2.3 Analysis

Styrene-butadiene copolymers have been identified using preparative gel permeation chromatography followed by analysis of the fractions by infra-red spectroscopy, solution viscosity and analytical gel permeation chromatography (Barlow et al., 1971).

Pyrolysis gas chromatography has been used to identify 57 plastics, rubbers and related materials (Fischer, 1967); to identify 37 commercial polymers (Okumoto & Takeuchi, 1972); and in a cooperative study of commercial styrene-butadiene block copolymers by 18 laboratories (Coupe *et al.*, 1970). In the last instance, the fingerprint pyrograms were useful; however, the reproducibility of quantitative results was poor.

Styrene-butadiene resins have been determined by infra-red spectrophotometry in solvent-based paints by measuring the ratio of absorbances at 3.3 nm/3.5 nm (Post, 1969); in masonry surface fillers, after extraction with benzene and pentane (Post, 1971); and in binders used in coating colour formulations in paper (Seves & Croce, 1970).

Spectrophotometric determination of styrene-butadiene latexes has been carried out using sequential treatment with hot nitric acid, potassium hydroxide, a reducing agent and *para*-dimethylaminobenzaldehyde. The optical density of the Schiff base obtained was measured and compared with a standard curve (Chene *et al.*, 1969a,b).

The components of paper coatings, including styrene-butadiene copolymers, have been identified by combined spectrophotometric methods in the visible, infra-red and ultra-violet regions and by liquid and gas chromatography (Luciani & Corradini, 1971).

Styrene-butadiene copolymers have been determined gravimetrically in latex paints by sequential extraction with methanolic hydrochloric acid, water and methanol, followed by drying at $50^{\circ}C$ under reduced pressure, and then identified by infra-red spectroscopy (Post, 1967).

## 3. Biological Data Relevant to the Evaluation
### of Carcinogenic Risk to Humans

### 3.1 Carcinogenicity studies in animals

No data were available to the Working Group.

### 3.2 Other relevant biological data

No data were available to the Working Group.

### 3.3 Case reports and epidemiological studies

McMichael *et al.* (1976) reported a 6-fold increase of malignancies of the lymphato-haematopoeietic system among a cohort of rubber workers with a history of SBR employment for more than 5 years. Smith & Ellis (1977) noted the small number of cases analysed (4 males) in this study and the variety of types among the malignancies.

A parallel study using the same design was conducted by Taulbee *et al.* (1976) in a different SBR plant. The authors reported no significant excess of malignancies of the lymphato-haematopoeietic system, and those cases that were found occurred among rubber workers who had no history of SBR exposure.

Lemen & Young (1976) reported 8 cases of leukaemia of various cell types among retired and active employees of two contiguous plants producing SBR. Block (1976) reported 2 lymphomas and 2 leukaemias among 72 deaths of workers at one plant producing SBR.

[The Working Group noted that each of the reported studies was limited due to small numbers, undefined latency and possible mixed exposures to industrial agents. The collective nature of the findings justifies suspicion and further investigation.]

No data were available regarding the carcinogenicity to humans of butadiene alone.

## 4.  Summary of Data Reported and Evaluation

### 4.1  Experimental data

Styrene was tested by oral administration to mothers and offspring of two strains of mice and of one strain of rats. In one strain of mice, high doses of styrene increased the incidence of lung tumours in offspring. In the other strain, a lower dose of styrene slightly increased the incidence of liver-cell tumours in male offspring. In rats, the total incidence of tumours was not statistically different in styrene-treated and control animals.

Styrene is mutagenic.

Subcutaneous implantation of polystyrene discs, rods, spheres or powder in rats induced local sarcomas, the incidences of which varied with the size and form of the implant.

No data on the carcinogenicity of styrene-butadiene copolymers were available to the Working Group.

### 4.2  Human data

The extensive production of styrene and polystyrene and the widespread use of the polymer and the copolymers derived from styrene for consumer products and medical applications suggest that occupationally and medically exposed groups may be identified for epidemiological investigation. Extensive data on toxicity in workers and hygienic measurements indicate that exposures do occur. Skin absorption of styrene has been reported. The widespread occurrence of styrene in the environment and the fact that in some countries styrene and some of its polymers are approved as food additives and for use in contact with food (e.g., disposable dinnerware and drinking glasses) indicate that the general population is also exposed.

The only report that relates to possible human carcinogenicity of styrene has methodological deficiencies: the population at risk was not clearly defined and may have been exposed to a variety of chemicals, such as benzene. No conclusion could be made concerning the carcinogenicity of styrene.

No case reports or epidemiological studies with regard to the carcinogenicity of polystyrene were available to the Working Group.

The case reports and epidemiological studies that concern the carcinogenic effects of styrene-butadiene copolymers also have limitations: the usual ones apply to the case reports; the epidemiological studies involved small numbers of workers. However, the collective nature of the findings, together with the similarity of tumour types observed, clearly indicate the need for further studies.

## 4.3 Evaluation

Although no information is available on carcinogenicity in humans attributable to styrene, its wide use and the facility with which it can be absorbed by inhalation indicate that it may be possible to carry out studies measuring both dose and cancer incidence in exposed workers. The finding of chromosomal aberrations in workers exposed to styrene further supports the need for epidemiological investigations.

Results from polystyrene implant studies in animals point to the need for further investigations with regard to the polymer. Recent epidemiological information on styrene-butadiene copolymer workers, which indicates lymphato-haematopoeietic malignancies, clearly requires elucidation by further studies.

## 5. References

Akhlyustina, L.V., Bokov, A.N. & Kosorotova, F.P. (1973)  Sanitary-hygienic evaluation of the plastic fittings of refrigerator 'Don-2' (Russ.). Gig. Toksikol. Polim. Stroit. Mater., 2, 317-325 [Chem. Abstr., 85, 76461b]

Anon. (1972)  Fire Protection Guide on Hazardous Materials, 4th ed., Boston, Mass., National Fire Protection Association, pp. 49-207-49-208

Anon. (1976)  B.F. Goodrich denies positive link between SBR, leukemia among workers. Occupational Safety and Health Reporter, 6 May, pp. 1751-1752

Araki, S., Abe, A., Ushio, K. & Fujino, M. (1971)  A case of skin atrophy, neurogenic muscular atrophy and anxiety reaction following long exposure to styrene. Jap. J. ind. Health, 13, 427-431

Åstrand, I. (1975)  Uptake of solvents in the blood and tissues of man. A review. Scand. J. Work. environ. Health, 1, 199-218

Åstrand, I., Kilbom, Å., Övrum, P., Wahlberg, I. & Vesterberg, O. (1974)  Exposure to styrene. I. Concentration in alveolar air and blood at rest and during exercise and metabolism. Work.-environ. Health, 11, 69-85

Austern, B.M., Dobbs, R.A. & Cohen, J.M. (1975)  Gas chromatographic determination of selected organic compounds added to wastewater. Environ. Sci. Technol., 9, 588-590

Axelson, O. (1976)  Some experiences from styrene studies. In: Third Swedish-Yugoslavian Symposium on Occupational Health, Stockholm, May, 1975, Arbete och Hälsa, Vol. 8, Stockholm, Arbetar-Skyddsverket, pp. 5-11

Baggett, M.S., Morie, G.P., Simmons, M.W. & Lewis, J.S. (1974)  Quantitative determination of semivolatile compounds in cigarette smoke. J. Chromatogr., 97, 79-82

Bardodej, Z. & Bardodejova, E. (1966)  The metabolism of ethylbenzene, styrene and alpha-methylstyrene. In: Proceedings of the XV International Congress on Occupational Health, Vienna, Vol. II-1, Vienna, Egermann, pp. 457-460

Bardodej, Z. & Bardodejova, E. (1970)  Biotransformation of ethylbenzene, styrene, and alpha-methylstyrene in man. Am. ind. Hyg. Assoc. J., 31, 206-209

Bardodĕj, Z., Málek, B., Volfová, B. & Zelená, E. (1960)  The hazard of styrene in the production of glass laminates (Czech.).  Ceskosl. Hyg., 5, 541-546

Barlow, A., Wild, L. & Roberts, T. (1971)  Structural evaluation of copolymers using preparative gel permeation chromatography.  J. Chromatogr., 55, 155-164

Barsotti, M., Parmeggiani, L. & Sassi, C. (1952)  Observations on occupational pathology in a polystyrene resin factory (Ital.).  Med. Lav., 43, 418-424

Bergman, K. & Lindberg, E. (1977)  Styrene exposure in plastic boat industry (Swed.).  Arbete och Hälsa, Vol. 3, Stockholm, Arbetar-Skyddsverket

Block, J.B. (1976)  A Kentucky study: 1950-1975.  In:  Ede, L., ed., Proceedings of NIOSH Styrene-Butadiene Briefing, Covington, Kentucky, 1976, HEW Publ. No. (NIOSH) 77-129, Cincinnati, Ohio, US Department of Health, Education and Welfare, pp. 28-32

Bos, R., Guicherit, R. & Hoogeveen, A. (1977)  Distribution of some hydrocarbons in ambient air near Delft and the influence on the formation of secondary air pollutants.  Sci. total Environ., 7, 269-281

Boyer, R.F. (1970)  Styrene polymers (physical properties-spectral).  In: Bikales, N.M., ed., Encyclopedia of Polymer Science and Technology, Plastics, Resins, Rubbers, Fibers, Vol. 13, New York, Interscience, pp. 251, 256-257, 259-260, 262-266, 277

Boyer, R.F. & Keskkula, H. (1970)  Styrene polymers (characterization).  In:  Bikales, N.M., ed., Encyclopedia of Polymer Science and Technology, Plastics, Resins, Rubbers, Fibers, Vol. 13, New York, Interscience, pp. 206, 210, 232

Brandrup, J. & Immergut, E.H., eds (1966)  Polymer Handbook, New York, Interscience, pp. VI-61-VI-62

Braun, D. & Disselhoff, R. (1972)  Pyrolysis-gas-chromatographic analysis of acrylonitrile-styrene copolymers (Ger.).  Angew. Makromol. Chem., 23, 103-115 [Chem. Abstr., 77, 88868n]

Braun, D. & Nixdorf, G. (1972)  Separation of synthetic resin for analysis. 4.  Soluble resins with neutral reaction of the pyrolysis products (Ger.).  Kunststoffe, 62, 318-322

Buchet, J.-P., Lauwerys, R. & Roels, H. (1974)  Evaluation of the exposure of workers to styrene by determination of their urinary metabolites: mandelic and phenylglyoxylic acids. I.  Technique for determination of the metabolites by gas chromatography (Fr.).  Arch. Mal. prof., 35, 511-516

Burnett, R.D. (1976)  Evaluation of charcoal sampling tubes.  J. Am. ind. Hyg. Assoc., 37, 37-45

Cakrtova, E. & Vanecek, M. (1974)  Evaluation of the styrene exposure in the production of glass fiber-reinforced laminated plastics (Czech.). Prac. Lek, 26, 370-374 [Chem. Abstr., 85, 112289n]

Chene, M., Martin-Borret, O. & Nott, M.A.J. (1969a)  Determination of high polymers in paper:  polyethylenimine and butadiene-styrene latex (Fr.).  Chim. anal. (Paris), 51, 237-241 [Chem. Abstr., 71, 31557g]

Chene, M., Martin-Borret, O. & Nott, M.A.J. (1969b)  Spectrophotometric determination of butadiene-styrene latex in papers (Fr.).  Papeterie, 91, 100-102 [Chem. Abstr., 70, 98027g]

Chmielewski, J. & Renke, W. (1976)  Clinical and experimental research into the pathogenesis of toxic effect of styrene.  Bull. Inst. Mar. Trop. Med. Gdynia, 27, 63-68

Chmielewski, J., Mikulski, P., Uselis, J. & Wiglusz, R. (1973)  Rating of the exposure to styrene of persons working at the production of poly-esteric laminates.  Bull. Inst. Mar. Med. Gdansk, 24, 203-209

Coulter, K.E. & Kehde, H. (1970)  Styrene polymers (monomers).  In: Bikales, N.M., ed., Encyclopedia of Polymer Science and Technology, Plastics, Resins, Rubbers, Fibers, Vol. 13, New York, Interscience, pp. 136-137

Coulter, K.E., Kehde, H. & Hiscock, B.F. (1971).  I.  Styrene and related monomers.  In:  Leonard, E.C., ed., Vinyl and Diene Monomers, Part 2, High Polymers, Vol. 24, New York, Wiley-Interscience, pp. 479-576

Coupe, N.B., Jones, C.E.R. & Perry, S.G. (1970)  Precision of pyrolysis-gas chromatography of polymers. A progress report.  J. Chromatogr., 47, 291-296

Danishefsky, I. & Willhite, M. (1954)  The metabolism of styrene in the rat. J. biol. Chem., 211, 549-553

Danishefsky, I., Oppenheimer, E.T., Willhite, M., Stout, A.P. & Fishman, M.M. (1959)  Biochemical changes during carcinogenesis by plastic films. Cancer Res., 19, 1234-1238

Davies, J.T. (1974)  Migration of styrene monomer from packaging material into food. Experimental verification of a theoretical model.  J. Food Technol., 9, 275-283

Dmitrieva, V.N., Meshkova, O.V. & Bezuglyi, V.D. (1975)  Determination of low contents of organic impurities in effluents from polymer production (Russ.).  Zh. anal. Khim., 30, 1406-1409

Dolgopolov, V.D. & Lishcheta, L.I. (1971)  Quantitative determination of by-products in technical samples of styrene chlorohydrin (Russ.). Khim. Farm. Zh., 5, 55-56

Dolmierski, R., Kwiatkowski, S.R. & Nitka, J. (1976)  Clinical and experimental research into the pathogenesis of toxic effect of styrene. VII.  Appraisal of the nervous system in the workers exposed to styrene. Bull. Inst. Mar. Trop. Med. Gdynia, 27, 193-196

Dowty, B.J., Carlisle, D.R. & Laseter, J.L. (1975)  New Orleans drinking water sources tested by gas chromatography-mass spectrometry. Occurrence and origin of aromatics and halogenated aliphatic hydro-carbons. Environ. Sci. Technol., 9, 762-765

Dutkiewicz, T. & Tyras, H. (1968)  Skin absorption of toluene, styrene, and xylene by man. Br. J. ind. Med., 25, 243

Engström, K., Härkönen, H., Kalliokoski, P. & Rantanen, J. (1976)  Urinary mandelic acid concentration after occupational exposure to styrene and its use as a biological exposure test. Scand. J. Work. environ. Health, 2, 21-26

Ermolova, E.A., Mazunina, G.N., Orlova, A.A. & Solov'eva, E.A. (1965) Clinical aspects of chronic poisoning with styrene and α-methylstyrene in the production of synthetic rubber (Russ.). In: Occupational Diseases in the Chemical Industry, Moscow, Meditsina, pp. 91-95 (Abstract)

Eurocop-Cost (1976)  A Comprehensive List of Polluting Substances Which have been Identified in Various Fresh Waters, Effluent Discharges, Aquatic Animals and Plants, and Bottom Sediments, 2nd ed., EUCO/MDU/73/76, XII/476/76, Luxembourg, Commission of the European Communities, p. 101

Fischer, W.G. (1967)  Pyrolytic gas-chromatography (Ger.). Glas-Instrum.-Tech., 11, 562, 567-570, 775-780, 1086-1088, 1091-1095 [Chem. Abstr., 68, 78636k]

Fišerova-Bergerová, V. & Teisinger, J. (1965)  Pulmonary styrene vapor retention. Ind. Med. Surg., 34, 620-622

Gage, J.C., Strafford, N. & Truhaut, R. (1962)  Methods for the Determination of Toxic Substances in Air. Styrene, Method II, International Union of Pure and Applied Chemistry, London, Butterworths

Gillette, J.R. (1963)  Metabolism of drugs and other foreign compounds by enzymatic mechanisms. Prog. Drug Res., 6, 11-73

Götell, P., Axelson, O. & Lindelöf, B. (1972)  Field studies on human styrene exposure. Work.-environ. Health, 9, 76-83

Grasselli, J.G. & Ritchey, W.M., eds (1975)  CRC Atlas of Spectral Data
    and Physical Constants for Organic Compounds, 2nd ed., Vol. IV,
    Cleveland, Ohio, Chemical Rubber Co., p. 538

Haken, J.K. & Ho, D.K.M. (1976)  Quantitative pyrolysis studies of styrene,
    acrylate ester systems, and their α-methyl-substituted homologs.
    J. Chromatogr., 126, 239-247

Halpern, B.D. & Karo, W. (1977)  Medical applications.  In:  Bikales, N.M.,
    ed., Encyclopedia of Polymer Science and Technology, Plastics, Resins,
    Rubbers, Fibers, Suppl. Vol. 2, New York, Interscience, pp. 369, 380,
    389, 402

Härkönen, H. (1977)  Relationship of symptoms to occupational styrene
    exposure and to the findings of electroencephalographic and psycho-
    logical examinations.  Int. Arch. occup. environ. Health, 40, 231-239

Härkönen, H., Kalliokoski, P., Hietala, S. & Hernberg, S. (1974)  Concen-
    trations of mandelic and phenylglyoxylic acid in urine as indicators
    of styrene exposure.  Work.-environ. Health, 11, 162-165

Härkönen, H., Lindström, K., Seppäläinen, A.M., Asp, S. & Hernberg, S.
    (1978)  Exposure-response relationship between styrene exposure
    and central nervous functions.  Scand. J. Work. environ. Health, 4,
    53-59

Hawley, G.G., ed. (1971)  The Condensed Chemical Dictionary, 8th ed.,
    New York, Van Nostrand-Reinhold, p. 712

Hawley, G.G., ed. (1977)  The Condensed Chemical Dictionary, 9th ed.,
    New York, Van Nostrand-Reinhold, pp. 758, 822

Holmberg, P.C. (1977)  Central nervous defects in two children of mothers
    exposed to chemicals in the reinforced plastics industry.  Scand. J.
    Work. environ. Health, 3, 212-214

Holzer, G., Shanfield, H., Zlatkis, A., Bertsch, W., Juarez, P.,
    Mayfield, H. & Liebich, H.M. (1977)  Collection and analysis of
    trace organic emissions from natural sources.  J. Chromatogr., 142,
    755-764

Hoshika, Y. (1977)  Gas chromatographic determination of styrene as its
    dibromide.  J. Chromatogr., 136, 95-103

Hrubá, E., Salcmanová, Z. & Schwartzová, K. (1975)  Long term follow-up
    of subjects exposed to possible styrene intoxication (Czech.)
    Cesk. Neurol. Neurochirurg., 38, 116-122

Hruza, D.E., Van Praag, M. & Heinsohn, H. (1974)  What tastes so good?
    Chem. Technol., 4, 512-513

Hŭzl, F., Sýkora, J., Mainerová, J., Janková, J., Šrŭtek, J., Junger, V. & Lahn, V. (1967) To the question of health hazard during the work with styrene (Czech.). Pracov. Lék., 19, 121-125

IARC (1978a) Information Bulletin on the Survey of Chemicals Being Tested for Carcinogenicity, No. 7, Lyon, pp. 35, 238, 256, 337, 382

IARC (1978b) Directory of On-Going Research in Cancer Epidemiology, 1978 (IARC Scientific Publications No. 26), Lyon, p. 330 (Abstract No. 873)

Ikeda, M., Ohtsuji, H. & Imamura, T. (1972) In vivo suppression of benzene and styrene oxidation by co-administered toluene in rats and effects of phenobarbital. Xenobiotica, 2, 101-106

Ikeda, M., Imamura, T., Hayashi, M., Tabuchi, T. & Hara, T. (1974) Evaluation of hippuric, phenylglyoxylic and mandelic acids in urine as indices of styrene exposure. Int. Arch. Arbeitsmed., 32, 93-101

Ioffe, B.V., Isidorov, V.A. & Zenkevich, I.G. (1977) Gas chromatographic-mass spectrometric determination of volatile organic compounds in an urban atmosphere. J. Chromatogr., 142, 787-795

Jensen, J.W., Holman, J.L. & Stephenson, J.B. (1974) Recycling and disposal of waste plastics. In: Yen, T.F., ed., Recycling and Disposal of Solid Wastes, Industrial, Agricultural, Domestic, Ann Arbor, Mich., Ann Arbor Science, pp. 219-249

Jermini, C., Weber, A. & Grandjean, E. (1976) Quantitative determination of various gas-phase components of the side-stream smoke of cigarettes in the room air as a contribution to the problem of passive-smoking (Ger.). Int. Arch. occup. environ. Health, 36, 169-181

Kalliokoski, P. & Pfäffli, P. (1975) Charcoal sampling method for determining the concentration of styrene in air. Scand. J. work. environ. Health, 1, 193-198

Katz, B.Y. (1962) Toxicochemical affection of the liver with styrene under operating conditions (Russ). Gig. Tr. Prof. Zabol., 10, 21-24

Kleshcheva, M.S., Usacheva, V.T. & Pozharova, V.N. (1971) Determination of residual monomers and non-polymerising impurities in polystyrene plastics by means of gas chromatography. Plast. Massy, 7, 57-58

Klimková-Deutschová, E. (1962) Neurologic factors in the plastic industry in styrene workers (Ger.). Int. Arch. Gewerbepath. Gewerbehyg., 19, 35-50

Klimková-Deutschová, E., Jandová, D., Salcmanová, Z., Schwartzová, K. & Titman, O. (1973) Recent advances concerning the clinical picture of professional styrene exposure (Czech.). Cesk. Neurol. Neurochir., 36, 20-25

Lambotte-Vandepaer, M., Noël, G., Rollmann, B., Mercier, M. & Roberfroid, M. (1978) Modifying effects of styrene on the catalytic properties of some microsomal enzymes. Arch. Toxicol. Suppl. 1, 287-290

Leibman, K.C. (1975) Metabolism and toxicity of styrene. Environ. Health Perspect., 11, 115-119

Leibman, K.C. & Ortiz, E. (1968) Styrene epoxide - An intermediate in microsomal oxidation of styrene to its glycol (Abstract No. 277). Pharmacologist, 10, 203

Leibman, K.C. & Ortiz, E. (1969) Oxidation of styrene in liver microsomes. Biochem. Pharmacol., 18, 552-554

Lemen, R.A. & Young, R. (1976) Investigations of health hazards in styrene butadiene rubber facilities. In: Ede, L., ed., Proceedings of NIOSH Styrene-Butadiene Briefing, Covington, Kentucky, 1976, HEW Publ. No. (NIOSH) 77-129, Cincinnati, Ohio, US Department of Health, Education and Welfare, pp. 3-8

Lilis, R. & Nicholson, W.J. (1976) Cancer experience among workers in a chemical plant producing styrene monomers. In: Ede, L., ed., Proceedings of NIOSH Styrene-Butadiene Briefing, Covington, Kentucky, 1976, HEW Publ. No. (NIOSH) 77-129, Cincinnati, Ohio, US Department of Health, Education and Welfare, pp. 22-27

Lilis, R., Lorimer, W.V., Diamond, S. & Selikoff, I.J. (1978) Neurotoxicity of styrene in production and polymerization workers. Environ. Res., 15, 133-138

Lindström, K., Härkönen, H. & Hernberg, S. (1976) Disturbances in psychological functions of workers occupationally exposed to styrene. Scand. J. work. environ. Health, 3, 129-139

Loprieno, N., Abbondandolo, A., Barale, R., Baroncelli, S., Bonatti, S., Bronzetti, G., Cammellini, A., Corsi, C., Corti, G., Frezza, D., Leporini, C., Mazzaccaro, A., Nieri, R., Rosellini, D. & Rossi, A.M. (1976) Mutagenicity of industrial compounds: styrene and its possible metabolite styrene oxide. Mutat. Res., 40, 317-324

Lorimer, W.V., Lilis, R., Nicholson, W.J., Anderson, H., Fischbein, A., Daum, S., Rice, C. & Selikoff, I.J. (1976a) Clinical studies of styrene workers: preliminary report. In: Ede, L., ed., Proceedings of NIOSH Styrene-Butadiene Briefing, Covington, Kentucky, 1976, HEW Publ. No. (NIOSH) 77-129, Cincinnati, Ohio, US Department of Health, Education and Welfare, pp. 163-169

Lorimer, W.V., Lilis, R., Nicholson, W.J., Anderson, H., Fischbein, A., Daum, S., Rom, W., Rice, C. & Selikoff, I.J. (1976b) Clinical studies of styrene workers: initial findings. Environ. Health Perspect., 17, 171-181

Lowenheim, F.A. & Moran, M.K. (1975) Faith, Keyes, and Clark's Industrial Chemicals, 4th ed., New York, Wiley-Interscience, pp. 779-785

Luciani, M. & Corradini, T. (1971) Spectrophotometric and chromatographic analysis of paper coatings (Ital.). Cellul. Carta, 22, 19-35 [Chem. Abstr., 76, 73969b]

Luciani, M., Corradini, T., & Fiorucci, P. (1972) Identification of synthetic binders for paper coatings by gas chromatographic analysis of their pyrolysis products (Ital.). Cellul. Carta, 23, 7-20 [Chem. Abstr., 78, 161105p]

Markelov, M.A. & Semenenko, E.I. (1976) Determination of microconcentrations of substances migrating from polymer materials to water (Russ.). Plast. Massy, 1, 57-59 [Chem. Abstr., 84, 155747g]

Martynenko, D.N. (1973) Hygienic characteristics of working conditions during production of articles from polymeric materials used in machine construction (Russ.). Gig. Tr., 9, 57-61 [Chem. Abstr., 85, 148321f]

McCormick, H. (1969) Quantitative aspects of pyrolysis/gas-liquid chromatography of some vinyl polymers. J. Chromatogr., 40, 1-15

McLaughlin, J., Jr, Marliac, J.-P., Verrett, M.J., Mutchler, M.K. & Fitzhugh, O.G. (1963) The injection of chemicals into the yolk sac of fertile eggs prior to incubation as a toxicity test. Toxicol. appl. Pharmacol., 5, 760-771

McLaughlin, J., Jr, Marliac, J.-P., Verrett, M.J., Mutchler, M.K. & Fitzhugh, O.G. (1964) Toxicity of fourteen volatile chemicals as measured by the chick embryo method. Am. ind. Hyg. Assoc. J., 25, 282-284

McMichael, A.J., Spirtas, R., Gamble, J.F. & Tousey, P.M. (1976) Mortality among rubber workers: relationship to specific jobs. J. occup. Med., 18, 178-185

de Meester, C., Poncelet, F., Roberfroid, M., Rondelet, J. & Mercier, M. (1977) Mutagenicity of styrene and styrene oxide. Mutat. Res., 56, 147-152

Meretoja, T., Vainio, H., Sorsa, M. & Härkönen, H. (1977) Occupational styrene exposure and chromosomal aberrations. Mutat. Res., 56, 193-197

Meretoja, T., Vainio, H. & Järventaus, H. (1978) Clastogenic effects of styrene exposure on bone marrow cells of rat. Toxicol. Lett., 1, 315-318

Meshkova, O.V. & Dmitrieva, V.N. (1974)  Extraction polarographic determination of styrene and methylmethacrylate in plant sewage.
(Exchange of experience) (Russ.).  Zavod. Lab., 40, 28-29

Milvy, P. & Garro, A.J. (1976)  Mutagenic activity of styrene oxide
(1,2-epoxyethylbenzene), a presumed styrene metabolite.  Mutat. Res.,
40, 15-18

Morimoto, T., Takeyama, K. & Konishi, F. (1976)  Composition of gaseous
combustion products of polymers.  J. appl. Polym. Sci., 20, 1967-1976
[Chem. Abstr., 85, 63597a]

Murav'eva, S.I. & Smolyar, N.Y. (1974)  Determination of styrene in the
biological fluids of experimental animals (Russ.).  Gig. Tr. Prof.
Zabol., 9, 52-53 [Chem. Abstr., 82, 167113u]

National Institute for Occupational Safety and Health (1977a)  Health
Hazard Evaluation Determination, Fuel Economy Engineering Co.,
Spurlock Power Station, Maysville, KY, Report No. 76-8-370, US Department of Health, Education, and Welfare, Cincinnati, Ohio, pp. 1, 14-15,
29-31

National Institute for Occupational Safety and Health (1977b)  Health
Hazard Evaluation Determination, Reinell Boats, Inc., Poplar Bluff,
Missouri, Report No. 75-150-378, US Department of Health, Education,
and Welfare, Cincinnati, Ohio, pp. 1, 10-14, 21-22, 24-26

Nicholson, W.J., Selikoff, I.J. & Seidman, H. (1979)  Mortality experience
of styrene-polystyrene polymerization workers.  Initial findings.
Scand. J. Work. environ. Health, 4, Suppl. 2 (in press)

Nothdurft, H. (1956)  Experimental formation of sarcomas due to foreign
bodies (Ger.).  Strahlentherapie, 100, 192-210

Ohtsuji, H. & Ikeda, M. (1970)  A rapid colorimetric method for the determination of phenylglyoxylic and mandelic acids.  Its application to
the urinalysis of workers exposed to styrene vapour.  Br. J. ind. Med.,
27, 150-154

Ohtsuji, H. & Ikeda, M. (1971)  The metabolism of styrene in the rat and
the stimulatory effect of phenobarbital.  Toxicol. appl. Pharmacol.,
18, 321-328

Okumoto, T. & Takeuchi, T. (1972)  Rapid characterization of polymeric
materials by pyrolysis-gas chromatography (Jap.).  Nippon Kagaku
Kaishi, 1, 71-78 [Chem. Abstr., 76, 141459n]

Oltramare, M., Desbaumes, E., Imhoff, C. & Michiels, W. (1974)  Toxicology
of Styrene Monomer.  Experimental and Clinical Studies in Man (Fr.),
Geneva, Editions Médecine et Hygiene

Oppenheimer, B.S., Oppenheimer, E.T., Stout, A.P., Willhite, M. & Danishefsky, I. (1958) The latent period in carcinogenesis by plastics in rats and its relation to the presarcomatous stage. Cancer, 11, 204-213

Orlova, A.A. & Solov'eva, E.A. (1962) Clinical picture of chronic exposure to various chemicals used in synthetic rubber (Russ.). Tr. Voronezhsk. Med. Inst., 47, 86-87

Pakhomova, A.D. & Berendeeva, V.L. (1974) Identification of styrene in waste waters (Russ.). Khim. Tekhnol. (Kiev), 3, 12-13 [Chem. Abstr., 81, 158428c]

Parkes, D.G., Ganz, C.R., Polinsky, A. & Schulze, J. (1976) A simple gas chromatographic method for the analysis of trace organics in ambient air. Am. ind. Hyg. Assoc. J., 37, 165-173

Parkki, M.G., Marniemi, J. & Vainio, H. (1976) Action of styrene and its metabolites styrene oxide and styrene glycol on activities of xeno-biotic biotransformation enzymes in rat liver in vivo. Toxicol. appl. Pharmacol., 38, 59-70

Parkki, M.G., Marniemi, J., Ekfors, T., Louhivuori, A. & Aitio, A. (1979) Hepatotoxic changes in hamster by styrene. In: Proceedings of the Industrial Toxicology Meeting, Prague, 1977 (in press)

Petrova, L.I., Boikova, Z.K. & Guricheva, Z.G. (1974) Spectrophotometric determination of small amounts of styrene in extracts in the presence of low-molecular-weight substances (Russ.). Plast. Massy, 3, 72-74 [Chem. Abstr., 81, 121536k]

Platt, A.E. (1970) Styrene polymers (polymerization). In: Bikales, N.M., ed., Encyclopedia of Polymer Science and Technology, Plastics, Resins, Rubbers, Fibers, Vol. 13, New York, Interscience, pp. 156, 201

Polikarpov, G.G. & Benzhitskii, O.G. (1975) Synthetic polymer materials in the hyponeustonlogical layer of the Mediterranean (Ukrain.). Visn. Akad. Nauk Ukr. RSR, 3, 93-96 [Chem. Abstr., 83, 47816z]

Ponomarkov, V. & Tomatis, L. (1979) Effects of long-term oral administration of styrene to mice and rats. Scand. J. Work. environ. Health, 4, Suppl. 2, pp. 127-135

Post, M.A. (1967) Qualitative and quantitative determination of emulsion-polymerized binders in latex paints. J. appl. Chem., 17, 315-320

Post, M.A. (1969) Determination of styrene-butadiene and styrene-acrylate resins in solvent-type paint. J. Paint Technol., 41, 567-580 [Chem. Abstr., 71, 126049g]

Post, M.A. (1971)  Copolymer determination in surface filler.  Paint Varn.
    Prod., 61, 31-38 [Chem. Abstr., 76, 35293u]

Pratt-Johnson, J.A. (1964)  Case report.  Retrobulbar neuritis following
    exposure to vinyl benzene (styrene).  Can. med. Assoc. J., 90, 975-977

Ragule, N. (1974)  Embryotoxic action of styrene (Russ.).  Gig. i Sanit.,
    11, 85-86

Rappaport, S.M. (1975)  The identification of effluents from rubber vulcani-
    zation.  In: Ayer, F.A., ed., Proceedings of a Conference on Environ-
    mental Aspects of Chemical Use in Rubber Processing Operations,
    Washington DC, US Environmental Protection Agency, pp. 185-216

Rappaport, S.M. & Fraser, D.A. (1976)  Gas chromatographic-mass spectro-
    metric identification of volatiles released from a rubber stock during
    simulated vulcanization.  Anal. Chem., 48, 476-481

van Rees, H. (1974)  The partition coefficients of styrene between blood
    and air and between oil and blood.  Int. Arch. Arbeitsmed., 33, 39-47

Riihimäki, V. & Pfäffli, P. (1979)  Percutaneous absorption of solvent
    vapours in man.  Scand. J. Work. environ. Health (in press)

Rivière, M.R., Chouroulinkov, I. & Guérin, M. (1960)  Sarcomas produced
    by implantation of polystyrene in rats:  results appreciably different
    according to the strain of animals used (Fr.).  C.R. Soc. Biol., 154,
    485-487

Rona, A. (1971)  Instrumental investigation of adhesives used in the build-
    ing industry.  In: Symposium on Synthetic Resins in Building Con-
    struction, Paper RILEM (Reunion Int. Lab. Essais Rech. Mater. Constr.)
    1967, Vol. 2, 464-471 [Chem. Abstr., 76, 100475w]

Roy, S.S. (1977)  Titrimetric determination of residual monomers in styrene-
    acrylonitrile copolymers.  Analyst, 102, 302-305

Rudd, J.F. (1970)  Styrene polymers, physical properties - general.  In:
    Bikales, N.M., ed., Encyclopedia of Polymer Science and Technology,
    Plastics, Resins, Rubbers, Fibers, Vol. 13, New York, Interscience,
    pp. 243-244, 251

Ryan, A.J., James, M.O., Ben-Zvi, Z., Law, F.C.P. & Bend, J.R. (1976)
    Hepatic and extrahepatic metabolism of [14]C-styrene oxide.  Environ.
    Health Perspect., 17, 135-144

Ryska, M. (1974)  Use of mass spectrometry in thermal analysis of polymers
    (Russ.).  Sb. Vys. Sk. Chem.-Technol. Praze, Technol. Paliv, D30,
    335-344 [Chem. Abstr., 83, 200931e]

Safe Drinking Water Committee (1977) Drinking Water and Health, Washington DC, National Academy of Sciences, pp. 763-765, 796-797

Saltman, W.M. (1965) Butadiene polymers. In: Bikales, N.M., ed., Encyclopedia of Polymer Science and Technology, Plastics, Resins, Rubbers, Fibers, Vol. 2, New York, Interscience, pp. 678-679, 754

Savolainen, H. & Pfäffli, P. (1977) Effects of chronic styrene inhalation on rat brain protein metabolism. Acta neuropath. (Berlin), 40, 237-241

Savolainen, H. & Vainio, H. (1977) Organ distribution and nervous system binding of styrene and styrene oxide. Toxicology, 8, 135-141

Selerowicz, A. (1976) Simple methods for the identification of thermoplastics (Pol.). Mechanik, 49, 30-31

Seppäläinen, A.M. & Härkönen, H. (1976) Neurophysiological findings among workers occupationally exposed to styrene. Scand. J. Work. environ. Health, 3, 140-146

Seves, A. & Croce, A. (1970) Identification of binders in coating colors (Ital.). Ind. Carta, 8, 53-59 [Chem. Abstr., 73, 26816c]

Seves, A., Croce, A. & Brizzi, P. (1972) Gas chromatography by pyrolysis for the identification of coating binders (Ital.). Ind. Carta, 10, 271-280 [Chem. Abstr., 77, 154171h]

Shackelford, W.M. & Keith, L.H. (1976) Frequency of Organic Compounds Identified in Water, EPA-600/4-76-062, Athens, Ga, US Environmental Protection Agency, pp. 213-214

Shugaev, B.B. (1969) Concentrations of hydrocarbons in tissues as a measure of toxicity. Arch. environ. Health, 18, 878-882

Simko, A., Jindřichová, J. & Pultarová, H. (1966) The effect of styrene on the health state of workers employed in laminate-production (Czech.). Pracov. Lék., 18, 348-352

Slob, A. (1973) A new method for determination of mandelic acid excretion at low level styrene exposure. Br. J. ind. Med., 30, 390-393

Smith, A.H. & Ellis, L. (1977) Styrene butadiene rubber synthetic plants and leukemia. J. occup. Med., 19, 441

Spagnolo, F. (1974) Ultraviolet determination of polystyrene in paper products. Appl. Spectrosc., 28, 259-261 [Chem. Abstr., 81, 123224f]

Spencer, H.C., Irish, D.D., Adams, E.M. & Rowe, V.K. (1942) The response of laboratory animals to monomeric styrene. J. ind. Hyg. Toxicol., 24, 295-301

Steichen, R.J. (1976) Modified solution approach for the gas chromatographic determination of residual monomers by head-space analysis.
Anal. Chem., 48, 1398-1402

Stewart, R.D., Dodd, H.C., Baretta, E.D. & Schaffer, A.W. (1968) Human
exposure to styrene vapor. Arch. environ. Health, 16, 656-662

Stöfen, D. (1973) The maximum permissible concentrations in the USSR for
harmful substances in drinking water. Toxicology, 1, 187-195

Sulzbacher, M. (1972) Hydrocarbons. Styrene. In: Codd, L.W.,
Dijkhoff, K., Fearon, J.H., Van Oss, C.J., Roebersenn, H.G. &
Stanford, G., eds, Chemical Technology: An Encyclopedic Treatment,
Vol. IV, New York, Barnes & Noble, pp. 178-179

Swiatecka, M. & Zowall, H. (1975) Determination of residual blowing agent
and styrene in styrofoam by gas chromatography (Pol.). Polimery
(Warsaw), 20, 33-34 [Chem. Abstr., 84, 5742n]

Taulbee, J., Andjelkovic, D., Williams, T., Gamble, J.F. & Wolf, P. (1976)
A study of possible associations between exposure to SBR processes and
mortality from leukemia and related diseases based on toxicologic,
industrial hygiene and epidemiologic considerations (for workers in
the 1951 and 1964 cohorts and deaths 1964-1973). In: Ede, L., ed.,
Proceedings of NIOSH Styrene-Butadiene Briefing, Covington, Kentucky,
1976, HEW Publ. No. (NIOSH) 77-129, Cincinnati, Ohio, US Department
of Health, Education, and Welfare, pp. 113-162

Union Carbide Corporation (1957) Toxicology studies: Styrene, New York,
Industrial Medicine and Toxicology Department

US Department of Commerce (1977a) US Imports for Consumption and General
Imports, TSUSA Commodity by Country of Origin, FT 246/Annual 1976,
Bureau of the Census, Washington DC, US Government Printing Office,
pp. 217-218

US Department of Commerce (1977b) US Exports, Schedule B Commodity
Groupings, Schedule B Commodity by Country, FT410/December, Bureau
of the Census, Washington DC, US Government Printing Office,
pp. 2-73-2-74, 2-121

US Environmental Protection Agency (1975) Preliminary Assessment of
Suspected Carcinogens in Drinking Water, Report to Congress,
Washington DC, pp. II-7

US Food and Drug Administration (1977) Food and drugs. US Code Fed.
Regul., Title 21, parts 172.515, 175.105, 175.300, 175.320, 176.170,
177.1010, 177.1640, 177.1810, 177.1820, 177.1830, 177.2420, 177.2600,
177.2710, 177.2800, 178.3790, 179.45, pp. 376, 382, 438, 448, 452, 455,
465-466, 471, 478, 481, 496, 531-533, 535-537, 548-549, 555, 557-560,
596, 607-608

US International Trade Commission (1977a) Synthetic Organic Chemicals, US Production and Sales, 1975, USITC Publication 804, Washington DC, US Government Printing Office, pp. 22, 41

US International Trade Commission (1977b) Synthetic Organic Chemicals, US Production and Sales, 1976, USITC Publication 833, Washington DC, US Government Printing Office, pp. 27, 30

US Occupational Safety and Health Administration (1976) Occupational safety and health standards, subpart Z - toxic and hazardous substances. US Code Fed. Regul., Title 29, Chapter XVII, Section 1910.1000, p. 31:8304

US Tariff Commission (1938) Dyes and Other Synthetic Organic Chemicals in the US, 1937, Report No. 132, Second Series, Washington DC, US Government Printing Office, p. 45

US Tariff Commission (1939) Synthetic Organic Chemicals, US Production and Sales, 1938, Report No. 136, Second Series, Washington DC, US Government Printing Office, p. 15

Vainio, H. & Mäkinen, A. (1977) Styrene and acrylonitrile induced depression of hepatic nonprotein sulfhydryl content in various rodent species. Res. Commun. chem. Pathol. Pharmacol., 17, 115-124

Vainio, H., Pääkkönen, R., Rönnholm, K., Raunio, V. & Pelkonen, O. (1976) A study on the mutagenic activity of styrene and styrene oxide. Scand. J. Work. environ. Health, 3, 147-151

Vainio, H., Hemminki, K. & Elovaara, E. (1977) Toxicity of styrene and styrene oxide on chick embryos. Toxicology, 8, 319-325

Vrba, J., Mádlo, Z. & Kovář, V. (1967) A study on styrene metabolism in the rat by means of gas chromatography (Czech.). Cs. Hyg., 12, 477-478

Wancheck, P.L. & Wolfram, L.E. (1976) Quantitative analysis of styrene monomer in styrene/butadiene latexes using Raman spectroscopy. Appl. Spectrosc., 30, 542-544

Weast, R.C., ed. (1976) CRC Handbook of Chemistry and Physics, 57th ed., Cleveland, Ohio, Chemical Rubber Co., p. C-500

Wilson, R.H., Hough, G.V. & McCormick, W.E. (1948) Medical problems encountered in the manufacture of American-made rubber. Ind. Med., 17, 199-207

Windholz, M., ed. (1976) The Merck Index, 9th ed., Rahway, NJ, Merck & Co., p. 1146

Winell, M. (1975)  An international comparison of hygienic standards for chemicals in the work environment. Ambio, 4, 34-36

Withey, J.R. (1976)  Quantitative analysis of styrene monomer in poly-styrene and foods including some preliminary studies of the uptake and pharmacodynamics of the monomer in rats.  Environ. Health Perspect., 17, 125-133

Withey, J.R. & Collins, P.G. (1978)  Styrene monomer in foods.  A limited Canadian survey.  Bull. environ. Contam. Toxicol., 19, 86-94

Wolf, M.A., Rowe, V.K., McCollister, D.D., Hollingsworth, R.L. & Oyen, F. (1956)  Toxicological studies of certain alkylated benzenes and benzene.  Arch. ind. Health, 14, 387-398

Wolff, M.S. (1976)  Evidence for existence in human tissues of monomers for plastics and rubber manufacture.  Environ. Health Perspect., 17, 183-187

Wolff, M.S., Daum, S.M., Lorimer, W.V., Selikoff, I.J. & Aubrey, B.B. (1977) Styrene and related hydrocarbons in subcutaneous fat from polymeriza-tion workers.  J. Toxicol. environ. Health, 2, 997-1005

Yamashita, T., Katsura, H. & Mori, Y. (1976)  Hygienic study on polystyrene containers.  I.  Determination of trace amounts of styrene monomer in milk products (Jap.).  Shokuhin Eiseigaku Zasshi, 17, 187-192 [Chem. Abstr., 85, 61572q]

Zeman, A. (1972)  Identification of high polymers by thermal degradation in the mass spectrometer.  In: Wiedemann, H.G., ed., Proceedings of the 3rd International Conference on Thermal Analysis, 1971, Vol. 3, Basel, Birkhaeuser, pp. 219-227 [Chem. Abstr., 78, 148551m]

Zielhuis, R.L. (1961)  Systemic toxicity from exposure to epoxy resins, hardeners, and styrene.  J. occup. Med., 3, 25-29

Zizin, V.G., Kazakova, M.G., Fainulin, I.F. & Perina, Y.V. (1974) Determination of monomers in polymer products (Russ.).  Zavod. Lab., 40, 929-931 [Chem. Abstr., 82, 18285z]

## STYRENE OXIDE

This substance was considered by a previous IARC Working Group, in February 1976 (IARC, 1976). Since that time new data have become available, and these have been incorporated into the monograph and taken into account in the present evaluation.

## 1. Chemical and Physical Data

### 1.1 Synonyms and trade names

Chem. Abstr. Services Reg. No.: 96-09-3

Chem. Abstr. Name: Phenyloxirane

(Epoxyethyl)benzene; 1,2-epoxyethylbenzene; epoxystyrene; $\alpha,\beta$-epoxystyrene; phenethylene oxide; 1-phenyl-1,2-epoxyethane; phenylethylene oxide; 2-phenyloxirane; styrene epoxide; styryl oxide

### 1.2 Structural and molecular formulae and molecular weight

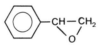

$C_8H_8O$                Mol. wt: 120.2

### 1.3 Chemical and physical properties of the pure substance

From Weast (1976), unless otherwise specified

(a) Description: Colourless-to-pale-straw-coloured liquid (Hawley, 1971)

(b) Boiling-point: 194.1°C

(c) Melting-point: -36.6°C (Hawley, 1971)

(d) Density: $d_4^{16}$ 1.0523

(e) Refractive index: $n_D^{20}$ 1.5342

(f)  Spectroscopy data:  $\lambda_{max}$ 250 nm (shoulder), 254 nm, 260 nm, 265 nm (shoulder) ($E_1^1$ = 13.2, 14.5, 16, 10);  infra-red, Raman, nuclear magnetic resonance and mass spectral data have been tabulated (Grasselli & Ritchey, 1975).

(g)  Solubility:  Slightly soluble in water (0.28% at 25°C); miscible with methanol, ether, carbon tetrachloride, benzene and acetone (Hine & Rowe, 1963)

(h)  Volatility:  Vapour pressure is 0.3 mm at 20°C (Hine & Rowe, 1963).

(i)  Stability:  Flash-point is 80°C (Hine & Rowe, 1963).

(j)  Reactivity:  Polymerizes exothermally and reacts vigorously with compounds possessing a labile hydrogen (e.g., alcohols), in the presence of catalysts such as acids, bases and certain salts (Hine & Rowe, 1967)

(k)  Conversion factor:  1 ppm in air = 4.9 mg/m³

## 1.4  Technical products and impurities

Styrene oxide (98 mol % pure) available in the US has the following specifications:  density, 1.0490-1.0515 (25/25°C);  distillation range at 760 mm:  fraction between 5 and 95% by volume shall boil within a 3.0°C range, which includes the temperature 194.1°C;  water, 0.25% by wt max (Mack *et al.*, 1967).

In Japan, styrene oxide is available commercially with a minimum purity of 98% and contains mono- and dichloroethylbenzene and unreacted styrene monomer as impurities.  Additional specifications include:  specific gravity, 1.0530-1.0560 (20/20°C);  refractive index, 1.5330-1.5355 (20°C);  boiling-point, 194.1°C;  and water, 0.1% max.

## 2.  Production, Use, Occurrence and Analysis

### 2.1  Production and use

#### (a)  Production

Styrene oxide was prepared in 1905 from α-phenyl-β-iodoethanol by treatment with potassium hydroxide (Fourneau & Tiffeneau, 1905).  It is produced commercially either by the chlorhydrin route or by epoxidation of styrene with peroxyacetic acid (Lapkin, 1967).

Commercial production of styrene oxide in the US was first reported in 1974 (US International Trade Commission, 1976). Annual production of the one US producer is 450-900 thousand kg.

Styrene oxide has been produced commercially in Japan since 1964. One company produced 1.8 million kg in 1976, and 10 thousand kg were exported.

(b)  Use

Styrene oxide is used as a reactive diluent in epoxy resins to reduce the viscosity of mixed systems prior to curing (Lee & Neville, 1967). It is also used as an intermediate in the preparation of agricultural and biological chemicals, cosmetics, surface coatings, and in the treatment of textiles and fibres.

In Japan, styrene oxide is used as a raw material for the production of phenylstearyl alcohol used in perfume.

In the US, the Food and Drug Administration has ruled that styrene oxide may be used as a catalyst and cross-linking agent for epoxy resins in coatings for containers with a capacity of 1000 gallons (3785 1) or more when such containers are intended for repeated use in contact with beverages containing up to 8% of alcohol by volume (US Food & Drug Administration, 1977).

2.2  Occurrence

Styrene oxide has been detected as a volatile component of a Burley tobacco concentrate (Demole & Berthet, 1972), as a by-product in commercial samples of styrene chlorhydrin (Dolgopolov & Lishcheta, 1971), and in effluent water from latex manufacturing plants in Louisville, Kentucky, and from chemical manufacturing plants in Louisville and in Memphis, Tennessee (Shackelford & Keith, 1976).

2.3  Analysis

Styrene oxide can be determined volumetrically in epoxide-glycol mixtures (Swan, 1954). It has been analysed by thin-layer chromatography at the microgram level (Dolgopolov & Lishcheta, 1971; Kulicka *et al.*, 1967) and in biological media by gas chromatography with flame-ionization detection and thin-layer chromatography of the picrate (Leibman & Ortiz, 1970). It has also been determined at the nanomole level by indirect spectrophotometry (Mishmash & Meloan, 1972).

The quantity of styrene oxide produced by the action of styrene oxidase on styrene has been determined by hydration to styrene glycol, followed by esterification using pentafluorobenzoyl chloride to a highly sensitive derivative analysed by gas chromatography-electron capture detection. The limit of detection was 0.01 ng/injection (van Bogaert *et al.*, 1978).

### 3. Biological Data Relevant to the Evaluation

### of Carcinogenic Risk to Humans

## 3.1 Carcinogenicity studies in animals[1]

### Skin application

Mouse: Forty 13-week-old C3H mice were painted on the clipped dorsal skin with a 5% solution of styrene oxide in acetone thrice weekly for life. No skin tumours were observed in 33 animals that survived 17-24 months (37 mice were alive at 12 months). Another group of C3H mice were similarly painted with a 10% solution of styrene oxide in acetone; 18 mice survived 12 months, only 2 mice survived to 17 months, and no skin tumours were observed (Weil *et al.*, 1963).

Of 30 8-week-old male Swiss ICR/Ha mice given thrice weekly applications of 0.1 ml of a 10% solution of styrene oxide in benzene on the clipped dorsal skin for life, 3 developed skin tumours; one of these was a squamous-cell carcinoma. The median survival time was 431 days. Of 150 benzene-painted controls, 11 developed skin tumours, and one of these was a squamous-cell carcinoma (Van Duuren *et al.*, 1963).

## 3.2 Other relevant biological data

### (a) Experimental systems

### Toxic effects

The oral $LD_{50}$ of styrene oxide in rats is 4290 mg/kg bw (Smyth *et al.*, 1954) or 3000 mg/kg bw (Weil *et al.*, 1963); the i.p. $LD_{50}$ is 460-610 mg/kg bw (Ohtsuji & Ikeda, 1971). The $LD_{50}$ by skin application in rabbits is 1060 mg/kg bw (Smyth *et al.*, 1954) or 930 mg/kg bw (Weil *et al.*, 1963). Inhalation of 4900 mg/m$^3$ (1000 ppm) in air killed 2/6 rats in 4 hours (Weil *et al.*, 1963).

Styrene oxide causes corneal injury in rabbits, even with dilutions as low as 1% (Hine & Rowe, 1963). Intradermal injections sensitized guinea-pigs (Weil *et al.*, 1963).

One i.p. dose of 375 mg/kg bw styrene oxide caused a significant decrease in the activities of mixed-function oxidases and in cytochrome P-450 content (Parkki *et al.*, 1976). Styrene oxide decreases liver gluta-thione content *in vivo* (Marniemi *et al.*, 1977).

---

[1]The Working Group was aware of studies in progress or planned to test the carcinogenicity of styrene oxide in mice and rats by oral administration (IARC, 1978).

## Embryotoxicity and teratogenicity

When styrene oxide was injected into the air space of fertilized eggs at concentrations of 0.5-5 µmol/egg, it was embryotoxic and caused malformations in developing chicks. The $LD_{50}$ for embryos was 1.5 µmol/egg when injected on the 4th day of incubation (Vainio *et al.*, 1977).

## Absorption, distribution and excretion

The main route of excretion of styrene oxide metabolites in animals is *via* the kidney; in rabbits, about 80% of a single oral dose was excreted in the urine (James & White, 1967).

## Metabolism (see also monograph on styrene, p. 240)

Styrene oxide is converted *in vitro* into styrene glycol (phenylethylene glycol) by microsomal epoxide hydrase from the liver, kidneys, intestine, lungs and skin of several mammalian species (Oesch, 1973).

The biotransformation of styrene oxide into styrene glycol was stimulated by pretreatment of rats with phenobarbital or 3-methyl cholanthrene; however, the further metabolism of styrene glycol to mandelic acid was not stimulated (Oesch *et al.*, 1971; Ohtsuji & Ikeda, 1971). Isolated perfused rat livers rapidly metabolized styrene oxide to approximately equal amounts of styrene glycol, mandelic acid and *S*-(1-phenyl-2-hydroxyethyl)glutathione (Ryan & Bend, 1977).

Styrene oxide injected intraperitoneally or incubated *in vitro* binds covalently to microsomes, protein and nucleic acid fractions of rat liver (Marniemi *et al.*, 1977).

## Mutagenicity and other short-term tests

Styrene oxide was mutagenic to *Salmonella typhimurium* TA1535 and TA100 in the absence of metabolic activation (de Meester *et al.*, 1977; Milvy & Garro, 1976; Vainio *et al.*, 1976).

A dose-dependent increase of forward mutations in *Schizosaccharomyces pombe* and gene conversion in *Saccharomyces cerevisiae* was obtained by treatment with styrene oxide (Loprieno *et al.*, 1976). In a host-mediated assay, 100 mg/kg bw styrene oxide given by gavage to male Swiss albino mice increased the frequency of gene conversions in *S. cerevisiae* but not of forward mutations in *Sch. pombe* (Loprieno *et al.*, 1976).

Styrene oxide caused a dose-dependent increase of mutation to 8-azaguanine resistance in cultured V79 Chinese hamster cells (Loprieno *et al.*, 1976).

(b)  Humans

Acute exposure to styrene oxide causes skin and eye irritation and skin sensitization.  It is absorbed slowly through the skin (Hine & Rowe, 1967).

3.3  Case reports and epidemiological studies

No data were available to the Working Group.

4.  Summary of Data Reported and Evaluation

4.1  Experimental data

Styrene oxide was tested in mice by skin application.  No increase in the incidence of skin tumours was observed.

Styrene oxide is mutagenic.

4.2  Human data

No case reports or epidemiological studies regarding the carcinogenicity of styrene oxide were available to the Working Group.  The fact that styrene oxide is used primarily as a chemical intermediate suggests that occupationally exposed groups could be identified for epidemiological investigation.

4.3  Evaluation

The data available to the Working Group do not permit an assessment of the carcinogenicity of styrene oxide.  Animal experiments and epidemiological studies should be undertaken (see also 'General Remarks on the Substances Considered', p. 35).

## 5. References

van Bogaert, M., Rollmann, B., Noël, G., Roberfroid, M. & Mercier, M. (1978)   A very sensitive gas chromatographic method for the evaluation of styrene oxidase and styrene oxide hydratase activities. Arch. Toxicol., Suppl. 1, 295-298

Demole, E. & Berthet, D. (1972)   A chemical study of Burley tobacco flavour (*Nicotiana tabacum* L.).   I.   Volatile to medium-volatile constituents (b.p. $\leq$ 84°/0.001 Torr).   Helv. chim. acta, 55, 1866-1882

Dolgopolov, V.D. & Lishcheta, L.I. (1971)   Qualitative determination of by-products in commercial samples of styrene chlorohydrin (Russ.). Khim.-Farm. Zh., 5, 55-56 [Chem. Abstr., 76, 27967b]

Fourneau & Tiffeneau (1905)   Some monosubstituted aromatic ethylene oxides (Fr.).   C.R. Acad. Sci. (Paris), 140, 1595-1597

Grasselli, J.G. & Ritchey, W.M., eds (1975)   CRC Atlas of Spectral Data and Physical Constants for Organic Compounds, 2nd ed., Vol. II, Cleveland, Ohio, Chemical Rubber Co., p. 304

Hawley, G.G., ed. (1971)   The Condensed Chemical Dictionary, 8th ed., New York, Van Nostrand-Reinhold, p. 832

Hine, C.H. & Rowe, V.K. (1963)   Epoxy compounds.   In:   Patty, F.A., ed., Industrial Hygiene and Toxicology, 2nd ed., Vol. II, New York, Interscience, pp. 1649-1651

IARC (1976)   IARC Monographs on the Evaluation of the Carcinogenic Risk of Chemicals to Man, 11, Cadmium, Nickel, Some Epoxides, Miscellaneous Industrial Chemicals and General Considerations on Volatile Anaesthetics, Lyon, pp. 201-208

IARC (1978)   Information Bulletin on the Survey of Chemicals Being Tested for Carcinogenicity, No. 7, Lyon, pp. 69, 227

James, S.P. & White, D.A. (1967)   The metabolism of phenethyl bromide, styrene and styrene oxide in the rabbit and rat.   Biochem. J., 104, 914-921

Kulicka, J., Baranowski, R. & Gregorowicz, Z. (1967)   Thin-layer chromatography of the oxidation products of ethylbenzene (Ger.).   Fresenius' Z. anal. Chem., 230, 357-359 [Chem. Abstr., 67, 104940f]

Lapkin, M. (1967)   Epoxides.   In:   Kirk, R.E. & Othmer, D.F., eds, Encyclopedia of Chemical Technology, 2nd ed., Vol. 8, New York, John Wiley and Sons, p. 289

Lee, N. & Neville, K. (1967)  Handbook of Epoxy Resins, New York, McGraw-Hill, p. 13-10

Leibman, K.C. & Ortiz, E. (1970)  Epoxide intermediates in microsomal oxidation of olefins to glycols.  J. Pharmacol. exp. Ther., 173, 242-246

Loprieno, N., Abbondandolo, A., Barale, R., Baroncelli, S., Bonatti, S., Bronzetti, G., Cammellini, A., Corsi, C., Corti, G., Frezza, D., Leporini, C., Mazzaccaro, A., Nieri, R., Rosellini, D. & Rossi, A.M. (1976)  Mutagenicity of industrial compounds:  styrene and its possible metabolite styrene oxide.  Mutat. Res., 40, 317-324

Mack, N.F., Gaylord, N.G. & Bikales, N.M., eds (1967)  Encyclopedia of Polymer Science and Technology, Plastics, Resins, Rubbers, Fibers, Vol. 6, New York, Interscience, p. 170

Marniemi, J., Suolinna, E.-M., Kaartinen, N. & Vainio, H. (1977)  Covalent binding of styrene oxide to rat liver macromolecules in vivo and in vitro.  In:  Ullrich, U., Roots, I., Hildebrandt, A., Estabrook, R.W. & Conney, A.H., eds, Microsomes and Drug Oxidations, Oxford, Pergamon Press, pp. 698-702

de Meester, C., Poncelet, F., Roberfroid, M., Rondelet, J. & Mercier, M. (1977)  Mutagenicity of styrene and styrene oxide.  Mutat. Res., 56, 147-152

Milvy, P. & Garro, A.J. (1976)  Mutagenic activity of styrene oxide(1,2-epoxyethylbenzene), a presumed styrene metabolite.  Mutat. Res., 40, 15-18

Mishmash, H.E. & Meloan, C.E. (1972)  Indirect spectrophotometric determination of nanomole quantities of oxiranes.  Anal. Chem., 44, 835-836

Oesch, F. (1973)  Mammalian epoxide hydrases:  inducible enzymes catalysing the inactivation of carcinogenic and cytotoxic metabolites derived from aromatic and olefinic compounds.  Xenobiotica, 3, 305-340

Oesch, F., Jerina, D.M. & Daly, J. (1971)  A radiometric assay for hepatic epoxide hydrase activity with [7-$^3$H]-styrene oxide.  Biochim. biophys. acta, 227, 685-691

Ohtsuji, H. & Ikeda, M. (1971)  The metabolism of styrene in the rat and the stimulatory effect of phenobarbital.  Toxicol. appl. Pharmacol., 18, 321-328

Parkki, M.G., Marniemi, J. & Vainio, H. (1976)  Action of styrene and its metabolites styrene oxide and styrene glycol on activities of xenobiotic biotransformation enzymes in rat liver in vivo.  Toxicol. appl. Pharmacol., 38, 59-70

Ryan, A.J. & Bend, J.R. (1977)  The metabolism of styrene oxide in the isolated perfused rat liver.  Identification and quantitation of major metabolites.  Drug Metab. Disposition, 5, 363–367

Shackelford, W.M. & Keith, L.H. (1976)  Frequency of Organic Compounds Identified in Water, EPA-600/4-76-062, Athens, Ga, US Environmental Protection Agency, p. 214

Smyth, H.F., Jr, Carpenter, C.P., Weil, C.S. & Pozzani, U.C. (1954)  Range-finding toxicity data. List V. Arch. ind. Hyg. occup. Med., 10, 61–68

Swan, J.D. (1954)  Determination of epoxides with sodium sulfite.  Anal. Chem., 26, 878–880

US Food and Drug Administration (1977)  Food and drugs.  US Code Fed. Regul., Title 21, part 175.300, pp. 452, 454

US International Trade Commission (1976)  Synthetic Organic Chemicals, US Production and Sales, 1974, USITC Publication 776, Washington DC, US Government Printing Office, p. 44

Van Duuren, B.L., Nelson, N., Orris, L., Palmes, E.D. & Schmitt, F.L. (1963)  Carcinogenicity of epoxides, lactones, and peroxy compounds.  J. natl Cancer Inst., 31, 41–55

Vainio, H., Pääkkönen, R., Rönnholm, K., Raunio, V. & Pelkonen, O. (1976)  A study on the mutagenic activity of styrene and styrene oxide.  Scand. J. Work. environ. Health, 3, 147–151

Vainio, H., Hemminki, K. & Elovaara, E. (1977)  Toxicity of styrene and styrene oxide on chick embryos.  Toxicology, 8, 319–325

Weast, R.C., ed. (1976)  CRC Handbook of Chemistry and Physics, 57th ed., Cleveland, Ohio, Chemical Rubber Co., p. C-164

Weil, C.S., Condra, N., Haun, C. & Striegel, J.A. (1963)  Experimental carcinogenicity and acute toxicity of representative epoxides.  Am. ind. Hyg. Assoc. J., 24, 305–325

TETRAFLUOROETHYLENE and
POLYTETRAFLUOROETHYLENE

## Tetrafluoroethylene

### 1.  Chemical and Physical Data

### 1.1  Synonyms and trade names

Chem. Abstr. Services Reg. No.:  116-14-3

Chem. Abstr. Name:  Tetrafluoroethene

Perfluoroethene;  perfluoroethylene

### 1.2  Structural and molecular formulae and molecular weight

$$\underset{F}{\overset{F}{>}}C=C\underset{F}{\overset{F}{<}}$$

$C_2F_4$                    Mol. wt:  100

### 1.3  Chemical and physical properties of the pure substance

From Weast (1976), unless otherwise specified

(a)  Description:  Colourless gas (Hawley, 1971)

(b)  Boiling-point:  $-76.3^{\circ}C$

(c)  Melting-point:  $-142.5^{\circ}C$

(d)  Density:  $d^{-76.3}$ 1.519 (Grasselli & Ritchey, 1975);  vapour density about 3 (air = 1) (Anon., 1972)

(e)  Spectroscopy data:  Infra-red and mass spectral data have been tabulated (Grasselli & Ritchey, 1975).

(f)  Solubility:  Insoluble in water

(g)  Stability:  Inflammable at 14-43% by volume in air at 760 mm (McCane, 1970)

(h)  Reactivity: Polymerizes at high pressure (McCane, 1970)

(i)  Conversion factor: 1 ppm in air = 4 mg/m$^3$

## 1.4  Technical products and impurities

A highly purified grade of tetrafluoroethylene is required for commercial production of polytetrafluoroethylene. Polymerization stabilizers such as dipentene, terpinolene and α-pinene are added if the tetrafluoroethylene is to be transported.

## 2.  Production, Use, Occurrence and Analysis

### 2.1  Production and use

(a)  Production

Tetrafluoroethylene was first prepared in 1933 by decomposition of tetrafluoromethane in an electric arc (McCane, 1970). It is produced commercially by the pyrolysis of chlorodifluoromethane at temperatures of 590-800°C.

Commercial production of tetrafluoroethylene in the US was first reported in 1960 (US Tariff Commission, 1961). In 1975, four companies reported production of 7.9 million kg (US International Trade Commission, 1977a), down from 11.2 million kg in 1974 (US International Trade Commission, 1976).

Six manufacturers in western Europe produced 11.5 million kg tetrafluoroethylene in 1977.

It was first produced commercially in Japan in 1953. In 1976, four companies produced a total of about 2-2.5 million kg.

Worldwide production of tetrafluoroethylene in 1977 is estimated to have been 15-20 million kg.

(b)  Use

Virtually all tetrafluoroethylene produced in the US is used as a monomer for the production of homopolymers, copolymers and terpolymers. The major end-product is the homopolymer, polytetrafluoroethylene (PTFE); in 1974, about 7.3 million kg PTFE were used in the US. For a detailed description of the uses of PTFE, see p. 291.

Use of tetrafluoroethylene copolymers and terpolymer is the US amounted to 1.4-1.6 million kg in 1974. Three copolymer resins are made by one US company: fluorinated ethylenepropylene (FEP) resins, copolymers of tetrafluoroethylene and hexafluoropropylene; ethylene-tetrafluoroethylene (ETFE)

resins;  and perfluoroalkoxy resins (PFA), copolymers of tetrafluoroethylene and perfluoropropyl vinyl ether.  In general, the copolymers are a
compromise of PTFE properties, resulting in lower temperature and specific
chemical resistance.  A terpolymer resin, vinylidene fluoride-hexafluoro-
propylene-tetrafluoroethylene, is used as a fluoroelastomer for:  (1)
applications requiring heat and fluid resistance or flame resistance for
oxygen-enriched atmospheres;  (2) critical automotive and aerospace components;  (3) high vacuum equipment;  and (4) equipment involving the use of
cryogenic temperatures and radiation.

FEP resins are used primarily in electrical applications:  75% for
wire and cable insulation and 25% for moulded electrical parts such as coil
forms and tube sockets.  Chemical applications of FEP resins include heat
exchangers, laboratory ware, lined pipe and overbraided hose.  FEP resins
are also used in mechanical parts, e.g., chute liners, conveyor belt
coatings, roll covers and seals.

ETFE resins are mainly used in wire and cable insulation but are also
used in moulded parts for chemical processing equipment, electronic components, automotive parts, labware and liners for valves and fittings.

PFA resins are used mainly in injection-moulded articles for the chemical processing industry and as injection- or transfer-moulded liners for
valves, pumps, pipes and fittings.  They are also used for a variety of
tubing, in film and roll covers, in wire insulation, and in extruded shapes
and profiles.

Total use of tetrafluoroethylene in the European Economic Community
in 1973 is estimated to have been 6.9 million kg.  Essentially all of the
monomer is used for production of fluorinated polymers, and more than two-
thirds is used for the homopolymer.

In Japan, 70-80% of tetrafluoroethylene is used for the production of
PTFE and 20-30% for FEP resins, ETFE resins and PFA resins.

## 2.2  Occurrence

Tetrafluoroethylene is not known to occur as a natural product.

No data were available concerning the content of tetrafluoroethylene
in typical commercial grade PTFE;  the very low boiling-point of tetrafluoroethylene suggests that the level of residues would be very small.

Tetrafluoroethylene has been detected as a decomposition product (1)
when PTFE is heated in the absence of air (more than 90% of the decomposition product is tetrafluoroethylene) (Zapp, 1962);  (2) during the high-
temperature (400°C) processing of PTFE resins (Marchenko, 1966);  and (3)
as a result of pyrolysis of PTFE in air at 450°C (Waritz, 1975).

2.3  Analysis

Gas chromatography has been used to separate and detect tetrafluoroethylene in air, with a limit of detection of 7 mg/m$^3$ (2 ppm) (Dolgina
et al., 1966), and to detect tetrafluoroethylene in the pyrolysis products
of PTFE (Waritz, 1975).

## 3.  Biological Data Relevant to the Evaluation

### of Carcinogenic Risk to Humans

3.1  Carcinogenicity studies in animals

No data were available to the Working Group.

3.2  Other relevant biological data

(a)  Experimental systems

The LC$_{50}$ in rats is 160 g/m$^3$ (40 000 ppm) in air for a 4-hour exposure
(Clayton, 1967).  Male rats exposed to 14 g/m$^3$ (3500 ppm) tetrafluoroethylene in air for 30 minutes excreted small amounts of fluoride ion in
the urine over a 14-day period, indicating that the compound can be metabolized.  No gross pathology was noted in any of the organs (Dilley et al.,
1974).

No data on the embryotoxicity or mutagenicity of this compound were
available to the Working Group.

(b)  Humans

No data were available to the Working Group.

3.3  Case reports and epidemiological studies

No data were available to the Working Group.

Polytetrafluoroethylene

## 1.  Chemical and Physical Data

1.1  Synonyms and trade names

Chem. Abstr. Services Reg. No.:  9002-84-0

Chem. Abstr. Name:  Tetrafluoroethene homopolymer

Poly(ethylene tetrafluoride); polytef; polytetrafluoroethene; PTFE; tetrafluoroethene polymer; tetrafluoroethylene homopolymer; tetrafluoroethylene polymers

Aflon; Algloflon; Algoflon SV; Alkathene RXDG33; AMIP 15M; Balfon 7000; BDH 29-801; Chromosorb T; Dixon 164; Duroid 5870; EK 1108GY-A; Ethicon PTFE; F 103; FBF 74D; F 4K20; Fluo-Kem; Fluon; Fluon CD 1; Fluon CD 023; Fluon CD 042; Fluon G4; Fluon G163; Fluon G201; Fluon GPI; Fluon L 169; Fluon L 170; Fluon L 171; Fluon L 169B; Fluoroflex; Fluorolon 4; Fluoropak 80; Fluoroplast 4B; Fluoroplast 4D; Fluoroplast 4M; Fluoropore FP 120; F 4MB; FN 3; FT-4; Ftorlon 4; Ftorlon 4M; Ftorlon F-4MB; Ftoroplast 4; Ftoroplast 4B; Ftoroplast 4D; Ftoroplast F-4; Ftoroplast F 4MB; Ftoroplast FBF 74D; Ftoroplast 4K20; Ftoroplast 4M; F 4Zh20; G 163; GORE-TEX; Halon G 80; Halon G 183; Halon G 700; Halon TFEG 180; Heydeflon; Hostaflon; Hostaflon TF; L 169; Molykote 522; Polifen; Politef; Polyfene; Polyflon; Polyflon D 1; Polyflon EK 4108GY; Polyflon EK 1108GY-A; Polyflon F 103; Polyflon M 12; Polyflon M 21; Polyflon M12A; PTFE-GM3; Soreflon 604; Soreflon 5A; T 8A; Tarflen; T 5B; TE 30; Teflon; Teflon 5; Teflon 6; Teflon 30; Teflon 110; Teflon 6C; Teflon K; Teflon T5; Teflon T 6; Teflon T 30; Tetran 30; Tetran PTFE; TL 102; TL 115; TL 125; TL 126; TL-R; TL-V; Unon P; Valflon; Zitex H 662-124; Zitex K 223-122

## 1.2 Structural and molecular formulae and molecular weight

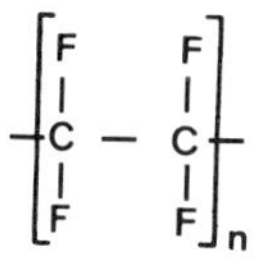

$$\left[\begin{array}{cc} F & F \\ | & | \\ C & - & C \\ | & | \\ F & F \end{array}\right]_n$$

$(C_2F_4)_n$                Mol. wt: 400 000-10 000 000

1.3  Chemical and physical properties of the polymer

From Windholz (1976), unless otherwise specified

(a)  Description: Soft, waxy, milk-white solid with a low coefficient of friction (Hawley, 1971)

(b)  Melting-point: Gels at 325°C

(c)  Density: 2.25

(d)  Solubility: No substance has been found which will dissolve the polymer.

(e)  Stability: Upon heating, weight loss varies from 0.001%/hr at 290°C to 4%/hr at 450°C (Waritz, 1975). Polytetrafluoroethylene (PTFE) has been degraded at various temperatures, and the following compounds were detected: (1) at 450°C, tetrafluoroethylene (Waritz, 1975); (2) at 460°C, hexafluoropropylene (Waritz, 1975); (3) at 475°C, perfluoroisobutylene (Waritz, 1975); (4) between 500°-650°C, carbonyl fluoride (Coleman et al., 1968); (5) above 650°C, carbon tetrafluoride and carbon dioxide (Coleman et al., 1968). When PTFE was burned in air in an electric oven at 475-575°C, the pH of the exhaust gases was 2.5, and fluoride ion was detected at a level of 1580 ppm (vol/vol) (van Grimbergen et al., 1975) [For studies of the toxic properties of thermal degradation products, see section 3.2 (a)].

(f)  Reactivity: Ignites in fluorine-oxygen mixtures under extreme conditions.

1.4  Technical products and impurities

PTFE is available in three forms: (1) granular, for moulded parts and for extruding thick-walled tubing and rods; (2) coagulated dispersions (also referred to as fine powders), for extruding thin sections; and (3) aqueous dispersions, for coating, impregnation and preparation of fibres and films. Filled polymers are also available; these are generally made by mixing fillers such as glass fibre, graphite, molybdenum disulphide, metal oxides or ceramics and finely-divided granular PTFE. Reprocessed scrap and off-grade material is also used.

No detailed information on the possible presence of unreacted monomer in the polymer was available to the Working Group.

## 2. Production, Use, Occurrence and Analysis

### 2.1 Production and use

#### (a) Production

PTFE was first isolated in 1938 by Plunkett (McCane, 1970); it is manufactured commercially by the polymerization of tetrafluoroethylene at 7-70 atmospheres (5320-53 200 mm) in the presence of water and free-radical initiators (e.g., peroxydisulphates and organic peroxides).

Commercial production in the US was first reported in 1960 (US Tariff Commission, 1961). In 1976, three companies reported production of 7.1 million kg (US International Trade Commission, 1977b), a reduction from the 8.4 million kg reported in 1974 (US International Trade Commission, 1976). US imports of PTFE amounted to 600 thousand kg in 1976 and were from the following countries (per cent of total): the Federal Republic of Germany (43), France (40), Japan (11) and the UK (6) (US Department of Commerce, 1977). Data on exports of PTFE itself are not available; however, exports of all fluoropolymers (of which PTFE is the major component) are over 450 thousand kg per year.

Six companies in western Europe produce PTFE, and it is also believed to be produced in the USSR. Production in western Europe in 1977 was 7.5 million kg.

PTFE has been produced commercially in Japan since 1953; two companies currently manufacture it. Total production of all fluoropolymers based on tetrafluoroethylene in Japan amounted to 1.15 million kg in 1975.

Production facilities were reported to have been started in the People's Republic of China in 1965.

Worldwide production of PTFE in 1977 is estimated to have been 15-20 million kg.

#### (b) Use

Of the 7.3 million kg PTFE resins sold in the US in 1974, 69% was in granular resin form (including over 1 million kg of reprocessed scrap and off-grade material and over 1 million kg of filled PTFE, which contains 75-80% resins); 15% in coagulated dispersions (fine powders); and 16% in aqueous dispersions.

PTFE was used in the US in 1974 in chemical equipment (36%), and mechanical (25%), electrical (20%) and miscellaneous applications (19%).

The primary chemical equipment applications are in fluid handling parts (e.g., valve and pump linings, dip tubes, expansion bellows, nozzles, valve seats), packings, basic shapes (rods, sheets and tubes) and in over-braided hose. The major mechanical applications for PTFE are in seals and piston rings (e.g., fluid transmission systems, hydraulic cylinders and nonlubricated compressors) and in machine bearings and bearing pads, and, to a lesser extent, in mechanical tapes and impregnated glass fabrics. Wire and cable insulations account for over 85% of the PTFE used in electrical/electronic applications; it is also used in electrical compo-nents such as cable connectors, circuit breakers and stand-off insulators. Miscellaneous applications include anti-stick uses (coatings for consumer products, e.g., cooking utensils and tools, and coatings for industrial products, such as conveyor belts, chute liners, rolls and roller covers), fibres and lubricant powders.

In 1975, an estimated 5000 kg PTFE were used in Europe and the US in the manufacture of plastic materials for medical applications, such as (1) vascular grafts when fabricated into textiles; (2) knitted fabrics for the treatment of aneurysms; (3) heart valves and aorta implants; (4) shunts in haemodialysis equipment; (5) bone replacements (e.g., ossicles in the ear); and (6) injections near the vocal cords for the treatment of dysphonia (Halpern & Karo, 1977).

Use of PTFE in western Europe in 1977 was as follows: mechanical industry (30-45%), chemical industry (35%), electric/electronic industry (15-20%) and miscellaneous applications such as industrial coatings, house-wares (10-15%).

In Japan, PTFE is used in chemical equipment (37%), appliances (31%), electrical/electronics (16%) and miscellaneous applications (16%).

Worldwide consumption of PTFE in 1974 is estimated to have been 13.6 million kg.

The US Food and Drug Administration permits the use of PTFE as a compo-nent of adhesives and in resinous and polymeric coatings (as release agents) intended for use in contact with food (US Food and Drug Administration, 1977).

## 2.2 Occurrence

PTFE is not known to occur as a natural product.

PTFE dust has been detected in workplace environments during the thermal processing of fluoroplastics (Okawa & Polakoff, 1973, 1974).

## 2.3 Analysis

PTFE elastomer has been identified by differential thermal analysis (Sircar & Lammond, 1972); and mass spectrometry (Okawa & Polakoff, 1973; Zeman, 1972) has been used in the identification and analysis of PTFE.

### 3. Biological Data Relevant to the Evaluation
### of Carcinogenic Risk to Humans

## 3.1 Carcinogenicity studies in animals

### (a) Subcutaneous and/or intramuscular administration

Mouse: A group of 89 random-bred female Swiss mice, 7-9-weeks old, received a s.c. implant in the left flank of a square sheet of polytetrafluoroethylene (PTFE) measuring 12 x 12 x 1.2 mm. The first local tumour developed 25 weeks after implantation; a total of 11 (12.5%) fibrosarcomas were found after an average latent period of 54.5 weeks (Tomatis & Shubik, 1963) [The Working Group noted that since the implant was not retained in 9 mice and since 70 mice were still alive at the appearance of the first tumour, the effective tumour incidence should be ≈16%].

Groups of 7-9-week old random-bred Swiss mice were given a s.c. implant of a 12 x 12 x 1.2 mm square of PTFE (89 females and 61 males) or of a 15 mm diameter PTFE disc (103 females), or of a Teflon fragment corresponding to one disc (size not specified) (53 females) or of a 20 mm diameter PTFE disc (54 females and 50 males). Tumours developed around the implant in 8/89 (10%) and 1/61 (2%), 23/103 (22.7%), 10/53 (21.2%) and 7/54 (15.2%) and 4/50 (8%) mice in the above groups, respectively. No similar tumours were seen in 200 female and 100 male untreated mice. Of 50 female mice implanted with 12 x 12 x 1.2 mm square glass coverslips, 6 developed sarcomas (13.6%); and of 48 females implanted with fragments of glass corresponding to one square, 2 developed sarcomas (4.3%). The average latent period for gross, palpable tumours was 55 weeks, with 2 tumours appearing as early as the 25th week and 9 at 65 weeks after implantation. All neoplasms were fibrosarcomas, and some had angiosarcomatous areas (Tomatis, 1963) [The Working Group noted that survival rates and the time at which the experiment was terminated were not reported. Mice at risk were considered to be those that retained the implant rather than those alive at the time of the appearance of the first tumour].

A group of 19 male and 27 female 7-9-week-old inbred C57BL mice received s.c. implants of 15 x 1.2 mm PTFE discs. At 50 weeks, 13 males and 13 females were still alive. Four local sarcomas (20%) developed in 20 females that retained the implant and were considered to be at risk at weeks 39, 47, 52 and 58, and 4 local sarcomas were found in the 15 males considered to be at risk (26%) at weeks 49, 51, 60 and 91. Mice were observed for 90 weeks, at which time only 3 males and 3 females were still alive. Tumours always occurred around the discs; 1 sarcoma tested was found to be transplantable in syngeneic mice. Tumours unrelated to the implant developed in 3 females and 1 male. In a control group of 30 male and 33 female non-implanted mice that were observed for 100 weeks, no s.c. sarcomas were found; 3 females and 2 males developed spontaneous tumours (Tomatis, 1966).

A group of 40 male and 40 female 8-week-old random-bred CTM albino
mice received s.c. implants into the right flank of 15 x 1.2 mm PTFE discs
and were observed for lifespan; 18 females and 9 males developed sarcomas
around the disc, a total incidence of 38% of the 69 mice still alive at
the time of the appearance of the first tumour. Average ages at death of
tumour-bearing animals were 72 and 69 weeks for females and males, respectively. No s.c. fibrosarcomas were found in 99 male and 98 female control
mice of the same strain observed for lifespan (Tomatis & Parmi, 1971).

Three groups of 38, 38 and 39, 6-7-week-old female BALB/c, C3Hf/Dp and
C57BL/He mice received s.c. implants of PTFE discs (15 x 1.2 mm) in the
dorsal area. Fibrosarcomas developed around the discs in 17/38 (44%)
BALB/c, 36/38 (94%) C3Hf/Dp and 12/39 (30%) C57BL/He animals, with mean
latent periods of 78, 61 and 82 weeks, respectively. All surviving mice
were sacrificed at 120 weeks of age. Of the 56 tumours examined histologically, 2 were rhabdomyosarcomas and the rest were fibrosarcomas (Ménard
& Della Porta, 1976) [The Working Group noted that the incidence of tumours
was calculated on the basis of the number of mice treated initially].

Rat: In rats implanted subcutaneously with PTFE films, 4 sarcomas
were produced after 2 years, at which time 15 animals were still alive
(Oppenheimer *et al.*, 1953) [The Working Group noted the incomplete reporting of the experiment].

A group of 65 weanling Wistar rats of both sexes received single s.c.
PTFE implants (4 x 5 x 0.16 mm) in the abdominal wall; 55 rats were still
alive after 300 days and 45 at the time of appearance of the first tumour
(659 days); all rats were killed within 800 days. Two s.c. sarcomas were
induced; no tumours were observed in 20 control animals receiving glass
implants, which survived 300 days and were observed for a similar period
of time (Russell *et al.*, 1959).

Two groups of Wistar rats were implanted subcutaneously with discs of
PTFE (15 x 0.02 mm) in the abdominal wall; in one group, the discs were
perforated. The numbers of rats that survived the minimum latent period
were 34 and 32 for the groups implanted with plain and perforated discs,
respectively. Eight sarcomas (23.5%) were observed in the first group and
6 sarcomas (18.7%) in the second (Oppenheimer *et al.*, 1955) [The Working
Group noted the incomplete reporting of the study].

A group of 39 male Evans rats received s.c. implants of squares (20 x
20 mm) of PTFE mesh surgical outflow patches. A further 40 rats were
implanted with the shredded material, and 41 non-implanted rats served as
controls. The experiment was terminated 19 months later, and no local
tumours were observed; at that time, 28 controls and 24 and 23 PTFE-
implanted rats were still alive (Bryson & Bischoff, 1969) [The Working
Group noted the short period of observation].

(b) Intraperitoneal administration

Rat: Weanling Wistar rats of both sexes were implanted intraperitoneally with 10 x 2 x 2 mm PTFE rods (16 rats) or with equivalent amounts
of PTFE powder (17 rats). After 365 days, 13/16 and 10/17 animals were
still alive in the two groups, respectively, and after 800 days, 9/16 and
3/17 animals. Surviving animals were killed 27 months after implantation.
No tumours were found in rod-implanted rats, whereas 2 sarcomas became
palpable in the powder-treated animals at 354 and 476 days after implantation. Extraperitoneal tumours included 1 fibroadenoma in the inguinal
region in rod-implanted rats and 1 liposarcoma in the upper part of the
leg, 1 fibrosarcoma in the shoulder and 1 inguinal fibroadenoma in powder-
treated rats. Among 25 untreated controls, 1 adenoma of the testis and a
possible carcinoma in the inguinal region were observed (Simmers *et al.*,
1963).

3.2 Other relevant biological data

(a) Experimental systems

No toxicity was observed in male and female rats fed PTFE for 90 days,
even with a level of 25% in the diet. The polymer has not been found to
produce skin irritation or to act as an allergenic agent (Clayton, 1962;
Zapp, 1962).

The toxicity of the pyrolysis products of PTFE, degraded at various
temperatures, has been tested in several animal species.

PTFE heated to $300^{\circ}$C in air was lethal to rats (Zapp, 1962). Gases
identified during pyrolysis of PTFE included tetrafluoroethylene, hexa-
fluorethylene, hexafluoropropylene, octafluorocyclobutane and octafluoroisobutylene (Lee *et al.*, 1976). Depending on the specific PTFE, generation
of toxic gases does not occur until the temperature reaches $350^{\circ}$C (Clayton,
1967). When the polymer is heated to $375^{\circ}$C in air, toxic fumes are generated, as demonstrated in inhalation studies in several animal species
(Treon *et al.*, 1955). One of the extremely toxic gases produced was reported to be octafluoroisobutylene, which has an approximate lethal concentration of 0.5 ppm in rats exposed for a few hours (Harris, 1959). At $400^{\circ}$C,
no lethal products were produced from PTFE similar to that used in cooking
utensils; tetrafluoroethylene was detected at $450^{\circ}$C, hexafluoropropylene
at $460^{\circ}$C and perfluoroisobutylene (octafluoroisobutylene) at $475^{\circ}$C (Waritz,
1975).

At temperatures above $500^{\circ}$C, other toxic thermodegradation products
are produced: when PTFE is heated in the temperature range of $500-650^{\circ}$C,
the predominant product is carbonyl fluoride. If the temperature is increased above $650^{\circ}$C, the products formed are carbon tetrafluoride and carbon
dioxide. The $LC_{50}$ of carbonyl fluoride was found to be 350-450 ppm for 1
hour exposure; this toxicity was found to correlate with that of PTFE
pyrolysed at $550^{\circ}$C (Coleman *et al.*, 1968). Exposure to pyrolysis products

equivalent to 50 ppm carbonyl fluoride for 1 hour daily increased the fluoride ion content of the urine of rats from 3 to 42 µg/ml in 5 days; the same exposure produced reversible fluoride toxicity in the lungs and liver of rats within 18 days (Scheel *et al.*, 1968a).

The toxicity of the pyrolysis products of PTFE is reduced and even suppressed by passing the pyrolysis stream through a 0.45 µ pore size filter (Clayton, 1967).

Rodents exposed to such pyrolysis products showed signs of pulmonary irritation and oedema and diffuse degeneration of the brain, liver and kidneys (Lee *et al.*, 1976;  Scheel *et al.*, 1968b;  Treon *et al.*, 1955).

No data on the embryotoxicity, teratogenicity, metabolism or mutagenicity of this compound were available to the Working Group.

(b)  Humans

Thermodegradation products of PTFE produce influenza-like symptoms ('polymer-fume fever') in humans.  These may include chills, headaches, rigour-like shaking of the limbs, mild respiratory discomfort and a high fever.  These symptoms disappear within a 24- or 48-hour period if the worker is removed from the working environment and rests (Barnes & Jones, 1967;  Brubaker, 1977;  Harris, 1951;  Kuntz & McCord, 1974;  Lewis & Kerby, 1965;  Okawa & Polakoff, 1974;  Welti & Hipp, 1968;  Williams *et al.*, 1974).

The chemical factor that causes the fever has not yet been identified (Evans, 1973).  Polymer-fume fever generally occurs when the worker is exposed to polymer at temperatures between 300 and 500°C;  a number of thermodegradation products have been identified in this temperature range (see section 1.3 (e)).

It has been suggested that smoking increases the risk of developing polymer-fume fever (Brubaker, 1977;  Lewis & Kerby, 1965;  Welti & Hipp, 1968).

Fluoride levels in urine are greater than normal in workers exposed to fumes of PTFE (Okawa & Polakoff, 1974).

Williams *et al.* (1974) reported a case of a female worker who had more than 40 attacks of polymer-fume fever without pulmonary oedema during a 9-month period.  A few months after the last attack, she had no symptoms; however, 18 months later she complained of shortness of breath on exertion. Chest X-ray revealed no abnormalities, but pulmonary function studies demonstrated alveolar-capillary block.  Robbins & Ware (1964) and Evans (1973) described 4 cases of pulmonary oedema that result from inhalation of fumes.  Brubaker (1977) described a case of pulmonary oedema in a person who had smoked PTFE-contaminated cigarettes.

## 3.3  Case reports and epidemiological studies

Herrmann *et al.* (1971) and Burns *et al.* (1972) both report a case of a fibrosarcoma in a 31-year old man, which was diagnosed 10½ years after implantation of a 5 cm woven PTFE-dacron arterial prosthesis.  The tumour (9 x 8 x 4 cm) constricted and encircled more than half of the length of the femoral artery, including the implant, but did not invade the vessel. There was no evidence of metastasis.  The authors suggested that the fibrosarcoma arose due to implantation of the plastic vascular prosthesis.

## 4.  Summary of Data Reported and Evaluation

## 4.1  Experimental data

No data on the carcinogenicity or mutagenicity of tetrafluoroethylene were available to the Working Group.  Polytetrafluoroethylene discs, squares, fragments or powder implanted subcutaneously or intraperitoneally in mice or rats induced local sarcomas.

## 4.2  Human data

No case reports or epidemiological studies relating to general or occupational exposure to tetrafluoroethylene or polytetrafluoroethylene were available to the Working Group.  There is one case report of a patient who received a woven polytetrafluoroethylene/dacron prosthesis to repair a lacerated femoral artery;  a fibrosarcoma was diagnosed at the site of the prosthesis 10½ years after the initial operation.

## 4.3  Evaluation

General and occupational exposure to tetrafluoroethylene and polytetrafluoroethylene and medical exposure to polytetrafluoroethylene are known to occur.  The induction of sarcomas by polytetrafluoroethylene implants in mice and rats, together with a single case of a fibrosarcoma in a patient treated with a polytetrafluoroethylene/dacron implant, provide insufficient evidence to assess the carcinogenic risk of exposure to tetrafluoroethylene and polytetrafluoroethylene in humans.  The long-term follow-up of patients with medical implants is recommended.

## 5.  References

Anon. (1972)  Fire Protection Guide on Hazardous Materials, 4th ed., Boston,
    Mass., National Fire Protection Association, pp. 49-212-49-213

Barnes, R. & Jones, A.T. (1967)  Polymer-fume fever.  Med. J. Aust., 54,
    60-61

Brubaker, R.E. (1977)  Pulmonary problems associated with the use of poly-
    tetrafluoroethylene.  J. occup. Med., 19, 693-695

Bryson, G. & Bischoff, F. (1969)  The limitations of safety testing.
    Progr. exp. Tumor Res., 11, 100-133

Burns, W.A., Kanhouwa, S., Tillman, L., Saini, N. & Herrmann, J.B. (1972)
    Fibrosarcoma occurring at the site of a plastic vascular graft.
    Cancer, 29, 66-72

Clayton, J.W., Jr (1962)  The toxicity of fluorocarbons with special
    reference to chemical constitution.  J. occup. Med., 4, 262-273

Clayton, J.W., Jr (1967)  Fluorocarbon toxicity and biological action.
    Fluorine Chem. Rev., 1, 197-252

Coleman, W.E., Scheel, L.D., Kupel, R.E. & Larkin, R.L. (1968)  The iden-
    tification of toxic compounds in the pyrolysis products of polytetra-
    fluoroethylene (PTFE).  Am. ind. Hyg. Assoc. J., 29, 33-40

Dilley, J.V., Carter, V.L., Jr & Harris, E.S. (1974)  Fluoride ion excre-
    tion by male rats after inhalation of one of several fluoroethylenes
    or hexafluoropropene.  Toxicol. appl. Pharmacol., 27, 582-590

Dolgina, A.I., Alekseeva, A.D. & Meshcheryakova, A.N. (1966)  Control of
    the content of difluorochloromethane and tetrafluoroethylene in
    air (Russ.).  Gazov. Khromatogr., 4, 120-122 [Chem. Abstr., 67,
    119996c]

Evans, E.A. (1973)  Pulmonary edema after inhalation of fumes from poly-
    tetrafluoroethylene (PTFE).  J. occup. Med., 15, 599-601

Grasselli, J.G. & Ritchey, W.M., eds (1975)  CRC Atlas of Spectral Data
    and Physical Constants for Organic Compounds, 2nd ed., Vol. III,
    Cleveland, Ohio, Chemical Rubber Co., p. 283

van Grimbergen, M., Reybrouck, G. & van de Voorde, H. (1975)  Air pollution
    due to the burning of thermoplastics. II. (Ger.).  Zbl. Bakt. Hyg.,
    I. Abt. Orig. B, 160, 139-147

Halpern, B.D. & Karo, W. (1977) Medical applications: In: Bikales, N.M., ed., Encyclopedia of Polymer Science and Technology, Plastics, Resins, Rubbers, Fibers, Suppl. Vol. 2, New York, Interscience, pp. 369, 383-384

Harris, D.K. (1951) Polymer-fume fever. Lancet, ii, 1008-1011

Harris, D.K. (1959) Some hazards in the manufacture and use of plastics. Br. J. ind. Med., 16, 221-229

Hawley, G.G., ed. (1971) The Condensed Chemical Dictionary, 8th ed., New York, Van Nostrand-Reinhold, pp. 712-713, 857

Herrmann, J.B., Kanhouwa, S., Kelley, R.J. & Burns, W.A. (1971) Fibrosarcoma of the thigh associated with a prosthetic vascular graft. New Engl. J. Med., 284, 91

Kuntz, W.D. & McCord, C.P. (1974) Polymer-fume fever. J. occup. Med., 16, 480-482

Lee, K.P., Zapp, J.A., Jr & Sarver, J.W. (1976) Ultrastructural alterations of rat lung exposed to pyrolysis products of polytetrafluoroethylene (PTFE, Teflon). Lab. Invest., 35, 152-160

Lewis, C.E. & Kerby, G.R. (1965) An epidemic of polymer-fume fever. J. Am. med. Assoc., 191, 103-106

Marchenko, E.N. (1966) Fundamental problems of industrial hygiene in processing of polyfluoroethylene resins (Russ.). Gig. Tr. Prof Zabol., 10, 12-18 [Chem. Abstr., 66, 68685v]

McCane, D.I. (1970) Tetrafluoroethylene polymers. In: Bikales, N.M., ed., Encyclopedia of Polymer Science and Technology, Plastics, Resins, Rubbers, Fibers, Vol. 13, New York, Interscience, pp. 623-624, 626-627, 654

Ménard, S. & Della Porta, G. (1976) Incidence, growth and antigenicity of fibrosarcomas induced by Teflon disc in mice. Tumori, 62, 565-573

Okawa, M.T. & Polakoff, P.L. (1973) Health Hazard Evaluation/Toxicity Determination, Modern Industrial Plastics Division, Duriron Co., Dayton, Ohio, available from US National Technical Information Service, PB Rep. No. 229167/2GA [Chem. Abstr., 81, 68004g]

Okawa, M.T. & Polakoff, P.L. (1974) Occupational health case reports - No. 7. J. occup. Med., 16, 350-355

Oppenheimer, B.S., Oppenheimer, E.T., Stout, A.P. & Danishefsky, I. (1953) Malignant tumors resulting from embedding plastics in rodents. Science, 118, 305-306

Oppenheimer, B.S., Oppenheimer, E.T., Danishefsky, I., Stout, A.P. & Eirich, F.R. (1955)  Further studies of polymers as carcinogenic agents in animals.  Cancer Res., 15, 333-340

Robbins, J.J. & Ware, R.L. (1964)  Pulmonary edema from Teflon fumes. Report of a case.  New Engl. J. Med., 271, 360-361

Russell, F.E., Simmers, M.H., Hirst, A.E. & Pudenz, R.H. (1959)  Tumors associated with embedded polymers.  J. natl Cancer Inst., 23, 305-315

Scheel, L.D., McMillan, L. & Phipps, F.C. (1968a)  Biochemical changes associated with toxic exposures to polytetrafluoroethylene pyrolysis products.  Am. ind. Hyg. Assoc. J., 29, 49-53

Scheel, L.D., Lane, W.C. & Coleman, W.E. (1968b)  The toxicity of polytetra-fluoroethylene pyrolysis products - including carbonyl fluoride and a reaction product, silicon tetrafluoride.  Am. ind. Hyg. Assoc. J., 29, 41-48

Simmers, M.H., Agnew, W.F. & Pudenz, R.H. (1963)  Effects of plastic polymers within the rat's peritoneal cavity.  Bol. Inst. Estud. Med. Biol. Méx., 21, 1-13

Sircar, A.K. & Lamond, T.G. (1972)  Identification of elastomers by thermal analysis.  Rubber Chem. Technol., 45, 329-345

Tomatis, L. (1963)  Studies in subcutaneous carcinogenesis with implants of glass and Teflon in mice.  Acta unio int. contra cancrum, 19, 607-611

Tomatis, L. (1966)  Subcutaneous carcinogenesis by implants and by 7,12-dimethylbenz[a]anthracene.  Tumori, 52, 1-16

Tomatis, L. & Parmi, L. (1971)  Effect of perinatal administration of 7,12-dimethylbenz[a]anthracene on the later response to a subcutaneous Teflon implant.  Tumori, 57, 55-62

Tomatis, L. & Shubik, P. (1963)  Influence of urethane on subcutaneous carcinogenesis by 'Teflon' implants.  Nature (Lond.), 198, 600-601

Treon, J.F., Cappel, J.W., Cleveland, F.P., Larson, E.E., Atchley, R.W. & Denham, R.T. (1955)  The toxicity of the products formed by the thermal decomposition of certain organic substances.  Am. ind. Hyg. Assoc. Q., 16, 187-195

US Department of Commerce (1977)  US Imports for Consumption and General Imports, TSUSA Commodity by Country of Origin, FT 246/Annual 1976, Bureau of the Census, Washington DC, US Government Printing Office, p. 234

US Food and Drug Administration (1977)  Food and drugs.  US Code Fed. Regul., Title 21, parts 175.105, 175.300, pp. 438, 446, 452, 457

US International Trade Commission (1976)  Synthetic Organic Chemicals, US Production and Sales, 1974, USITC Publication 776, Washington DC, US Government Printing Office, pp. 128, 131, 203, 229

US International Trade Commission (1977a)  Synthetic Organic Chemicals, US Production and Sales, 1975, USITC Publication 804, Washington DC, US Government Printing Office, pp. 198, 221

US International Trade Commission (1977b)  Synthetic Organic Chemicals, US Production and Sales, 1976, USITC Publication 833, Washington DC, US Government Printing Office, pp. 182, 186

US Tariff Commission (1961)  Synthetic Organic Chemicals, US Production and Sales, 1960, TC Publication 34, Washington DC, US Government Printing Office, p. 180

Waritz, R.S. (1975)  An industrial approach to evaluation of pyrolysis and combustion hazards.  Environ. Health Perspect., 11, 197–202

Weast, R.C., ed. (1976)  CRC Handbook of Chemistry and Physics, 57th ed., Cleveland, Ohio, Chemical Rubber Co., p. C-298

Welti, D.W. & Hipp, M.J. (1968)  Polymer fume fever.  Possible relationship to smoking.  J. occup. Med., 10, 667–671

Williams, N., Atkinson, W. & Patchefsky, A.S. (1974)  Polymer-fume fever: not so benign.  J. occup. Med., 16, 519–522

Windholz, M., ed. (1976)  The Merck Index, 9th ed., Rahway, NJ, Merck & Co., pp. 985–986

Zapp, J.A., Jr (1962)  Toxic and health effects of plastics and resins. Arch. environ. Health, 4, 335–346

Zeman, A. (1972)  Identification of high polymers by thermal degradation in the mass spectrometer.  In: Wiedemann, H.G., ed., Proceedings of the 3rd International Conference on Thermal Analysis, Basel, Vol. 3, Basel, Birkhaeuser, pp. 219–227 [Chem. Abstr., 78, 148551m]

2,4- and 2,6-TOLUENE DIISOCYANATES, 1,5-NAPHTHALENE DIISOCYANATE, 4,4'-METHYLENEDIPHENYL DIISOCYANATE and POLYMETHYLENE POLYPHENYL ISOCYANATE and FLEXIBLE and RIGID POLYURETHANE FOAMS

## 2,4- and 2,6-Toluene diisocyanates

### 1. Chemical and Physical Data

#### 1.1 Synonyms and trade names

##### 2,4-Toluene diisocyanate

Chem. Abstr. Services Reg. No.: 584-84-9

Chem. Abstr. Name: 2,4-Diisocyanato-1-methylbenzene

2,4-Diisocyanatotoluene; isocyanic acid, 4-methyl-*meta*-phenylene ester; 4-methyl-*meta*-phenylene diisocyanate; 4-methyl-*meta*-phenylene isocyanate; 2,4-TDI; toluene 2,4-diisocyanate; 2,4-tolylene diisocyanate

Hylene T; Hylene TCPA; Hylene TIC; Hylene TM; Hylene TM-65; Hylene TRF; Mondur TDS; Nacconate 100; NIAX TDI; NIAX TDI-P

##### 2,6-Toluene diisocyanate

Chem. Abstr. Services Reg. No.: 91-08-7

Chem. Abstr. Name: 1,3-Diisocyanato-2-methylbenzene

2,6-Diisocyanatotoluene; isocyanic acid, 2-methyl-*meta*-phenylene ester; 2-methyl-*meta*-phenylene isocyanate; 2,6-TDI; toluene 2,6-diisocyanate; tolylene 2,6-diisocyanate; *meta*-tolylene diisocyanate

Hylene TCPA; Hylene TIC; Hylene TM; Hylene TM-65; Hylene TRF; NIAX TDI; NIAX TDI-P

1.2  Structural and molecular formulae and molecular weight

2,4-Toluene diisocyanate

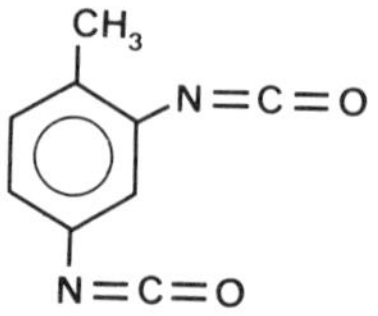

$C_9H_6N_2O_2$                  Mol. wt:  174.2

2,6-Toluene diisocyanate

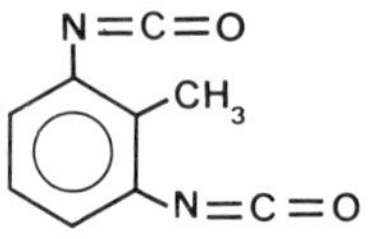

$C_9H_6N_2O_2$                  Mol. wt:  174.2

1.3  Chemical and physical properties of the pure substance

2,4-Toluene diisocyanate

From Windholz (1976), unless otherwise specified

(a)  Description:  Colourless liquid with a sharp, pungent odour

(b)  Boiling-point:  251°C

(c)  Melting-point:  19.5–21.5°C

(d)  Density:  $d_4^{20}$ 1.2244

(e)  Refractive index:  $n_D^{25}$ 1.5654 (Pigott, 1969)

(f)  Spectroscopy data:  Infra-red, Raman and nuclear magnetic
     resonance spectral data have been tabulated (Grasselli &
     Ritchey, 1975).

(g)  Solubility:  Miscible with ether, acetone, carbon tetrachloride,
     benzene, chlorobenzene, kerosene and olive oil

(h)  Stability: Flash-point, 132°C;  darkens on exposure to light;
polymerized rapidly by bases

(i)  Reactivity: Reacts violently with water;  with limited amounts
of water disubstituted amides are formed;  in the presence of
excess water, 2,4-diaminotoluene (IARC, 1978) is formed.  It
reacts rapidly with 'active hydrogen' compounds (e.g., alcohols,
carboxylic acids, primary and secondary amines) (Pigott, 1970).

(j)  Conversion factor: 1 ppm in air = 7 mg/m$^3$

2,6-Toluene diisocyanate

Boiling-point: 129-133°C (18 mm) (Pollock & Stevens, 1974)

1.4  Technical products and impurities

The most widely marketed grade of toluene diisocyanate in the US is
a mixture of 80% 2,4-isomer and 20% 2,6-isomer;  this 80/20 mixture accounts
for over 90% of US toluene diisocyanate production.  A mixture of 65%
2,4-isomer and 35% 2,6-isomer is also available.  Small quantities of
2,4-toluene diisocyanate (which has a somewhat greater reactivity than the
2,6-isomer) are used for special applications.

A typical analysis of 80/20 toluene diisocyanate available in the US
is as follows:  purity, 99.7% min;  2,4-isomer, 80± 1%;  2,6-isomer, 20±
1%;  total chloride, 0.1% max;  hydrolysable chloride, 0.01% max;  and
acidity (as hydrochloric acid), 0.002-0.01% (Chadwick & Hardy, 1967).  The
vapour pressure of the technical product is 1.9 mm at 94°C (Woolrich & Rye,
1969).

In Japan, commercially available pure 2,4-toluene diisocyanate has
the following specifications:  purity, 99.5% min;  2,4-isomer, 97.5% min;
2,6-isomer, 2.5% max;  acidity (as hydrochloric acid), 0.010-0.013%;
hydrolytic hydrochloric acid, 0.010-0.013%;  total hydrochloric acid, 0.05%
max;  and freezing-point, 21.0°C min.  The commercially available 80/20
toluene diisocyanate mixture has the following specifications:  purity,
99.6% min;  2,4-isomer, 78.0-81.0%;  2,6-isomer, 19.0-22.0%;  acidity (as
hydrochloric acid), 0.004% max;  hydrolytic hydrochloric acid, 0.01% max;
total hydrochloric acid, 0.07% max;  freezing-point, 11.8-13.4°C.  A
commercially available 65/35 toluene diisocyanate mixture has the following specifications:  purity, 99.5% min;  2,4-isomer, 63-67%;  2,6-isomer,
33-37%;  acidity (as hydrochloric acid), 0.010-0.013%;  hydrolytic hydrochloric acid, 0.01-0.013%;  and total hydrochloric acid, 0.05% max.

## 2.  Production, Use, Occurrence and Analysis

### 2.1  Production and use

#### (a)  Production

The first organic isocyanate was prepared by Wurtz in 1849;  however, commercial production of isocyanates was first begun in the late 1930's in Germany (Chadwick & Hardy, 1967).

Toluene diisocyanate (80% 2,4-isomer and 20% 2,6-isomer) is produced commercially by nitrating toluene with a nitric acid-sulphuric acid mixture and catalytically reducing the resultant dinitrotoluene (a mixture of at least 76% 2,4-isomer, less than 24% 2,6-isomer and small amounts of 2,3- and 3,4-isomers) to a toluenediamine mixture (see monograph on 2,4-diamino-toluene, IARC, 1978);  this is dissolved in monochlorobenzene or *ortho*-dichlorobenzene and treated with phosgene to produce the diisocyanates.

Although pilot-plant quantities of 2,4-toluene diisocyanate were made in the US in the late 1940's (Pigott, 1970), commercial production was first reported in 1953 (US Tariff Commission, 1954).  In 1976, two US companies reported production of 2,4-toluene diisocyanate;  2 companies produced the 65/35 mixture and 8 companies reported production of 255 million kg of the 80/20 mixture (US International Trade Commission, 1977a). US exports of toluene diisocyanate (isomer ratios unspecified) amounted to 60.8 million kg in 1976 and went to the following countries (% of total): Argentina (3.2), Australia (5.3), Belgium (8.6), Brazil (25.1), Canada (9.8), the Federal Republic of Germany (5.3), Japan (2.4), Mexico (9.2), The Netherlands (10.7), Venezuela (5.5), and at least 34 other countries (14.9) (US Department of Commerce, 1977).  US imports of toluene diisocyanate are believed to be negligible.

Canadian production of toluene diisocyanate in 1975 amounted to 9 million kg.

Total western Europe production in 1976 amounted to 225 million kg. Among the major producers were the following countries (production in millions of kg):  the Federal Republic of Germany (70), France (65), Italy (30), Spain (15) and the UK (25).  Exports from western Europe in that year were 85 million kg and imports 35 million kg.

Toluene diisocyanate has been produced commercially in Japan since 1962.  Six companies produced a total of 64 million kg toluene diisocyanate in 1976, and 17 million kg were exported, primarily to countries in south-east Asia and Oceania.

Worldwide production of toluene diisocyanate in 1976 is estimated to have been 660 million kg.

(b) Use

In 1975, 20/80 toluene diisocyanate mixture produced in the US was used in the production of polyurethane flexible foams (90-92%), polyurethane coatings (4%), polyurethane elastomers (3%), and other applications (1%). In the 1950's, a toluene diisocyanate mixture was used to produce some of the early rigid foams. Today, a crude toluene diisocyanate product, which is recovered from the reaction residue of toluene diisocyanate production, is used for the production of polyurethane rigid foams. For a detailed description of the uses of polyurethane flexible and rigid foams, see p. 324.

Polyurethane coatings made from toluene diisocyanate mixture fall into various categories, including urethane-modified alkyds, moisture-curing one-component types, two-component systems, blocked isocyanate systems and polyurethane lacquers. In general, they are used in floor finishes, wood finishes and sealers, trade sales paints, concrete sealers, and in coatings for aircraft, tank trucks, truck trailers and truck fleets.

Polyurethane elastomers made from toluene diisocyanates are used in coated fabrics and clay-pipe seals. Toluene diisocyanates are also used in adhesives of the polyurethane and other types.

Use of toluene diisocyanates in western Europe in 1975 was in the production of polyurethane flexible foams (90-95%) and for polyurethane coatings (5-10%).

In Japan in 1976, toluene diisocyanates were used for the production of polyurethane flexible foams (75%) and for polyurethane coatings and elastomers (25%).

The US Food and Drug Administration permits the use of 2,4- and 2,6-toluene diisocyanates as a raw material in the production of adhesives intended for use in contact with food (US Food and Drug Administration, 1977).

The US Occupational Safety and Health Administration's health standards for exposure to air contaminants require that an employee's exposure to 2,4-toluene diisocyanate not exceed a ceiling concentration limit of 0.14 mg/m$^3$ (0.02 ppm) at any time (US Occupational Safety and Health Administration, 1976). Workers should not be exposed to a time-weighted average of more than 0.036 mg/m$^3$ (0.005 ppm) toluene diisocyanate for any eight-hour work day (National Institute for Occupational Safety and Health, 1973).

Work environment hygiene standards (all in terms of eight-hour time-weighted averages) for 2,4-toluene diisocyanate reported by Winell (1975) are as follows: Czechoslovakia, 0.07 mg/m$^3$ (0.01 ppm); the Federal Republic of Germany, 0.1 mg/m$^3$ (0.014 ppm) and the German Democratic Republic, 0.14 mg/m$^3$ (0.02 ppm). The maximum acceptable ceiling concentration of 2,4-toluene diisocyanate in Sweden is 0.07 mg/m$^3$ (0.01 ppm) and in the USSR 0.5 mg/m$^3$ (0.07 ppm).

## 2.2 Occurrence

2,4- and 2,6-Toluene diisocyanate are not known to occur as natural products.

Production workers were exposed to 2,4- and 2,6-toluene diisocyanates in concentrations of less than 0.07 mg/m$^3$ (0.01 ppm) in air in almost all samples examined during the manufacture of polyurethane foams; a concentration of 0.09 mg/m$^3$ was found in one sample (Ciosek et al., 1969).

Toluene diisocyanate has been found in the working environment: (1) during the manufacture of foam cushions and slabs, in concentrations of 0.014-0.09 mg/m$^3$ (0.002-0.013 ppm) (Wegman et al., 1974); (2) in the production room of a polyurethane footwear plant, in concentrations of 7-14 mg/m$^3$ (1-2 ppm) over a three-year period (Sova, 1974); and (3) above a mixing tank used in the preparation of polyurethane cement, in concentrations of $\leq$ 1.45 mg/m$^3$ (0.2 ppm) (Tonkoshkurov, 1969).

Toluene diisocyanate has been found as free monomer in a urethane foam fabric coating, in concentrations of less than 200 mg/kg (ppm) (Scott & Carey, 1976).

## 2.3 Analysis

Toluene diisocyanate occurs mainly as a mixture of the 2,4- and 2,6-isomers. The analytical methods to determine toluene diisocyanate, unless otherwise noted, are not specific and can measure the presence of either isomer.

A sampling and analytical method in general use for determining 2,4-toluene diisocyanate concentrations in workplace atmospheres is a colorimetric method based on the N-(1-naphthyl)ethylenediamine complex; it has a useful range of 0.05-1 mg/m$^3$ (0.007-0.140 ppm) in air (National Institute for Occupational Safety and Health, 1973, 1977a). Modifications of this method involve various complexing agents, including: (1) glutaconic aldehyde, with a limit of detection of 0.035 mg/m$^3$ (0.005 ppm) (Belisle, 1969); (2) chromotropic acid, with a limit of detection of 2 µg (Simonov et al., 1971); and (3) thiotrithiazyl chloride, with a limit of detection of 0.07 mg/m$^3$ (0.01 ppm) (Levin et al., 1967).

A simple and rapid method for determining toluene diisocyanate vapour in air uses a test paper prepared by treating filter paper with a solution of sodium nitrite, 2-hydroxy-11H-benzo[a]carbazole-3-carboxy-para-anisidine, ammonium acetate and diethyl phthalate in methanol. The useful range is 0.07-0.7 mg/m$^3$ (0.01-0.10 ppm) (Reilly, 1968).

Gas chromatography with electron capture detection has been used to determine 2,4-toluene diisocyanate in a standard air sample, in the range of 1-30 ng (Wheals & Thomson, 1967), and in air, with a lower limit of detection of 0.035 mg/m$^3$ (0.005 ppm) (Schanche & Hermann, 1974). Gas chromatography has also been used to determine 2,4-toluene diisocyanate in polyurethane lacquer samples (Potapova *et al.*, 1974) and polyurethane pre-polymers (Potapova *et al.*, 1975), with a relative error of ±10%.

Liquid chromatography has been used to separate the toluene diiso-cyanate isomers as the urea derivatives from a prepared mixture of iso-cyanates, with detection by ultra-violet spectroscopy. The limit of detec-tion was 1.2 ng of 2,4- or 2,6-isomer (Hastings Vogt *et al.*, 1977). High-performance liquid chromatography has also been used to determine free toluene diisocyanate in polyurethane pre-polymers in concentrations of about 1% (McFadyen, 1976).

Toluene diisocyanate has been determined in the workplace atmosphere by thin-layer chromatography of the *N*-4-nitrobenzyl-*N*-*n*-propylamine deriva-tive. The useful range of the method for the 2,4- and 2,6-isomers was 0.08-34.0 mg/m$^3$ (0.01-5 ppm) (Keller *et al.*, 1974).

Free monomeric toluene diisocyanate has been determined in polyurethane paints at levels of less than 1% by combined thin-layer and gas chromato-graphic analysis and infra-red and ultra-violet spectral analysis (Heuser *et al.*, 1971). Potentiometric titration has also been used, with an error of ±1.3% (De Moran & Biondi, 1973).

2,6-Toluene diisocyanate has been determined in the presence of the 2,4-isomer using a dielectric constant method, with an error of ±0.2% (Mulyanov *et al.*, 1974).

### 3.  Biological Data Relevant to the Evaluation
### of Carcinogenic Risk to Humans

3.1  Carcinogenicity studies in animals[1]

No data were available to the Working Group.

_____

[1]The Working Group was aware of a study in progress to assess the carcinogenicity of a mixture of 80% 2,4-toluene diisocyanate and 20% 2,6-toluene diisocyanate in mice and rats by oral administration (Toxicology Information Program, 1976).

3.2  Other relevant biological data

Two reviews on 2,4- and 2,6-toluene diisocyanates are available (Gustavsson, 1977; National Institute of Occupational Safety and Health, 1973). Almost none of the published papers on toluene diisocyanate (TDI) specify which isomer was used, or its purity.

(a)  Experimental systems

In rats, the oral $LD_{50}$ of TDI was 5800 mg/kg bw (mean value) (Zapp, 1957) or 7500 mg/kg bw (Union Carbide Corporation, 1967).

The $LC_{50}$ following exposure to TDI for 14 days was: mouse, 70 mg/m$^3$ (10 ppm), guinea-pig, 90 mg/m$^3$ (13 ppm) and rat, 100 mg/m$^3$ (14 ppm). The $LC_{50}$ following exposure for 7 days was 80 mg/m$^3$ (11 ppm) in rabbits. During exposure, mice, rats and guinea-pigs exhibited lachrymation, salivation, restlessness and hyperactivity (Duncan *et al.*, 1962).

In acute 6-hour inhalation studies in rats, a concentration of 4200 mg/m$^3$ (600 ppm) was lethal, whereas 420 mg/m$^3$ (60 ppm) was not. The animals that died showed acute pulmonary congestion and oedema (Zapp, 1957).

Acute skin absorption tests with TDI on rabbits produced severe local irritation but failed to kill, even with doses as high as 16 g/kg bw; there was no anatomical injury to internal organs. A 10% solution in dimethylphthalate irritated the intact skin of guinea-pigs. Application of TDI to the rabbit eye resulted in marked irritation of the eyelids and mild damage to the corneal epithelium (Zapp, 1957).

Exposure by inhalation to 70 mg/m$^3$ (10 ppm) 2,4-TDI, 2,6-TDI or a 65/35 mixture for 6 hours/day for 3-5 days was lethal to rats; exposure to 35 mg/m$^3$ (5 ppm) of the mixture for 4 days killed 65% of rats. Following 24 hours' exposure to 3.5 mg/m$^3$ (0.5 ppm) of the mixture, 55% of young rats, 100% of older rats and 60% of guinea-pigs survived (Henschler *et al.*, 1962).

Following exposure by inhalation of rats and rabbits to 0.7 mg/m$^3$ (0.1 ppm) TDI for a 6-hour period on 1 day/week for 38 weeks, or exposure of rats, rabbits and guinea-pigs for 6 hours/day on 5 days/week for a total of 58 exposures, rats showed proliferation of fibrous tissue in the walls of the bronchioles as well as pneumonitis, tracheitis and bronchitis. In rabbits and guinea-pigs, no proliferation of fibrous tissue was seen (Niewenhuis *et al.*, 1965).

Exposure of guinea-pigs by inhalation to 14-35 mg/m$^3$ (2-5 ppm) TDI in air for 6 hours/day for 3 days rendered them more sensitive when 3 weeks later they were exposed to 0.14 mg/m$^3$ (0.02 ppm) for 5 hours, as shown by a more pronounced reduction of breath rate when compared with animals that had not been previously exposed (Stevens & Palmer, 1970).

No data on the embryotoxicity, teratogenicity, metabolism or mutagenicity of this compound were available to the Working Group.

(b) Humans

Workers exposed to toluene diisocyanate (TDI) frequently develop irritation of the eyes, irritation or dryness of throat and/or tightness of the
chest (Adams, 1975; Bruckner et al., 1968; Dodson, 1971; Elkins et al.,
1962; Munn, 1965; Peters & Wegman, 1975; Peters et al., 1968; Walworth
& Virchow, 1959; Weill et al., 1975; Williamson, 1964, 1965). Exposure
to levels as low as 0.014 mg/m$^3$ (0.002 ppm) can result in chronic loss of
pulmonary function (Wegman et al., 1977). A more acute, asthmatic type of
bronchitis is not uncommon, and sometimes typical, frank asthma may occur.
Respiratory symptoms rapidly improve during the few days after removal from
exposure, but it has been widely reported that re-exposure to even minimal
concentrations of TDI vapours produced a recurrence of very severe symptoms
(Peters & Wegman, 1975; Weill et al., 1975).

The hypersensitivity to TDI arises only after vapour inhalation, and
it has been related to immunological changes (IgE antibody response)
(Porter et al., 1975) and to altered β-adrenergic function (Butcher et al.,
1977).

Wegman et al. (1977) demonstrated a dose-reponse relationship of acute
pulmonary function changes among 112 workers exposed to TDI at levels of
0.0035-0.06 mg/m$^3$ (0.0005-0.009 ppm). A 2-year follow-up examination of
57 of the workers disclosed decreases in pulmonary function that were
related to exposure levels, controlling for age, months employed, smoking
habits and physique. The authors concluded that chronic occupational exposure to TDI at levels of 0.02 mg/m$^3$ (0.003 ppm) in air or higher is unsafe.

3.3  Case reports and epidemiological studies

No data were available to the Working Group.


1,5-Naphthalene diisocyanate

1.  Chemical and Physical Data

1.1  Synonyms and trade names

Chem. Abstr. Services Reg. No.: 3173-72-6

Chem. Abstr. Name: 1,5-Diisocyanatonaphthalene

Isocyanic acid, 1,5-naphthylene ester; 1,5-naphthylene diisocyanate

Desmodur N

1.2  Structural and molecular formulae and molecular weight

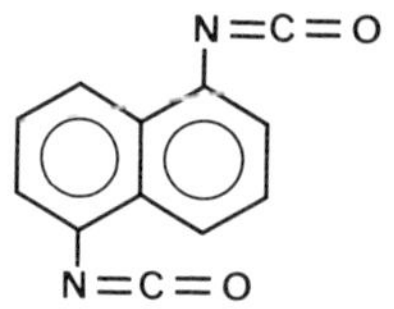

$$N=C=O$$

$$N=C=O$$

$C_{12}H_6N_2O_2$          Mol. wt:  210.2

1.3  Chemical and physical properties of the pure substance

   (a)  Description:  White-to-light-yellow, crystalline solid
        (Hawley, 1971)

   (b)  Melting-point:  130–132°C (Siefken, 1949)

   (c)  Conversion factor:  1 ppm in air = 8.6 mg/m³

1.4  Technical products and impurities

    In Japan, 1,5-naphthalene diisocyanate available commercially has
the following specifications:  purity, 99.5% min.;  hydrolytic chlorine,
0.004–0.008%;  total chlorine, 0.04% max;  total isocyanate, 39.8% min.
1,8-Naphthalene diisocyanate occurs as an impurity.


            2.  Production, Use, Occurrence and Analysis

2.1  Production and use

   (a)  Production

    1,5-Naphthalene diisocyanate has been prepared by the reaction of
phosgene and 1,5-naphthalenediamine dihydrochloride (Siefken, 1949).
In Japan, it is produced commercially by the nitration of naphthalene,
followed by reduction with iron to 1,5-naphthalenediamine, which is then
treated with phosgene.

    One company in the Federal Republic of Germany produces approximately
1000 kg 1,5-naphthalene diisocyanate per year.

    1,5-Naphthalene diisocyanate was first produced commercially in Japan
in 1967.  One Japanese company produced about 70 thousand kg in 1976, and
imports in that year amounted to 70 thousand kg.

    1,5-Naphthalene diisocyanate has never been produced commercially in
the US.  However, in 1976, two chemical manufacturers were reportedly
offering it for sale in research quantities.

(b) Use

1,5-Naphthalene diisocyanate is used in Japan and western Europe for the production of polyurethane elastomers.

It has been patented in the US for use in preparing polyurethane elastomers and other polymers with good resistance to water and heat, but no evidence has been found that it has ever been used in the US other than for research purposes.

2.2 Occurrence

1,5-Naphthalene diisocyanate is not known to occur as a natural product.

Workers were exposed to unspecified levels of 1,5-naphthalene diisocyanate in the production of polyurethane rubber and to levels of 0.59-0.74 mg/m$^3$ (0.07-0.09 ppm) in air in the shoe manufacturing industry (Hassman, 1969).

2.3 Analysis

1,5-Naphthalene diisocyanate has been determined in the pyrolysate of polyurethanes by gas chromatography (Gnauck, 1975).

## 3. Biological Data Relevant to the Evaluation of Carcinogenic Risk to Humans

3.1 Carcinogenicity studies in animals

No data were available to the Working Group.

3.2 Other relevant biological data

(a) Experimental systems

No data were available to the Working Group.

(b) Humans

Acute damage to the respiratory tract (pharyngites and bronchitis) as well as conjunctivitis were observed in workers employed in the production of polyurethane rubber (Vulkollan) in which 1,5-naphthalene diisocyanate was the basic substance (Hassman, 1968, 1969).

An association between exposure to isocyanates, particularly 1,5-naphthalene diisocyanate, and bronchitis was observed with levels of less than 0.17 mg/m$^3$ (0.02 ppm) 1,5-naphthalene diisocyanate in air, a threshold limit value tentatively proposed for this substance (Hill, 1970).

3.3  Case reports and epidemiological studies

No data were available to the Working Group.

4,4'-Methylenediphenyl diisocyanate and
polymethylene polyphenyl isocyanate

1.  Chemical and Physical Data

1.1  Synonyms and trade names

4,4'-Methylenediphenyl diisocyanate

Chem. Abstr. Services Reg. No.:  101-68-8

Chem. Abstr. Name:  1,1-Methylenebis(4-isocyanatobenzene)

Bis(1,4-isocyanatophenyl)methane;  bis(4-isocyanatophenyl)methane;
bis(*para*-isocyanatophenyl)methane;  4,4'-diisocyanatodiphenylmethane;
4,4'-diphenylmethane diisocyanate;  *para,para*'-diphenylmethane
diisocyanate;  diphenylmethane 4,4'-diisocyanate;  isocyanic acid
methylenedi-*para*-phenylene ester;  MDI;  methylenebis(4-isocyanato-
benzene);  methylenebis(4-phenylene isocyanate);  methylenebis(*para*-
phenylene isocyanate);  4,4'-methylenebis(phenyl isocyanate);
*para,para*'-methylenebis(phenyl isocyanate);  methylenebis(4-phenyl
isocyanate);  methylenebis(*para*-phenyl isocyanate);  methylenedi-
*para*-phenylene diisocyanate;  4,4'-methylenediphenylene isocyanate;
methylenedi-*para*-phenylene isocyanate

Caradate 30;  Desmodur 44;  Hylene M50;  Isonate 125M;  Isonate
125 MF;  Nacconate 300

Polymethylene polyphenyl isocyanate

Chem. Abstr. Services Reg. No.:  9016-87-9

Chem. Abstr. Name:  Isocyanic acid, polymethylenepolyphenylene ester

Polymeric MDI;  poly(methylene phenylene isocyanate);  polymethylene
polyphenylene isocyanate;  polymethylenepolyphenylene isocyanate
polymer;  polymethylenepolyphenylene polyisocyanate;  polymethylene

poly(phenyl isocyanate);   polymethylene polyphenyl polyisocyanate;

polymethyl polyphenyl polyisocyanate;   poly(phenylenemethylene

isocyanate);   polyphenylene polymethylene polyisocyanate;   polyphenyl-

polymethylene polyisocyanate

Isocyanate 390P;   Millionate MR;   Mirionate MR;   Mondur MR:   Mondur

MRS;   PAPI;   PAPI 901;   Thanate P 210;   Thanate P 220;   Thanate P 270

1.2   Structural and molecular formulae and molecular weight

4,4'-Methylenediphenyl diisocyanate

$$O=C=N-\langle\bigcirc\rangle-\underset{\underset{H}{\overset{H}{|}}}{C}-\langle\bigcirc\rangle-N=C=O$$

$C_{15}H_{10}N_2O_2$                         Mol. wt:   246.3

Polymethylene polyphenyl isocyanate

$$C_{15}H_{10}N_2O_2-[C_8H_5NO]_n$$

1.3   Chemical and physical properties of the pure substance

4,4'-Methylenediphenyl diisocyanate

From Chadwick & Hardy (1967), unless otherwise specified

(a)   Description:   Light-yellow, fused solid (Hawley, 1977)

(b)   Boiling-point:   $196^\circ$C at 5 mm Hg

(c)   Melting-point:   $38^\circ$C

(d)   Density:   $d^{50}$ 1.19

(e)   Refractive index:   $n_D^{50}$ 1.5906

(f)  Solubility:  Soluble in acetone, benzene, kerosene and nitrobenzene (Hawley, 1977)

(g)  Stability:  Flash-point, 201°C (open cup)

(h)  Conversion factor:  1 ppm in air = 10 mg/m$^3$

Polymethylene polyphenyl isocyanate

Description:  Dark-amber, viscous liquid (Wooldrich & Rye, 1969)

1.4  Technical products and impurities

4,4'-Methylenediphenyl diisocyanate

4,4'-Methylenediphenyl diisocyanate (MDI) is available commercially
in the US as white-to-pale-yellow flakes and has the following typical
properties:  assay, 99.5% min;  acidity, as hydrochloric acid, 0.002% max;
hydrolysable chloride, 0.002% max;  total chloride, 0.10% max;  hexane
insolubles, 0.5% max;  crystallizing-point, 37°C min; and specific
gravity (d$_{15.5}^{50}$), 1.19.  The vapour pressure of the technical product is
0.0075 mm at 94°C (Woolrich & Rye, 1969).

In Japan, it is available as a white solid with the following typical
properties:  purity, 99.5% min;  hydrolytic hydrochloric acid, 0.005% max;
and freezing-point, 38.0°C min.  A crude grade is also available as a light-
yellow liquid, with the following typical properties:  purity, 28.5-29.5%;
acidity, 0.01% max;  hydrolytic hydrochloric acid, 0.02% max;  and
freezing-point, -10°C max.

Polymethylene polyphenyl isocyanate

Polymethylene polyphenyl isocyanate available commercially in the US
has the following typical properties:  isocyanate equivalent, 132-137 g/Eq;
hydrolysable chloride, 0.28-0.5%;  specific gravity (d$_{20}^{20}$), 1.2;  flash-
point, 215-218°C;  isocyanate content, 30.5-32% min;  acidity, as hydrochloric acid, 0.2-0.3%;  and vapour pressure at 25°C, <1x10$^{-4}$ mm.

## 2.  Production, Use, Occurrence and Analysis

2.1  Production and use

(a)  Production

A method for preparing MDI by heating bis(4-aminophenyl)methane with
phosgene in toluene, with the addition of $N,N$-dimethylaniline was first
patented in the US in 1942 (Boit, 1973).

MDI and polymethylene polyphenyl isocyanate are produced commercially by the following steps: (1) aniline is condensed with formaldehyde to give diphenylmethane diamine (methylene dianiline), and the reaction conditions are modified to control the composition of the polyamine product, especially the isomer distribution; (2) the diamine is phosgenated, which results in a mixture of aromatic isocyanates corresponding to the composition of the polyamine; (3) this mixture commonly consists of MDI and its dimer, trimer and some tetramer and is polymethylene polyphenyl isocyanate; the pure MDI can then be distilled from the mixture.

Commercial production of MDI in the US was first reported in 1953 (US Tariff Commission, 1954) and that of polymethylene polyphenyl isocyanate in 1957 (US Tariff Commission, 1958). In 1976, two US companies reported production of an undisclosed amount of MDI (see preamble, p. 22), and four companies reported production of 142.1 million kg polymethylene polyphenyl isocyanate (US International Trade Commission, 1977a); production of poly-methylene polyphenyl isocyanate in 1975 amounted to 112.4 million kg (US International Trade Commission, 1977b). US imports of MDI through principal customs districts in 1975 amounted to 1000 kg; imports of polymethylene polyphenyl isocyanate were 120 kg in 1975 and 454 thousand kg in 1976 (US International Trade Commission, 1977c,d). US exports of polymethylene polyphenyl isocyanate in 1974 were 31.8-36.4 million kg.

Demand for MDI and polymethylene polyphenyl isocyanate in Europe in 1973 was 115-150 million kg. MDI is currently produced by at least 12 companies in western Europe, in Belgium (3 producers), the Federal Republic of Germany (2), France (1), Italy (2), The Netherlands (2), Spain (1) and the UK (1).

MDI has been produced commercially in Japan since 1964. In 1976, four companies produced 29 million kg; imports were about 3 million kg and exports about 5 million kg.

(b) Use

In 1975, 3.6-4.5 million kg of MDI and 8.36-85.9 million kg of poly-methylene polyphenyl isocyanate were used in the US. MDI was used for the production of polyurethane coatings (25-30%), polyurethane elastomers (20-25%) and other polyurethane applications (50%). Polymethylene poly-phenyl isocyanate was used for the production of polyurethane rigid foam (80.4-82.8%), polyurethane flexible foams (7.6-8.5%), polyurethane elasto-mers (2.7-3.2%) and other polyurethane applications (7.1-7.9%).

For a discussion of the uses of polyurethane flexible and rigid foams, see p. 324.

MDI is used in two-component polyurethane coating systems which are used for aircraft, tank trucks and truck trailers due to their durability and toughness. It is also used to produce polyurethane lacquer coatings applied to certain automobile body components and, to a small extent, to patent leather.

Polyurethane elastomers based on MDI are used as cast elastomers for front- and rear-end automobile components and as fabric coatings. Polyurethane elastomers based on polymethylene polyphenyl isocyanate are used in microcellular products, including shoes and automobile bumpers.

Other uses of MDI are in the production of thermoplastic polyurethane resins, millable gums and spandex fibres. Additional applications for polymethylene polyphenyl isocyanate include the production of polyurethane adhesives and special adhesives based on other polymer systems, and foundry resin sand binders used in the casting of steel, grey iron, modular iron and nonferrous metals.

In Japan, MDI is used for the production of polyurethane rigid foams (65%) and for other uses (35%), including fibres, paints, elastomers and synthetic leather.

The US Food and Drug Administration permits the use of polyurethane resins produced from MDI in contact with bulk quantities of dry food (US Food and Drug Administration, 1977).

The US Occupational Safety and Health Administration's health standards for exposure to air contaminants require that an employee's exposure to MDI not exceed at any time during an eight-hour work shift the ceiling concentration limit of 0.2 mg/m$^3$ (0.02 ppm) (US Occupational Safety and Health Administration, 1976). In Japan, the threshold limit value for MDI is 0.2 mg/m$^3$ (0.02 ppm).

## 2.2  Occurrence

MDI and polymethylene polyphenyl isocyanate are not known to occur as natural products.

Emissions of MDI into the workplace air from twelve polyurethane coatings during application and drying did not exceed 0.20 mg/m$^3$ (0.02 ppm) in the US and 0.07 mg/m$^3$ (0.007 ppm) in Italy (Scrima & Salvadori, 1976).

## 2.3  Analysis

2,4'- and 4,4'-Methylenediphenyl diisocyanate have been determined in their isomeric mixtures by measuring the dielectric constant of the mixture (Mulyanov *et al.*, 1973).

Colorimetric methods are used for determining isocyanates, including MDI, in air in which the isocyanate is converted to the amine and diazotized and the absorbance of the coloured complex of the azo component is measured with: (1) *N*-(1-naphthyl)ethylenediamine at 350-690 nm, with a limit of detection of 0.05 mg/m$^3$ (0.005 ppm) (Fantuzzi *et al.*, 1973); (2) *N*-(1-naphthyl)ethylenediamine at 555 nm, for a concentration range of 0.07-0.7 mg/m$^3$ (0.007-0.07 ppm) (National Institute for Occupational Safety and Health, 1977b); and (3) β-naphthol at 495 or 520 nm, with a limit of detection of 2-3 μg (Pilz, 1965). These colorimetric methods are not specific for MDI, as no separation is involved;  thus, other isocyanates and amines can interfere.

Thin-layer chromatography has been used to separate isocyanates, including MDI, by first converting them to:  (1) the urea derivatives, which are then reacted with *N*-4-nitrobenzyl-*N*-*n*-propylamine and determined colorimetrically, for an MDI concentration range of 0.08-50 mg/m$^3$ (0.008-5 ppm) (Keller *et al.*, 1974);  (2) the amines, which are then reacted with *para*-dimethylaminobenzaldehyde and determined colorimetrically (Lesiak & Orlikowska, 1971);  and (3) the urea or carbamate derivatives, with detection using cerium sulphate (Kozlowski *et al.*, 1976).

MDI has been detected in isocyanate mixtures by liquid chromatographic separation of the urea derivatives and detection by ultra-violet spectroscopy in amounts as low as 2 ng (Hastings Vogt *et al.*, 1977). High-performance liquid chromatography with detection by ultra-violet spectroscopy has been used to separate and detect MDI in blends with toluene diisocyanate and in pre-polymers based on these isocyanates (McFadyen, 1976).

No data on polymethylene polyphenyl isocyanate were available to the Working Group.

## 3.   Biological Data Relevant to the Evaluation
## of Carcinogenic Risk to Humans

### 3.1   Carcinogenicity studies in animals

No data were available to the Working Group.

### 3.2   Other relevant biological data

#### (a)   Experimental systems

The LD$_{50}$ of MDI is more than 10 000 mg/kg bw (Woolrich & Rye, 1969). It is an irritant for the skin and eye of rabbits.  In guinea-pigs, it induces skin sensitivity similar to contact allergy (Duprat *et al.*, 1976).

No data on the embryotoxicity, metabolism or mutagenicity of this compound were available to the Working Group.

#### (b)   Humans

MDI is less toxic than toluene diisocyanate because of its low vapour pressure (Anon., 1966;  Munn, 1965, 1968).

Asthma and tightness of the chest have been observed in workers exposed to MDI (Longley, 1964;  Munn, 1968;  Tanser *et al.*, 1973).  Of 44 workers exposed during the production of polyurethane foam for an average of 16 months, 19 (43.5%) had stress breathlessness but no changes in the lung ventilation, and 70% had hyperaemia of the conjunctiva (Hassmann, 1973). Of 180 workers exposed to MDI, 19% had chronic obstructive lung disease and 21% simple bronchitis (Saia *et al.*, 1976).

Antibodies to MDI were found in workers exposed to 1.3 ppm-min (13 mg/m$^3$-min), but not when they were exposed to 0.9 ppm-min (9 mg/m$^3$-min) (Konzen *et al.*, 1966).

No data on polymethylene polyphenyl isocyanate were available to the Working Group.

## 3.3 Case reports and epidemiological studies

No data were available to the Working Group.

## Flexible and rigid polyurethane foams

### 1. Chemical and Physical Data

### 1.1 Synonyms and trade names[1]

Chem. Abstr. Services Reg. No.: 9009-54-5

Chem. Abstr. Name: Polyurethane foam

### 1.2 Structural and molecular formulae

#### Flexible foam

The general structure of a polyurethane derived from a dihydroxy compound and 2,4-toluene diisocyanate is given by the structure:

$$[C_9H_8N_2O_4R]_n$$

---

[1]For these polyurethane foams we were unable to obtain either synonyms and trade names or molecular weights, with the exception of Y-238, Etheron and Polyfoam as referred to in Section 3.1.

## Rigid foam

Rigid polyurethane foams are typically the reaction products of poly-methylene polyphenyl isocyanate with polyether polyols and have the follow-ing general structure, in which R represents the polyether polyol moieties:

$$C_{15}H_{12}N_2O_4R_2-[C_8H_6NO_2R]_n$$

## 1.3  Chemical and physical properties of the substance

### Flexible foam

(a)  Description:  Cellular plastic foams (Hawley, 1977)

(b)  Density:  Variable, 0.025-0.04 g/cm$^3$ (Pigott, 1969)

(c)  Stability:  Degrades at 300-1000°C in an inert atmosphere to give a complex and variable mixture which may include benzene, 3-amino-4-methylphenylisocyanate and 2,4-diaminotoluene (Hileman *et al.*, 1976;  IARC, 1978);  gaseous products formed by pyrolysis in air at 700°C include methane, ethylene and acetylene (Morimoto *et al.*, 1976).

### Rigid foam

(a)  Description:  Rigid foam (Hawley, 1977)

(b)  Density:  0.017-0.66 g/cm$^3$;  most widely used, 0.025-0.058 g/cm$^3$ (Buist *et al.*, 1971)

(c)  Maximum service temperature:  94-149°C (Agranoff, 1976)

(d)  Softening temperature:  128-145°C (Buist *et al.*, 1971)

(e)  Stability:  Burns or reacts violently with gaseous and liquid fluorine-oxygen mixtures containing 50-100% fluorine (Anon., 1972)

## 1.4 Technical products and impurities

### Flexible foam

A wide variety of flexible polyurethane foams are available in the US, and their composition varies with the processing qualities desired and the preparation methods used. All flexible polyurethane foams are made using toluene diisocyanate (80% 2,4-isomer, 20% 2,6-isomer), polyfunctional polyols, blowing agents, catalysts and surfactants. A typical formulation for a grade of foam used in furniture has a density of approximately 0.025 $g/cm^3$ and may consist of the following ingredients: 100 parts by wt of a polyol (a polyether triol with a molecular weight of 3000 and a hydroxyl number of 56); 41-50 parts by wt of toluene diisocyanate (80/20 mixture), 3.3-4.1 parts by wt water (used to generate carbon dioxide as a blowing agent); 0.5-1.5 parts by wt catalysts (e.g., stannous octoate, sometimes a mixture with tertiary amines such as triethylenediamine, $N$-methyl morpholine, trialkylamines, etc); 1.0-2.0 parts by wt surfactant (usually silicone copolymers); and 2-4 parts by wt trichlorofluoromethane (Fluorocarbon 11) used as a blowing agent (SRI International, 1976). Special properties may be obtained by adding modifiers, fillers and plasticizers (Pigott, 1970).

### Rigid foam

Rigid polyurethane foam is available in the US in board stock (30-35% of foam produced in the US) and as foam systems, which are proportioned, premixed, machine-ready components (typically where the polyols are pre-blended with the surfactants and catalysts as one package and the isocyanate comprises the other component).

A typical formulation for rigid polyurethane foam is as follows: a mixture of primarily sucrose-(or sorbitol-)based polyether polyols with other polyols, 100 parts by wt; polymethylene polyphenyl isocyanate, 110-140 parts by wt; Fluorocarbon 11, 25-35 parts by wt; flame retardant, such as $O,O$-diethyl-$N,N$-bis(hydroxyethylaminomethylphosphonate), 0-15 parts by wt; catalysts, usually mixtures of dibutyltin dilaurate and a tertiary amine, 1.5-3 parts by wt; and a surfactant, 1.3-3 parts by wt. The ingredients used vary depending on the end-use requirements of the foam (SRI International, 1976).

No detailed information on the possible presence of unreacted monomers in the polymers was available to the Working Group.

## 2. Production, Use, Occurrence and Analysis

A review article on polyurethanes has been published (Pigott, 1970).

## 2.1 Production and use

### (a) Production

### Flexible foam

Urethane polymers based on diisocyanate addition polymerization were first discovered by Bayer and coworkers in 1937, and development of flexible polyurethane foams was first disclosed in the Federal Republic of Germany in 1952 (Pigott, 1970). Commercial production of polyurethanes in the US was first reported in 1957 (US Tariff Commission, 1958).

Almost all commercial flexible polyurethane foam production is based on the reaction of toluene diisocyanate (80/20 mixture) with a polyether triol (e.g., polypropylene glycols or propylene oxide adducts of glycerin, 1,2,6-hexanetriol, or trimethylolpropane), or in some cases polyester polyols derived from adipic acid and glycols, in water with added catalysts, surfactants and blowing agents. The reactants are usually metered and mixed together continuously and discharged onto a moving belt upon which the mixture polymerizes and concurrently expands to a cellular mass.

Over 50 companies in the US produce flexible polyurethane foams; production in 1976 was 500 million kg. US exports are believed to be negligible.

Flexible polyurethane foams have been produced commercially in Japan since 1962. In 1976, fourteen companies produced 130 million kg; there are no imports or exports.

### Rigid foam

Rigid polyurethane foams were first made in Germany in 1940-1945, using toluene diisocyanate; however, technical deficiencies and toxicity problems existed with this system. A low-toxicity system based on 4,4'-methylenediphenyl diisocyanate compositions was developed in the UK in the early 1950's, and rigid polyurethane foams based on 4,4'-methylene-diphenyl diisocyanate and polyester resin were first marketed in 1957. Polyether resins with lower viscosities than polyesters were developed for use with 4,4'-methylenediphenyl diisocyanate in 1959 (Buist et al., 1971).

Rigid polyurethane foam is produced commercially by controlled mixing of the components (see the typical formulation described in section 1.4).

Commercial production in the US of polyurethane resins based on diisocyanates was first reported in 1957 (US Tariff Commission, 1958). Production of rigid polyurethane foam was 168.2 million kg in 1974 and 172.7 million kg in 1973. About twelve companies produce board stock, and fifteen companies supply foam systems (including flexible foam).

Rigid polyurethane foams have been produced commercially in Japan since 1964. In 1976, fourteen companies produced 41 million kg; there were no imports or exports.

### (b) Use

#### Flexible foam

In 1975, flexible polyurethane foams were used in the US as follows: furniture (38%), transportation (31%), bedding (14%), carpet underlay (8%), packaging (2%), textile laminates (1%) and miscellaneous applications (6%).

Flexible polyurethane foam is primarily used as a cushioning or padding material: it accounts for about 80% of all furniture cushioning. Transportation applications include passenger car and other motor vehicle seating and miscellaneous padding in door panels, head rests, arm rests, sun visors, etc. High-density, high-resilient flexible foam is used in mattresses; foam padding is used as carpet underlay. Miscellaneous applications include use as scrap for the fabrication of bonded carpet underpadding and packaging. Shredded flexible foam is used as filling material for pillows. Other uses are in insulation, floor mats, sporting goods, novelties and toys, and for the construction of shoes and purses.

In Japan, flexible polyurethane foam is used in furniture (55%) and automotive (45%) applications.

It has been used as a prosthetic breast implant (Clarkson, 1960).

#### Rigid foam

In 1975, 129 million kg of rigid polyurethane foam, based on 4,4'-methylenediphenyl diisocyanate and polymethylene polyphenyl isocyanate, were used in the US, as follows: construction (47.5%), transportation (14.1%), refrigerators and freezers (12.3%), industrial insulation (9.9%), furniture (7.0%), floatation (4.6%) and other applications (4.6%).

Rigid polyurethane foam is primarily used as an insulating material. In construction, it may be used as board stock, spray applied or poured in place, almost entirely in non-residential construction. These uses include roofing insulation, cold storage structures, pipe covering and mobile home construction.

In transport, rigid foam is used for insulation in lorry trailers and bodies and in railroad freight cars, primarily those that have mechanical refrigeration for the transportation of food. It is also used to insulate tank cars that transport chlorine.

Rigid polyurethane foam is used as insulation material for household and commercial refrigerators (it is used in 50% of all refrigerators produced in the US) and for freezers (85% of all freezers produced in the US). An estimated 20.5 million kg of rigid polyurethane foam based on crude toluene diisocyanate was also used in refrigerator and freezer insulation in the US in 1975.

Industrially, rigid foam is used to insulate fuel oil tanks, liquid natural gas pipelines and refrigerated compartments on ships.

It is used in the US as an ornamental trim to simulate carved wood in furniture; and in Europe it is used more extensively, for frames for sofas and lounge chairs.

Floatation applications for rigid foam include its use in marine salvage operations, the reparation of steel barges and, to a smaller extent, in the construction of pleasure boats and commercial vessels.

Other uses are as a packaging material, as picnic coolers and for other recreational items.

In Japan, polyurethane rigid foams are used as insulation in refrigerators and freezers (55%), as insulation in construction applications (23%), as insulation in transportation equipment (10%) and in furniture and miscellaneous applications (12%).

## 2.2 Occurrence

Flexible and rigid polyurethane foams are not known to occur as natural products.

## 2.3 Analysis

Various polyurethanes have been determined by pyrolysis with identification of the pyrolysis products by gas chromatography (Cianetti & Pecci, 1969; Iglauer & Bentley, 1974; Tsuge et al., 1976). The composition of industrial polyurethane elastomers has been determined by aminolysis in morpholine, followed by analysis of the product by infra-red spectroscopy and gas chromatography (Kopusov & Zharkov, 1973).

Twelve groups of plastics, including polyurethanes, were identified by characteristic thermograms using differential thermal analysis (Bosch, 1975). High-resolution nuclear magnetic resonance spectrometry has been used to determine the composition and molecular weight of polyester urethanes (Yeager & Becker, 1977).

### 3.  Biological Data Relevant to the Evaluation

### of Carcinogenic Risk to Humans

## 3.1  Carcinogenicity studies in animals

### (a)  Oral administration

Rat:  Polyurethane foam (ester from linear polyester of adipic acid
and diethylene glycol, coupled with toluene diisocyanate, plus 5 additives)
was cut into strips, saturated with beef extract and then dried in an oven.
Bethesda black rats consumed about 1 g daily per cage of 10-15 rats, for 2
years.  Seven tumours were detected among 43 rats, 27 of which survived 21
months or more.  This incidence was not considered to be different from
that observed in controls (Hueper, 1964) [The Working Group noted the low
dose used].

### (b)  Inhalation and/or intratracheal or intrabronchial administration[1]

Rat:  Two groups of 39 and 45 male Sprague-Dawley rats were submitted
to inhalation of rigid isocyanate polyurethane foam powder (composition
not given) for 6 hours/day on 5 days/week for 6 weeks, at concentrations of
3.6 and 20 mg/m$^3$, respectively.  One bronchial squamous-cell carcinoma was
observed in animals at each dose level after 544 and 349 days, respectively.
The median lifespan was 50 and 62 weeks, and the durations of the experiments were 139 and 101 weeks.  No tumours were found in 20 untreated rats
(Laskin et al., 1972) [The Working Group noted the short duration of treat-
ment].

---

[1]Subsequent to the finalization of the monograph by the Working Group
in February 1978, the Secretariat became aware of an inhalation study in a
group of 50 male and 50 female Sprague-Dawley rats, 8-weeks of age, exposed
to a freshly generated rigid polyurethane foam dust synthesized from
Desmophen FWFA/2 (polyol based on a sucrose-polyether) and Desmodur 44V20
(a polymeric isocyanate based on 4,4'-methylenediphenyl diisocyanate) at a
concentration of 8.65 mg/m$^3$ air for 6 hours/day on 5 days/week for 12 weeks;
the experiment was terminated after 140 weeks.  There was no difference in
tumour incidences between the polyurethane group and 2 groups of controls
given titanium oxide or air alone (Thyssen et al., 1978).

Five mg of powder from an old polyurethane dust (same product as the one used by Laskin *et al.*, 1972) or a freshly prepared polyurethane (composition not given) were suspended in 0.2 ml saline and introduced by intubation into the trachea of white rats of different ages (2-3 months or 11-19 months). This dose is equivalent to inhalation for 8 hours/day for 30 days of a concentration between the minimal and maximal levels used in the experiment by Laskin *et al.* (1972). Pulmonary fibrosis appeared after 6 months. A sub-pleural adenoma was seen in an old rat given the old sample, and 4 benign lesions reported as intrabronchial adenomas were observed 18 months after intubation among 15 young rats given the freshly prepared sample (Stemmer *et al.*, 1975).

A polyether chlorinated polyurethane sheet [Y-238, polymer formed by reaction of toluene diisocyanate with polyether and cured with MOCA, 4,4'-methylenebis(2-chloroaniline)[1]] was cut into strips of approximately 1 x 1 x 6 mm (5-8 mg) and 1 x 1 x 10 mm (9-10 mg). Fine, stainless-steel surgical wire was passed through each sample and bent to form 2 hooks. The strips were then introduced *via* tracheotomy into the left inferior bronchus by means of trochar; 2 groups of 35 male Bethesda black rats were used. One squamous-cell carcinoma of the lung was observed after 21.5 months in the first group, in which 31 animals survived 1 year or more; and 3 squamous-cell carcinomas of the lung were observed after 17-21 months in the second group, in which 32 animals survived 1 year or more. No lung tumours were observed in controls implanted with surgical wire alone (Autian *et al.*, 1976).

Hamster: Two groups of 40 and 50 male Syrian hamsters were exposed to respirable dust (0.5-3 μ) generated from rigid polyurethane foam (composition not given) at concentrations of 3.6 and 20 mg/m$^3$ in air, respectively, for 6 hours/day on 5 days/week for 6 weeks. Median survival times were 76 and 87 weeks, and the durations of the experiment were 139 and 101 weeks, respectively. No lung tumours were reported (Laskin *et al.*, 1972) [The Working Group noted the short duration of exposure and the fact that histopathology was not complete at the time of reporting].

(c)  Other experimental systems

Subcutaneous and/or intraperitoneal implantation: Three forms of polyurethane (made from toluene diisocyanate), each weighing 65 mg, were introduced into the nape of the neck or into the right side of the abdominal cavity of 6 groups of 30 3-month-old female Bethesda black rats. The form was either a disc cut from a sheet, or cubes cut from polyurethane foam, or a powder derived from the foam by micropulverization. A control group was

---

[1]See also IARC (1974)

given i.p. injections of saline. The experiment lasted 24 months. The sheet gave rise to 1 s.c. tumour, the foam caused one s.c. and 9 abdominal tumours, and the powder gave 1 abdominal tumour. The latency of tumour appearance was 10 months for the foam and 22 months for the sheet (Hueper, 1960); see Table 1.

Table 1

Sites and types of tumours observed in rats with implants of polyurethane

| Type of polyurethane | Site of implantation | No. of tumours | |
|---|---|---|---|
| | | local | remote |
| Sheet | s.c. | 1 | 5 |
| | i.p. | 0 | 6 |
| Foam | s.c. | 1 | 5 |
| | i.p. | 9 | 4 |
| Powdered foam | s.c. | 0 | 4 |
| | i.p. | 1 | 6 |
| Controls | | 0 | 4 |

S.c. (in the nape of the neck) or i.p. implants of polyurethane sheet, foam cubes or powder were made in groups of 30 3-month-old female Bethesda black rats. The sheet, made by reacting toluene diisocyanate 80/20, adipic acid and diethylene glycol, and containing the flame retardant tris(β-chloroethyl)phosphate, was cut into 2 discs (3 and 5 mm in diameter). The foam was cut into cubes measuring 25 x 20 x 3 mm; each cube was further subdivided into 4 pieces for s.c. implantation. Powder was obtained by micropulverizing the foam. All samples weighed 65 mg each. Female rats (200) were used as controls. Polyurethane sheet and foam each produced only one s.c. sarcoma; however, i.p. implantation of the foam produced 8 adenocarcinomas of the caecum within a latency of 10-19 months. S.c. implants of the powdered form produced one s.c. sarcoma, and i.p. implants caused one invading adenocarcinoma of the caecum (Hueper, 1961).

Two polyurethane foams (linear polyester of adipic acid and diethylene glycol coupled with toluene diisocyanate, old or freshly prepared) and 3 rigid types of polyurethane were implanted into the s.c. tissue of the nape of the neck and/or into the abdominal cavity (pericoecal and perigastric region) of Bethesda black rats. The 65 mg implants varied from 6 x 5 x 2 mm to 25 x 20 x 2 mm in size because of density differences. Each group of 35 (20 males and 15 females) rats was observed for 24 months. Among the 140 rats that received i.p. implantations of foam, 20 tumours related to the implant were detected (including 5 stomach sarcomas and 9 adenocarcinomas of the colon). The s.c. implants of rigid polyurethane foams resulted in 9 sarcomas in 135 rats; the i.p. implantation of rigid foam produced 2 abdominal fibrosarcomas and 1 lymphangiosarcoma of the vaginal region in 135 rats (Hueper, 1964).

Two polyurethane foams (Etheron, derived from diisocyanate polyethers, and Polyfoam, from toluene diisocyanate) were implanted in the cervical s.c. tissue of albino rats as 20 x 20 x 5 mm pieces. Etheron produced 2 sarcomas in 18 animals that lived for 19-28 months. Polyfoam produced 4 sarcomas in 10 animals, the average age at death being 22.5 months. The two foams disappeared almost entirely after 2 years of implantation (Walter & Chiaramonte, 1965).

Seventeen isocyanate polyurethane samples containing various substituent groups (aromatic, aliphatic or ester groups) were implanted intraperitoneally into groups of 30 or more male Bethesda black rats. Thirteen polyurethane samples were furnished as sheets and 4 as granular powders. The sheets were cut into rectangular pieces with a dimension of 0.3 cm or less. Thirteen of the polyurethane samples were similarly studied in females. Each rat received 1.5 g of test samples. Of the 1015 rats implanted with polyurethane samples, 292/577 males and 248/438 females developed malignant tumours during the 24-month study, about 90% of which were fibrosarcomas. In addition, 4/37 sham operated male controls and 7/37 female controls developed malignant tumours (Autian *et al.*, 1975) [The Working Group noted that insufficient pathological data were given].

A chlorinated polyether polyurethane [Y-238, formed from toluene diisocyanate and cured with 4,4'-methylenebis(*o*-chloroaniline) (MOCA)[1]], which demonstrated the highest relative tumorigenicity of 17 polyurethane samples tested in the study reported above, was selected for further evaluation. Discs 3.1 mm in diameter were implanted intraperitoneally into 5 groups of 35 male Bethesda black rats to give doses of 93.8, 187.5, 375, 750 and 1500 mg/rat. The animals were observed for 2 years. None, 1, 2, 8 and 24 local fibrosarcomas were observed in the 5 groups, respectively, suggesting a dose-related incidence of tumours (Autian *et al.*, 1975, 1976).

Intravaginal insertion: Soft polyurethane sponge tampons, either impregnated or not with ethylene glycol, were introduced twice weekly into the vaginas of 30 random-bred and 23 C57BL mice. The controls received the same treatment but with tampons of rubber sponge. After 64 and 322-596 days, respectively, vaginal lesions described as precancerous were observed in both treated groups (15/30 and 23/23), with signs of malignancy in 2 mice of the first group. In the control group, 17/18 C57BL mice had precancerous lesions, 3 of which showed possible signs of malignancy (Volfson, 1969, 1973).

Three groups of CL57W or A mice received insertions of polyurethane foam tampons into the vagina. Group 1 received repeated insertions during the experiment (155-464 days); group 2 received repeated insertions during all but the last 27-64 days of the experiment (215-439 days); group 3 had

---

[1]See also IARC (1974)

tampons inserted permanently during 65-120 days.  The incidences of lesions of the ovary and vagina were:

| Group | No. of mice | Ovarian folliculoma | Vagina | |
|-------|-------------|---------------------|--------|-------|
|       |             |                     | precancer | cancer |
| 1 | 41 | 0 | 28 | 3 |
| 2 | 15 | 5 | 8 | 0 |
| 3 | 12 | 1 | 8 | 0 |

(Volfson, 1976).

## 3.2  Other relevant biological data

### (a)  Experimental systems

The distribution of both ring- and side-chain-labelled rigid poly-urethane rods (prepared from toluene diisocyanate) was slow, and approximately three-fourths of the implanted material remained *in situ* (in the marrow cavity of the tibia of rats) for at least 2 years after implantation. Studies of homogenates indicated that the aromatic ring from the polyure-thane was not retained in appreciable amounts in the organs examined (Sherman & Lyons, 1969).

No data on the toxicity, embryotoxicity, teratogenicity, metabolism or mutagenicity of this compound were available to the Working Group.

### (b)  Humans

Allergic contact dermatitis has been reported among polyurethane plastic moulders (Emmett, 1976).

## 3.3  Case reports and epidemiololgical studies

No data were available to the Working Group.

## 4.  Summary of Data Reported and Evaluation

## 4.1  Experimental data

No data on the carcinogenicity or mutagenicity of 2,4- and 2,6-toluene diisocyanates, 1,5-naphthalene diisocyanate, 4,4'-methylenediphenyl diisocyanate or polymethylene polyphenyl isocyanate were available to the Working Group.

Polyurethanes of various chemical compositions were tested for carcino-genicity in a number of physical forms (discs, strips, foams, powder) by subcutaneous, intraperitoneal, intravaginal, intratracheal and intrabronchial administration and by inhalation of the dust in mice and rats. Fibrosarcomas were induced at the sites of subcutaneous and intraperitoneal implantation. The incidence of sarcomas varied with the physical and chemical characteristics of the implants. In one experiment with intraperitoneal implantation, epithelial tumours were also induced. No association can be made between lung tumours in rats and inhalational exposure or intrabronchial or intratracheal implantation of polyurethane on the basis of the data available to the Working Group.

## 4.2  Human data

No case reports or epidemiological studies relating to the carcinogenicity of either 2,4- or 2,6-toluene diisocyanate, 1,5-naphthalene diisocyanate, 4,4'-methylenediphenyl diisocyanate or polymethylene polyphenyl isocyanate or polyurethane foams were available to the Working Group. In view of the massive production of these isocyanates and the wide distribution of polyurethane foam products in general consumer products, it should be possible to identify and follow up exposed groups (particularly occupational).

## 4.3  Evaluation

The insufficient experimental data and the absence of data in humans preclude assessment of the carcinogenicity of 2,4- and 2,6-toluene diisocyanates, 1,5-naphthalene diisocyanate, 4,4'-methylenediphenyl diisocyanate and polymethylene polyphenyl isocyanate and polyurethane foams in humans. Efforts should be made to obtain further experimental and epidemiological evidence (see also 'General Remarks on the Substances Considered', p. 35).

# 5. References

Adams, W.G.F. (1975)  Long-term effects on the health of men engaged in the manufacture of tolylene di-isocyanate. Br. J. ind. Med., 32, 72-78

Agranoff, J., ed. (1976)  Modern Plastics Encyclopedia 1976-1977, Vol. 53, No. 10A, New York, McGraw-Hill, pp. 480-481

Anon. (1966)  Hazards of di-isocyanates. Lancet, i, 32-33

Anon. (1972)  Fire Protection Guide on Hazardous Materials, 4th ed., Boston, Mass., National Fire Protection Association, pp. 491M-118, 491M-186

Autian, J., Singh, A.R., Turner, J.E., Hung, G.W.C., Nunez, L.J. & Lawrence, W.H. (1975)  Carcinogenesis from polyurethans. Cancer Res., 35, 1591-1596

Autian, J., Singh, A.R., Turner, J.E., Hung, G.W.C., Nunez, L.J. & Lawrence, W.H. (1976)  Carcinogenic activity of a chlorinated polyether polyurethan. Cancer Res., 36, 3973-3977

Belisle, J. (1969)  A portable field kit for the sampling and analysis of toluene diisocyanate in air. Am. ind. Hyg. Assoc. J., 30, 41-45

Boit, H.-G., ed. (1973)  Beilsteins Handbuch der Organischen Chemie, 4th ed., Vol. 13, Syst. No. 1787/H243-244, Berlin, Springer, p. 461

Bosch, K. (1975)  Thermoanalytical identification of plastics (Ger.). Beitr. Gerichtl. Med., 33, 280-284 [Chem. Abstr., 84, 60332d]

Bruckner, H.C., Avery, S.B., Stetson, D.M., Dodson, V.N. & Ronayne, J.J. (1968)  Clinical and immunologic appraisal of workers exposed to diisocyanates. Arch. environ. Health, 16, 619-625

Buist, J.M., Crowley, G.P. & Lowe, A. (1971)  Polyurethan technology. In: Bikales, N.M., ed., Encyclopedia of Polymer Science and Technology, Plastics, Resins, Rubbers, Fibers, Vol. 15, New York, Interscience, pp. 458, 462, 467-471, 479

Butcher, B.T., Salvaggio, J.E., O'Neil, C.E., Weill, H. & Garg, O. (1977)  Toluene diisocyanate pulmonary disease: immunopharmacologic and mecholyl challenge studies. J. Allergy clin. Immunol., 59, 223-227

Chadwick, D.H. & Hardy, E.E. (1967)  Isocyanates, organic. In: Kirk, R.E. & Othmer, D.F., eds, Encyclopedia of Chemical Technology, 2nd ed., Vol. 12, New York, John Wiley and Sons, pp. 46-47, 59, 64

Cianetti, E. & Pecci, G. (1969) Identification of elastomers by gas chromatography of pyrolysis products at a given temperature (Ital.). Ind. Gomma, 13, 45-54, 56-57 [Chem. Abstr., 72, 13554v]

Ciosek, A., Gesicka, E. & Kesy-Dabrowska, I. (1969) The evaluation of occupational exposure of workers employed at the production of polyurethane foam (Pol). Med. Pracy, 20, 417-424

Clarkson, P. (1960) Sponge implants for flat breasts. Proc. R. Soc. Med., 53, 880-881

De Moran, J.A. & Biondi, A.C. (1973) Potentiometric determination of toluene diisocyanate (Span.). Arch. Bioquim., Quim. Farm., 18, 177-180 [Chem. Abstr., 83, 125878n]

Dodson, V.N. (1971) Isocyanate anhelation. J. occup. Med., 13, 238-241

Duncan, B., Scheel, L.D., Fairchild, E.J., Killens, R. & Graham, S. (1962) Toluene diisocyanate inhalation toxicity: pathology and mortality. Am. ind. Hyg. Assoc. J., 23, 447-456

Duprat, P., Gradiski, D. & Marignac, B. (1976) Irritant and allergenic capacity of two isocyanates. Toluene diisocyanate (TDI). Diphenyl-methane diisocyanate (MDI) (Fr.). Eur. J. Toxicol., 9, 41-53

Elkins, H.B., McCarl, G.W., Brugsch, H.G. & Fahy, J.P. (1962) Massachusetts experience with toluene di-isocyanate. Am. ind. Hyg. Assoc. J., 23, 265-272

Emmett, E.A. (1976) Allergic contact dermatitis in polyurethane plastic moulders. J. occup. Med., 18, 802-804

Fantuzzi, A., Consonni, G. & Locati, G. (1973) Method for the determination of isocyanates in the atmosphere (Ital.). Ann. Ist. Super. Sanita, 9, 528-533 [Chem. Abstr., 83, 151466w]

Gnauck, R. (1975) Identification of polymers by pyrolysis-gas chromato-graphy. I. Determination of isocyanate components in polyurethanes (Ger.). Plaste Kautsch., 22, 795-796 [Chem. Abstr., 84, 5414g]

Grasselli, J.G. & Ritchey, W.M., eds (1975) CRC Atlas of Spectral Data and Physical Constants for Organic Compounds, 2nd ed., Vol. IV, Cleveland, Ohio, Chemical Rubber Co., p. 663

Gustavsson, P. (1977) Diisocyanates. A review of the literature on medi-cal and toxicological observations (Swed.). Arbete och Hälsa, Vol. 11, Stockholm, Arbetar-Skyddsverket

Hassman, P. (1968) Damage of respiratory ways in production of polyurethane foam (Czech.). Pracov. Lék., 20, 105-108

Hassman, P. (1969)  Rate of disease of the respiratory ways in workers
    employed in production of polyurethane rubber (Czech.).  Pracov. Lék.,
    21, 197-201

Hassman, P. (1973)  The health status of workers with diphenylmethane-
    4.4'-diisocyanate (MDI) (Czech.).  Pracov. Lék., 25, 242-244

Hastings Vogt, C.R., Ko, C.Y. & Ryan, T.R. (1977)  Simple ureas derived
    from diisocyanates and their liquid chromatography on a 5-cm column.
    J. Chromatogr., 134, 451-458

Hawley, G.G., ed. (1971)  The Condensed Chemical Dictionary, 8th ed.,
    New York, Van Nostrand-Reinhold, p. 603

Hawley, G.G., ed. (1977)  The Condensed Chemical Dictionary, 9th ed.,
    New York, Van Nostrand-Reinhold, pp. 317, 705-706

Henschler, D., Assmann, W. & Meyer, K.-O. (1962)  Toxicology of toluene
    diisocyanates (Ger.).  Arch. Toxikol., 19, 364-387

Heuser, E., Reusche, W., Wrabetz, K. & Fauss, R. (1971)  Determination of
    free monomeric tolylene diisocyanates and hexamethylene diisocyanate
    in polyurethane paints (Ger.).  Fresenius' Z. anal. Chem., 257,
    119-125 [Chem. Abstr., 76, 114874n]

Hileman, F.D., Voorhees, K.J. & Einhorn, I.N. (1976)  Pyrolysis of a
    flexible-urethane foam.  In: Physiological and Toxicological Aspects
    of Combustion Products, International Symposium, March 18-20, 1974,
    University of Utah, Salt Lake City, Washington DC, National Academy
    of Sciences, pp. 226-244

Hill, R.N. (1970)  A controlled study of workers handling organic diiso-
    cyanates.  Proc. R. Soc. Med., 63, 375

Hueper, W.C. (1960)  Experimental production of cancer by means of
    implanted polyurethane plastic.  Am. J. clin. Pathol., 34, 328-333

Hueper, W.C. (1961)  Carcinogenic studies on water-insoluble polymers.
    Pathol. Microbiol., 24, 77-106

Hueper, W.C. (1964)  Cancer induction by polyurethan and polysilicone
    plastics.  J. natl Cancer Inst., 33, 1005-1027

IARC (1974)  IARC Monographs on the Evaluation of Carcinogenic Risk
    of Chemicals to Man, 4, Some Aromatic Amines, Hydrazine and Related
    Substances, N-Nitroso Compounds and Miscellaneous Alkylating Agents,
    Lyon, pp 65-71

IARC (1978)  IARC Monographs on the Evaluation of the Carcinogenic Risk of Chemicals to Humans, 16, Some Aromatic Amines and Related Nitro Compounds - Hair Dyes, Colouring Agents and Miscellaneous Industrial Chemicals, Lyon, pp. 83-95

Iglauer, N. & Bentley, F.F. (1974)  Pyrolysis GLC [gas-liquid chromatography] for the rapid identification of organic polymers. J. chromatogr. Sci., 12, 23-33 [Chem. Abstr., 81, 64416v]

Keller, J., Dunlap, K.L. & Sandridge, R.L. (1974)  Determination of isocyanates in the working atmosphere by thin-layer chromatography. Anal. Chem., 46, 1845-1846

Konzen, R.B., Craft, B.F., Scheel, L.D. & Gorski, C.H. (1966)  Human response to low concentrations of $p,p$-diphenylmethane diisocyanate (MDI). Am. ind. Hyg. Assoc. J., 27, 121-127

Kopusov, L.I. & Zharkov, V.V. (1973)  Determination of the composition of industrial elastic polyurethanes (Russ.). Plast. Massy, 9, 64-66 [Chem. Abstr., 80, 71829q]

Kozlowski, K., Goraczko, A. & Turowiec, G. (1976)  Identification of aromatic isocyanates by thin-layer chromatography (Pol.). Chem. Anal. (Warsaw), 21, 1357-1360 [Chem. Abstr., 87, 95033w]

Laskin, S., Drew, R.T., Cappiello, V.P. & Kuschner, M. (1972)  Inhalation studies with freshly generated polyurethane foam dust.  In: Mercer, T.T., ed., Assessment of Airborne Particles, Fundamentals, Applications and Implications to Inhalation Toxicity, Springfield, Ill., C.C. Thomas, pp. 382-404

Lesiak, T. & Orlikowska, H. (1971)  Colorimetric determination of diphenylmethane-4,4'-diisocyanate in commercial products after chromatographic separation of their hydrolysates (Pol.). Chem. Anal. (Warsaw), 16, 1233-1239 [Chem. Abstr., 76, 94330b]

Levin, V., Nippoldt, B.W. & Rebertus, R.L. (1967)  Spectrophotometric determination of primary aromatic amines with thiotrithiazyl chloride. Application to determination of toluene-2,4-diisocyanate in air. Anal. Chem., 39, 581-584

Longley, E.O. (1964)  Methane diisocyanate:  a respiratory hazard? Arch. environ. Health, 8, 898

McFadyen, P. (1976)  Determination of free toluene diisocyanate in polyurethane prepolymers by high-performance liquid chromatography. J. Chromatogr., 123, 468-473

Morimoto, T., Takeyama, K.-I. & Konishi, F. (1976)  Composition of gaseous combustion products of polymers. J. appl. Polym. Sci., 20, 1967-1976

Mulyanov, P.V., Moncharzh, N.M., Bogdanova, T.M. & Golov, V.G. (1973) Determination of the isomeric composition of diphenylmethane diisocyanate by a dielectric-constant method (Russ.). Zh. anal. Khim., 28, 1628-1631 [Chem. Abstr., 79, 152652h]

Mulyanov, P.V., Moncharzh, N.M., Bogdanova, T.M. & Golov, V.G. (1974) Determination of the isomeric composition of tolylene diisocyanate by a dielectric constant method (Russ.). Zavod. Lab., 40, 65-66 [Chem. Abstr., 81, 32993q]

Munn, A. (1965) Hazards of isocyanates. Ann. occup. Hyg., 8, 163-169

Munn, A. (1968) Health hazards from isocyanates. Adv. Polyurethane Technol., 16, 299-306

National Institute for Occupational Safety and Health (1973) Criteria for a Recommended Standard. Occupational Exposure to Toluene Diisocyanate, Contract HSM 73-11022, Washington DC, US Department of Health, Education and Welfare

National Institute for Occupational Safety and Health (1977a) NIOSH Manual of Analytical Methods, 2nd ed., Part I, Vol. 1, Method No. P&CAM 141, Publ. No. 77-157-B, Washington DC, US Government Printing Office, pp. 141-1-141-8

National Institute for Occupational Safety and Health (1977b) NIOSH Manual of Analytical Methods, 2nd ed., Part I, Vol. 1, Method No. P&CAM 142, Publ. No. 77-157-B, Washington DC, US Government Printing Office, pp. 142-1-142-7

Niewenhuis, R., Scheel, L., Stemmer, K. & Killens, R. (1965) Toxicity of chronic low level exposures to toluene diisocyanate in animals. Am. ind. Hyg. Assoc. J., 26, 143-149

Peters, J.M. & Wegman, D.H. (1975) Epidemiology of toluene diisocyanate (TDI)-induced respiratory disease. Environ. Health Perspect., 11, 97-100

Peters, J.M., Murphy, R.L.H., Pagnotto, L.D. & Van Ganse, W.F. (1968) Acute respiratory effects in workers exposed to low levels of toluene diisocyanate (TDI). Arch. environ. Health, 16, 642-647

Pigott, K.A. (1969) Polyurethans. In: Bikales, N.M., ed., Encyclopedia of Polymer Science and Technology, Plastics, Resins, Rubbers, Fibers, Vol. 11, New York, Interscience, pp. 510, 537-544

Pigott, K.A. (1970) Urethan polymers. In: Kirk, R.E. & Othmer, D.F., eds, Encyclopedia of Chemical Technology, 2nd ed., Vol. 21, New York, John Wiley and Sons, pp. 56-106

Pilz, W. (1965) Determination of diphenylmethane-4,4'-diisocyanate (Desmodur 44) in the air (Ger.) Mikrochim. ichnoanal. acta, 4, 687-698 [Chem. Abstr., 63, 17153d]

Pollock, J.R.A. & Stevens, R., eds (1974) Dictionary of Organic Compounds, 4th ed., Suppl. 10, New York, Oxford University Press, p. 337

Porter, C.V., Higgins, R.L. & Scheel, L.D. (1975) A retrospective study of clinical, physiologic and immunologic changes in workers exposed to toluene diisocyanate. Am. ind. Hyg. Assoc. J., 36, 159-168

Potapova, M.P., Lushchik, V.I., Ermolaeva, T.A. & Pronina, I.A. (1974) Chromatographic determination of free monomers in polyurethane systems (Russ.). Lakokras. Mater. Ikh Primen., 4, 73-74 [Chem. Abstr., 82, 45126e]

Potapova, M.P., Lushchik, V.I., Ermolaeva, T.A. & Pronina, I.A. (1975) Gas chromatographic determination of free monomers of hexamethylene and tolylene diisocyanates in polyurethane prepolymers (Ger.). Plaste Kautsch., 22, 988-989 [Chem. Abstr., 84, 60290p]

Reilly, D.A. (1968) A test-paper method for the determination of tolylene di-isocyanate vapour in air. Analyst (Lond.), 93, 178-185

Saia, B., Fabbri, L., Mapp, C., Marcer, G. & Mastrangelo, G. (1976) Epidemiology of chronic non-specific lung disease in a population exposed to isocyanate. I. Analysis of symptoms. Med. Lav., 67, 278-284

Schanche, G.W. & Hermann, E.R. (1974) Micrograms of TDI by chromatography. Am. ind. Hyg. Assoc. J., 35, 47-52

Scott, P.H. & Carey, D.A. (1976) Fabrethane, a one component urethane foam fabric coating. J. Coated Fabr., 6, 13-19 [Chem. Abstr., 85, 178572f]

Scrima, M. & Salvadori, P. (1976) Determination of TDI from polyurethane paints and in the work environment (Ital.). Lav. Um., 28, 48-59 [Chem. Abstr., 86, 160431v]

Sherman, R.T. & Lyons, H. (1969) The biological fate of implanted rigid polyurethane foam. J. surg. Res., 9, 167-171

Siefken, W. (1949) Mono- and polyisocyanates. IV. Polyurethanes (Ger.). Justus Liebigs Ann. Chem., 562, 75, 91-92, 129

Simonov, V.A., Nekhorosheva, E.V. & Zavorovskaya, N.A. (1971) Photometric determination of 2,4-tolylene diisocyanate in air using chromotropic acid (Russ.). Nauch. Rab. Inst. Okhr. Tr. Vses. Tsent. Sov. Prof. Soyuz., 70, 67-68 [Chem. Abstr., 77, 105225v]

Sova, B. (1974)  Experience with isocyanates in the footwear industry (Czech.).
    Kozarstvi, 24, 20-22 [Chem. Abstr., 81, 67963g]

SRI International (1976)  Polyurethane foams - continued.  Plastics and
    resins, diisocyanates and polyisocyanates - continued.  Isocyanates.
    Chemical Economics Handbook, January, Menlo Park, California,
    pp. 580.1562A-580.1562D, 666.5022M-662.5022O

Stemmer, K.L., Bingham, E. & Barkley, W. (1975)  Pulmonary response to poly-
    urethane dust.  Environ. Health Perspect., 11, 109-113

Stevens, M.A. & Palmer, R. (1970)  The effect of tolylene diisocyanate on
    certain laboratory animals.  Proc. R. Soc. Med., 63, 380-382

Tanser, A.R., Bourke, M.P. & Blandford, A.G. (1973)  Isocyanate asthma:
    respiratory symptoms caused by diphenyl-methane di-isocyanate.
    Thorax, 28, 596-600

Thyssen, J., Kimmerle, G., Dickhaus, S., Emminger, E. & Mohr, U. (1978)
    Inhalation studies with polyurethane foam dust in relation to respir-
    atory tract carcinogenesis.  J. environ. Pathol. Toxicol., 1, 501-508

Tonkoshkurov, Y.S. (1969)  Sanitary and hygienic conditions during the
    preparation and use of the polymer cement 'Polief' (Russ.).  Gig. Tr.
    Prof. Zabol., 13, 41 [Chem. Abstr., 72, 70364g]

Toxicology Information Program (1976)  Carcinogenesis bioassay of toluene
    diisocyanate (TDI).  Tox-Tips, 1(5), 17

Tsuge, K., Hashimoto, K. & Matsuo, T. (1976)  Analysis of polyurethane
    elastomers (Jap.).  Nippon Gomu Kyokaishi, 49, 643-647 [Chem. Abstr.,
    85, 144390e]

Union Carbide Corporation (1967)  Toxicological studies:  'Niax' Isocyanate
    TDI, 11 July, New York, Industrial Medicial and Toxicology Department

US Department of Commerce (1977)  US Exports, Schedule B Commodity Groupings,
    Schedule B Commodity by Country, FT410/December, Bureau of the Census,
    Washington DC, US Government Printing Office, p. 2-74

US Food and Drug Administration (1977)  Food and drugs.  US Code Fed. Regul.,
    Title 21, parts 175.105, 177.1680, pp. 438-439, 534

US International Trade Commission (1977a)  Synthetic Organic Chemicals,
    US Production and Sales, 1976, USITC Publication 833, Washington DC,
    US Government Printing Office, pp. 37, 59

US International Trade Commission (1977b)  Synthetic Organic Chemicals,
    US Production and Sales, 1975, USITC Publication 804, Washington DC,
    US Government Printing Office, pp. 22, 36

US International Trade Commission (1977c)  Imports of Benzenoid Chemicals and Products, 1975, USITC Publication 806, Washington DC, US Government Printing Office, pp. 18, 25

US International Trade Commission (1977d)  Imports of Benzenoid Chemicals and Products, 1976, USITC Publication 828, Washington DC, US Government Printing Office, p. 24

US Occupational Safety and Health Administration (1976)  Occupational safety and health standards, subpart Z - toxic and hazardous substances, US Code Fed. Regul., Title 29, Chapter XVII, Section 1910.1000, p. 31:8303

US Tariff Commission (1954)  Synthetic Organic Chemicals, US Production and Sales, 1953, Report No. 194, Second Series, Washington DC, US Government Printing Office, p. 71

US Tariff Commission (1958)  Synthetic Organic Chemicals, US Production and Sales, 1957, Report No. 203, Second Series, Washington DC, US Government Printing Office, pp. 76, 123

Volfson, N.I. (1969)  Precancerous changes of the cervical uterine and vaginal epithelium of the mouse in intravaginal administration of plastic sponge. Bjull. eksp. Biol. Med., 67, 91-95

Volfson, N.I. (1973)  The genesis of glandlike changes of uterine cervix. Neoplasma, 20, 189-196

Volfson, N.I. (1976)  On the genesis of experimental granulosa cell tumors of the ovary. Vop. Onkol., 22, 68-75

Walter, J.B. & Chiaramonte, L.G. (1965)  The tissue responses of the rat to implanted Ivalon, Etheron, and polyfoam plastic sponges. Br. J. Surg., 52, 49-54

Walworth, H.T. & Virchow, W.E. (1959)  Industrial hygiene experiences with toluene diisocyanate. Am. ind. Hyg. Assoc. J., 20, 205-210

Wegman, D.H., Pagnotto, L.D., Fine, L.J. & Peters, J.M. (1974)  A dose-response relationship in TDI workers. J. occup. Med., 16, 258-260

Wegman, D.H., Peters, J.M., Pagnotto, L. & Fine, L.J. (1977)  Chronic pulmonary function loss from exposure to toluene diisocyanate. Br. J. ind. Med., 34, 196-200

Weill, H., Salvaggio, J., Neilson, A., Butcher, B. & Ziskind, M. (1975)  Respiratory effects in toluene diisocyanate manufacture: a multidisciplinary approach. Environ. Health Perspect., 11, 101-108

Wheals, B.B. & Thomson, J. (1967)  The determination of trace levels of toluene-2,4-diisocyanate by electron capture gas chromatography. Chemistry & Industry, 6 May, 753-754

Williamson, K.S. (1964)  Studies of diisocyanate workers. Trans. Assoc. Ind. med. Officers, 14, 81-88

Williamson, K.S. (1965)  Studies of diisocyanate workers (2). Trans. Assoc. Ind. med. Officers, 15, 29-35

Windholz, M., ed. (1976)  The Merck Index, 9th ed., Rahway, NJ, Merck & Co., pp. 1225-1226

Winell, M. (1975)  An international comparison of hygienic standards for chemicals in the work environment. Ambio, 4, 34-36

Woolrich, P.F. & Rye, W.A. (1969)  Urethanes. Engineering, medical control and toxicologic considerations. J. occup. Med., 11, 184-190

Yeager, F.W. & Becker, J.W. (1977)  Determination of composition and molecular weight of polyester urethanes by high resolution proton magnetic resonance spectrometry. Anal. Chem., 49, 722-724

Zapp, J.A., Jr (1957)  Hazards of isocyanates in polyurethane foam plastic production. Arch. ind. Health, 15, 324-330

## VINYL ACETATE, POLYVINYL ACETATE and POLYVINYL ALCOHOL

Vinyl acetate

### 1.  Chemical and Physical Data

1.1  Synonyms and trade names

Chem. Abstr. Services Reg. No.:  108-05-4

Chem. Abstr. Name:  Acetic acid ethenyl ester

Acetic acid vinyl ester;  1-acetoxyethylene;  vinyl A monomer;
VAc;  VyAc

1.2  Structural and molecular formulae and molecular weight

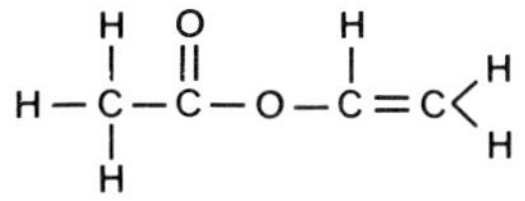

$$H-\underset{\underset{H}{|}}{\overset{\overset{H}{|}}{C}}-\overset{\overset{O}{\|}}{C}-O-\overset{\overset{H}{|}}{C}=C\overset{H}{\underset{H}{\big<}}$$

$C_4H_6O_2$                 Mol. wt:  86.1

1.3  Chemical and physical properties of the pure substance

From Weast (1976), unless otherwise specified

(a)  Description:  Colourless liquid (Hawley, 1971)

(b)  Boiling-point:  72.2-72.3°C

(c)  Melting-point:  -93.2°C

(d)  Density:  $d_4^{20}$ 0.9317;  vapour-air density at 42°C is 1.5;
vapour density is 3 (air = 1) (Anon., 1972).

(e)  Refractive index:  $n_D^{20}$ 1.3959

(f)  Spectroscopy data:  $\lambda_{max}$ 258 (shoulder) ($E_1^1$ = 0.06);  infra-red,
Raman, nuclear magnetic resonance and mass spectral data have
been tabulated (Grasselli & Ritchey, 1975).

(g) Solubility: Insoluble in water; soluble in ethanol, ether,
acetone, benzene, chloroform and carbon tetrachloride

(h) Volatility: Vapour pressure is 100 mm at 23.3°C (Perry &
Chilton, 1973).

(i) Stability: Flash-point (open cup), between -9° and -5°C
(Rhum, 1970); inflammable limits, 2.6-13.4% (Anon., 1972);
polymerizes in light (Windholz, 1976); hydrolysed by acids
and bases (Rhum, 1970)

(j) Conversion factor: 1 ppm in air = 3.5 mg/m$^3$

## 1.4 Technical products and impurities

Three grades of vinyl acetate are available in the US, which differ
only in the amount of inhibitor added: 3-7 mg/kg (ppm) hydroquinone (see
IARC, 1977) are present when use is expected within two months of delivery;
12-17 mg/kg (ppm) hydroquinone for up to four months of storage; and 200-
300 mg/kg (ppm) diphenylamine when indefinite storage is anticipated. Typi-
specifications are: vinyl acetate, 99.8% min; boiling-point, 72.3-73.0°C;
acidity (as acetic acid), 0.007% max; carbonyls (as acetaldehyde), 0.013%
max; water, 0.04% max; and suspended matter, none (Rhum, 1970).

In western Europe, vinyl acetate produced by the gas-phase ethylene
process has the following typical specifications: vinyl acetate, 99.9%
min; ethyl acetate, 323 mg/kg (ppm); water, 240 mg/kg (ppm); methyl
acetate, 175 mg/kg (ppm); acetaldehyde, 6 mg/kg (ppm); and acrolein,
1 mg/kg (ppm).

Typical specifications for vinyl acetate in Japan are as follows:
density, 0.932-0.936; free acid (as acetic acid), 0.01% max; free aldehydes (as acetaldehyde), 0.05% max; distillation residue, 0.05% max;
moisture, 0.2% max; and distillation range, 71.0-73.5°C.

## 2. Production, Use, Occurrence and Analysis

### 2.1 Production and use

(a) Production

Vinyl acetate was first isolated in 1912 as a minor by-product in the
preparation of ethylidene diacetate from acetylene and acetic acid (Rhum,
1970). It is produced commercially by two processes: (1) in the acetylene
process (used since 1920), acetylene and acetic acid are reacted in the
vapour phase over a catalyst bed; (2) in the ethylene process (predominant

in the US and Japan), ethylene is reacted with acetic acid in the presence
of oxygen.

Commercial production of vinyl acetate was first reported in the US
in 1928 (US Tariff Commission, 1930a).  In 1976, six companies reported
production of 673 million kg (US International Trade Commission, 1977);
exports were 149 million kg and went to the following countries (% of total):
Brazil (19), Canada (11), The Netherlands (34), Taiwan (8), and more than
27 other countries (28) (US Department of Commerce, 1977a).  US imports of
vinyl acetate are negligible.

Annual production capacity for vinyl acetate in western Europe in 1976
was 285 million kg, in the following countries (millions of kg):  the
Federal Republic of Germany (150), France (60), Spain (25) and the UK (50).
Annual production capacity in other countries in 1976 was as follows
(millions of kg):  Australia (12), Brazil (11) and Mexico (18).

Commercial production of vinyl acetate in Japan first began in 1936.
Four companies produced a total of 426 million kg vinyl acetate in 1976,
and 22 million kg were exported.

(b)  Use

In 1976, vinyl acetate was used in the US for the production of polyvinyl acetate homopolymer emulsions and resins (including copolymers with
more than 60% vinyl acetate), 61%;  polyvinyl alcohol, 22%;  polyvinyl
butyral, 6%;  vinyl chloride-vinyl acetate copolymers (see monograph,
p. 377), 5%;  ethylene-vinyl acetate resins and emulsions, 5%;  other
uses, 1%.

In 1976, 310 million kg vinyl acetate were used in the US for the
production of polyvinyl acetate emulsions and resins;  for a detailed
description of the uses of polyvinyl acetate, see p. 349.

Polyvinyl alcohol is produced from vinyl acetate by the hydrolysis of
polyvinyl acetate.  Polyvinyl alcohol was used in the US in 1976 as a
textile warp sizing and finishing agent (47%), in adhesives (23%), as a
polymerization aid in polyvinyl acetate emulsions used in adhesives (14%),
as a paper sizing and coating (8%) and for miscellaneous applications,
which include thickening and binding applications (8%) (see also p. 354).

Polyvinyl butyral is produced from vinyl acetate by the reaction of
polyvinyl alcohol with butyraldehyde.  Polyvinyl butyral is used primarily
as an adhesive film in the lamination of automobile safety glass;  it is
also used in the production of architectural safety glass and in wash
primers for steel.  Minor uses are in reprographics and as a special textile
finish component.

For a detailed description of the uses of vinyl chloride-vinyl acetate
copolymers, see p. 377.

Ethylene-vinyl acetate resins usually contain about 28% vinyl acetate and are used for hot-melt adhesives and coatings. Ethylene-vinyl acetate emulsions contain less than 60% vinyl acetate and are used in the same applications as polyvinyl acetate.

Minor applications for vinyl acetate are as a comonomer in a modacrylic carpet fibre (for a detailed description of the uses of modacrylic fibres, see p. 89) and in the manufacture of polyvinyl formal for magnet wire coatings.

In Japan, vinyl acetate was used as follows in 1976: polyvinyl alcohol, 70%; polyvinyl acetate resins and emulsions, 20%; ethylene-vinyl acetate resins, 9%; and vinyl chloride-vinyl acetate copolymers, 1%.

The American Conference of Governmental Industrial Hygienists recommends that an employee's exposure to vinyl acetate not exceed an eight-hour time-weighted average of 10 ppm, cited as 30 mg/m$^3$, in the workplace air in any eight-hour work shift of a forty-hour work week. They recommend an absolute ceiling concentration limit of 20 ppm, cited as 60 mg/m$^3$, during any 15-minute period, provided the eight-hour time-weighted average limit is not exceeded (American Conference of Governmental Industrial Hygienists, 1976).

The National Institute of Occupational Safety and Health recommends that exposure to vinyl acetate in the workplace be controlled so that employees are not exposed to concentrations greater than 15 mg/m$^3$ (4 ppm), measured as a ceiling concentration in samples collected during any 15-minute period (National Institute of Occupational Safety and Health, 1978).

In the USSR, the maximum allowable concentration for exposure at any one time is 0.2 mg/m$^3$ (Ryazanov, 1962).

2.2  Occurrence

Vinyl acetate is not known to occur as a natural product.

It has been detected in waste-waters from a polyvinyl acetate plant in concentrations of 50 mg/l (ppm) (Stepanyan et al., 1970), and in the air of production units, at levels of 17.5-35 mg/m$^3$ (5-10 ppm), with acute levels as high as 1050 mg/m$^3$ (300 ppm) (Deese & Joyner, 1969).

## 2.3  Analysis

Vinyl acetate has been determined in air by reaction with ethanolic mercuric acetate, paper chromatography of the mercury salt and elution with a basic solvent;  the limits of detection were 1 µg/sample (Kaznina, 1972; Khrustaleva & Osokina, 1970) and 0.3 µg/sample (Osokina, 1972).  Vinyl acetate has also been determined in air, water, alcoholic solutions and food by formation of the mercury complex and colorimetric dosage of the uncomplexed mercury by reaction with diphenylcarbazide;  the method was accurate to 50 µg/l (ppb) (Petrova & Boikova, 1975).

Gas chromatography can be used to determine vinyl acetate:  (1) in aqueous vinyl polymer latexes used in the paper and textile industry (Bollini *et al.*, 1974, 1975);  (2) as unreacted monomer in emulsions of acrylic-vinyl acetate copolymers, using flame-ionization detection, with a limit of detection of 10 mg/kg (ppm), with direct gas chromatography and a limit of 200 mg/kg (ppm) with extraction prior to gas chromatography (Zaitseva *et al.*, 1973);  (3) in aqueous dispersions of vinyl acetate-butyl acrylate copolymers, with a minimum detectable limit of 100 mg/kg (ppm) (Shiryaev & Pozharova, 1974);  and (4) in ethylene-vinyl acetate copolymers (Itsikson *et al.*, 1973).  Gas chromatography has also been used to determine vinyl acetate in waste-waters from a polyvinyl acetate plant, with a limit of detection of 100 mg/l (ppm) (Stepanyan *et al.*, 1970).

Vinyl acetate has been determined in air using chromotropic acid, with a limit of detection of 2.5 µg/sample (Gronsberg, 1970), and as a residual monomer in emulsion polymers by gel-chromatographic separation with detection by ultra-violet spectroscopy (Schmoetzer, 1972).

### 3.  Biological Data Relevant to the Evaluation
### of Carcinogenic Risk to Humans

## 3.1  Carcinogenicity studies in animals

### Inhalation and/or intratracheal administration

Rat:  A group of 96 Sprague-Dawley rats (sex not specified) were exposed for 4 hours/day on 5 days/week for 52 weeks to the maximum tolerated concentration, 8.8 g/m$^3$ (2500 ppm), vinyl acetate in air.  No tumours were reported to have occurred during 135 weeks.  Early mortality was high: 49 animals survived for 26 or more weeks (Maltoni & Lefemine, 1974, 1975; Maltoni *et al.*, 1974) [The Working Group noted that the time of death of animals that lived longer than 26 weeks was not indicated].

3.2  Other relevant biological data

(a)  Experimental systems

The oral $LD_{50}$ in rats was 2920 mg/kg bw.  The $LC_{50}$ in rats for a 2-hour exposure to vapours was 14 $g/m^3$ (4000 ppm).  The $LD_{50}$ in rabbits by skin application was more than 5 ml/kg bw;  0.5 ml vinyl acetate caused severe irritation to the rabbit eye (Union Carbide Corporation, 1958).

No data on the embryotoxicity, teratogenicity or metabolism of this compound were available to the Working Group.

Exposure of *Salmonella typhimurium* TA100 and TA1530 to vapours of vinyl acetate in the presence or absence of a 9000 x *g* supernatant fraction of liver from phenobarbital-pretreated mice caused no mutagenic effects (Bartsch *et al.*, 1976, 1979).

(b)  Humans

In a vinyl acetate production unit, levels of 75.6 $mg/m^3$ (21.6 ppm) produced eye and throat irritation (Deese & Joyner, 1969).

3.3  Case reports and epidemiological studies

No data were available to the Working Group.


Polyvinyl acetate

1.  Chemical and Physical Data

1.1  Synonyms and trade names

Chem. Abstr. Services Reg. No.:  9003-20-7

Chem. Abstr. Name:  Acetic acid ethenyl ester homopolymer

Acetic acid vinyl ester polymers;  poly(vinylacetate);  vinyl acetate homopolymer;  vinyl acetate polymer;  vinyl acetate resin

Asahisol 1527;  ASB 516;  AYAA;  AYAF;  AYJV;  Bakelite AYAA; Bakelite AYAF;  Bakelite AYAT;  Bakelite LP 90;  Bond CH 3; Bond CH 1200;  Borden 2123;  Cemedine 196;  Cevian 380;  Cevian A 678;  D 50;  D 50(polymer);  DCA 70;  D 50 M;  Duvilax;  Duvilax BD 20;  Duvilax HN;  Elvacet 81-900;  Emultex F;  En-Cor;  EP 1208;

EP 1436;   EP 1437;   EP 1463;   Esnil P 18;   Everflex B;   Formvar 1285;
Gelva;   Gelva CSV 16;   Gelva GP 702;   Gelva S 55H;   Gelva TS 22;
Gelva TS 23;   Gelva TS 30;   Gelva TS 85;   Gelva V 25;   Gelva V 100;
Gelva V 800;   Gohensil E 50Y;   Kurare OM 100;   Lemac;   Lemac 1000;
Meikatex 5000NG60;   Merckogel OR;   Merckogen 6000;   Mokotex D 2602;
Movinyl;   Movinyl 801;   Movinyl 50M;   Mowilith 30;   Mowilith 50;
Mowilith 70;   Mowilith 90;   Mowilith D;   Mowilith DV;   Mowilith M 70;
National 120-1207;   National Starch 1014;   NS 2842;   OM 100;   OR 1500;
P-170;   Pioloform F;   Plyamul 40-155;   Plyamul 40-350;   Polisol S-3;
Polyco 953;   Polyco 2116;   Polyco 2134;   Polyco 117FR;   Polyfox P 20;
Polyfox PO;   Polysol 1000;   Polysol 1200;   Polysol PS 10;   Polysol
S 6;   Protex;   Protex (polymer);   PS 3h;   PVAE;   R 10688;   Resyn
25-1025;   Rhodopas;   Rhodopas 010;   Rhodopas 5425;   Rhodopas A 10;
Rhodopas AM 041;   Rhodopas B;   Rhodopas BB;   Rhodopas HV 2;   Rhodopas
5000SMR:   RV 225-5B;   S-nyl-p 42;   Soloid;   Soviol;   SP 60;   SP 60
(ester);   Toabond 2;   Toabond 6;   Toabond 40H;   TS2;   Ucar 15;   Ucar
130;   UK 131;   V 501;   VA-0112;   VA 0112;   Vinac ASB 10;   Vinac B 7;
Vinalite D 50N;   Vinalite DS 41/11;   Vinamul 9300;   Vinapol A 16;
Vinnapas B;   Vinnapas B 17;   Vinnapas UW 50;   Vinylite AYAF;   Vinylite
AYAT;   Vinyl Products R 10688;   Winacet D

## 1.2  Structural and molecular formulae and molecular weight

$$(C_4H_6O_2)_n \qquad \text{Mol. wt: } 11\,000\text{-}1\,500\,000 \text{ (Rhum, 1970)}$$

## 1.3  Chemical and physical properties of the homopolymer

From Lindemann (1971a), unless otherwise specified

(a)  Description:  Colourless, odourless, tasteless, transparent
     solid (Hawley, 1971)

(b)  Melting-point:  35-50°C (softening)

(c) Density: $d^{25}$ 1.19

(d) Refractive index: $n_D^{20.7}$ 1.4669

(e) Solubility: Soluble in ethanol, 2-propanol, 1-butanol, benzene, acetone, chloroform, carbon tetrachloride, trichloroethylene and methylene chloride; insoluble in higher alcohols, aliphatic hydrocarbons, carbon disulphide and cyclohexane

(f) Stability: Degrades at 220-250°C; the principal pyrolysis product is acetic acid (Cascaval & Schneider, 1972).

(g) Reactivity: Hydrolysed by water to polyvinyl alcohol

## 1.4 Technical products and impurities

Polyvinyl acetate is available commercially in the US in emulsion and resin forms. Most polyvinyl acetate is not a homopolymer but rather a copolymer; predominant comonomers are $n$-butyl acrylate, 2-ethylhexyl acrylate and ethylene; minor comonomers include dibutyl maleate and dibutyl fumarate. The comonomers are used to impart a plasticizing or hardening effect on the polyvinyl acetate. Polyvinyl acetate copolymers are generally regarded as 'polyvinyl acetate' as long as the copolymer contains at least 60% vinyl acetate units (the average vinyl acetate content of these copolymers is believed to be about 85%). Polyvinyl acetate emulsions usually contain about 55% resin in an aqueous solution; however, emulsions are available with a solids content of 48%. The emulsions are compounded with thickeners, flow control and suspension agents, plasticizers, biocides, pigments and fillers to achieve the desired properties. Solid resins are also available in the form of powders or beads.

In Japan, polyvinyl acetate is available in the form of an emulsion (50% solids) and as a solution (30% solids) and may contain as impurities: vinyl acetate, emulsifiers (e.g., potassium peroxide) and initiators (e.g., benzoyl peroxide).

No detailed information on the possible presence of unreacted monomers in the polymer was available to the Working Group.

## 2. Production, Use, Occurrence and Analysis

### 2.1 Production and use

#### (a) Production

Industrial processes for the manufacture of polyvinyl acetate had been developed by 1925 (Rhum, 1970). Most polyvinyl acetate is produced by the

emulsion polymerization of vinyl acetate in water in the presence of surfactants and a free-radical initiator (e.g., a suitable peroxide, persulphate or diazo compound).  Solid polyvinyl acetate resins are primarily
made by suspension polymerization, which is very similar to emulsion polymerization, except that a suspension agent (e.g., partially hydrolysed
polyvinyl alcohol) is added.

Commercial production in the US was first reported in 1929 (US Tariff
Commission, 1930b).  In 1976, 32 US companies reported the production of
280 million kg polyvinyl acetate (US International Trade Commission, 1977);
exports were 14.6 million kg and went to the following countries (% of
total):  Belgium (6), Canada (41), Mexico (7), The Netherlands (8), UK (9)
and more than 18 other countries (38) (US Department of Commerce, 1977a).
Separate data on US imports of polyvinyl acetate are not available.

Western European production of polyvinyl acetate in 1977 was 350
million kg.

Polyvinyl acetate has been produced commercially in Japan since 1936.
At least seven companies produced a total of 80 million kg polyvinyl acetate
in 1976.

Worldwide production of polyvinyl acetate in 1977 was approximately
900 million kg.

(b)  Use

In 1976, polyvinyl acetate (homopolymers and copolymers) was used in
the US in adhesives (37%), paints (36%), paper coatings (13%), textile
treatment (6%), nonwoven binders (2%) and miscellaneous uses (6%).  It is
also used as an unisolated intermediate in the production of polyvinyl
alcohol (see also p. 354).

Polyvinyl acetate emulsions and resins are used in adhesives for
packaging and labelling (42%), construction (31%) and miscellaneous applications (27%).  It is used to bind paper fibres in folding boxboard, bag
seams, laminations, tube winding and remoistenable labels.  Adhesive uses
in construction are to smooth plaster-board tape joints, in spackling paste,
in wallboard and as a cement additive.  It is also used in consumer adhesives, secondary furniture gluing and bookbinding.

Polyvinyl acetate emulsions are the major vehicle in latex paints,
mainly in interior flat paints.  It is also used as an extender for interior
semigloss latex paint and for exterior house paint.  The most frequently
used comonomers in these emulsions are 2-ethylhexyl and butyl acrylates.

Polyvinyl acetate is used as a binder in paper coatings primarily for
paper and paperboard used in publications, labels and boxboard.  It is used
in textile treating applications - finishing, fabric coating and laminating
and as a binder in nonwoven fabrics.

Miscellaneous uses for polyvinyl acetate resins are in solution coatings, inks and chewing-gum bases.  Emulsions are used for the factory pre-
finishing of ceiling tiles.

In western Europe in 1976, polyvinyl acetate was used in adhesives
(45%), paint (40%), textiles (10%) and others (5%).

In Japan in that year, it was used in adhesives (55%), paint (38%),
textile treating (5%) and gum (2%).

The US Food and Drug Administration permits the use of polyvinyl
acetate homopolymers and copolymers as components of adhesives, resinous
and polymeric coatings, and paper and paperboard (for aqueous, fatty or
dry food) when they are intended for use in contact with food (US Food and
Drug Administration, 1977).

## 2.2  Occurrence

Polyvinyl acetate is not known to occur as a natural product.

## 2.3  Analysis

Pyrolysis gas chromatography can be used to determine polyvinyl acetate
in plastics and rubbers (Fischer, 1967) and in adhesives (Fischer & Meuser,
1967).  Pyrolysis-mass spectrometry can be used to identify some commercial
polymers, including polyvinyl acetate (Zeman, 1973).

Liquid and gas chromatography and infra-red, ultra-violet and visible
spectrophotometric techniques can be used to identify polyvinyl acetate in
paper coatings (Luciani & Corradini, 1971).  Infra-red spectroscopy has also
been used to identify polyvinyl acetate in latex paints (Post, 1967), textile sizing finishes (Lanciault, 1967) and paper binders (Seves & Croce,
1970).

Polyvinyl acetate has also been identified and analysed by hydrolysis,
followed by potentiometric titration of the total acid, and qualitative and
quantitative gas chromatographic analysis of the acid (Aydin *et al.*, 1973).

It can be determined quantitatively by colorimetry of its iodine complex at 510 nm (Hayashi & Kawamura, 1969).

## 3.  Biological Data Relevant to the Evaluation
### of Carcinogenic Risk to Humans

## 3.1  Carcinogenicity studies in animals

For data on the carcinogenicity of vinyl chloride-vinyl acetate copolymers, see p. 377.

Other experimental systems

Implantation: Polyvinyl acetate powder (amount unspecified) was
implanted (route unspecified) in 100 Wistar rats and in 100 mice (strain
unspecified); no local sarcomas were observed within 16-20 months after
implantation (Nothdurft, 1956) [The Working Group noted that the results
of the experiment were given, without details, as a footnote to another
experiment].

3.2 Other relevant biological data

(a) Experimental systems

After single oral administration of 25 g/kg bw polyvinyl acetate to
rats and mice, lymphoid infiltration of the liver, epithelial dystrophy
of the kidney and a slight increase in the number of polynucleated cells
in the spleen were observed. Oral administration of 250 mg/kg bw to mice
and rats for 12 months caused fluctuations in weight, changes in blood
composition, changes in liver:body weight ratio and changes in activity of
catalase and cholinesterase (Scherbak *et al.*, 1975).

No data on the embryotoxicity, teratogenicity, metabolism or mutagenicity of this compound were available to the Working Group.

(b) Humans

No data were available to the Working Group.

3.3 Case reports and epidemiological studies

No data were available to the Working Group.


Polyvinyl alcohol

1. Chemical and Physical Data

1.1 Synonyms and trade names

Chem. Abstr. Services Reg. No.: 9002-89-5

Chem. Abstr. Name: Ethenol homopolymer

Poly(vinyl alcohol); PVA; vinyl alcohol polymer

Alcotex 88/05; Alcotex 88/10; Alkotex; Alvyl; Aracet APV;
Cipoviol W 72; Covol; Covol 971; Elvanol; Elvanol 50-42;
Elvanol 52-22; Elvanol 70-05; Elvanol 71-30; Elvanol 90-50;

Elvanol 522-22;   Elvanol 73125G;   EP 160;   Gelvatol;   Gelvatol 1-30;
Gelvatol 1-60;   Gelvatol 1-90;   Gelvatol 3-91;   Gelvatol 20-30;
Gelvatol 2090;   GH 20;   GL 02;   GL 03;   GLO 5;   GM 14;   Gohsenol;
Gohsenol AH 22;   Gohsenol GH;   Gohsenol GH 17;   Gohsenol GH 20;
Gohsenol GH 23;   Gohsenol GL 03;   Gohsenol GL 05;   Gohsenol GL 08;
Gohsenol GM 14;   Gohsenol GM 14L;   Gohsenol GM 94;   Gohsenol KH 17;
Gohsenol NH 05;   Gohsenol NH 17;   Gohsenol NH 18;   Gohsenol NH 20;
Gohsenol NH 26;   Gohsenol NK 114;   Gohsenol NL 05;   Gohsenol NM 14;
Kuralon VP;   Kurare Poval 120;   Kurare Poval 1700;   Kurare PVA 205;
Lemol;   Lemol 5-88;   Lemol 5-98;   Lemol 12-88;   Lemol 16-98;   Lemol
24-98;   Lemol 30-98;   Lemol 51-98;   Lemol 60-98;   Lemol 75-98;   Lemol
GF-60;   M 13/20;   Mowiol;   Mowiol N 30-88;   Mowiol N 50-98;   Mowiol N
70-98;   NH 18;   NM 11;   NM 14;   Polydesis;   Polysizer 173;   Polyvinol;
Polyviol;   Polyviol M 13/140;   Polyviol MO 5/140;   Polyviol W 25/140;
Polyviol W 40/140;   Poval 117;   Poval 120;   Poval 203;   Poval 205;
Poval 217;   Poval 1700;   Poval C 17;   PVA 008;   PVS 4;   Resistoflex;
Rhodoviol;   Rhodoviol 4/125;   Rhodoviol 16/200;   Rhodoviol 4-125P;
Rhodoviol R 16/20;   Solvar;   Sumitex H 10;   Vibatex S;   Vinacol MH;
Vinalak;   Vinarol;   Vinarol DT;   Vinarole;   Vinarol ST;   Vinavilol
2-98;   Vinnarol;   Vinol;   Vinol 125;   Vinol 205;   Vinol 351;   Vinol
523;   Vinylon Film 2000

## 1.2   Structural and molecular formulae and molecular weight

$$\left[\begin{array}{cc} \overset{\displaystyle H}{\underset{\displaystyle H}{\mid}} & \overset{\displaystyle H}{\underset{\displaystyle OH}{\mid}} \\ C & - C \end{array}\right]_n$$

$(C_2H_4O)_n$               Mol. wt:   25 000-300 000

## 1.3   Chemical and physical properties of the polymer

The physical properties of polyvinyl alcohol polymers are dependent
on the degree of hydrolysis, water content and molecular weight.  The
following properties apply to a fully hydrolysed grade of polyvinyl alcohol, unless otherwise noted.  From Lindemann (1971b), unless otherwise
specified

(a) <u>Description</u>: White-to-light-straw-coloured, granular powder

(b) <u>Melting-point</u>: 228°C (decomposition)

(c) <u>Density</u>: d 1.19-1.31

(d) <u>Refractive index</u>: 1.49-1.53

(e) <u>Spectroscopy data</u>: Ultra-violet, infra-red and nuclear magnetic resonance spectra have been reported.

(f) <u>Solubility</u>: Soluble in hot or boiling water (Windholz, 1976); water solubility for different grades of polyvinyl alcohol increases as molecular weight decreases (Hawley, 1977). Insoluble in petroleum solvents (Windholz, 1976)

(g) <u>Stability</u>: Flash-point, 78.4°C, open cup (mixture of polymers) (Anon., 1972); degrades slowly at more than 100°C, with rapid degradation and decomposition at more than 200°C. Degrades under ultra-violet radiation. Softens or dissolves in acids and alkalis

(h) <u>Reactivity</u>: Undergoes chemical reactions typical of compounds with secondary hydroxyl groups, including esterification and etherification

## 1.4  Technical products and impurities

Polyvinyl alcohol is available in many grades which differ in the molecular weight and the degree of hydrolysis of the polymer. Standard 4% solutions are generally available in low, medium and high viscosity grades and are either fully hydrolysed (98-99.8 mol %) or partially hydrolysed (79-83 mol % or 87-89 mol %). Polyvinyl alcohol films are also available.

In Japan, polyvinyl alcohol fibres are available, in addition to resins, emulsions and films.

No detailed information on the possible presence of unreacted monomer in the polymer was available to the Working Group.

## 2.  Production, Use, Occurrence and Analysis

A review on polyvinyl alcohol has been published (Lindemann, 1971b).

2.1  Production and use

(a)  Production

Polyvinyl alcohol was first prepared by Herrmann and Haehnel in 1924
by hydrolysing polyvinyl acetate in ethanol with potassium hydroxide
(Lindemann, 1971b).  It was first used commercially in Germany in the
1920's (Leeds, 1970).

Polyvinyl alcohol is produced commercially from polyvinyl acetate,
usually by a continuous process.  The acetate groups are hydrolysed by
ester interchange with methanol in the presence of anhydrous sodium methy-
late or aqueous sodium hydroxide.

Commercial production of polyvinyl alcohol in the US was first reported in 1940 (US Tariff Commission, 1941).  In 1976, three US companies
reported the production of 57.5 million kg polyvinyl alcohol, excluding
that amount which was used as a reactive intermediate for polyvinyl butyral
or other vinyl resins (US International Trade Commission, 1977);  imports
were 4.6 million kg, from Japan (92.9% of total imports), the Federal
Republic of Germany (3.5%), Italy (2.1%), the UK (0.9%) and other countries (0.6%) (US Department of Commerce, 1977b).  The US exported an estimated 1.4 million kg polyvinyl alcohol in 1976.

Polyvinyl alcohol is produced in western Europe by at least three
companies in the Federal Republic of Germany (one of which has an annual
production capacity of 25 million kg), two companies in France, two in
Italy, two in Spain and two in the UK.

At least one company (with an annual production capacity of 10 million
kg) produces polyvinyl alcohol in Taiwan;  and India also has at least one
producer.  A plant with an annual production capacity of 2.5 million kg
was expected to be constructed in Mexico by late 1978 (Anon., 1977).

Polyvinyl alcohol has been produced commercially in Japan since 1936.
In 1976, five companies produced 158 million kg;  exports were 46 million
kg in 1976, and there were no imports.

(b)  Use

In the US in 1976, polyvinyl alcohol (excluding that which was used
as a captive intermediate in the production of polyvinyl butyral) was used
as a textile warp sizing and finishing agent (47.0%), as a component of
adhesives (23.1%), as a polymerization aid (13.7%), as a paper sizing and
coating (8.5%) and in miscellaneous applications (7.7%).

The major use for polyvinyl alcohol in the US is as a textile warp
size, which contributes to high weaving efficiency at low levels.  It is
also used as a textile finish to provide stiffness.

It is used as an additive to polyvinyl acetate and starch adhesives used in bag making, carton sealing, tube winding and solid board lamination and in the manufacture of remoistenable labels and tapes, often in a mixture with starch or carboxymethyl cellulose. It is used as a thickener in combination with polyvinyl acetate in commonly used household 'white glue' and in furniture assembly adhesives. It is also used as an additive in gypsum-based joint cements and in ceramic tile cement.

Polyvinyl alcohol is used as a polymerization aid, acting as a protective colloid, in polyvinyl acetate emulsions for adhesive uses. It is used in paper sizings, as a grease-resistant paper coating (e.g., on potato crisp bags), and as a pigment binder in certain paper coatings.

Miscellaneous applications are as a thickener in latex coatings; as a water-soluble film used to make hospital laundry bags that are hot-water soluble, release films for vacuum-bag moulding of reinforced plastics, consumer bleach packages and herbicide packages; as a binder in disposable, nonwoven milk filters; as an aid in certain photoengraving processes; as an ingredient in insecticide and fungicide sprays; as a binder for phosphorescent pigments in television picture tubes; in cosmetic face masks; and in photographic film.

A cationic polyvinyl alcohol hydrogel has been prepared to lubricate cartilage prostheses. Polyvinyl alcohol has also been investigated for use as a synthetic cartilage, by crosslinking a fully hydrolysed grade in aqueous solution under an electron beam (Halpern & Karo, 1977). Polyvinyl alcohol sponge has been used as a prosthetic breast implant (Clarkson, 1960; Hamit, 1957).

In Japan, polyvinyl alcohol is used as a fibre (37%), in textile sizing and finishing (16%), in adhesives (16%), as a film (11%), in paper coatings (10%) and in other applications (10%).

The US Food and Drug Administration permits the use of polyvinyl alcohol (usually specified as a 4% aqueous solution having a minimum viscosity of 4 centipoises at $20^{\circ}$C) as a component of the following products when they are intended for use in contact with food: (1) adhesives; (2) resinous and polymeric coatings, including those for polyolefin film; (3) paper and paperboard (in contact with dry, aqueous, and fatty food); (4) cellophane; (5) resin-bonded filters; (6) textiles and textile fibres; and (7) surface lubricants used in the manufacture of metallic articles. Polyvinyl alcohol film used in contact with food must not result in more than 0.5 mg extractives per square inch ($0.07$ mg/cm$^2$) of food-contact surface (US Food and Drug Administration, 1977).

No threshold limit values were found for polyvinyl alcohol.

## 2.2  Occurrence

Polyvinyl alcohol is not known to occur as a natural product.

2.3  Analysis

Several reviews have been published on methods of analysis for polyvinyl alcohol (Finch, 1973;  Urbanski, 1977).

Filter paper treated with potassium iodide and iodine solutions has
been suggested for measuring polyvinyl alcohol concentrations in waste-
water in a concentration range of 1 000-20 000 mg/l (ppm) (Taniguchi &
Ohkita, 1977).  The colours of polymers, including polyvinyl alcohol, and
their nitrated derivatives in various solvents have been used to identify
them (El-Kodsi & Schurz, 1973).  The green complex formed by the reaction
of polyvinyl alcohol with boric acid has been used to detect small amounts
in polyvinyl chloride resins (Eliassaf, 1972).  A method has been described for determining polyvinyl alcohol photometrically by turbidity in
biological media (blood, urine, etc) (Maslov & Kolerko, 1972).

Spectrophotometric techniques in the ultra-violet, visible and infra-
red regions have been used to identify polyvinyl alcohol in paper coatings
(Luciani & Corradini, 1971).  Infra-red spectroscopy has also been used
to identify polyvinyl alcohol in postage stamp adhesives (Cleverley &
Goldman, 1972) and in textile sizing materials (Jitianu & Georgescu, 1976).

Various polymers, including polyvinyl alcohol, have been identified
by first pyrolysing the polymer and then identifying the pyrolysis products
by a combination of ultra-violet analysis, colour-forming reactions and
thin-layer chromatography (Braun & Nixdorf, 1972).

### 3.  Biological Data Relevant to the Evaluation
### of Carcinogenic Risk to Humans

3.1  Carcinogenicity studies in animals

Subcutaneous implantation

Rat:  Male Wistar rats were given s.c. implants of polyvinyl alcohol
(Ivalon sponge) of unspecified size into the abdominal wall and were observed for lifespan.  Three local sarcomas were found in 34 animals still alive
at the appearance of the first local sarcoma at 567 days (Oppenheimer
et al., 1955).

Polyvinyl alcohol sponges (4 x 5 x 0.16 mm) were implanted subcutaneously into the abdominal tissues of 25 Wistar rats of both sexes;  21
animals survived 300 days.  All animals had died or were killed within 800
days.  Multiple sections were taken from each implantation site;  but no
local tumours were detected (Russell et al., 1959).

Thick (20 x 20 x 5 mm) and thin (20 x 20 x 2 mm) polyvinyl alcohol
(Ivalon) sponges were implanted subcutaneously into the right flank of

groups of 20 Chester Beatty 70-day-old rats (sex not specified). Fourteen of the rats implanted with thick sponges lived 10 months or longer and developed local sarcomas, whereas only one of the rats bearing thin sponges had a local sarcoma among 18 rats that lived 12 months or longer (Dukes & Mitchley, 1962).

Male Holtzman rats, 5-6-weeks-old, each received 2 s.c. implants of polyvinyl alcohol (Ivalon) sponges (20 mm diameter, 3-4 mm thick). Local sarcomas were found in 9/12 rats (75%) that lived for at least 18 months (only one animal had tumours at both implanted sites) (Dasler & Milliser, 1963).

Polyvinyl alcohol (Ivalon) sponges (20 x 20 x 5 mm) were implanted into the s.c. tissue of the back in 39 albino rats (sex unspecified). Twenty were killed at intervals of 2 days to 1 year; the remaining 19 were kept until they died or were killed at 29 months. Local tumours developed in 3 rats (2 sarcomas and 1 fibroma or low-grade fibrosarcoma) (Walter & Chiaramonte, 1965).

The possible role of the thickness of sponge implants was investigated in 8-week-old Chester Beatty male rats. Of animals given 20 x 20 x 5 mm (2000 $mm^3$) s.c. implants of polyvinyl alcohol (Prosthex) in the right flank, 9/24 developed local sarcomas, whereas only 1/24 with 33 x 33 x 2 mm (2000 $mm^3$) implants developed a local sarcoma. In addition, 5 sarcomas arose in 24 rats with 12.6 x 12.6 x 5 mm (800 $mm^3$) s.c. implants, and only 1/24 in animals with 20 x 20 x 2 mm (800 $mm^3$) implants and 1/24 with 8 x 8 x 5 mm (320 $mm^3$) implants. The incidence of local sarcomas in inbred Woodruff hooded rats given 20 x 20 x 5 mm (2000 $mm^3$) implants of Prosthex was similar to that in Chester Beatty rats (12/24). The experiment lasted 800 days (Roe et al., 1967).

Single doses of 500 mg/animal polyvinyl alcohol powder (molecular weight, 120 000) were implanted into the s.c. tissue in 25 Bethesda black rats, which were observed for up to 2 years. No local tumours were seen, but 3 benign and 6 malignant tumours at various sites were observed in treated rats, and 3 benign and 17 malignant tumours were found among 200 controls (Hueper, 1959).

3.2  Other relevant biological data

(a)  Experimental systems

In dogs, repeated i.v. and i.p. injections of a 5% aqueous solution of polyvinyl alcohol caused anaemia and atheromatous lesions in the aorta and in the carotid and femoral arteries (Hueper, 1941; Hueper et al., 1940).

Polyvinyl alcohol (Ivalon) sponges of varying sizes (10 x 5 x 5 mm, 8 x 5 x 5 mm and 10 x 5 x 2 mm) were implanted into the s.c. tissue of male Bar Harbor C57 mice (number not specified). Biopsies taken at

intervals ranging from 1-18 weeks after insertion showed a fibrous capsule
extending into the interstices of the sponges, accompanied by collagen-like
material. From week 6 onward, vessels were seen to extend into the sponge
(Moore & Brown, 1952).

Polyvinyl alcohol (Ivalon) sponge proposed for use as a plastic
prosthetic material induced no host reaction in dogs (Cameron & Lawson,
1960; Grindlay & Waugh, 1951).

Polyvinyl alcohol given subcutaneously, intravenously or orally to
rats and rabbits was retained for up to 6 weeks in various organs, including brain, liver and kidney (Hueper, 1939). Only small amounts were depo-
sited in the kidneys and liver of guinea-pigs following its i.p. administration (Foster & Jenkins, 1944).

No data on the embryotoxicity, teratogenicity, metabolism or mutagenicity of this compound were available to the Working Group.

(b)  Humans

Implantation of polyvinyl alcohol sponge as a breast prosthesis has
been associated with fibrosis (Hamit, 1957).

3.3  Case reports and epidemiological studies

Prout & Davis (1977) reported a case of haemangiopericytoma of the
bladder in a 40-year-old man who had worked with polyvinyl alcohol; they
speculated that there might be a relationship similar to that between
vinyl chloride and angiosarcoma of the liver.


4.  Summary of Data Reported and Evaluation

4.1  Experimental data

In the only study available, vinyl acetate was tested in rats by
inhalation exposure; it produced no evidence of carcinogenicity.

Vinyl acetate was non-mutagenic in the only test system used.

Subcutaneous or intraperitoneal implantation of polyvinyl acetate
powder in mice and rats did not result in local sarcomas. Subcutaneous
implantation of polyvinyl alcohol sponges in rats produced local sarcomas,
whereas negative results were obtained with polyvinyl alcohol powder.

For data on vinyl chloride-vinyl acetate copolymers, see monograph
on vinyl chloride polymers and copolymers, p. 377.

## 4.2  Human data

No case reports or epidemiological studies relating to the carcinogenicity of either vinyl acetate or polyvinyl acetate were available to
the Working Group.  One case of haemangiopericytoma was reported in a man
exposed to polyvinyl alcohol.

The high levels of production of vinyl acetate, polyvinyl acetate
and polyvinyl alcohol indicate that occupationally exposed groups could
be identified for epidemiological investigation.  The widespread use of
polyvinyl acetate and polyvinyl alcohol in diverse applications indicates
that the general population is also exposed.

## 4.3  Evaluation

No case reports or epidemiological studies concerning vinyl acetate
were available to the Working Group.  Animal studies involving implantation
of polyvinyl acetate and polyvinyl alcohol powder in rats did not result
in local sarcomas, whereas in similar experiments with polyvinyl alcohol
sponges, local sarcomas were produced.  Both polyvinyl acetate and polyvinyl alcohol have substantial commercial applications.  Further studies
are required before an evaluation can be made of the carcinogenicity of
these compounds.

## 5. References

American Conference of Governmental Industrial Hygienists (1976) TLVs ®
Threshold Limit Values for Chemical Substances in Workroom Air
Adopted by ACGIH for 1976, Cincinnati, Ohio, p. 30

Anon. (1972) Fire Protection Guide on Hazardous Materials, 4th ed.,
Boston, Mass., National Fire Protection Association, pp. 325M-120,
325M-136, 49-225-49-226

Anon. (1977) PVA plant slated by Polivin in Mexico. Chemical Marketing
Reporter, 5 December, p. 13

Aydin, O., Kaczmar, B.U. & Schulz, R.C. (1973) Analysis of vinyl acetate-
vinyl propionate copolymers (Ger.). Angew. Makromol. Chem., 33,
153-157 [Chem. Abstr., 80, 27626x]

Bartsch, H., Malaveille, C., Barbin, A., Planche, G. & Montesano, R. (1976)
Alkylating and mutagenic metabolites of halogenated olefins produced
by human and animal tissues (Abstract No. 67). Proc. Am. Assoc.
Cancer Res., 17, 37

Bartsch, H., Malaveille, C., Barbin, A. & Planche, G. (1979) Mutagenic
and alkylating metabolites of halo-ethylenes, chlorobutadienes and
dichlorobutenes produced by rodent or human liver tissues; evidence
for oxirane formation by P450-linked microsomal mono-oxygenases.
Arch. Toxicol. (in press)

Bollini, M., Seves, A. & Focher, B. (1974) Determination of free monomers
in water emulsions of synthetic polymers or copolymers (Ital.).
Ind. Carta, 12, 234-240 [Chem. Abstr., 81, 121672b]

Bollini, M., Seves, A. & Focher, B. (1975) Determination of free monomers
in aqueous emulsions of synthetic polymers and copolymers (Ital.).
Textilia, 51, 25-28 [Chem. Abstr., 83, 60039t]

Braun, D. & Nixdorf, G. (1972) Simple separation method for analysis of
plastics. 4. Soluble compounds with neutral reaction of pyrolysis
products (Ger.). Kunststoffe, 62, 318-322

Cameron, J.M. & Lawson, D.D. (1960) The failure of polyvinyl sponge as a
bone substitute. Res. vet. Sci., 1, 230-231

Cascaval, C.N. & Schneider, I.A. (1972) Pyrolytic chromatographic study
of vinyl polymers (Fr.). Rev. Roum. Chim., 17, 835-840 [Chem. Abstr.,
77, 89052d]

Clarkson, P. (1960) Sponge implants for flat breasts. Proc. R. Soc. Med.,
53, 880-881

Cleverley, B. & Goldman, A. (1972) Infrared spectroscopy in the service of the post office. Chem. N. Z., 36, 5-8 [Chem. Abstr., 77, 35367s]

Dasler, W. & Milliser, R.V. (1963) Induction of tumors in rats by subcutaneous implants of surgical sponges. Experientia, 19, 424-426

Deese, D.E. & Joyner, R.E. (1969) Vinyl acetate: a study of chronic human exposure. Am. ind. Hyg. Assoc. J., 30, 449-457

Dukes, C.E. & Mitchley, B.C.V. (1962) Polyvinyl sponge implants: experimental and clinical observations. Br. J. plast. Surg., 16, 225-235

Eliassaf, J. (1972) Detection of small quantities of poly(vinyl alcohol) in poly(vinyl chloride) resins. Polym. Lett., 10, 697-698

El-Kodsi, G. & Schurz, J. (1973) Chemical characterization of high polymers. I. Nitration and subsequent reactions (Ger.). Papier (Darmstadt), 27, 253-255 [Chem. Abstr., 79, 54022h]

Finch, C.A. (1973) Analytical methods for poly(vinyl alcohol). In: Finch, C.A., ed., Polyvinyl Alcohol, London, Wiley, pp. 561-572 [Chem. Abstr., 82, 4816m]

Fischer, W.G. (1967) Pyrolytic gas-chromatography (Ger.). Glas-Instrum.-Tech., 11, 562, 567-570, 775-780, 1086-1088, 1091-1095 [Chem. Abstr., 68, 78636k]

Fischer, W. & Meuser, H. (1967) The application of physical-chemical methods of analysis (Ger.). Adhaesion, 11, 145-150 [Chem. Abstr., 67, 33189e]

Foster, R.H.K. & Jenkins, L. (1944) Fate of polyvinyl alcohol introduced intraperitoneally in rats. Arch. Pathol., 37, 279-281

Grasselli, J.G. & Ritchey, W.M., eds (1975) CRC Atlas of Spectral Data and Physical Constants for Organic Compounds, 2nd ed., Vol. II, Cleveland, Ohio, Chemical Rubber Co., p. 79

Grindlay, J.H. & Waugh, J.M. (1951) Plastic sponge which acts as a framework for living tissue. Experimental studies and preliminary report of use to reinforce abdominal aneurysms. Arch. Surg., 63, 288-297

Gronsberg, E.S. (1970) Determination of vinyl acetate and ethyl acrylate during analysis of air (Russ.). Tr. Khim. Khim Tekhnol., 1, 186-189 [Chem. Abstr., 75, 88995k]

Halpern, B.D. & Karo, W. (1977) Medical applications. In: Bikales, N.M., ed., Encyclopedia of Polymer Science and Technology, Plastics, Resins, Rubbers, Fibers, Suppl. Vol. 2, New York, Interscience, p. 380

Hamit, H.F. (1957)  Implantation of plastics in the breast.  Complications in a case.  Arch. Surg., 75, 224-229

Hawley, G.G., ed. (1971)  The Condensed Chemical Dictionary, 8th ed., New York, Van Nostrand-Reinhold, pp. 714, 926

Hawley, G.G., ed. (1977)  The Condensed Chemical Dictionary, 9th ed., New York, Van Nostrand-Reinhold, p. 706

Hayashi, S. & Kawamura, C. (1969)  Poly(vinyl acetate) and its derivatives. 4.  Colorimetric determination of poly(vinyl acetate) by color reaction with iodine (Jap.).  Kogyo Kagaku Zasshi, 72, 2491-2493 [Chem. Abstr., 72, 122206d]

Hueper, W.C. (1939)  Organic lesions produced by polyvinyl alcohol in rats and rabbits.  A toxicopathologic investigation of an experimental thesaurosis.  Arch. Pathol., 28, 510-531

Hueper, W.C. (1941)  Experimental studies in cardiovascular pathology. III.  Polyvinyl alcohol atheromatosis in the arteries of dogs. Arch. Pathol., 31, 11-24

Hueper, W.C. (1959)  Carcinogenic studies on water-soluble and insoluble macromolecules.  Arch. Pathol., 67, 589-617

Hueper, W.C., Landsberg, J.W. & Eskridge, L.C. (1940)  The effects of intravenous and intraperitoneal introduction of polyvinyl alcohol solutions upon the blood.  J. Pharmacol. exp. Ther., 70, 201-210

IARC (1977)  IARC Monographs on the Evaluation of the Carcinogenic Risk of Chemicals to Man, 15, Some Fumigants, the Herbicides 2,4-D and 2,4,5-T, Chlorinated Dibenzodioxins and Miscellaneous Industrial Chemicals, Lyon, pp. 155-175

Itsikson, L.B., Yudkina, L.N., Terteryan, R.A. & Monastyrskii, V.M. (1973) Determination of the amount of free vinyl acetate in its copolymers with ethylene by a gas chromatographic method (Russ.).  Neftepererab. Neftekhim. (Moscow), 10, 72-73 [Chem. Abstr., 80, 71135k]

Jitianu, A. & Georgescu, M. (1976)  Infrared spectrophotometry study on several sizing agents used in the textile industry (Rom.).  Ind. Usoara: Text., Tricotaje, Confectii Text., 27, 213-219 [Chem. Abstr., 85, 109939u]

Kaznina, N.I. (1972)  Determination of unsaturated compounds in the air by mercury salt addition (Russ.).  Gig. i Sanit., 37, 63-66 [Chem. Abstr., 77, 92364n]

Khrustaleva, V.A. & Osokina, S.K. (1970)  Separate determination of vinyl acetate and 2-ethylhexyl acrylate in the presence of dibutyl maleate in air (Russ.).  Gig. i Sanit., 35, 80-83 [Chem. Abstr., 73, 38277r]

Lanciault, G.E. (1967)  A chemical method for the identification of sizes – including infrared spectra. Am. Dyest. Rep., 56, P351–P356 [Chem. Abstr., 67, 33755m]

Leeds, M. (1970)  Poly(vinyl alcohol). In:  Kirk, R.E. & Othmer, D.F., eds, Encyclopedia of Chemical Technology, 2nd ed., Vol. 21, New York, John Wiley and Sons, pp. 353–368

Lindemann, M.K. (1971a)  Vinyl ester polymers. In:  Bikales, N.M., ed., Encyclopedia of Polymer Science and Technology, Plastics, Resins, Rubbers, Fibers, Vol. 15, New York, Interscience, pp. 611, 617–619, 625–627, 643–648

Lindemann, M.K. (1971b)  Vinyl alcohol polymers.  Poly(vinyl alcohol). In:  Bikales, N.M., ed., Encyclopedia of Polymer Science and Technology, Plastics, Resins, Rubbers, Fibers, Vol. 14, New York, Interscience, pp. 149–207

Luciani, M. & Corradini, T. (1971)  Spectrophotometric and chromatographic analysis of paper coatings (Ital.). Cellul. Carta, 22, 19–35 [Chem. Abstr., 76, 73969b]

Maltoni, C. & Lefemine, G. (1974)  Carcinogenicity bioassays of vinyl chloride.  I.  Research plan and early results. Environ. Res., 7, 387–405

Maltoni, C. & Lefemine, G. (1975)  Carcinogenicity bioassays of vinyl chloride:  current results. Ann. NY Acad. Sci., 246, 195–218

Maltoni, C., Lefemine, G., Chieco, P. & Carretti, D. (1974)  Vinyl chloride carcinogenesis:  current results and perspectives. Med. Lav., 65, 421–444

Maslov, V.I. & Kolerko, F.M. (1972)  Methods for determining the components of iodopoly(vinyl alcohol) in biological media (Russ.). Lab. Delo, 5, 295–297 [Chem. Abstr., 77, 96696v]

Moore, A.M. & Brown, J.B. (1952)  Investigation of polyvinyl compounds for use as subcutaneous prostheses. Plast. reconstr. Surg., 10, 453–459

National Institute for Occupational Safety and Health (1978)  Criteria for a Recommended Standard.  Occupational Exposure to Vinyl Acetate, DHEW (NIOSH) Publ. No. 78–205, Washington DC, US Department of Health, Education, and Welfare

Nothdurft, H. (1956)  Experimental formation of sarcomas due to foreign bodies (Ger.). Strahlentherapie, 100, 192–210

Oppenheimer, B.S., Oppenheimer, E.T., Danishefsky, I., Stout, A.P. & Eirich, F.R. (1955)  Further studies of polymers as carcinogenic agents in animals. Cancer Res., 15, 333–340

Osokina, S.K. (1972)  Chromatographic determination of vinyl acetate in
the air by preliminary mercuration in a medium of lower aliphatic
alcohols (Russ.).  Gig. i Sanit., 37, 72-74

Perry, R.H. & Chilton, C.H., eds (1973)  Chemical Engineer's Handbook,
5th ed., New York, McGraw-Hill, p. 3-61

Petrova, L.I. & Boikova, Z.K. (1975)  Determination of small amounts of
vinyl acetate in air, water, alcohol solutions, and foods (Russ.).
Gig. i Sanit., 6, 48-49 [Chem. Abstr., 83, 94994r]

Post, M.A. (1967)  Qualitative and quantitative determination of emulsion-
polymerized binders in latex paints.  J. appl. Chem., 17, 315-320

Prout, M.N. & Davis, H.L., Jr (1977)  Hemangiopericytoma of the bladder
after polyvinyl alcohol exposure.  Cancer, 39, 1328-1330

Rhum, D. (1970)  Poly(vinyl acetate).  In: Kirk, R.E. & Othmer, D.F., eds,
Encyclopedia of Chemical Technology, 2nd ed., Vol. 21, New York,
John Wiley and Sons, pp. 317-353

Roe, F.J.C., Dukes, C.E. & Mitchley, B.C.V. (1967)  Sarcomas at the site of
implantation of a polyvinyl plastic sponge:  incidence reduced by use
of thin implants.  Biochem. Pharmacol., 16, 647-650

Russell, F.E., Simmers, M.H., Hirst, A.E. & Pudenz, R.H. (1959)  Tumors
associated with embedded polymers.  J. natl Cancer Inst., 23, 305-315

Ryazanov, V.A. (1962)  Sensory physiology as basis for air quality
standards.  The approach used in the Soviet Union.  Arch. environ.
Health, 5, 480-494

Scherbak, B.I., Broitman, L.Y., Yatsenko, T.B. & Kolesnikov, S.I. (1975)
Toxicological characteristics of some poly(vinyl acetate) dispersions
(PVAD) (Russ.) (Abstract).  Uch. Zap.-Mosk. Nauch. Issled. Inst. Gig.,
22, 74-80

Schmoetzer, G. (1972)  Determination of residual monomers in emulsion
polymers (Ger.).  Fresenius' Z. anal. Chem., 260, 10-24 [Chem. Abstr.,
77, 127080w]

Seves, A. & Croce, A. (1970)  Identification of binders in coating colors
(Ital.).  Ind. Carta, 8, 53-59 [Chem. Abstr., 73, 26816c]

Shiryaev, B.V. & Pozharova, V.P. (1974)  Chromatographic determination of
monomers in dispersions of copolymers based on vinyl acetate and
butyl acrylate.  Khim Prom. (Moscow), 6, 475 (Translation in Soviet
Chem. Ind., 6, 404-405)

Stepanyan, I.S., Padaryan, G.M., Airapetyan, L.K. & Maslyukova, D.F. (1970) Ionization-chromatographic method for determining some components of waste waters from the plant 'Polivinilatsetat' (Russ.). Prom. Arm., 9, 76-78 [Chem. Abstr., 74, 90928p]

Taniguchi, J. & Ohkita, K. (1977) Testing paper for measuring poly(vinyl alcohol) concentration. Japanese Patent 7765,495, 30 May, to Shikishima Spinning Co., Ltd [Chem. Abstr., 88, 54762k]

Union Carbide Corporation (1958) Toxicology Studies - Vinyl Acetate, H.Q., 25 April, New York, Industrial Medicine and Toxicology Department

Urbanski, J. (1977) Analysis of poly(vinyl alcohol) and its derivatives. In: Handbook of Analysis and Synthesis of Polymers and Plastics, Chichester, UK, Ellis Horwood Ltd, pp. 388-402

US Department of Commerce (1977a) US Exports, Schedule B Commodity Groupings, Schedule B Commodity by Country, FT410/December, Bureau of the Census, Washington DC, US Government Printing Office, pp. 2-86, 2-122

US Department of Commerce (1977b) US Imports for Consumption and General Imports, TSUSA Commodity by Country of Origin, FT246/Annual 1976, Bureau of the Census, Washington DC, US Government Printing Office, p. 234

US Food and Drug Administration (1977) Food and drugs. US Code Fed. Regul., Title 21, parts 175.105, 175.300, 175.320, 176.170, 176.180, 177.1200, 177.1670, 177.2260, 177.2800, 178.3910, pp. 438, 446, 452, 455, 465-467, 471-472, 479, 481-482, 486-487, 489, 504, 506, 534, 545-546, 559-560, 600

US International Trade Commission (1977) Synthetic Organic Chemicals, US Production and Sales, 1976, USITC Publication 833, Washington DC, US Government Printing Office, pp. 183, 187, 301, 327

US Tariff Commission (1930a) Census of Dyes and of Other Synthetic Organic Chemicals, 1928, Tariff Information Series No. 38, Washington DC, US Government Printing Office, p. 137

US Tariff Commission (1930b) Census of Dyes and of Other Synthetic Organic Chemicals, 1929, Tariff Information Series No. 39, Washington DC, US Government Printing Office, p. 144

US Tariff Commission (1941) Synthetic Organic Chemicals, US Production and Sales, 1940, Report No. 148, Second Series, Washington DC, US Government Printing Office, p. 47

Walter, J.B. & Chiaramonte, L.G. (1965) The tissue responses of the rat to implanted Ivalon, Etheron, and polyfoam plastic sponges. Br. J. Surg., 52, 49-54

Weast, R.C., ed. (1976)  CRC Handbook of Chemistry and Physics, 57th ed.,
    Cleveland, Ohio, Chemical Rubber Co., p. C-86

Windholz, M., ed. (1976)  The Merck Index, 9th ed., Rahway, NJ, Merck &
    Co., pp. 986, 1283

Zaitseva, N.A., Tolstobrova, S.A. & Il'in, D.T. (1973)  Chromatographic
    determination of unreacted monomers in emulsions of acrylic copoly-
    mers (Russ.).  Lakokrasoch. Mater. Ikh Primen., 6, 48-49 [Chem.
    Abstr., 80, 134147p]

Zeman, A. (1973)  Identification of some commercially available polymers by
    thermal degradation in a mass spectrometer (Ger.).  Angew. Makromol.
    Chem., 31, 1-24

VINYL BROMIDE

## 1.  Chemical and Physical Data

1.1  Synonyms and trade names

Chem. Abstr. Services Reg. No.:  593-60-2

Chem. Abstr. Name:  Bromoethene

Bromoethylene

1.2  Structural and molecular formulae and molecular weight

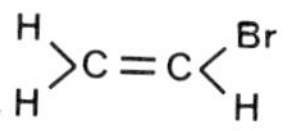

$$\underset{H}{\overset{H}{>}}C=C\underset{H}{\overset{Br}{<}}$$

$C_2H_3Br$              Mol. wt:  106.9

1.3  Chemical and physical properties of the pure substance

From Weast (1976), unless otherwise specified

(a)  Description:  Gas (Hawley, 1971)

(b)  Boiling-point:  +15.8°C

(c)  Melting-point:  -139.5°C

(d)  Density:  $d_4^{20}$ 1.4933

(e)  Refractive index:  $n_D^{20}$ 1.4410

(f)  Spectroscopy data:  Infra-red, nuclear magnetic resonance and mass spectral data have been tabulated (Grasselli & Ritchey, 1975).

(g)  Solubility:  Insoluble in water;  soluble in ethanol, ether, acetone, benzene and chloroform

(h)  Stability:  Inflammable;  polymerizes rapidly in light (Pollock & Stevens, 1965)

(i)  Conversion factor:  1 ppm in air = 4.4 mg/m$^3$

1.4  Technical products and impurities

Vinyl bromide available commercially in the US contains a minimum of 99.5% vinyl bromide, 175-225 mg/kg (ppm) of an undisclosed inhibitor and a maximum of 300 mg/kg (ppm) water.


2.  Production, Use, Occurrence and Analysis

2.1  Production and use

(a)  Production

Vinyl bromide was first prepared in 1835 by heating ethylene dibromide with alkali.  It is prepared commercially in the US by the reaction of acetylene with hydrogen bromide in the presence of a catalyst such as the halides of mercury, cerium or copper (Ramey & Lini, 1971).  In Japan, it is prepared by the reaction of potassium hydroxide on ethylene dibromide.

Commercial production of vinyl bromide in the US was first reported in 1968 (US Tariff Commission, 1970).  In 1975, two companies reported the manufacture of an undisclosed amount (see preamble, p. 22) (US International Trade Commission, 1977).

It is produced commercially in Japan by one company.

(b)  Use

Vinyl bromide is a reactive flame retardant used in small amounts as a comonomer with acrylonitrile and other vinyl monomers in modacrylic fibres (see also p. 86).  Modacrylic fibres containing vinyl bromide are used in fabrics and fabric blends with polyesters for children's sleepwear and other clothing, home furnishings and industrial applications (LeBlanc, 1977).

In Japan, vinyl bromide is also used as a comonomer in modacrylic fibres, all of which are exported.

Vinyl bromide has been used to prepare polyvinyl bromide, but the polymer is unstable even at room temperature and, consequently, has been of little commercial significance (Ramey & Lini, 1971) (see however, section 3.1, p. 370).

The American Conference of Governmental Industrial Hygienists has proposed that an employee's exposure to vinyl bromide not exceed an eight-hour time-weighted average of 22 mg/m$^3$ (5 ppm) in the workplace air in any eight-hour work shift of a forty-hour work week (Anon., 1977).  This is a revision of their previous recommended threshold limit value for vinyl bromide, which was 1100 mg/m$^3$ (250 ppm) (American Conference of Governmental Industrial Hygienists, 1976).

## 2.2 Occurrence

Vinyl bromide is not known to occur as a natural product.

It has been detected as an impurity in commercial vinyl chloride (Kurosaki *et al.*, 1968;  Sassu *et al.*, 1968).

## 2.3 Analysis

A sampling technique for air pollutants, including vinyl bromide, has been evaluated using different gas chromatographic packings.  The compounds are desorbed thermally and analysed by gas chromatography using flame-ionization detection.  The limit of detection is 4.4 µg/m$^3$ (1 ppb) (Russell, 1975).

Vinyl bromide in commercial vinyl chloride can be determined by gas chromatography and flame-ionization detection, with a limit of detection of several ppm (Sassu *et al.*, 1968), or collected by preparative gas chromatography and identified by infra-red spectrophotometry, mass spectrometry, elemental analysis and measurement of its physical properties (Kurosaki *et al.*, 1968).

## 3.  Biological Data Relevant to the Evaluation
## of Carcinogenic Risk to Humans

## 3.1  Carcinogenicity studies in animals[1]

### (a)  Skin application

Mouse:  Vinyl bromide was tested as an initiator and as a complete carcinogen in a two-stage skin carcinogenesis study using groups of 30 female ICR/Ha Swiss mice, at a dose of 15 mg/animal in 0.1 ml acetone per application.  When applied alone 3 times weekly for 420 days, there were no skin tumours.  When applied once only, followed by application of phorbol myristyl acetate (PMA) at 2.5 µg/0.1 ml acetone 3 times weekly, 1/30 mice developed a skin papilloma at 412 days.  One skin carcinoma occurred among 30 PMA-treated controls after 44 days.  Untreated controls (160 animals)

---

[1]The Working Group was aware of studies in progress to determine the carcinogenicity of vinyl bromide and polymerized vinyl bromide in rats by oral administration (IARC, 1978) and in mice and rats by inhalation exposure (Toxicology Information Program, 1976).

developed no skin tumours within 420 days. The positive control group (7,12-dimethylbenz[$a$]anthracene followed by PMA) showed the expected high number of skin tumours (Van Duuren, 1977) [The Working Group noted that there was incomplete pathological examination of the animals].

A solution of polymerized vinyl bromide was also tested in groups of 30 female ICR/Ha Swiss mice. A dose of 0.1 ml of a commercial aqueous latex suspension was applied 3 times weekly for 420 days; no skin tumours developed. When applied once only, followed by application of PMA at 2.5 µg/0.1 ml acetone 3 times weekly, 1/30 mice developed a papilloma at 175 days. Untreated controls (160 animals) showed no skin tumours (Van Duuren, 1977) [The Working Group noted that there was incomplete pathological examination of the animals].

(b)  Subcutaneous and/or intramuscular administration

Mouse: A group of 30 female ICR/Ha Swiss mice were injected with 25 mg/animal vinyl bromide in 0.05 ml trioctanoin once weekly for 48 weeks and observed up to 420 days. No local tumours were seen in treated mice, nor in 30 mice given 48 weekly injections of trioctanoin alone, nor in 60 untreated controls observed up to 420 days (Van Duuren, 1977) [The Working Group noted that there was incomplete pathological examination of the animals].

A group of 30 female ICR/Ha mice were injected once weekly for 48 weeks with 0.05 ml of a commercial polymerized vinyl bromide aqueous latex suspension and observed for 420 days. Nineteen mice developed sarcomas at the injection site. In a positive control group of 30 mice injected with β-propiolactone (0.3 mg/0.05 ml trioctanoin), the expected high incidence of tumours at the injection site was seen (18 sarcomas and 3 squamous-cell carcinomas). No local tumours were observed in 60 untreated mice or in 30 control mice injected with trioctanoin alone (Van Duuren, 1977) [The Working Group noted that there was incomplete pathological examination of the animals].

3.2  Other relevant biological data

(a)  Experimental systems

Toxic effects

The oral LD$_{50}$ of a 50% solution of vinyl bromide in corn oil in male rats was approximately 500 mg/kg bw. In acute inhalation studies, exposure of rats to 440 g/m$^3$ (100 000 ppm) resulted in deep anaesthesia and death within 15 minutes; but if exposure was terminated before death, all animals recovered and survived. Exposure to 220 g/m$^3$ (50 000 ppm) rendered rats unconscious in 25 minutes and was lethal after 7 hours' exposure; slight liver and kidney damage were observed. No histopathological changes were found in rats exposed for 7 hours to 110 g/m$^3$ (25 000 ppm) vinyl bromide (Torkelson, unpublished report cited in Leong & Torkelson, 1970).

In subacute inhalation studies, rats were exposed to 44 g/m$^3$ (10 000 ppm) vinyl bromide in air for 7 hours a day on 5 days a week for 4 weeks; or rats, rabbits and monkeys were exposed to 1.1 or 2.2 g/m$^3$ (250 or 500 ppm) vinyl bromide for 6 hours a day on 5 days a week for 6 months. No significant changes were detected in food consumption, haematology, gross pathology or histopathology. Non-volatile bromide levels in the blood increased with duration of exposure in all three species and were proportional to the concentrations of vinyl bromide inhaled (Leong & Torkelson, 1970).

Phenobarbital pretreatment of rats induced acceleration of vinyl bromide debromination in animals exposed to 2% (88 g/m$^3$; 20 000 ppm) vinyl bromide for 5 hours a day, once, twice or for 5 or 10 consecutive days. Toxic injury to the liver observed during the first two days of exposure was reversed by day 5 (VanStee *et al.*, 1977).

Aroclor 1254-pretreated rats exposed by inhalation for 4 hours to 44 or 132 g/m$^3$ (10 000 or 30 000 ppm) vinyl bromide showed increases in serum alanine-α-ketoglutarate transaminase and serum sorbital dehydrogenase. The effect was more pronounced in fasted than in fed rats (Conolly & Jaeger, 1978; Conolly *et al.*, 1977).

No data on the embryotoxicity or teratogenicity of this compound were available to the Working Group.

### Metabolism

When a mixture of vinyl bromide in air was passed through a mouse-liver microsomal system, a volatile alkylating metabolite was formed, as demonstrated by trapping with 4-(4-nitrobenzyl)pyridine (Barbin *et al.*, 1975; Bartsch *et al.*, 1976, 1979).

### Mutagenicity and other short-term tests

Exposure of *Salmonella typhimurium* TA1530 or TA100 to vapours of vinyl bromide in air caused mutagenic effects. The addition of 9000 x *g* liver supernatant fractions from phenobarbital-pretreated mice or from human liver biopsies enhanced the mutagenicity (Bartsch, 1976; Bartsch *et al.*, 1976, 1979).

### (b)  Humans

No data were available to the Working Group.

## 3.3  Case reports and epidemiological studies

No data were available to the Working Group.

## 4. Summary of Data Reported and Evaluation[1]

### 4.1 Experimental data

Vinyl bromide was tested in mice by skin application and by subcutaneous injection. No local tumours were produced.

Vinyl bromide was mutagenic in the only test system used.

A commercial suspension of polymerized vinyl bromide produced no skin tumours in mice when tested by skin application, but local sarcomas were produced following its subcutaneous injection.

### 4.2 Human data

No case reports or epidemiological studies regarding the carcinogenicity of vinyl bromide were available to the Working Group. The fact that workers are exposed to vinyl bromide indicates that it may be possible to identify occupational groups for epidemiological investigation.

### 4.3 Evaluation

The limited data from two studies in which vinyl bromide and polymerized vinyl bromide were tested for local (skin and subcutaneous) carcinogenesis in animals and the absence of human data preclude an evaluation of the carcinogenicity of these materials.

---

[1]Subsequent to the finalization of this evaluation by the Working Group in February 1978, the Secretariat became aware of an inhalation study in progress in male and female Sprague-Dawley rats which were exposed to vinyl bromide at concentrations of 5500, 1100, 220 and 44 mg/m$^3$ (1250, 250, 50 and 10 ppm) in air. Preliminary unpublished results after 18 months indicated an increase in the incidence of liver angiosarcomas (similar to those produced by vinyl chloride) at the 3 highest dose levels and an increase in the incidence of Zymbal gland carcinomas at the 2 highest dose levels (Huntingdon Research Center, 1978; National Institute for Occupational Safety and Health/Occupational Safety and Health Administration, 1978).

## 5. References

American Conference of Governmental Industrial Hygienists (1976)  TLVs ®
Threshold Limit Values for Chemical Substances in Workroom Air
Adopted by ACGIH for 1976, Cincinnati, Ohio, p. 30

Anon. (1977)  News items:  new and proposed threshold limit values for
chemical substances.  Ind. Hyg. Digest, 41, 1

Barbin, A., Brésil, H., Croisy, A., Jacquignon, P., Malaveille, C.,
Montesano, R. & Bartsch, H. (1975)  Liver-microsome-mediated formation
of alkylating agents from vinyl bromide and vinyl chloride.  Biochem.
biophys. Res. Commun., 67, 596-603

Bartsch, H. (1976)  Mutagenicity tests in chemical carcinogenesis.  In:
Rosenfeld, C. & Davis, W., eds., Environmental Pollution and Carcinogenic Risks (IARC Scientific Publications No. 13), Lyon, pp. 229-240

Bartsch, H., Malaveille, C., Barbin, A., Planche, G. & Montesano, R. (1976)
Alkylating and mutagenic metabolites of halogenated olefins produced
by human and animal tissues (Abstract No. 67).  Proc. Am. Assoc.
Cancer Res., 17, 17

Bartsch, H., Malaveille, C., Barbin, A. & Planche, G. (1979)  Mutagenic
and alkylating metabolites of halo-ethylenes, chlorobutadienes and
dichlorobutenes produced by rodent or human liver tissues;  evidence
for oxirane formation by P450-linked microsomal mono-oxygenases.
Arch. Toxicol. (in press)

Conolly, R.B. & Jaeger, R.J. (1977)  Acute hepatotoxicity of ethylene and
halogenated ethylenes after PCB pretreatment.  Environ. Health
Perspect., 21, 131-135

Conolly, R.B., Jaeger, R.J. & Szabo, S. (1977)  Acute hepatotoxicity of
ethylene, vinyl fluoride, vinyl chloride, and vinyl bromide after
Aroclor 1254 pretreatment (Abstract No. 36).  Toxicol. appl. Pharmacol.,
41, 146

Grasselli, J.G. & Ritchey, W.M., eds (1975)  CRC Atlas of Spectral Data
and Physical Constants for Organic Compounds, 2nd ed., Vol. III,
Cleveland, Ohio, Chemical Rubber Co., p. 279

Hawley, G.G., ed. (1971)  The Condensed Chemical Dictionary, 8th ed.,
New York, Van Nostrand-Reinhold, p. 926

Huntingdon Research Center (1978)  Oncogenic Potential of Vinyl Bromide
during Chronic Inhalation Exposure, 18-month Sacrifice, Pathology
Report, Project 7511-253, 26 June, New York

IARC (1978)  Information Bulletin on the Survey of Chemicals Being Tested
    for Carcinogenicity, No. 7, Lyon, pp. 277-278

Kurosaki, M., Taima, S., Hatta, T. & Nakamura, A. (1968)  Identification
    of high-boiling materials as by-products in vinyl chloride manufacture
    (Jap.).  Kogyo Kagaku Zasshi, 71, 488-491 [Chem. Abstr., 69, 56857b]

LeBlanc, R.B. (1977)  Flame resistant fibers.  Fiber Producer, April,
    pp. 10, 12, 16, 64

Leong, B.K.J. & Torkelson, T.R. (1970)  Effects of repeated inhalation of
    vinyl bromide in laboratory animals with recommendations for industrial
    handling.  Am. ind. Hyg. Assoc. J., 31, 1-11

National Institute for Occupational Safety and Health/Occupational Safety
    and Health Administration (1978)  Vinyl Halides Carcinogenicity.
    Vinyl Bromide, Vinyl Chloride, Vinylidene Chloride, Current Intelli-
    gence Bulletin 28, Washington DC, US Department of Health, Education,
    and Welfare

Pollock, J.R.A. & Stevens, R., eds (1965)  Dictionary of Organic Compounds,
    4th ed., Vol. 1, New York, Oxford University Press, p. 443

Ramey, K.C. & Lini, D.C. (1971)  Vinyl bromide polymers.  In:  Bikales, N.M.,
    ed., Encyclopedia of Polymer Science and Technology, Plastics, Resins,
    Rubbers, Fibers, Vol. 14, New York, Interscience, pp. 273-281

Russell, J.W. (1975)  Analysis of air pollutants using sampling tubes and
    gas chromatography.  Environ. Sci. Technol., 9, 1175-1178

Sassu, G.M., Zilio-Grandi, F. & Conte, A. (1968)  Gas chromatographic
    determination of impurities in vinyl chloride.  J. Chromatogr., 34,
    394-398

Toxicology Information Program (1976)  Carcinogenesis bioassay of vinyl
    bromide.  Tox-Tips, 1(7), 3

US International Trade Commission (1977)  Synthetic Organic Chemicals,
    US Production and Sales, 1975, USITC Publication 804, Washington DC,
    US Government Printing Office, p. 221

US Tariff Commission (1970)  Synthetic Organic Chemicals, US Production
    and Sales, 1968, TC Publication 327, Washington DC, US Government
    Printing Office, p. 240

Van Duuren, B.L. (1977)  Chemical structure, reactivity, and carcinogenicity
    of halohydrocarbons.  Environ. Health Perspect., 21, 17-23

VanStee, E.W., Patel, J.M., Gupta, B.N. & Drew, R.T. (1977)  Consequences
    of vinyl bromide debromination in the rat (Abstract No. 105).
    Toxicol. appl. Pharmacol., 41, 175

Weast, R.C., ed. (1976)  CRC Handbook of Chemistry and Physics, 57th ed.,
    Cleveland, Ohio, Chemical Rubber Co., p. C-298

## VINYL CHLORIDE, POLYVINYL CHLORIDE and VINYL CHLORIDE-VINYL ACETATE COPOLYMERS

### Vinyl chloride

This substance was considered by a previous IARC Working Group, in June 1974 (IARC, 1974). Since that time new data have become available, and these have been incorporated into the monograph and taken into account in the present evaluation.

A literature compilation (Warren *et al.*, 1978) and a review (Milby, 1977) are available.

### 1. Chemical and Physical Data

#### 1.1 Synonyms and trade names

Chem. Abstr. Services Reg. No.: 75-01-4

Chem. Abstr. Name: Chloroethene

Chloroethylene; monochloroethylene; VC; VCM; Vinyl C monomer

#### 1.2 Structural and molecular formulae and molecular weight

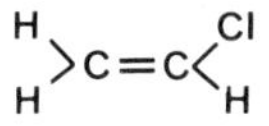

$$\underset{H}{\overset{H}{>}}C=C\underset{H}{\overset{Cl}{<}}$$

$C_2H_3Cl$          Mol. wt: 62.5

#### 1.3 Chemical and physical properties of the pure substance

From Weast (1976), unless otherwise specified

(a) Description: Colourless gas (Windholz, 1976)

(b) Boiling-point: -13.37°C

(c) Melting-point: -153.8°C

(d) Density: $d_4^{20}$ 0.9106; vapour density, 2.2 (air = 1) (Anon., 1972)

(e) Refractive index: $n_D^{20}$ 1.3700

(f) Spectrosocpy data: Infra-red, nuclear magnetic resonance and mass spectral data have been tabulated (Grasselli & Ritchey, 1975).

(g) Solubility: Slightly soluble in water (0.11 g/100 g at 25°C) (Hardie, 1964); soluble in ethanol; very soluble in ether, carbon tetrachloride and benzene

(h) Volatility: Vapour pressure is 2530 mm at 20°C (Hardie, 1964)

(i) Stability: Flash-point, -78°C (closed cup) (Hardie, 1964); polymerizes in light or in the presence of a catalyst (Windholz, 1976); on combustion it degrades to hydrogen chloride, carbon monoxide, carbon dioxide and traces of phosgene (O'Mara et al., 1971)

(j) Reactivity: On treatment with strong alkalis at high temperatures it loses hydrogen chloride (Miller, 1969).

(k) Conversion factor: 1 ppm in air = 2.6 mg/m³

## 1.4 Technical products and impurities

Vinyl chloride is generally supplied as a liquid under pressure. Usually no inhibitor is added when it is to be shipped within the US. A typical analysis of a commercial US grade is as follows: water, 50 mg/kg (ppm); nonvolatile residue, 5 mg/kg (ppm); acetaldehyde, <1 mg/kg (ppm); acetylene, <1 mg/kg (ppm); iron, 0.1 mg/kg (ppm); hydrogen chloride, <0.1 mg/kg (ppm); and hydrogen peroxide, 0.01 mg/kg (ppm).

In Japan, commercial vinyl chloride meets the following specifications: purity, 99.9% min; water, 200 mg/kg (ppm) max; hydrogen chloride, 1 mg/kg (ppm) max; iron, 1 mg/kg (ppm) max; and evaporation residue, 50 mg/kg (ppm) max. Chlorinated hydrocarbons may be present as impurities.

## 2. Production, Use, Occurrence and Analysis

## 2.1 Production and use

### (a) Production

The first synthesis of vinyl chloride appears to have been made in 1835 (Regnault, 1835). Addition of hydrogen chloride to acetylene, formerly the most important route of synthesis, has been displaced by the halogenation of ethylene; over 95% of the vinyl chloride monomer produced in the US and Japan in 1976 was made from ethylene. In this process, ethylene is reacted with hydrogen chloride and oxygen to give ethylene dichloride, which is subsequently cracked to produce vinyl chloride and hydrogen chloride.

Vinyl chloride has been produced commercially in the US for over fifty years (US Tariff Commission, 1928). In 1976, nine companies reported the production of 2580 million kg (US International Trade Commission, 1977). US imports have been negligible; exports amounted to 291 million kg in 1976 (US Department of Commerce, 1977), and in 1977, exports were about 150 million kg to the following countries (% of total): Brazil (28), Canada (8), Colombia (11), Mexico (14), Norway (12) and Yugoslavia (14).

Total western European production in 1976 amounted to 3925 million kg, in the following countries (millions of kg): Belgium (490), the Federal Republic of Germany (990), Finland (25), France (620), Greece (25), Italy (690), The Netherlands (340), Spain (190), Sweden (95), Switzerland (30) and the UK (430). Exports from western Europe in that year were 44 million kg.

In Japan, commercial production of vinyl chloride began prior to 1946. In 1976, eighteen companies produced a total of 1281 million kg vinyl chloride; 115 million kg were exported.

(b) Use

About 96% of the 2274 million kg vinyl chloride used in the US in 1976 was for the production of vinyl chloride homopolymer and copolymer resins. The remainder was used (essentially by one company internally) in the production of methyl chloroform and as a comonomer with vinylidene chloride in the production of resins. For a detailed description of the uses of vinylidene chloride-vinyl chloride copolymers, see p. 450.

The largest use for polyvinyl chloride resins is in the production of plastic piping and conduit. Other important uses are in floor coverings, in consumer goods, in electrical applications and in transport applications. For detailed descriptions of the uses of polyvinyl chloride and vinyl chloride-vinyl acetate copolymers, see pp. 406 and 414.

Hardie (1964) reported that vinyl chloride has been used as a refrigerant, as an extraction solvent for heat-sensitive materials and in the production of chloroacetaldehyde (an intermediate in the synthesis of sulphonamides); however no evidence was found that vinyl chloride is presently being used for these purposes.

Limited quantities of vinyl chloride were used in the US as an aerosol propellant, but in 1974 it was banned from use in pesticide aerosol products (US Environmental Protection Agency, 1974a), in self-pressurized household containers, and as an ingredient of drug and cosmetic products (US Consumer Product Safety Commission, 1974a,b).

Vinyl chloride was used in western Europe in 1977 in the production of polyvinyl chloride (95%) and for other uses, including the production of methyl chloroform (5%).

In Japan in 1976, vinyl chloride was used in the production of poly-vinyl chloride (92-94%) and for other uses, such as in copolymers (6-8%).

The US Occupational Safety and Health Administration's health standards for exposure to air contaminants require that an employees's exposure to vinyl chloride not exceed an eight-hour time-weighted average of 2.6 mg/m$^3$ (1 ppm) in the workplace air in any eight-hour work shift of a forty-hour work week. During any work shift an employee's exposure may not exceed a ceiling concentration limit of 13 mg/m$^3$ (5 ppm), averaged over any period of 15 minutes or less (US Occupational Safety and Health Administration, 1974).

The work environment hygiene standards for exposure to vinyl chloride in various countries, in terms of time-weighted averages (8-hr) and ceiling concentrations (10- or 15-min), were as follows in 1977: Canada, 10 ppm (8-hr) and 25 ppm (15-min); Finland, 5 ppm (8-hr) and 10 ppm (10-min); Italy, 50 ppm (8-hr), although this is expected to change to 25 ppm (8-hr); Japan, expected to be 10 ppm; The Netherlands, 10 ppm (8-hr); Norway, 1 ppm (8-hr) and 5 ppm (15-min); Sweden, 1 ppm (8-hr) and 5 ppm (15-min); USSR, 12 ppm (Bertram, 1977). In France, the standards were reported to be 5 ppm for 1 week, with a ceiling concentration of 15 ppm, in already existing factories, and 1 ppm and 5 ppm, respectively, for new factories; in Spain, no limits; in Denmark, 1 ppm (8-hr); in Belgium, 5 ppm (1 week), ceiling 15 ppm; in the Federal Republic of Germany, the same as for France in existing factories, and 2 ppm (1 year) and ceiling 15 ppm (1-hr) for new factories; in the UK, 10 ppm (8-hr), ceiling 30 ppm max; and in Switzerland, 10 ppm (1 week, 8-hr day for 5 days) (Thomas, 1977).

In August 1977, the proposed European value was 3 ppm over one year for existing and future plants, with an 'alarm-value' of 15 ppm (Commission of the European Communities, 1977a).

The US Environmental Protection Agency has proposed new rules to reduce the national emission standard for vinyl chloride from 10 ppm to 5 ppm in order to reduce vinyl chloride emissions by one-half within 3 years of the actual rulemaking. This would result in hourly emissions (based on new average-sized plants) of 5.1 kg from an ethylene dichloride-vinyl chloride plant (instead of 10.3 kg); 9 kg from a dispersion process polyvinyl chloride plant (instead of 17.5 kg); and 13.5 kg from a sus-pension process polyvinyl chloride resin plant (instead of 16 kg) (US Environmental Protection Agency, 1977).

In the Federal Republic of Germany, the emission in the environment is limited to 3 kg/hr/source or 150 mg/m$^3$/source, with a ground level of 0.3 mg/m$^3$ (99% confidence) in inhabited areas (Thomas, 1977).

The Commission of the European Communities has adopted a level of 1 mg/kg (1 ppm) as the amount of vinyl chloride which can be present in packaging and 0.01 mg/kg (ppm) in foodstuffs packed in polyvinyl chloride (Commission of the European Communities, 1977b, 1978). A maximum migration level of 0.05 mg/kg has been adopted in Belgium, Denmark, the Federal Republic of Germany, France, Italy, The Netherlands, Spain and Sweden (Thomas, 1977).

## 2.2 Occurrence

Vinyl chloride is not known to occur as a natural product.

The occurrence of vinyl chloride in ambient air near vinyl chloride and polyvinyl chloride plants, in water, and in food has been reviewed (US Environmental Protection Agency, 1975a,b).

### (a) Occupational exposure

The air concentration of vinyl chloride in a polymerization reactor prior to ventilation is of the order of 7800 mg/m$^3$ (3000 ppm); during the scraping procedure, 130-260 mg/m$^3$ (50-100 ppm); and that close to the hands during scraping, 1560-2600 mg/m$^3$ (600-1000 ppm) (Cook et al., 1971). Between 1950 and 1959, concentrations up to 10.4 g/m$^3$ (4000 ppm) were found in one factory near the polymerization reactors (Ott et al., 1975). Air concentrations of vinyl chloride in working places in polyvinyl chloride-producing factories have been reported variously to range from 100-800 mg/m$^3$ (40-312 ppm), with peaks up to 87.3 g/m$^3$ (33 500 ppm) (Filatova & Gronsberg, 1957); from 112-556 mg/m$^3$ (43-214 ppm) (Anghelescu et al., 1969); and >195 mg/m$^3$ (>75 ppm) in a Yugoslav plant (Orusev et al., 1976). In a Russian synthetic leather plant, <113.6 mg/m$^3$ (44 ppm) (Bol'shakov, 1969) and in three UK cable factories, 0.4-0.9 mg/m$^3$ (0.15-0.35 ppm) (Murdoch & Hammond, 1977) were detected. In 1974, it was estimated that 20 000 US workers, past and present, had been exposed to vinyl chloride in manufacturing plants (Heath et al., 1975).

On a time-weighted average, the concentration of vinyl chloride monomer to which coagulator operators are exposed ranges from 130-650 mg/m$^3$ (50-250 ppm) (Baretta et al., 1969). However, in a more recent survey for the US National Institute for Occupational Safety and Health of three vinyl chloride plants it was reported that the time-weighted average exposure to vinyl chloride ranged from 0.2-70 mg/m$^3$ (0.07-27 ppm) (Milby, 1977). Barnhart et al. (1975) found <0.03-15 mg/m$^3$ (<0.01-5.89 ppm), 0.03-220 mg/m$^3$ (0.01-84.77 ppm) and 0.05-57 mg/m$^3$ (0.02-21.8 ppm) in 3 vinyl chloride plants in the US.

In 1974, it was reported that polyvinyl chloride leaving certain manufacturing plants may have contained 200-400 mg/kg (ppm) vinyl chloride monomer; on delivery to the customer, this level was about 250 mg/kg (ppm); and after processing, levels of 0.5-20 mg/kg (ppm) were reached, depending on the method of fabrication (Anon., 1974). Wilkinson *et al.* (1964) found 100 mg/kg (ppm) residual vinyl chloride monomer in polyvinyl chloride dispersions. However, new processing methods leave as little as 1-2 mg/kg (ppm) residual vinyl chloride in vinyl chloride resins (US Food and Drug Administration, 1975). Residual vinyl chloride in commercial food grade resins has been reduced by processing and stripping techniques to 115 µg/kg (ppb) for resin, less than 0.048 µg/kg (ppb) for compound and less than 0.043 µg/kg (ppb) for sheet polyvinyl chloride (Saggese *et al.*, 1976). Industrial grade polyvinyl chloride-coated films used for food packaging were found to contain 5-71 µg/kg (ppb) of monomer (Gilbert *et al.*, 1975) and plastic bottles up to 7.9 mg/kg (ppm) (Breder *et al.*, 1975).

(b) Air

It has been estimated that prior to 1975 vinyl chloride emissions from US polyvinyl chloride plants amounted to 110 million kg/year (US Environmental Protection Agency, 1975b) and that the average concentration of vinyl chloride in air around these plants was 44 µg/m³ (17 ppb) (US Environmental Protection Agency, 1976). Vinyl chloride has been determined in the air in the Houston, Texas, area (where an estimated 40% of the US production capacity is located) in concentrations of 8 µg/m -3.2 mg/m³ (3.1-1250 ppb) (Gordon & Meeks, 1977) and in the ambient air near two vinyl chloride plants in the Long Beach, California, area in concentrations of 0.26-8.8 mg/m³ (0.1-3.4 ppm) (National Field Investigations Center, 1974). It has also been detected in the air in Delaware City, Delaware, in maximum concentrations of 3.9 mg/m³ (1.5 ppm) with a mean of 2 mg/m³ (0.8 ppm) (Lillian *et al.*, 1975).

(c) Water

Vinyl chloride has been detected in effluent discharged by chemical and latex manufacturing plants and in raw water in the US (Shackelford & Keith, 1976). The highest concentration of vinyl chloride detected in finished drinking-water in the US was 10.0 µg/l (Safe Drinking Water Committee, 1977; US Environmental Protection Agency, 1975a).

In 1974, it was estimated that about 12.3 kg/day vinyl chloride were discharged in the waste-water effluent from 2 vinyl chloride plants in the Long Beach, California, area (National Field Investigations Center, 1974).

(d) Food

In May 1973, a branch of the US Treasury Department banned the use of polyvinyl chloride for the packaging of alcoholic beverages (Anon., 1973a), as a result of studies reported by the US Food and Drug Administration indicating that up to 20 mg/kg (ppm) vinyl chloride monomer were present in

alcoholic beverages packaged in this material (Anon., 1973b).  Vinyl
chloride has been found in a variety of alcoholic drinks at levels of 0-2.1
mg/kg (ppm) (Williams, 1976a,b;  Williams & Miles, 1975) and in vinegars at
levels of up to 9.4 mg/kg (ppm) (Williams & Miles, 1975).

It has been found in edible oils, in concentrations of 0.05-14.8 mg/kg
(ppm) (Roesli *et al.*, 1975;  Williams, 1976a;  Williams & Miles, 1975), and
in butter and margarine, in concentrations of 0.05 mg/kg (ppm) (Fuchs
*et al.*, 1975), when these products were packaged and stored in polyvinyl
chloride containers.

(e)  Other

Vinyl chloride has been found in 2/7 new automobile interiors in
concentrations of 1-3 mg/m$^3$ (0.4-1.2 ppm) (Hedley *et al.*, 1976).  In
another study (Going, 1976), no concentrations above 10 ppb were found in
16 new or used automobiles or in 4 new or old mobile homes.

Vinyl chloride has been detected in domestic and foreign cigarettes
and little cigars, in concentrations of 5.6-27 ng/cigarette, and in a
marijuana cigarette at a level of 5.4 ng/cigarette (Hoffmann *et al.*, 1976).

2.3  Analysis

A comprehensive critical review, containing over 100 references, of
methods of sampling and analysis of vinyl chloride in the workplace atmosphere, ambient air, water, food, cigarette smoke and polyvinyl chloride
is available (Egan *et al.*, 1979).  Methods of collection and analysis of
vinyl chloride have also been reviewed (US Environmental Protection Agency,
1975b).  A review of methods used to determine vinyl chloride in air,
water, and water piping is available (Laramy, 1977).

A gas chromatographic method of analysis has been accepted by the US
National Institute for Occupational Safety and Health for determining vinyl
chloride in the workplace atmosphere, in the range of 0.008-5.2 mg/m$^3$ in a
5-litre air sample (National Institute for Occupational Safety and Health,
1977).

A gas chromatographic analytical method has been proposed by the Commission of the European Communities for determining vinyl chloride in
foodstuffs and in vinyl chloride polymers and copolymers intended to come
into contact with food (Commission of the European Communities, 1977b).

An official analytical method has been drafted in the Federal Republic
of Germany for determining residual vinyl chloride in polyvinyl chloride.
It is based on treatment of the polymer with $N,N$-dimethylacetamide, followed
by gas chromatographic analysis of the solution with flame-ionization detection and has a limit of detection of 0.5 mg/kg (ppm) (Deutsche Industrie
Normen Ausschuss, 1977).

3. Biological Data Relevant to the Evaluation

of Carcinogenic Risk to Humans

## 3.1 Carcinogenicity studies in animals[1,2]

(a) Oral administration

Rat: Groups of 40 male and 40 female 13-week-old Sprague-Dawley rats received gastric intubations of 0, 3.33, 16.65 or 50 mg/kg bw vinyl chloride dissolved in olive oil 4-5 times/week for 52 weeks. After 85 weeks from the initial treatment, 35, 39, 32 and 23 animals were still alive. At 120 weeks, 9 liver angiosarcomas, 2 Zymbal gland carcinomas and 3 nephroblastomas occurred in rats administered the 16.65 mg/kg bw dose; and 16 liver angiosarcomas, 2 nephroblastomas, 1 Zymbal gland carcinoma, and 1 thymic and 1 intra-abdominal angiosarcoma were found in the 50 mg/kg bw group. One intra-abdominal angiosarcoma was seen in the low-dose group, and 1 Zymbal gland tumour occurred in the control group (Maltoni, 1977a; Maltoni et al., 1975).

(b) Inhalation and/or intratracheal administration

Mouse: Groups of 30 male and 30 female 11-week-old Swiss mice were exposed to concentrations of 130-26 000 mg/m$^3$ (50, 250, 500, 2500, 6000, or 10 000 ppm) vinyl chloride in air for 4 hours/day on 5 days/week for 30 weeks. A total of 344 mice (176 males and 168 females) died within 61 weeks. At 81 weeks (end of experiment), 176 animals (3.5, 57, 66, 57, 70 and 70% in the different groups, respectively) had adenomas and/or adeno-carcinomas of the lung, 60 animals (33, 32, 24, 30, 28 and 47%, respec-tively) had mammary adenocarcinomas and 47 animals (2, 19, 19, 20, 5 and 16%, respectively) had angiosarcomas of the liver. Except for lung tumours, which were not increased in the group treated with 50 ppm, a significantly higher number of neoplasms occurred in all treated groups. In 80 male and 70 female untreated controls, 8 pulmonary tumours and 3 lymphomas were observed (Maltoni, 1977; Maltoni et al., 1974).

---

[1]The Working Group was aware of studies in progress to assess the carcinogenicity of vinyl chloride in rats by administration in the drinking-water and by administration in the diet, and of complete but unpublished studies by inhalation in rats (IARC, 1978a).

[2]In all his experiments, Maltoni used vinyl chloride that contained the following impurities (mg/kg): water, 100; acetic aldehyde, 5; ace-tylene, 2; allene, 5; butane, 8; 1,3-butadiene, 10; chloroprene (see also, p. 131), 10; diacetylene, 4; vinyl acetylene, 10; propine, 3; methyl chloride, 100.

Groups of 100 male and 100 female CDI Swiss/ChR mice (age unspecified) were exposed to 130, 520 or 6500 mg/m$^3$ (50, 200 or 2500 ppm) vinyl chloride in air (purity unspecified) for 7 hours/day on 5 days/week for 9 months and were observed for an additional 9 months. After 8 months' exposure, 49 treated animals died with tumours. A total of 42 pulmonary adenomas, 41 liver angiosarcomas and 11 mammary gland adenocarcinomas were observed (histological evaluation was carried out on grossly visible tumours only). A dose-related carcinogenic effect was evident (see Table I). At 8 months, no tumours were observed in 200 controls (100 females and 100 males). The study was still in progress at the time of reporting (Keplinger et al., 1975).

Table I

Incidence of tumours in mice exposed to vinyl chloride
(purity unspecified) for 8 months[1]

| Exposed groups | No. of mice with tumours at death | | | Type and location of tumour | | |
|---|---|---|---|---|---|---|
| | | | | Adenomas | Angiosarcomas | Adenocarcinomas |
| | Male | Female | Total | lung | liver | mammary gland |
| 50 ppm | 1 | 3 | 4 | 2 | 2 | 2 |
| 200 ppm | 3 | 12 | 15 | 12 | 11 | 3 |
| 2500 ppm | 6 | 24 | 30 | 28 | 28 | 6 |
| Control | 0 | 0 | 0 | 0 | 0 | 0 |

[1]From Keplinger et al. (1975), preliminary results

Two groups each of 12 male and 12 female 3-month-old NMRI outbred albino mice were exposed to either 130 or 1300 mg/m$^3$ (50 or 500 ppm) vinyl chloride in air for 6 hours/day on 5 days/week. The 500 ppm group was exposed for 26 weeks only (due to the poor condition of the mice); the 50 ppm group was exposed for 52 weeks, at which time the experiment was terminated. In the low-dose group, 18/24 animals had developed tumours, including pulmonary adenomas in 13/24, angiosarcomas at various sites in 15/24 and a mammary carcinoma in 1 mouse. Inhalation of 500 ppm vinyl chloride for 26 weeks induced pulmonary adenomas in all mice; in addition, 8 mice had angiosarcomas, mammary adenocarcinomas were found in 4 animals, 1 mouse had an angiosarcoma of the liver, 1 an adenoma of the kidney and 1 an angiosarcoma of brown fat. In the control group, 3/48 had tumours: 1 adenocarcinoma of the mammary gland, 1 dysgerminoma of the ovary and 1 reticulum-cell sarcoma of the spleen (Holmberg et al., 1976).

Groups of 36 male and 36 female 2-month-old albino CD mice were exposed to 130, 650 and 2600 mg/m$^3$ (50, 250 and 1000 ppm) vinyl chloride (99.8% pure) in air for 6 hours/day on 5 days/week for 52 weeks; at that time, 70, 52, 46 and 38 animals were still alive, respectively. A total of 12, 22 and 48 mice developed lung adenomas in the exposed groups, respectively; 1 lung adenoma was found in untreated control animals. In addition, angiosarcomas of the liver developed in 3, 23 and 31 treated mice, respectively, and angiosarcomas in other organs in 7, 5 and 9 mice. Mammary gland tumours were found in 9, 3 and 13 mice, respectively; most of these tumours metastasized to the lungs (Lee *et al.*, 1977, 1978).

Rat: A group of 26 male 3-month-old Ar/IRE Wistar rats were exposed to an atmospheric concentration of 3% v/v (equivalent to 78 g/m$^3$ or 30 000 ppm) commercial grade vinyl chloride (99% pure) for 4 hours/day on 5 days/week for 12 months; the experiment was terminated at 54 weeks. Skin tumours developed in the submaxillary parotid region in all 17 surviving rats (14 epidermoid carcinomas, 2 mucoepidermoid carcinomas, 1 papilloma); in addition, lung tumours developed in 7 rats and osteochondromas in 5. No tumours were observed in 25 untreated controls killed at an unstated time (Viola *et al.*, 1971) [Maltoni & Lefemine (1974) examined slides from this experiment and concluded that the skin tumours were Zymbal gland tumours and that the lung tumours were metastases from these].

Groups of 30 male and 30 female 21-week-old Sprague-Dawley rats were exposed by inhalation to 130-26 000 mg/m$^3$ (50, 250, 500, 2500, 6000 or 10 000 ppm) vinyl chloride in air for 4 hours/day on 5 days/week for 17 weeks. At 86 weeks, 18, 15, 37, 33, 16 and 9 animals were still alive in the 6 groups. At 155 weeks (end of experiment), carcinomas of the Zymbal gland were found in 0, 1, 1, 3, 6 and 7 animals, respectively (1 in untreated controls), nephroblastomas in 1, 2, 0, 2, 1 and 1 animals, liver angiosarcomas in 0, 0, 1, 1, 1 and 0 animals and angiosarcomas at other sites in 2, 0, 1, 2, 1 and 1 (1 in controls). Brain neuroblastomas were seen in 0, 0, 0, 2, 2 and 6 animals, respectively (Maltoni, 1977a; Maltoni *et al.*, 1974).

Groups of 64-96 13-week-old Sprague-Dawley rats were also treated for 52 weeks with the above concentrations of vinyl chloride in air. The following tumours developed in various organs by the end of the experiment, at 135 weeks: carcinomas of the Zymbal gland in 29/239 rats at the 4 highest dose levels, and nephroblastomas (26/257 rats) and angiosarcomas of the liver (47/357 rats) in all the treated groups (the numbers of rats given were those alive at 26 weeks); a total of 14 angiosarcomas was observed in organs other than the liver. The tumours of the liver and kidney metastasized to other organs. No such tumours were observed in 58 untreated controls alive at 26 weeks (see Table II). In a group of 60 17-week-old Sprague-Dawley rats treated with 78 g/m$^3$ (30 000 ppm) vinyl chloride in air for 4 hours/day on 5 days/week for 43 weeks, 30 (50%) developed Zymbal gland carcinomas, 13, liver angiosarcomas and 1, a lung angiosarcoma within the 61 weeks of observation (Maltoni *et al.*, 1974).

Table II[1]

Incidence of tumours in Sprague-Dawley rats exposed to vinyl chloride
for 4 hours/day on 5 days/week for 52 weeks and surviving up to 130 weeks

| Concentration of vinyl chloride (ppm) | Total no. of animals at start | No. of animals alive at 26 weeks | No. of Zymbal gland tumours | No. of nephro-blastomas | No. of angio-sarcomas of the liver | No. of angio-sarcomas at other sites | No. of brain neuro-blastomas | No. of other tumours |
|---|---|---|---|---|---|---|---|---|
| 10 000 | 69 | 61 | 16 | 5 | 9 | 3 | 7 | 11 |
| 6000 | 72 | 60 | 7 | 4 | 13 | 3 | 3 | 10 |
| 2500 | 74 | 59 | 2 | 6 | 13 | 3 | 5 | 7 |
| 500 | 67 | 59 | 4 | 4 | 7 | 2 | 0 | 8 |
| 250 | 67 | 59 | 0 | 6 | 4 | 2 | 0 | 7 |
| 50 | 64 | 59 | 0 | 1 | 1 | 1 | 0 | 10 |
| Controls | 68 | 58 | 0 | 0 | 0 | 0 | 0 | 10 |

[1]From Maltoni *et al.* (1974)

Wistar rats were also exposed by inhalation to 130-26 000 mg/m$^3$ (50, 250, 500, 2500, 6000 and 10 000 ppm) vinyl chloride in air for 52 weeks. After 136 weeks of observation, 1 Zymbal gland carcinoma was found, whereas at a comparable time the Sprague-Dawley rats had developed 29 such tumours. In the Wistar rats, 1 nephroblastoma, 8 liver angiosarcomas and 1 brain neuroblastoma were found in the 10 000 ppm group; 3 nephroblastomas, 2 liver angiosarcomas and 1 brain neuroblastoma in the 6000 ppm group; 3 liver angiosarcomas in the 2500 ppm group; and 1 nephroblastoma and 4 liver angiosarcomas in the 500 ppm group (Maltoni, 1977a; Maltoni *et al.*, 1974).

The effect of length of treatment by inhalation of vinyl chloride on the incidence of liver angiosarcomas was investigated. Groups of 60-120 Sprague-Dawley rats were given either 15.6 or 26 g/m$^3$ (6000 or 10 000 ppm) vinyl chloride in air for 4 hours/day on 5 days/week for 5, 17 or 52 weeks. The experiment was terminated at 155 weeks. Liver angiosarcomas developed in 13 (22%) and 9 (15%) of the 6000 and 10 000 ppm groups exposed for 52 weeks; 1 (0.6%) liver angiosarcoma was found in a rat exposed to 6000 ppm for 17 weeks and none in the 10 000 ppm group. No such tumours were induced in rats treated for 5 weeks (Maltoni, 1977b) [No information was given about tumours occurring at other sites].

The influence of age on the incidence of liver tumours was examined in Sprague-Dawley rats exposed to 15.6 or 26 g/m$^3$ (6000 or 10 000 ppm) vinyl chloride in air for 4 hours/day on 5 days/week for 5 weeks, starting at the age of 13 weeks (120 rats/group) or 1 day (43 and 46 rats). The animals were observed for 135 weeks. One hepatoma was reported in the older rats treated with 10 000 ppm. In the newborn rats, 10 angiosarcomas and 13 hepatomas were observed in the 6000 ppm group, and 10 angiosarcomas and 15 hepatomas were found in rats treated with 10 000 ppm. No liver tumours were reported in the 249 untreated rats (Maltoni, 1977b).

Groups of 36 male and 36 female 2-month-old CD rats were exposed to 0, 130, 650 and 2600 mg/m$^3$ (0, 50, 250 and 1000 ppm) vinyl chloride in air (99.8% pure) for 6 hours/day on 5 days/week for 12 months, at which time the surviving animals (72, 70, 58 and 51) were killed. In rats treated with 250 and 1000 ppm, liver angiosarcomas occurred in 12 and 22 and lung angiosarcomas developed in 3 and 13 (Lee *et al.*, 1977).

In a report of a study in progress, 4 groups of 80 Sprague-Dawley male rats received either 5% ethanol in the drinking-water or drinking-water only for 4 weeks prior to beginning inhalation of 1560 mg/m$^3$ (600 ppm) vinyl chloride for 4 hours/day on 5 days/week for 12 months or air; ethanol-water was given until death or sacrifice. After 60 weeks from the first exposure to vinyl chloride, 55 rats had died or had been sacrificed; liver tumours were found in 21/28 (75%) in the vinyl chloride-ethanol group and 5/13 (38%) in the vinyl chloride only group (Radike *et al.*, 1977).

Hamster: Groups of 32-35 male 11-week-old golden hamsters were exposed by inhalation to 130-26 000 mg/m$^3$ (50, 250, 500, 2500, 6000 and 10 000 ppm) vinyl chloride in air for 4 hours/day on 5 days/week for 30 weeks. At 48 weeks from the initial treatment, 60/198 treated animals were still alive. At 109 weeks (end of treatment), 2 liver angiosarcomas were seen in hamsters treated with 500 ppm and 1 in those treated with 6000 ppm. Skin trichoepitheliomas developed in 22 treated hamsters (in 1-6 animals/group) and in 2/70 controls. Two animals treated with 6000 ppm and 1 each treated with 50, 2500 and 10 000 ppm developed melanomas. In addition, 6 lymphomas and 35 forestomach papillomas and acanthomas were found in treated animals, and 2 and 2, respectively, in controls (Maltoni, 1977a; Maltoni *et al.*, 1974).

Rabbit: A group of 40 rabbits were exposed for 4 hours/day on 5 days/week for 12 months to air containing 26 g/m$^3$ (10 000 ppm) vinyl chloride. Between 9-15 months of exposure, 12 skin acanthomas and 6 lung adenocarcinomas were seen. No similar tumours occurred in 20 controls after 15 months of observation (Caputo *et al.*, 1974) [The Working Group noted the inadequacy of reporting].

## (c)  Subcutaneous and/or intramuscular administration

A group of 75 male and female 21-week-old Sprague-Dawley rats were given single s.c. injections of 4.25 mg/animal vinyl chloride in 1 ml olive oil. One nephroblastoma occurred in the treated animals (Maltoni, 1977a) [The Working Group noted that survival times and period of observation were not given].

## (d)  Intraperitoneal administration

Groups of 30 male and 30 female 13-week-old Sprague-Dawley rats received single injections of 4.25 mg/animal vinyl chloride in 1 ml olive oil, 2, 3 or 4 times in 2 months. One nephroblastoma and 1 s.c. angiosarcoma were found (Maltoni, 1977a) [The Working Group noted that survival times and period of observation were not given].

## (e)  Other experimental systems

Prenatal exposure: Two groups of 30 female Sprague-Dawley rats were given 15.6-26 g/m$^3$ (6000 or 10 000 ppm) vinyl chloride in air for 4 hours/day by inhalation from the 12-18th day of pregnancy. Of the offspring, 17/32 and 23/54 had died by the 95th week after birth. After 143 weeks (end of experiment), 1 s.c. angiosarcoma was observed in each group of offspring; 1 animal exposed *in utero* to 6000 ppm had a Zymbal gland carcinoma; and 3 animals exposed to 10 000 ppm had Zymbal gland carcinomas, and 1, a nephroblastoma. One female rat treated with 10 000 ppm developed a Zymbal gland carcinoma (Maltoni, 1974; Maltoni, 1977a).

## 3.2  Other relevant biological data

### (a)  Experimental systems

#### Toxic effects

The 2-hour $LC_{50}$ of vinyl chloride for mice was 294 $g/m^3$ (113 000 ppm); for rats, 390 $g/m^3$ (150 000 ppm); for guinea-pigs, 595 $g/m^3$ (230 000 ppm); and for rabbits, 295 $g/m^3$ (113 000 ppm). Vinyl chloride gas had a narcotic effect on experimental animals, the most sensitive species being mice, followed by rats, guinea-pigs and rabbits. The death of animals was preceded by excitement, contractions and convulsions, accelerated respiration, followed by respiratory failure. Rabbits and guinea-pigs had more accentuated muscular contractions and convulsions than mice and rats. Microscopically, congestion of the internal organs with more intense damage to the lungs, liver and kidneys were found (Prodan *et al.*, 1975a).

The hepatotoxicity of vinyl chloride has been shown to be increased after administration of cytochrome P-450 inducers such as phenobarbital, Aroclor 1254 and hexachlorobenzene (Ivanetich *et al.*, 1977; Reynolds *et al.*, 1975a,b). The extent of liver damage has been measured by the release of alanine α-ketoglutarate, glutamic oxalacetic and glutamic pyruvic transaminases (Reynolds *et al.*, 1975b, 1976) and of sorbitol dehydrogenase (Conolly & Jaeger, 1977) into the serum.

A single 6-hour inhalation exposure to 130 $g/m^3$ vinyl chloride (50 000 ppm) produced acute liver injury in male Sprague-Dawley rats pretreated with phenobarbital or Aroclor 1254. The degree of injury, as indicated by elevation of serum levels of enzymes derived from the liver, correlated with the magnitude of induction of cytochrome P-450 and morphological changes in the endoplasmic reticulum (Reynolds *et al.*, 1975a,b, 1976). Similar findings were reported in phenobarbital-pretreated male Holtzman rats (Jaeger *et al.*, 1974) and in phenobarbital-treated male Charles River CD-1 rats that received 10 daily exposures for 6 hours/day to 35 $g/m^3$ (13 500 ppm) vinyl chloride in air (Drew *et al.*, 1975).

Cytochrome P-450 concentration decreased during *in vivo* exposure or during *in vitro* incubation of liver homogenate from phenobarbital or 3-methylcholanthrene-induced rats (Ivanetich *et al.*, 1977; Reynolds *et al.*, 1975c).

In an abstract, it was reported that male rats pretreated by gavage with Aroclor 1254 for 3 consecutive days and exposed on day 4 by inhalation to 62.5 $g/m^3$ (24 000 ppm) vinyl chloride for 4 hours showed significant elevations of serum alanine-α-ketoglutarate transaminase and severe degeneration and necrosis of the liver (Conolly *et al.*, 1977). Overnight fasting, which depletes hepatic glutathione, of Aroclor-pretreated male Holtzman rats before exposure to 26 $g/m^3$ (10 000 ppm) for 4 hours significantly increased the hepatotoxic effects, as measured by sorbitol dehydrogenase levels in the serum (Conolly & Jaeger, 1977).

Simultaneous exposure to 1.75 g/m$^3$ (671 ppm) vinyl chloride with 200 ppm vinylidene chloride prevented vinylidene chloride-induced hepatic injury in fasted male rats. However, pre-exposure to concentrations of vinyl chloride which depleted hepatic glutathione concentrations significantly enhanced early acute hepatotoxic response to vinylidene chloride in fed rats (Jaeger *et al.*, 1975a,b).

Exposure of guinea-pigs to 260 g/m$^3$ (100 000 ppm) vinyl chloride for 2 hours/day for 3 months resulted in marked growth disturbances and intense histopathological and histochemical lesions in the liver, kidneys, spleen and lungs. Interruption of the exposure resulted in a regenerative effect, denoting a certain degree of reversibility of the hepatorenal lesions. Large quantities of vitamin C reduced the gravity of the lesions caused by vinyl chloride (Prodan *et al.*, 1975b).

Mice were exposed to 130, 650 or 2600 mg/m$^3$ (50, 250 or 1000 ppm) vinyl chloride for 6 hours/day on 5 days/week. The highest dose caused some acute deaths with toxic hepatitis and marked tubular necrosis in the renal cortex. From the 6th month of treatment, all mice became lethargic, lost weight quickly and died. Only a few mice exposed to 50 ppm survived for 12 months (Lee *et al.*, 1977).

The non-protein, free SH-groups of the liver are depleted in rats exposed to 390-5200 mg/m$^3$ (150-2000 ppm) vinyl chloride for 1-7 hours, as a function both of concentration and duration of exposure (Watanabe *et al.*, 1976a).

Vinyl chloride and two of its presumed metabolites, chloroethylene oxide and chloroacetaldehyde, depressed DNA synthesis in rat liver *in vivo* (Border & Webster, 1977).

## Embryotoxicity and teratogenicity

Pregnant CF-1 mice were exposed by inhalation to 130 and 1300 mg/m$^3$ (50 and 500 ppm) vinyl chloride on days 6-15 of gestation, Sprague-Dawley rats to 1300 and 6500 mg/m$^3$ (500 and 2500 ppm) on days 6-15 of gestation, and New Zealand rabbits to 1300 and 6500 mg/m$^3$ (500 and 2500 ppm) on days 6-18 of gestation, for 7 hours/day, with or without simultaneous exposure to 15% ethanol in the drinking-water. A significantly increased incidence of several skeletal anomalies was observed in offspring of mice that received vinyl chloride plus ethanol (John *et al.*, 1977; Schwetz *et al.*, 1975).

## Absorption, distribution, excretion and metabolism

The *in vivo* and *in vitro* metabolism of vinyl chloride has been studied and reviewed (Antweiler, 1976; Bartsch & Montesano, 1975; Bonse & Henschler, 1976; Green & Hathway, 1975, 1977; Haley, 1975; Hefner *et al.*, 1975; Malaveille *et al.*, 1975; Müller & Norpoth, 1975; Müller *et al.*, 1976; Plugge & Safe, 1977; Watanabe & Gehring, 1976; Watanabe *et al.*, 1976b,c).

Low concentrations (130 mg/m$^3$, 50 ppm, for 65 min) of vinyl chloride
are readily metabolized in rats exposed by inhalation and are converted
into polar metabolites, which are predominantly excreted in the urine;
a very small amount is expired in air as unchanged vinyl chloride (Hefner
et al., 1975).

Following exposure of male rats by inhalation to 26 mg/m$^3$ (10 ppm)
$^{14}$C-vinyl chloride for 6 hours, urinary $^{14}$C-activity and expired vinyl
chloride comprised 68 and 2%, respectively, of the recovered radioactivity;
after exposure to 2600 mg/m$^3$ (1000 ppm) $^{14}$C-vinyl chloride, the proportion
of the radioactivity in the urine was lower and that expired as vinyl
chloride higher, representing 56 and 12%, respectively. The pattern of
pulmonary elimination of 10 and 1000 ppm vinyl chloride per se was described by apparently similar first-order kinetics, with half-lives of 20.4 and
22.4 min, respectively; the half-lives for the initial phase of excretion
of $^{14}$C-radioactivity in the urine were 4.6 and 4.1 hours, respectively.
$^{14}$C-Radioactivity recovered from the carcass after 72 hours was 14 and 15%,
respectively; no vinyl chloride per se was found in tissues. The propor-
tions of 3 urinary metabolites, N-acetyl-S-(2-hydroxyethyl)cysteine, thiodiglycolic acid (thiodiacetic acid) and an unidentified metabolite, were
not markedly influenced by the level of exposure (Watanabe et al., 1976b).

Following single oral administration of 0.05, 1 or 100 mg/kg bw $^{14}$C-
vinyl chloride to male rats, excretion in the urine was 59, 68 and 11%,
respectively; the $^{14}$CO$_2$ in expired air accounted for 9, 13 and 3%, respectively; pulmonary elimination of unchanged vinyl chloride represented only
1-3% of the lower dose levels and 67% of the higher level. The pulmonary
clearance of 0.05 and 1 mg/kg bw doses of vinyl chloride was monophasic,
with half-lives of 53.3 and 57.8 min, respectively; it was biphasic after
administration of 100 mg/kg bw, with half-lives of 14.4 and 40.8 min for
the fast and slow phases, respectively. The percentages of the doses left
in the carcass after 72 hours were 10, 11 and 2% of the 0.05, 1 and 100
mg/kg doses, respectively. Two of 3 urinary metabolites were identified as
N-acetyl-S-(2-hydroxyethyl)cysteine and thiodiglycolic acid; their propor-
tions were not influenced by dose (Watanabe et al., 1976c). It has been
suggested that the metabolism of vinyl chloride in rats following oral and
inhalation exposure is a saturable process (Watanabe et al., 1976b,c).

The kinetic parameters and half-lives for the elimination of vinyl
chloride from rats after inhalation and i.v. administration have also been
reported by Withey (1976).

When rats were exposed to initial concentrations of less than 260 mg/m$^3$
(100 ppm) [1,2-$^{14}$C]-vinyl chloride, about 40% of that inspired was absorbed
by the lung. Highest radioactivity levels were observed in the liver and
kidney immediately after exposure. Most of the radioactive metabolites
were excreted rapidly, largely by the kidneys: the radioactivity in the
urine amounted to 70% within 24 hours. Some metabolites, however, remained
in tissues (mostly in spleen, liver, kidneys) even 48 hours after exposure
(Bolt et al., 1976). Metabolites that were not excreted in urine were partly

excreted *via* faeces and partly *via* expiration of $^{14}CO_2$ (Bolt *et al.*, 1976; Green & Hathway, 1975).

Vinyl chloride is metabolized by microsomal mixed-function oxidases to chloroethylene oxide, which can rearrange spontaneously to chloroacetaldehyde (Fig. 1). Although there is no direct evidence for this pathway *in vivo*, the following data are consistent with this hypothesis. Vinyl chloride in the presence of a mouse liver microsomal fraction, rat liver homogenate, an NADPH generating system and oxygen yielded an alkylating intermediate which reacted with either 3,4-dichlorobenzenethiol (Göthe *et al.*, 1974) or with 4-(4-nitrobenzyl)pyridine. The absorption spectra of the latter adduct was identical to those obtained with the product formed with synthetic chloroethylene oxide (Barbin *et al.*, 1975; Bartsch *et al.*, 1976). These studies indicate that the primary *in vitro* metabolite of vinyl chloride is chloroethylene oxide, which can rearrange to chloroacetaldehyde.

Metabolism of vinyl chloride occurs predominantly through the cytochrome P-450 system (Ivanetich *et al.*, 1977; Reynolds *et al.*, 1975c; Salmon, 1976). Inhibitors of microsomal mixed-function oxidases, such as 3-bromophenyl-4(5)-imidazole or 6-nitro-1,2,3-benzothiadiazole, reduced vinyl chloride metabolism *in vivo* (Bolt *et al.*, 1976). Chloroethylene oxide, with a half-life of 1.6 min in aqueous solution at neutrality (Barbin *et al.*, 1975), rearranges to chloroacetaldehyde (Bonse *et al.*, 1975). Chloroacetaldehyde combines directly or enzymatically *via* glutathione *S*-transferase with glutathione to form *S*-formylmethylglutathione, which is excreted as *N*-acetyl-*S*-(2-hydroxyethyl)cysteine (Green & Hathway, 1977) (Fig. 1). Chloroacetaldehyde can be oxidized to chloroacetic acid, which is either excreted as such or bound to glutathione to form *S*-carboxymethyl glutathione, which upon further enzymic degradation is excreted as thiodiglycolic acid (thiodiacetic acid) (Plugge & Safe, 1977).

Chloroacetic acid was metabolized in rats to two major urinary metabolites, *S*-carboxymethylcysteine and thiodiacetic acid (Yllner, 1971). *N*-Acetyl-*S*-(2-hydroxyethyl)cysteine (a major metabolite) (Green & Hathway, 1977; Watanabe *et al.*, 1976b,c), *S*-(carboxymethyl)cysteine and *N*-acetyl-*S*-vinylcysteine have been shown to be metabolites of vinyl chloride in rats after oral administration (Green & Hathway, 1977) and *N*-acetyl-*S*-(2-hydroxyethyl)cysteine after inhalation (Watanabe *et al.*, 1976b); *S*-(2-chloroethyl)cysteine was also identified after oral administration of vinyl chloride to rats (Green & Hathway, 1975). As thiodiglycolic acid was obtained as a common metabolite in rats dosed separately with chloroacetaldehyde, chloroacetic acid or *S*-(carboxymethyl)cysteine, the identification of the same *S*-containing metabolite from vinyl chloride-treated animals gives further support to the hypothesis that chloroethylene oxide or chloroacetaldehyde are formed and react with glutathione (Green & Hathway, 1977).

Following oral administration of $^{14}C$-vinyl chloride, $^{14}CO_2$ (Green & Hathway, 1975; Watanabe *et al.*, 1976c), $^{14}C$-labelled urea and glutamic acid were identified as minor metabolites (Green & Hathway, 1975).

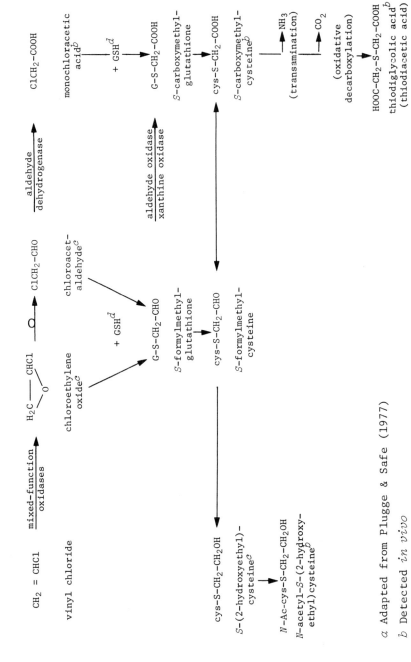

Figure 1[a]

a Adapted from Plugge & Safe (1977)

b Detected *in vivo*

c Detected *in vitro*

d GSH = glutathione

*In vitro* binding of $^{14}$C-vinyl chloride was shown to be dependent on the thiol content of proteins (Bolt & Filser, 1977), and binding was dependent on the presence of NADPH, oxygen and microsomal enzymes (Kappus *et al.*, 1976). It has been suggested that an epoxide of vinyl chloride is involved in the covalent binding reaction (Kappus *et al.*, 1975). In the presence of a rat liver microsomal system, vinyl chloride binds to RNA *in vitro* (Kappus *et al.*, 1975) and to RNA and DNA *in vivo* (Laib & Bolt, 1977).

Chloroacetaldehyde reacts with adenosine to give $1,N^6$-ethenoadenosine (Barrio *et al.*, 1972). Chloroethylene oxide and vinyl chloride, incubated in the presence of a mouse liver-microsomal preparation with adenosine *in vitro*, produced the same product (Barbin *et al.*, 1975). Reaction of chloroacetaldehyde with cytidine gives $3,N^4$-ethenocytidine (Barrio *et al.*, 1972). $1,N^6$-Ethenoadenosine was isolated after hydrolysis of polyadenosine that had been incubated with rat liver microsomes and $^{14}$C-vinyl chloride or with liver RNA of rats treated with $^{14}$C-vinyl chloride (Laib & Bolt, 1977). The corresponding etheno-derivatives of deoxyadenosine and deoxy-cytidine were identified in hydrolysis products obtained from calf thymus DNA treated with chloroacetaldehyde *in vitro* and from liver DNA of rats fed 250 mg/l vinyl chloride in their drinking-water (Green & Hathway, 1978).

The 2-hydroxyethyl derivatives of guanine, cysteine and histidine were identified after chemical reduction of the hydrolysis products of DNA and proteins isolated from the livers of mice treated with $^{14}$C-vinyl chloride (Osterman-Golkar *et al.*, 1977).

### Mutagenicity and other short-term tests

The mutagenicity of vinyl chloride has been reviewed by Bartsch & Montesano (1975), Bartsch *et al.* (1976) and Fishbein (1976).

Vinyl chloride vapour induced reverse mutations of the base-pair substitution type in *Salmonella typhimurium* G46, TA1530, TA1535 and TA100 in the presence of a 9000 x *g* supernatant from rat liver (Andrews *et al.*, 1976; Bartsch *et al.*, 1975; Garro *et al.*, 1976; Malaveille *et al.*, 1975; McCann *et al.*, 1975; Rannug *et al.*, 1974), mouse liver (Bartsch *et al.*, 1975; Garro *et al.*, 1976; Malaveille *et al.*, 1975) and human liver biopsy specimens (Bartsch *et al.*, 1975, 1979; Malaveille *et al.*, 1975). Although vinyl chloride also induced mutations in the absence of a metabolic activation system, a much higher mutagenic response was observed when a 9000 x *g* supernatant from liver was added (Andrews *et al.*, 1976; Bartsch *et al.*, 1975; McCann *et al.*, 1975).

Vinyl chloride in aqueous or methanolic solution was not mutagenic in the *Salmonella* test system (Bartsch *et al.*, 1975; Rannug *et al.*, 1974) but produced reverse mutations in *Escherichia coli* K12 (Greim *et al.*, 1975), forward mutations in *Schizosaccharomyces pombe* and mitotic gene conversions in *Saccharomyces cerevisiae* in the presence of a 9000 x *g* supernatant from mouse liver. Forward mutations in *S. pombe* were also induced in the host-mediated assay in mice (Loprieno *et al.*, 1976, 1977).

Vinyl chloride as vapour or as ethanol solution was not mutagenic in *Neurospora crassa* in the presence or absence of a metabolic activation system (Drozdowicz & Huang, 1977).

In inhalation experiments in *Drosophila melanogaster*, vinyl chloride was mutagenic in the recessive lethal test (Magnusson & Ramel, 1976; Verburgt & Vogel, 1977) but not mutagenic in tests for dominant lethals, translocations and sex-chromosome loss (Verburgt & Vogel, 1977).

No dominant lethals were observed in male CD-1 mice after exposure by inhalation to 7.8, 26, or 78 g/m$^3$ (3000, 10 000 or 30 000 ppm) vinyl chloride in air for 6 hours/day for 5 days (Anderson *et al.*, 1976, 1977).

Exposure to vinyl chloride vapour in the presence of a 15 000 x *g* supernatant from phenobarbital-pretreated rat liver induced forward mutations in V79 Chinese hamster cells in terms of 8-azaguanine and ouabain resistance (Drevon *et al.*, 1977).

The mutagenicity of several possible metabolites of vinyl chloride has also been examined. Chloroethylene oxide was the strongest mutagen among those tested in *S. typhimurium* TA1530 and TA1535 (Bartsch *et al.*, 1975; Malaveille *et al.*, 1975; Rannug *et al.*, 1976), *E. coli* (Hussain & Osterman-Golkar, 1976), *S. pombe* (Loprieno *et al.*, 1977), *S. cerevisiae* (Loprieno *et al.*, 1977) and V79 Chinese hamster cells (Huberman *et al.*, 1975). Chloroacetaldehyde was mutagenic in *S. typhimurium* TA1535, TA1530 and TA100 (Bartsch *et al.*, 1975; Malaveille *et al.*, 1975; McCann *et al.*, 1975; Rannug *et al.*, 1976) and V79 Chinese hamster cells (Huberman *et al.*, 1975). Chloroethanol was a weak mutagen in *S. typhimurium* TA1530, TA1535 and TA100 (Bartsch *et al.*, 1976; Malaveille *et al.*, 1975; McCann *et al.*, 1975; Rannug *et al.*, 1976; Rosenkranz *et al.*, 1974). Chloroacetic acid was not mutagenic in *S. typhimurium* TA1530, TA100 or TA1535 (Bartsch *et al.*, 1975; Malaveille *et al.*, 1975; McCann *et al.*, 1975; Rannug *et al.*, 1976).

1,2-Dichloroethane, a possible by-product of vinyl chloride production and a main component of waste products from vinyl chloride industries (EDC-tar), was mutagenic in *S. typhimurium* TA1535 (Rannug & Ramel, 1977) and in *S. typhimurium* TA100 (McCann *et al.*, 1975) in the presence or absence of a liver microsomal metabolic activation system.

(b)  Humans

Toxic effects

Exposure to vinyl chloride is associated with multiple systemic disorders, including a sclerotic syndrome, acro-osteolysis (sometimes associated with a Raynaud-like symptomatology), thrombocytopenia and liver damage, consisting of parenchymal damage, fibrosis of the liver capsule, periportal fibrosis associated with hepatomegaly, and splenomegaly (Lange *et al.*, 1974a; Thomas *et al.*, 1975).

Examination of 70 workers from a single polyvinyl chloride-producing factory showed a high frequency of signs and symptoms of vinyl chloride disease.  Although skin and bone changes may disappear when the patient is removed from contact with vinyl chloride, the thrombocytopenia persists after termination of exposure (Veltman *et al.*, 1975).

Non-cirrhotic portal fibrosis with associated portal hypertension was found in 7 patients who had been involved in the production of vinyl chloride monomer for 4-15 years.  An angiosarcoma developed in one patient, but fibrosis was a more common lesion and was considered to be probably not premalignant (Smith *et al.*, 1976a).

Of 487 workers involved in polyvinyl chloride production, two cases presenting with thrombocytopenia were found to have portal hypertension due to periportal fibrosis, with oesophageal varices and splenomegaly (Williams *et al.*, 1975, 1976).

Exposure to vinyl chloride was not only associated with circulatory and liver dysfunction and skin and bone disorders, but also deafness, vision failure and giddiness (Jühe & Lange, 1972).

Elevated carcino-embryonic antigen levels have been found in 48% of 200 polyvinyl chloride workers, as compared with 9% of a normal healthy population (Pagé *et al.*, 1976).  No evidence of an auto-immune disorder was found in 13 patients employed in polyvinyl chloride production who had symptoms of 'vinyl chloride disease' (Lange *et al.*, 1974a);  however, immunological data from 19/28 patients with vinyl chloride disease and in 2/30 workers exposed to vinyl chloride suggested an immune complex disorder (Ward *et al.*, 1976).

A group of 168 workers (114 from one factory and 54 from another) were examined medically at various times during 1962-1969.  Manifestations of disorders of the nervous system were recorded commonly;  hepatomegaly and splenomegaly occurred in 30% and 6% of workers;  and some cases of anaemia and leucopenia were also observed.  The incidence of Raynaud's syndrome fell from 6% in 1962 to 2.9% in 1966;  this phenomenon cleared spontaneously upon removal of the subjects from exposure:  these different incidence figures were associated with a 22-fold decrease in vinyl chloride levels during the period of the study.  A much higher percentage of vaso-spastic changes was found in the two groups (66 and 55%, respectively), suggesting that vinyl chloride acts as an irritant in the reticuloendothelial system to produce reactive splenic enlargement (Suciu *et al.*, 1975).

Reduced pulmonary function has been observed in workers exposed to vinyl chloride (Gamble *et al.*, 1976;  Miller *et al.*, 1975).  The prevalence of this impairment was similar in smokers and nonsmokers, suggesting that occupational or other environmental factors were operative (Miller *et al.*, 1975).

### Embryotoxicity and teratogenicity

A significant excess of foetal deaths was reported in women whose husbands were exposed to vinyl chloride: 15.8%, or 23, foetal deaths in 139 pregnancies, as compared with 8.8% (24/273) in the age-adjusted control group. This excess of foetal deaths was shown not to be a function of chronic abortions, i.e., the association was maintained after excluding pregnancies of women who had had more than 2 abortions (Infante *et al.*, 1976a). The significance of this study was questioned because data collection methods were not specified and there was no statistical treatment of the data (Paddle, 1976). Subsequently, the data collection methods were described, showing that there had been no interviewer-respondent bias, and details of statistical analyses were specified (Infante *et al.*, 1976b).

In a registry-based study, Infante (1976) reported that an excess of central nervous system defects, of deformities of the upper alimentary and genital tracts, and of clubfoot has been observed in stillborn and live children in 3 cities in Ohio in which vinyl chloride polymerization plants are located.

In hospital-based studies in newborns in Painesville (Ohio), where there are two polyvinyl chloride plants, and in Kanawha county (West Virginia), where there is one plant, excesses of anencephaly and spina bifida were reported, but no association was made with vinyl chloride (Edmonds, 1977; Edmonds *et al.*, 1975, 1978).

### Mutagenicity and other short-term tests

Chromosome aberrations were found in workers occupationally exposed to vinyl chloride in the US (Ducatman *et al.*, 1975; Heath *et al.*, 1977), Sweden (Funes-Cravioto *et al.*, 1975), the UK (Purchase *et al.*, 1975), Belgium (Léonard *et al.*, 1977), Hungary (Szentesi *et al.*, 1976) and Norway (Hansteen *et al.*, 1976). These aberrations were in most cases fragments, dicentrics and rings, and breaks and gaps.

### 3.3 Case reports and epidemiological studies[1]

In 1974, more than 40 years after the introduction of vinyl chloride into industry, Creech & Johnson (1974) first reported an association of exposure to this chemical with cancer in man. Three cases of liver angiosarcoma were reported in men who were employed in the manufacture of polyvinyl chloride resins (one had cleaned reactor vessels) in a single vinyl chloride polymerization plant in the US.

---

[1]The Working Group was aware of a study in progress on the occupational and community carcinogenic risk of vinyl chloride (IARC, 1978b).

By reviewing medical records and pathological material and by systematic medical screening, the association between exposure to vinyl chloride
and angiosarcoma of the liver has been reported from a number of other
countries: Canada (Delorme & Thériault, 1978; Noria *et al.*, 1976);
Czechoslovakia (Lloyd, 1975); the Federal Republic of Germany (Lange
*et al.*, 1974b, 1975); France (Couderc *et al.*, 1976; Ravier *et al.*, 1975;
Roche *et al.*, 1978); Italy (Maltoni, 1974); Norway (Lloyd, 1975);
Romania (Lloyd, 1975); Sweden (Byrén & Holmberg, 1975); the UK (Lee &
Harry, 1974; Smith *et al.*, 1976b); the US (Block, 1974; Falk *et al.*,
1974a; Makk *et al.*, 1974); and Yugoslavia (Sarić *et al.*, 1976). A review
of 64 reported cases in various countries as of October 1977 is available
(Spirtas & Kaminski, 1978).

No history of acro-osteolysis and no evidence of exposure to hepatotoxic materials other than vinyl chloride was reported in a clinical
review of 7 cases of liver angiosarcoma among US vinyl chloride polymerization workers (Heath *et al.*, 1975). In a pathological evaluation of cases
of liver angiosarcoma among exposed US vinyl chloride workers, it was concluded that these tumours were often multicentric: angiosarcomas were also
detected in the wall of the duodenum, in the heart and kidney, and in other
organs (Thomas & Popper, 1975).

The cancer risk among a cohort of males in the US who had at least
one year of occupational exposure to vinyl chloride was studied. When
compared with the US male population, an excess of cancer of the digestive
system, of the liver (primarily angiosarcoma), of the respiratory system,
of the brain and of unknown sites, as well as lymphomas was observed in
those members of the study cohort with the greatest estimated exposure to
vinyl chloride (Tabershaw & Gaffey, 1974) [Vital status was undetermined
for 15% of the study cohort, and only 50% had 15 or more years since onset
of exposure to vinyl chloride].

In a proportional-mortality analysis of 161 deceased workers in two US
plants producing and polymerizing vinyl chloride, a 50% excess of deaths
due to all cancers was reported. Sites of cancer with the greatest excess
were liver and biliary tract, brain, digestive tract and lung (Monson *et al.*,
1974). Falk *et al.* (1974b) questioned the authors' conclusion, on the
grounds that not all deaths studied were among workers in activities directly
related to vinyl chloride production or polymerization and that the study
failed to include deaths among workers who had terminated employment prior
to retirement or death.

The cancer mortality experience of 257 US workers (255 were traced),
each of whom had been occupationally exposed to vinyl chloride for at least
5 years and observed after 10 years from onset was studied using union
seniority and company employment records. Among 24 deaths from all causes,
a 2.3-fold excess was observed in deaths from cancer; of the 24 deaths,
3 were due to haemangiosarcoma of the liver (Nicholson *et al.*, 1975).

No excess of total or cause-specific mortality was reported in a study of 2100 male workers in the UK exposed to vinyl chloride for periods of up to 27 years; in addition, the authors reported a decreasing risk of mortality with increasing duration of exposure to vinyl chloride (Duck et al., 1975). Wagoner et al. (1976) challenged the conclusions of the study on the grounds of analytical shortcomings. After reanalysing the data, the authors (Duck & Carter, 1976) reported an increased risk of cancer of the digestive system 15 years after initial exposure to vinyl chloride.

The cancer mortality of 594 US workers exposed occupationally to vinyl chloride and to lesser amounts of vinylidene chloride (see p. 439) and other compounds (such as methyl methacrylate, see p. 187, and acrylonitrile, see p. 73) was studied. Although no angiosarcomas were found (no deaths due to any liver cancer), an excess of all malignancies combined was reported among those workers classified as having been highly exposed to vinyl chloride when compared with all other exposure categories. However, the number of workers in the lower exposure categories who were exposed for more than 10 years was small, resulting in part from the fact that workers first took jobs in the dry end of the polymerization process where exposures to vinyl chloride were low; many employees who remained with the units and established seniority would subsequently have moved to the higher exposure areas (Ott et al., 1975).

The incidence of abnormal sputum cytology among workers in the vinyl chloride-polyvinyl chloride industry in Italy was much higher than expected, even when compared with a population of heavy smokers who did not work in chemical industries (Maltoni, 1976).

Waxweiller et al. (1976) studied the cancer mortality experience of 1294 individuals with 5 or more years of employment and 10 years since onset of employment in departments or jobs with direct exposure to vinyl chloride at 1 of 4 vinyl chloride-polyvinyl chloride production plants in the US. When compared with the US white male population, an excess of cancer was found in four organ systems: brain and central nervous system, respiratory system, hepatic system, and lymphatic and haematopoietic systems. This excess of organ-specific cancer was restricted to those workers with 15 or more years since onset of vinyl chloride exposure. For all malignant neoplasms combined, the standard mortality ratio was 184; for the brain and central nervous system, 498; for the respiratory system, 194; for the hepatic system, 1606; and for the lymphatic and haematopoietic system, 176. Of 14 histologically confirmed cases of biliary and liver cancer among workers from these 4 plants, 11 were angiosarcoma of the liver. Of 10 cases of brain cancer, 9 were classified histologically as glioblastoma multiforme, a cell type of brain cancer reported to be unusual in the US. Of the 14 cases of primary lung cancer, 5 were large-cell undifferentiated and 3 were adenocarcinoma.

In 771 workers employed in a Swedish vinyl chloride-polyvinyl chloride plant since its start in the early 1940's, a 4- to 5-fold excess of cancer of the liver and pancreas was found. Although the risks of cancer of the brain and of the lung were also increased, they were not statistically significant (Byrén *et al.*, 1976).

Whereas no excess mortality from lung cancer was demonstrated among currently employed individuals 15 years after initial occupational exposure to vinyl chloride, a 56% excess of lung cancer was observed among those individuals who had terminated employment less than 15 years since initial exposure; this excess was found for each duration of exposure (Fox & Collier, 1976).

Fox & Collier (1977) investigated the cancer mortality among 7561 males who were exposed to vinyl chloride in the manufacture of polyvinyl chloride in the UK at some time between 1940 and 1974. An excess mortality from liver cancer was reported for each group of workers, whether exposure was thought to be high, medium or low; however, the authors reported no evidence of an excess mortality from cancers other than of the liver. Relatively few subjects had long-term exposure to vinyl chloride, and even in cases in which men had completed 20 years of employment, the follow-up period was judged to be too short to evaluate the carcinogenic effect of vinyl chloride.

A study was reported of cancer mortality among 7021 males employed in the production and polymerization of vinyl chloride in the Federal Republic of Germany. When compared with the national male population, an excess of cancers was found for 4 organs: liver, brain, lung and lymphatic organs. This excess of organ-specific cancer was shown to increase with duration of exposure (von Reinl *et al.*, 1977).

The risk of cancer mortality was investigated among residents 45-years of age and older in three US communities with vinyl chloride polymerization facilities. Among males, the death rate from central nervous system cancer was higher than that for the state as a whole. No excess mortality from leukaemia and aleukaemic leukaemia or from lymphoma was found (Infante, 1976).

The incidence of liver and lung cancer was studied for a 4-year period in a city in Yugoslavia with a factory in which vinyl chloride was polymerized and polyvinyl chloride processed. Polyvinyl chloride workers were included in the study. Except for liver angiosarcoma, no association was found between cancer incidence and place of work or residence (Šarić *et al.*, 1976).

Polyvinyl chloride

## 1.  Chemical and Physical Data

### 1.1  Synonyms and trade names

Chem. Abstr. Services Reg. No.:  9002-86-2

Chem. Abstr. Name:  Chloroethene homopolymer

Atactic poly(vinyl chloride);  chloroethylene polymer;  poly(chloroethylene);  poly(vinyl chloride);  poly(vinylchloride);  polyvinylchloride;  PVC;  vinyl chloride homopolymer;  vinyl chloride polymer

Airex;  AL 30;  AL 31;  Armodour;  Aron compound HW;  Astralon;
Bakelite OYNV;  Bakelite QSAH 7;  Bakelite QYAC 10;  Bakelite QYJV 1;
Bakelite QYOH-1;  Bakelite QYSJ;  Bakelite QYSL 7;  Bakelite QYTO 7;
Bakelite UCA 3310;  Benvic;  Blacar 1716;  Bolatron 6200;  Bonloid;
Breon;  Breon 107;  Breon 113;  Breon 121;  Breon 125/10;  Breon 151;
Breon 4121;  Breon 111EP;  Breon 112EP;  Breon P 130/1;  Breon S 110/10;
Breon S 125/12;  C 65;  Caliplast;  Carina S 70-01;  Carina S 70-71;
Chemosol;  Chlorostop;  Cobex (polymer);  Contizell;  Corvic 55/9;
Corvic 65/50;  Corvic 206573;  Corvic 20560600;  Corvic 20650600;
Corvic C 65/02;  Corvic D 55/9;  Corvic D 57/15;  Corvic D 57/17;
Corvic D 60/11;  Corvic D 65;  Corvic D 65/02;  Corvic D 65/8;
Corvic D 75/10;  Corvic D 6518;  Corvic H 55/34;  Corvic P 65/50;
Corvic P 65/54;  Corvic P 65/55;  Corvic R 65/81;  Corvic S 46/70;
Dacovin;  Dacovin 2082;  Danuvil 70;  Darvic 110;  Darvis Clear 025;
Daycell;  Decelith H;  Denka Vinyl SS 80;  Denka Vinyl SS-Y;  Diamond
Shamrock 40;  Diamond Shamrock 71;  Diamond Shamrock 450;  Diamond
Shamrock 7602;  DN 4;  DN 5;  Dorlyl;  Durofol P;  Dynadur;  E 62;
E 66;  Ekavyl SD 2;  Ekavyl SDF 58;  Ekavyl SK64;  Ekavyl SK66;
E 66P;  103EP8;  E-PVC;  Escambia 2160;  Escambia 2200;  Europhan;
Exon 605;  Exon 640;  Exon 654;  Exon 965;  Exon 9269;  Exon 9290;
Exon 9269A;  FC 4648;  Flocor;  Genotherm;  Genotherm N;  Genotherm
UG 200;  Geon 51;  Geon 59;  Geon 72;  Geon 101;  Geon 103;  Geon
110X233;  Geon 120X241;  Geon 121;  Geon 124;  Geon 126;  Geon 128;
Geon 131;  Geon 151;  Geon 85542;  Geon 101EP;  Geon 102EP;  Geon

Geon 103EP; Geon 103EP8; Geon 103EPF7; Geon 135J; Geon 121L; Geon Latex 151; Guttagena; Halvic 223; Halvic 229; HC 825; Hi-S Film No. 111L; Hishirex 502; Hishirex 502Z; Hispavic 229; Hostalit; Hostalit E; Hostalit P 7078; Hostalit PVP 3475; Hostalit PVP 5470; Hostalit S; Hostalit S 4070; HX-M; Igelite F; Igelite P; Improved Wilt Pruf; Kanevinyl PSH 10; Kanevinyl PSL 81; Kanevinyl S 1001; Kanevinyl S 1007; KhS 010; KhSE 3; Klegecell; Kohiner R 687; KR 800; Kureha S 901; L 5; Lak Kh SL; Lonza 380 ES; Lonza G; Lucoflex; Lucovyl BB 800; Lucovyl BB 8010; Lucovyl GB 1150; Lucovyl GB 9550; Lucovyl GS 1200; Lucovyl GS 8001; Lucovyl PB 1302; Lucovyl PE; Lucovyl PE 1100; Lucovyl PE 1290; Lucovyl PE 1311; Lucovyl PE 1355; Lucovyl RB 8010; Lutofan; Marvinal; Marvinol; Marvinol 14; Marvinol 53; Marvinol 57; Marvinol 7000; Marvinol VR 50; Marvinol VR 53; Mirrex MCFD 1025; Movinyl 100; Mowilith F; Myraform; NIKA-TEMP; Nikavinyl SG 700; Nipeon A 21; Nipol 576; Nipolit CM 081; Nipolit SK; Nipolit SK 081; Nipolit SL 082; Nipolit SM 092; Nipolit SV 13081; Norvinyl; Norvinyl P 2; Norvinyl P10; Norvinyl S 1-70; Norvinyl S 1-80; Norvinyl S 3-68; Novon 712; Ongrovil S 165; Ongrovil S 470; Opalon; Opalon 410; Opalon 440; Opalon 610; Opalon 630; Opalon 650; Opalon 660; Opalon R 7611; Ortodur; P 400 (vinyl polymer); Pantasote R 873; Pattina V 82; Pevikon D 61; Pevikon KL 2; Pevikon PE 709; Pevikon PE 712; Pevikon PS 690; Pevikon R 23; Pevikon R 25; Pevikon R 45; Pevikon R 341; Pevikon S 602; Pliovic D 100X; Pliovic DB 80V; Pliovic K 906; Pliovic K 90E; Pliovic S 50; POK 60; Polivinit; Polwinit; Polyco 2622; Polytherm; Porodur; Prototype III Soft; PVKhL 4; PVKhS 60; PVKh-S 60; PVKh-S 65; PVKh-S 63Zh; QSAH 7; QSAN 7; Quirvil; Quirvil 278; QYSA; Ravinil R 100/65D; Rucon B 20; Ryurene S 800B; S 61; S 65 (polymer); S 70; S 901; Scon 5300; Sicron; Sicron 530; Sicron 540; Sicron 548; Sicron 548FM; SKhV 71; S-Lon; SM 200; Solvic; Solvic 223; Solvic 229; Solvic 239; Solvic 334; Solvic 340; Solvic 406; SP 60; SP 60 (chlorocarbon); SR11; Sumilit EXA 13; Sumilit PXA 13; Sumilit PX-A; Sumilit PX-N; Sumilit PXNH;

Sumilit PX-NL;  Sumilit SX 11;  Sumilit SX 13;  Sumilit S χ-D;
Sumilit SX 7G;  Sumilit VS 9200;  Sumitomo PX 11;  SV 55;  SX 11;
SX 7G;  SX 8T;  Takilon;  Technopor;  Tenneco 1742;  TK 1000;
Tocryl C 440;  Trovidur;  Trovidur N;  Trovithern HTL;  TS 1100;
U 1;  U 1 (polymer);  Ultron;  VA 15;  VC 100;  VC 410;  Veron P
130/1;  Vestolit B 7021;  Vestolit GH;  Vestolit S 60;  Vestolit S
6554;  Vestolit S 6857;  Vestolit S 7054;  Vestolit S 7554;
Vestolit S 8054;  Vinika KR 600;  Vinika KR 800;  Vinika 37M;
Vinika 35R;  Vinikulon;  Viniplast;  Viniplen P 73;  Viniplen P 74;
Viniplen P 73E;  Viniplen P 73EM;  Vinnol E 75;  Vinnol H 100/65;
Vinnol H 100/70;  Vinnol H 60d;  Vinnol H 70D;  Vinnol H 100/70d;
Vinnol H 75F;  Vinnol P 70;  Vinnol P 70E;  Vinnol P 100/70e;
Vinnol Y;  Vinoflex;  Vinoflex P 313;  Vinylchlon 4000LL;  Vinylite
QYJV;  Viplast RA/F;  Volgovinyl E 62;  Volgovinyl E 62P;  Volgovinyl
E 66P;  VSKh-S;  Vygen 85;  Vygen 110;  Vygen 120;  Vygen 313;
Welvic G 2/5;  Welvic PRIO 953;  Welvic PRO 686;  Welvic R 7/622;
Welvic RI 7/316;  Welvic RIO 715;  Wilt Pruf;  Winidur;  X-AB;
Yugovinyl

## 1.2 Structural and molecular formulae and molecular weight

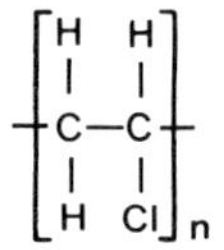

$$\left[\begin{array}{ccc} & H & H \\ & | & | \\ -\!\!\!-C & -\!\!\!- & C-\!\!\!- \\ & | & | \\ & H & Cl \end{array}\right]_n$$

$(C_2H_3Cl)_n$          Mol. wt:  60 000-150 000 (average)

## 1.3 Chemical and physical properties of the polymer

From Windholz (1976), unless otherwise specified

(a) Description:  White or colourless granules (Hawley, 1971)

(b) Density:  1.406

(c) Refractive index:  n 1.54

(d) Solubility: Solvents for unmodified polyvinyl chloride (PVC) of high molecular weight are: cyclohexanone, methyl cyclo-hexanone, dimethyl formamide, nitrobenzene, tetrahydrofuran, isophorone and mesityl oxide. Solvents for lower polymers are: di-*n*-propyl ketone, methyl amyl ketone, methyl isobutyl ketone, acetonylacetone, methyl ethyl ketone, dioxane and methylene chloride.

(e) Stability: PVC is unstable to heat and light in the absence of added stabilizers. Thermal decomposition products can include ethylene, benzene, toluene (Eckardt & Hindin, 1973), 1,3,5-trichlorobenzene (Tsuge, 1969) and naphthalene (Dyer & Esch, 1976).

## 1.4  Technical products and impurities

A wide variety of vinyl chloride homo- and copolymers are available, with varying properties designed for specific applications. Consequently, the specifications vary widely.

PVC resins for the production of rigid plastics are processed essentially without plasticizer: the polymer may be a homopolymer or a copolymer made with low levels of comonomer such as vinyl acetate or ethylene. The comonomers are used to aid in the processing of the resulting polymer.

Most of the flexible and semirigid PVC plastics contain plasticizers at a level of 10-100% of the resin weight. The plasticizers most commonly used are dialkyl phthalates (e.g., dioctyl phthalate). Other compounding materials (such as pigments, fillers and light- and heat-stabilizers) are also used.

PVC dispersion or paste resins are used in the form of plastisols (PVC resin dispersed in plasticizer). In Europe, significant amounts of PVC are used in the form of latexes; in the US very little of the latex form is used.

For concentrations of unreacted vinyl chloride monomer in various PVC samples, see p. 382.

## 2. Production, Use, Occurrence and Analysis

### 2.1 Production and use

#### (a) Production

A method for the synthesis of PVC was reported in 1872 (Baumann, 1872). Commercial homopolymers of vinyl chloride were introduced in 1933 (Darby & Sears, 1968). Vinyl chloride polymer is currently produced by one of four processes: suspension, emulsion, bulk or solution polymerization. In the US in 1976, over 80% of homopolymers and copolymers were produced by the suspension polymerization process.

In 1976, 22 US companies reported production of 2065 million kg PVC resins of all types (US International Trade Commission, 1977); approximately 230 million kg of the total were copolymers. US exports of uncompounded PVC resins in 1977 were about 72 million kg, and exports of compounded PVC (excluding any additives in compounded products) were approximately 39 million kg. These exports went primarily to Belgium (13%), Brazil (12%), Canada (21%), Iran (6%), New Zealand (7%) and Venezuela (13%). US imports of PVC resins are negligible (approximately 1% of domestic production).

Total western Europe production in 1976 amounted to 3745 million kg. The major producers were the following countries (production in millions of kg): Austria (40), Belgium (200), the Federal Republic of Germany (1020), Finland (35), France (615), Greece (25), Italy (675), The Netherlands (290), Norway (55), Portugal (15), Spain (215), Switzerland (30), Sweden (110) and the UK (415). Exports from western Europe in that year were 1050 million kg and imports 690 million kg.

PVC was first produced commercially in Japan prior to 1946. In 1976, nineteen companies produced a total of 1044 million kg; 121 million kg were exported, and 15 million kg imported.

#### (b) Use

Use of PVC resins in the US in 1976 was as follows: building and construction industries (49%), consumer goods (15%), electrical applications (8%), packaging (9%) and transportation (7%), with miscellaneous uses accounting for the remainder. Since 1968, the major uses have been in the building and construction industries, in consumer goods, packaging and electrical wire insulation.

In building and construction, PVC resins are used in piping and conduits (including water pipes), in flooring, in windows and other rigid structures, in pipe fittings, in sidings and as swimming-pool liners. They are used in such consumer products as upholstery, wall coverings, garden hoses and appliances and also in gramophone records, stationery supplies, footwear, toys, outerwear and sporting goods. Electrical applications consist primarily of wire and cable insulation.  The major uses of PVC in packaging are in plasticized film, bottles and bottle-cap liners and gaskets;  however, in the US, its use for packaging of alcoholic beverages has been banned because of migration of vinyl chloride monomer into the alcohol.  Major uses in transport include upholstery and seat covers, automotive tops and automotive floor mats.

In 1975, 27 million kg PVC were used in Europe and 14 million kg in the US in plastic materials for medical applications, including external tubing and catheters;  in sheet form for splints;  and in shunts, balloons, blood storage bags, cannulae, surgical drapes and packaging containers for parenteral substances (Halpern & Karo, 1977).

The 1977 western Europe use pattern for PVC was as follows:  piping and fittings (24%), rigid and flexible films (20%), profiles (12%), cable (10%), artifical leather cloth (8%), bottles (7%), gramophone records (3%) and other uses (16%).

In Japan in 1976, it was used as follows:  piping (31%), film (17%), sheet (14%), extrusions and artifical leather (12%), wire/cable (11%) and other, including flooring (15%).

The US Food and Drug Administration permits the use of PVC as a component of the following products when they are intended for use in contact with food:  (1) adhesives;  (2) resinous and polymeric coatings; (3) paper and paperboard (in contact with dry food only);  and (4) semi-rigid and rigid acrylic and modified acrylic plastics.  The amount present may not exceed that which is reasonably required to produce the intended effect (US Food and Drug Administration, 1977).

An estimated 700 000 to 2 million workers are employed in the production of PVC in the USA (Infante, 1977).

2.2  Occurrence

PVC is not known to occur as a natural product.

It has been estimated that prior to 1975 more than 22.7 million kg PVC may have been discharged into the environment in the US.  These losses occurred as particulates in air emissions, suspended solids in water effluents, and components of solid wastes (US Environmental Protection Agency, 1974b).  Workers in the USSR have been exposed to PVC dust in the production of block polymer (Filatova et al., 1974).

The disposal of PVC by ocean dumping, as solid waste, as landfilling and by incineration has been reviewed (US Environmental Protection Agency, 1974b,c).

2.3  Analysis

No information was available to the Working Group on methods for determining PVC residues in foods or other parts of the environment.

A rapid and simple way of identifying fifteen packaging films, including PVC, has been described in which the films were treated with ten different solvents and the solubility and physical appearance of the film at room temperature and at the boiling-points of the solvents were noted (Van Gieson, 1969).

Plastics, including PVC, have been identified by measurement of the pH of an aqueous solution of the pyrolysis products, followed by thin-layer chromatography, and by reaction of PVC with pyridine (Braun & Nixdorf, 1972).

PVC has been separated from plasticizers, stabilizers, modifiers, fillers, pigments and other inorganic additives by gel permeation chromatography or sequential solvent extraction. The resulting additive-free fraction has been analysed by chlorine analysis, infra-red spectroscopy, molecular-weight determination by viscosity measurements and thermal gravimetry and differential thermal analysis (Brookman, 1974).

Pyrolysis-gas chromatography has been proposed to identify PVC in polymers used in medical applications (Nematollahi *et al.*, 1970), in three commercial polymers (in this case, pyrolysis-gas chromatography was used in combination with thermogravimetric analysis and differential thermal analysis) (Boettner *et al.*, 1969), and among some chlorine-containing polymers (Tsuge *et al.*, 1969). Pyrolysis-gas chromatography has also been used to identify polymers, including PVC, among 37 commercial polymers (Okumoto & Takeuchi, 1972), in plastics and rubbers (Fischer, 1967) and in adhesives used in building (in this case, pyrolysis-gas chromatography was used in combination with thermogravimetry, differential thermogravimetry and differential thermal analysis) (Rona, 1971).

Thin-layer chromatography of pyrolysis products has been used to identify high polymers, including PVC (Pastuska, 1969).

Thermogravimetry and infra-red spectral analysis have been used to determine PVC in floor tiles (Powell, 1974).

3. Biological Data Relevant to the Evaluation

of Carcinogenic Risk to Humans

## 3.1 Carcinogenicity studies in animals[1]

### Subcutaneous or intraperitoneal administration

Rat: A group of 45 adult Wistar rats were given s.c. implants in the abdominal wall of squares or discs of a commercial PVC known to contain some additives; the implants were 0.04 mm thick and 15 mm wide. At the appearance of the first tumour, 44 animals were still alive. Seventeen (38.6%) malignant tumours (fibrosarcomas and 1 liposarcoma) developed at the site of film implantation, with a latent period of 189-727 days; a similar but perforated film did not produce local tumours in 27 rats at risk. No local tumours were found in a group of 50 rats given a s.c. implant of cotton (Oppenheimer *et al.*, 1952, 1955). With a pure PVC film of 0.03 mm thickness, 4 malignant tumours were obtained after 533 days in a similar group (Oppenheimer *et al.*, 1955) [The Working Group noted that the reporting of this experiment was preliminary and that final results were never forthcoming].

Groups of 35 (male and female) Wistar rats were given a s.c. implant into the abdomen of PVC film 4 x 5 x 0.16 mm. A group of 25 control rats received an implant of glass of similar size. After 300 days, 30 and 20 animals were still alive in the two groups, respectively; all surviving rats were killed 800 days after implantation. One sarcoma and one fibroma were found after 580 days in the PVC-treated rats, whereas no local tumours developed in the control group (Russell *et al.*, 1959).

A group of 80 outbred albino rats (sex unspecified) received implants (of unstated size) of PVC film by laparotomy to surround the kidney. The animals were sacrificed at 3, 10, 15, 30, 90, 195, 285, 300 and 380 days after the implantation. Of rats that survived 285-375 days, 6/16 developed fibrosarcomas at the site of implantation (Raikhlin & Kogan, 1961).

In rats implanted in the kidney with either PVC capsules, whole PVC films or perforated PVC films, 5/16, 2/5 and 1/5 sarcomas were observed (Kogan & Tugarinova, 1959).

--------------

[1]The Working Group was aware of a study in progress to assess the carcinogenicity of PVC powder by inhalation exposure and intrapleural administration to rats (IARC, 1978a).

## 3.2  Other relevant biological data

### (a)  Experimental systems

Rats and guinea-pigs exposed continuously to PVC dust for 24 hours/
day for periods varying from 2-7 months were found to have extensive lung
damage (Frongia et al., 1974).

The growth of granulation tissue around PVC particles implanted into
the muscles of rabbits has been reported (Guess & Stetson, 1968).  Severe
fibroblastic reactions were found in rats (Calnan, 1963) and dogs (Harrison
et al., 1957) which received PVC sponge implants into the s.c. tissue of
the anterior abdominal wall.

Ingested and rectally absorbed PVC particles (5-110 μm) were found to
be transported by both the lymphatic and the portal system from the intestinal wall of rats, guinea-pigs, rabbits, chickens, dogs and pigs
(Volkheimer, 1975).

In rats, inhalation of fumes from heated PVC produced interstitial
oedema, as well as focal bronchial and intra-alveolar haemorrhage in the
lungs of some animals (Cornish & Abar, 1969).

No data on the embryotoxicity, teratogenicity, metabolism or mutagenicity of this compound were available to the Working Group.

### (b)  Humans

Workers exposed to PVC dust during the manufacture of articles made
from PVC showed alterations in the respiratory organs (e.g., changed bron-
chovascular pattern, increased pulmonary ventilation at rest) (Vertkin
& Mamontov, 1970).

Pneumoconiosis due to inhalation of PVC dust was suggested following
pulmonary biopsies in a male patient who had inhaled PVC dust for 1 year
and exhibited granulomatous lesions due to foreign bodies.  The severity of
the disease was shown by the observed dyspnoea, secondary polyglobulia and
reduced respiratory function (Szende et al., 1970).

Fibrotic lung changes and altered pulmonary function tests have been
reported in 96 workers exposed to PVC dust;  the changes were more pronounced in those with long exposure (Lilis et al., 1976;  Waxweiler et al.,
1976).

Reduced pulmonary function and an enhancement of pulmonary function
defects associated with an increased risk of respiratory impairment were
noted in a number of nonsmoking workers exposed to an occupational environment contaminated with vinyl chloride fumes and PVC dust (Miller, 1975;
Miller et al., 1975).

In 15 polyvinyl production workers employed in 'PVC-processing industries', where stabilizers, colours and bulk materials were added to and
mixed with the basic PVC powder, the following pathological findings were
reported:  in 7, slight to moderate thrombocytopenia;  in 7, increased
bromosulphalein retention;  in 6, reticulocytosis;  in 1, leucopenia;  and
in 1, slight splenomegaly.  Neither scleroderma-like skin changes nor
Raynaud's syndrome were observed (Lange *et al.*, 1975).  A large proportion
of abnormal liver function tests and platelet counts were found in a group
of 37 PVC process workers:  20% had abnormal alkaline phosphatase, 60%
abnormal lactic dehydrogenase, 30% abnormal serum glutamic-oxaloacetic
transaminase, 10% abnormal serum glutamic-pyruvic transaminase, and 35%
abnormal platelets (Wegman, 1975).

Cases of 'meat-wrappers' asthma' have been reported, in which meat
wrappers developed respiratory symptoms when exposed to fumes of PVC film
sealed and cut with a hot wire.  The identity of the causative agent(s)
has not been established (Brooks & Vandervort, 1977;  Falk & Portnoy, 1976;
Polakoff *et al.*, 1975;  Sokol *et al.*, 1973).

During the period 1970-1975, 175 fire-fighters experienced respiratory
distress due to the toxicity of hydrogen chloride gas released from the
combustion of PVC plastics (Dyer & Esch, 1976).  Carbon monoxide, hydrochloric acid and phosgene (Cornish & Abar, 1969;  Dyer & Esch, 1976) have
been reported as the major PVC pyrolysis products of toxicological importance, although more than 75 components have been identified following the
thermal degradation of PVC (Dyer & Esch, 1976).

The few cases of dermatitis that have been reported are believed to
be caused by sensitivity to plasticizers in polyvinyl plastics (Morris,
1953).

## 3.3 Case reports and epidemiological studies[1]

A proportional mortality study was carried out using death certificates from 1970-1972 of 707 male plastic workers (extruding, moulding,
cutting, turning or otherwise machining plastics, and including PVC fabricating).  A statistically significant excess of stomach cancer mortality
was found (24 observed *versus* 16.4 expected, P<0.05) (Baxter & Fox, 1976)
[The study is limited by the use of proportionate mortality methodology and
by the fact that not all deaths studied were among workers engaged in activities directly involving PVC].

---

[1]The Working Group was aware of a study in progress on workers
exposed to PVC (IARC, 1978c).

In a cross-sectional mortality study of 4341 deaths during 1964-1973 among current and former employees of 17 PVC fabricators, an excess in total cancer mortality, particularly that of the digestive system, was reported among both white males and white females. The risk of cancer of the breast and urinary organs was also reported to be in excess among white females (Chiazze *et al.*, 1977) [The study is limited by the use of proportionate mortality methodology and by the fact that not all deaths were among workers engaged in activities directly involving PVC].

Casterline *et al.* (1977) reported a case of a 22-year-old male who developed a squamous-cell carcinoma of the buccal mucosa as a result of a habit, acquired at the age of 8 years, of chewing plastic materials containing PVC. No prior history of mouth or lip lesions, of smoking tobacco or drinking alcohol, or of occupational exposure to vinyl chloride was noted.

## Vinyl chloride-vinyl acetate copolymers

### 1.  Chemical and Physical Data

1.1  Synonyms and trade names

Chem. Abstr. Services Reg. No.:  9003-22-9

Chem. Abstr. Name:  Acetic acid ethenyl ester polymer with chloroethene

Acetic acid vinyl ester polymer with chloroethylene;  chloroethylene-vinyl acetate polymer;  polyvinyl chloride-polyvinyl acetate;  vinyl acetate-vinyl chloride copolymer;  vinyl acetate-vinyl chloride polymer;  vinyl chloride-vinyl acetate polymer

A 15;  A 15 (polymer);  A 15-0;  A 15S;  Bakelite LP 70;  Bakelite VLFV;  Bakelite VMCC;  Bakelite VSJD 10;  Bakelite VYHD;  Bakelite VYHH;  Bakelite VYNS;  Bakelite VYNW;  Breon 351;  Breon 425;  Breon AS 60/41;  Corvic 51/83;  Corvic 236581;  Corvic R 46/88;  Denkalac 41M;  Denka Vinyl MM 90;  Diamond Shamrock 744;  Diamond Shamrock 7401;  Exon 450;  Exon 454;  Exon 470;  Exon 481;  Exon 760;  Flovic;  Geon 100x150;  Geon 130x10;  Geon 135;  Geon 351;  Geon 400x47;  Geon 421;  Geon 427;  Geon 434;  Geon 103EP-J;  Geon 440L2;  Geon 450x150PN;  Geon 150XML;  Geon 103ZX;  Hostalit PVP;  Leucovyl PA 1302;  Lucovyl GA 8502;  Lucovyl MA 6028;  Lucovyl PA 1208;  Marvinol VP 56;  50ME;

Norvinyl P 6; Opalon 400; Pevikon C 870; Pliovac AO; Pliovic AO;
PVC Cordo; Resin 4301; Rhodopas 6000; Rhodopas AX; Rhodopas
AX 30/10; Rhodopas AX 85/15; Sarpifan HP 1; Solvic 523KC; Solvic
PA 513; Solvic 513PB; Sumilit PCX; Tennus 0565; VA 3 (copolymer);
VAGD; VH 10/60; Vilit 40; Vinnol H 10/60; Vinnol H 15/45; Vinnol
H 40/60; Vinylite VGHH; Vinylite VYDR; Vinylite VYDR 21; Vinylite
VYFS; Vinylite VYHD; Vinylite VYHH; Vinylite VYNS; Vinylite VYNW;
Vinyon; VLVF; VMCC; VYHH; VYNS; VYNW

## 1.2  Structural and molecular formulae and molecular weight

$(C_2H_3Cl)_x-(C_4H_6O_2)_y$     Mol. wt: ~100 000

## 1.3  Chemical and physical properties of the copolymers

(a)  Description: White powder

(b)  Stability: Sensitive to excessive exposure to heat and light
in the absence of added stabilizers. Hydrogen chloride gas
is a decomposition product of degradation.

## 1.4  Technical products and impurities

Low levels of vinyl acetate are copolymerized with vinyl chloride
to obtain resins with specific properties. Depending upon the use, the
vinyl acetate level may vary from 2-20%, with an average of 11-12%. As
described in the monograph on polyvinyl chloride, p. 405, various additives are used to aid in processing the resins.

No detailed information on the possible presence of unreacted monomers
in the copolymers was available to the Working Group.

## 2. Production, Use, Occurrence and Analysis

### 2.1 Production and use

#### (a)  Production

Vinyl chloride-vinyl acetate copolymers were introduced commercially in 1934 (Darby & Sears, 1968). Most of these copolymers are manufactured by free-radical-initiated suspension and emulsion polymerization techniques; solution polymerization is used for the manufacture of some special coating resins.  In the US, over 80% of vinyl chloride-vinyl acetate copolymer resins are made by suspension processes.

In 1976, five US companies produced 230 million kg vinyl chloride-vinyl acetate copolymer resins.

Western European production in 1977 was 200 million kg.

About thirty Japanese companies produced a total of 6 million kg of these copolymers in 1976.

#### (b)  Use

In the US, the major use for vinyl chloride-vinyl acetate copolymers is in the production of vinyl asbestos flooring tiles (a declining market) and gramophone records.  Other applications include injection moulding, rigid sheet production and coatings.

Copolymers containing about 13% vinyl acetate are used for floor tiles and gramophone records;  others with lower levels of vinyl acetate are used for sheet extrusion and injection moulding.  The resins used for soluble coating resins contain from 4-10% vinyl acetate and may be further modified. Solutions of these copolymers in solvents such as cyclohexane and tetrahydrofuran are used in coatings of tin cans and metals, and for maintenance coatings.

In western Europe vinyl chloride-vinyl acetate copolymers were used in 1977 in gramophone records (50%), vinyl asbestos flooring tiles (35%), film (10%) and coatings (5%).

The US Food and Drug Administration permits the use of vinyl chloride-vinyl acetate copolymers as components of the following products when they are intended for use in contact with food:  (1) adhesives;  (2) resinous and polymeric coatings, including those for polyolefin films;  (3) paper and paperboard;  (4) semirigid and rigid acrylic and modified acrylic plastics.  The amount present may not exceed that which is reasonably required to produce the intended effect (US Food and Drug Administration, 1977).

## 2.2 Occurrence

Vinyl chloride-vinyl acetate copolymers are not known to occur as natural products.

## 2.3 Analysis

Pyrolysis-gas chromatography has been used to identify vinyl acetate-vinyl chloride copolymers in paints and plastics (May *et al.*, 1973) and polymeric materials, including these copolymers, in 37 commercial polymers (Okumoto & Takeuchi, 1972). Combined pyrolysis-gas chromatography, thermogravimetry, differential thermogravimetry and differential thermal analysis have been used to identify polymers, including vinyl acetate-vinyl chloride copolymers, in adhesives used in building (Rona, 1971).

The vinyl resin content of vinyl floor tiles, including vinyl acetate-vinyl chloride copolymers, has been determined by thermogravimetric and infra-red spectrophotometry (Powell, 1974).

## 3. Biological Data Relevant to the Evaluation
## of Carcinogenic Risk to Humans

### 3.1 Carcinogenicity studies in animals

#### Subcutaneous and/or intramuscular administration

Mouse: A group of 82 (male and female) 1.5-2-month-old CBA/H-T6 mice received a s.c. implant of a piece of 15 x 22 x 0.2 mm film made of vinyl chloride-vinyl acetate copolymer. Sarcomas at the site of implantation developed in 65% of males within 9-12 months and in almost all the females after 7-12 months. A control group of 80 mice with no implants developed no s.c. tumours (Brand *et al.*, 1967a,b, 1975).

Groups of 30 male and 46 female 6-week-old CBA mice were given s.c. implants of vinyl chloride-vinyl acetate copolymer powder (particle size, 50-100 μ), corresponding by weight to two films of 15 x 22 x 0.2 mm, and were observed until death. No treatment-related tumours were reported; however, one sarcoma found in a female was attributable to clumping of the powder (Brand *et al.*, 1975).

Groups of 9-124 male and female mice of 18 strains were given s.c. implants of 15 x 22 x 0.2 mm or 7 x 15 x 0.2 mm vinyl chloride-vinyl acetate copolymer films to test strain differences in response. The incidence of tumours was 90-100% in CBA/H and CBA/H-T6 female mice, AKR/J males, BALB/cJ and BALB/cWat females, C57BL/10ScSn females and (C57BL/10ScSnxCBA/H)F1 males and females. No tumours were induced in males of strain I/LnJ or strain SJL/J. The tumour incidence in other strains was intermediate, the males being less sensitive than females, except for AKR mice (Brand *et al.*, 1977).

3.2 Other relevant biological data

(a) Experimental systems

An aqueous dispersion of a vinyl chloride-vinyl acetate copolymer administered orally at a dose of 10 ml/day to rats or rabbits decreased the reticulocyte count and caused changes in the blood serum protein fractions and histological changes in the stomach and liver.  Inhalation of the dry residue at concentrations of 4.2 mg/m$^3$ in air decreased body-weight gain and caused pneumonia and peribronchitis.  Application of this preparation to the skin decreased reticulocyte and leucocyte counts and haemoglobin levels (Ivanova & Shamina, 1973).

In rats, inhalation of fumes from heated vinyl chloride-vinyl acetate copolymer produced focal oedema and intra-alveolar haemorrhages of the lung (Cornish & Abar, 1969).

No toxic effects were reported in Wistar albino rats of both sexes following daily intakes of 0.61 or 5.75 g/kg bw vinyl resin (copolymer of 95% vinyl chloride and 5% vinyl acetate) for 2 years (Smyth & Weil, 1966).

No data on the embryotoxicity, teratogenicity, metabolism or muta-genicity of this compound were available to the Working Group.

(b) Humans

Two cases of dermatitis have been reported in people wearing Elasti-glass garters (vinyl chloride-vinyl acetate copolymer) (Zeisler, 1940).

3.3 Case reports and epidemiological studies

No data were available to the Working Group.


4.  Summary of Data Reported and Evaluation

4.1 Experimental data

Vinyl chloride was tested in rats by oral, subcutaneous and intraperi-toneal administration and in mice, rats and hamsters by inhalation exposure. Following oral and inhalation exposure, vinyl chloride was carcinogenic in all three species, producing tumours at different sites, including angio-sarcomas of the liver.  Vinyl chloride was carcinogenic in rats following prenatal exposure.  A dose-response effect has been demonstrated.

The results of subcutaneous and intraperitoneal injection studies in rats are incomplete and cannot be evaluated.

Vinyl chloride is mutagenic.

Polyvinyl chloride was tested in rats by subcutaneous and intraperitoneal implantation;   local sarcomas were induced, the incidence of which varied with the size and form of the implant.

Vinyl chloride-vinyl acetate copolymers were tested in rats by subcutaneous implantation as films or powder;   local sarcomas were induced following implantation of films.

## 4.2   Human data

Vinyl chloride is manufactured on a vast scale, and exposure involves workers in the production, polymerization and processing industries. Also, large sections of the general population may have some exposure to vinyl chloride, particularly through direct or indirect contact with polymer products.

Several independent but mutually confirmatory studies have shown that exposure to vinyl chloride results in an increased carcinogenic risk in humans, involving the liver, brain, lung and haemo-lymphopoietic system.

In one epidemiological study, an excess of foetal mortality was reported among wives of workers who had been exposed to vinyl chloride, indicating a possible mutagenic effect in human germ cells.  Several investigations have detected an increase in chromosomal aberrations in the lymphocytes of workers exposed to vinyl chloride.  Increased rates of birth defects among children of parents residing in communities where vinyl chloride-polyvinyl chloride or other chemical processing plants are located have been reported in several other studies.  These suggest teratogenic and/or mutagenic effects of vinyl chloride in humans.

In two proportionate mortality studies, in which death certificates of workers who had been involved in the fabrication of plastics, including polyvinyl chloride, were analysed, there appeared to be an increased proportion of cancer of the digestive system in both sexes and possibly of the urinary system and of the breast in women.

## 4.3   Evaluation

Vinyl chloride is a human carcinogen.  Its target organs are the liver, brain, lung and haemo-lymphopoietic system.  Similar carcinogenic effects were first demonstrated in rats and were later confirmed in mice and hamsters.  Although evidence of a carcinogenic effect of vinyl chloride in humans has come from groups occupationally exposed to high doses of vinyl chloride, there is no evidence that there is an exposure level below which no increased risk of cancer would occur in humans.

Epidemiological reports regarding clastogenic effects among vinyl chloride-exposed workers and a single study of increased foetal mortality among the wives of workers who had been exposed to vinyl chloride suggest that vinyl chloride could be mutagenic to humans.  Additional support for this suggestion derives from experimental evidence of its mutagenicity.

Studies which indicate increased rates of birth defects among the
children of parents residing in communities where vinyl chloride production
and polymerization plants are located indicate the necessity for further
investigation of the teratogenicity of vinyl chloride and its polymers in
both animals and humans.

The available studies on polyvinyl chloride, which indicate an
elevated proportion of digestive system cancer in male and female workers
and possibly of cancers of the breast and urinary organs in female workers
involved in the fabrication of plastics, including polyvinyl chloride, are
insufficient to evaluate the carcinogenicity of this compound.

## 5. References

Anderson, D., Hodge, M.C.E. & Purchase, I.F.H. (1976) Vinyl chloride: dominant lethal studies in male CD-1 mice. Mutat. Res., 40, 359-370

Anderson, D., Hodge, M.C.E. & Purchase, I.F.H. (1977) Dominant lethal studies with the halogenated olefins vinyl chloride and vinylidene dichloride in male CD-1 mice. Environ. Health Perspect., 21, 71-78

Andrews, A.W., Zawistowski, E.S. & Valentine, C.R. (1976) A comparison of the mutagenic properties of vinyl chloride and methyl chloride. Mutat. Res., 40, 273-276

Anghelescu, F., Otoiu, M., Dobrinescu, E., Hagi-Paraschiv-Dossios, L., Dobrinescu, G. & Ganea, V. (1969) Clinico-pathogenic considerations on Raynaud's phenomenon in the employees of the polyvinyl chloride industry (Rom.). Med. interna (Buc.), 21, 473-482

Anon. (1972) Fire Protection Guide on Hazardous Materials, 4th ed., Boston, Mass., National Fire Protection Association, pp. 325M-137, 49-226-49-227

Anon. (1973a) 'Prior sanction' regulation proposed for PVC. Food Chemical News, 21 May, p. 42

Anon. (1973b) FDA to propose ban on use of PVC for liquor use. Food Chemical News, 14 May, pp. 3-4

Anon. (1974) CIA argues case against zero VCM exposure limits. Eur. Chemical News, 24 May, p. 24

Antweiler, H. (1976) Studies on the metabolism of vinyl chloride. Environ. Health Perspect., 17, 217-219

Barbin, A., Brésil, H., Croisy, A., Jacquignon, P., Malaveille, C., Montesano, R. & Bartsch, H. (1975) Liver-microsome-mediated formation of alkylating agents from vinyl bromide and vinyl chloride. Biochem. biophys. Res. Commun., 67, 596-603

Baretta, E.D., Stewart, R.D. & Mutchler, J.E. (1969) Monitoring exposures to vinyl chloride vapor: breath analysis and continuous air sampling. Am. ind. Hyg. Assoc. J., 30, 537-544

Barnhart, W.L., Toney, C.R. & Devlin, J.B. (1975) Environmental/Industrial Hygiene Surveys of Vinyl Chloride Monomer Manufacturing Operations and Operations Where Polyvinyl Chloride and Copolymers of Polyvinyl Chloride Are Processed, Contract No. CDC-99-74-50, Washington DC, US Department of Health, Education, and Welfare, National Institute for Occupational Safety and Health, pp. 1-8, 101-110

Barrio, J.R., Secrist, J.A., III & Leonard, N.J. (1972) Fluorescent adenosine and cytidine derivatives. Biochem. biophys. Res. Commun., 46, 597-604

Bartsch, H. & Montesano, R. (1975) Mutagenic and carcinogenic effects of vinyl chloride. Mutat. Res., 32, 93-114

Bartsch, H., Malaveille, C. & Montesano, R. (1975) Human, rat and mouse liver-mediated mutagenicity of vinyl chloride in S. typhimurium strains. Int. J. Cancer, 15, 429-437

Bartsch, H., Malaveille, C., Barbin, A., Brésil, H., Tomatis, L. & Montesano, R. (1976) Mutagenicity and metabolism of vinyl chloride and related compounds. Environ. Health Perspect., 17, 193-198

Bartsch, H., Malaveille, C., Barbin, A. & Planche, G. (1979) Mutagenic and alkylating metabolites of halo-ethylenes, chlorobutadienes and dichlorobutenes produced by rodent or human liver tissues; evidence for oxirane formation by P450-linked microsomal mono-oxygenases. Arch. Toxicol. (in press)

Baumann, E. (1872) Some vinyl compounds (Ger.). Justus Liebig's Ann. Chem., 163, 308-322

Baxter, P.J. & Fox, A.J. (1976) Angiosarcoma of the liver in P.V.C. fabricators. Lancet, i, 245-246

Bertram, C.G. (1977) Minimizing emissions from vinyl chloride plants. Environ. Sci. Tech., 11, 864-868

Block, J.B. (1974) Angiosarcoma of the liver following vinyl chloride exposure. J. Am. med. Assoc., 229, 53-54

Boettner, E.A., Ball, G. & Weiss, B. (1969) Analysis of the volatile combustion products of vinyl plastics. J. appl. Polym. Sci., 13, 377-391

Bol'shakov, A.M. (1969) Working conditions in the production of synthetic leather (Russ.). In: Proceedings of a Conference on Hygienic Problems in Manufacture and Use of Polymer Materials, Moscow, Moscovic Research Institute of Hygiene, pp. 47-52 [Chem. Abstr., 75, 143701p]

Bolt, H.M. & Filser, J.G. (1977) Irreversible binding of chlorinated ethylenes to macromolecules. Environ. Health Perspect., 21, 107-112

Bolt, H.M., Kappus, H., Buchter, A. & Bolt, W. (1976) Disposition of [1,2-$^{14}$C]vinyl chloride in the rat. Arch. Toxicol., 35, 153-162

Bonse, G. & Henschler, D. (1976) Chemical reactivity, biotransformation, and toxicity of polychlorinated aliphatic compounds. CRC Crit. Rev. Toxicol., 4, 395-409

Bonse, G., Urban, T., Reichert, D. & Henschler, D. (1975) Chemical reactivity, metabolic oxirane formation and biological reactivity of chlorinated ethylenes in the isolated perfused rat liver preparation. Biochem. Pharmacol., 24, 1829-1834

Border, E.A. & Webster, I. (1977) The effect of vinyl chloride monomer, chloroethylene oxide and chloracetaldehyde on DNA synthesis in regenerating rat liver. Chem.-biol. Interact., 17, 239-247

Brand, I., Buoen, L.C. & Brand, K.G. (1977) Foreign-body tumors of mice: strain and sex differences in latency and incidence. J. natl Cancer Inst., 58, 1443-1447

Brand, K.G., Buoen, L.C. & Brand, I. (1967a) Premalignant cells in tumorigenesis induced by plastic film. Nature (Lond.), 213, 810

Brand, K.G., Buoen, L.C. & Brand, I. (1967b) Carcinogenesis from polymer implants: new aspects from chromosomal and transplantation studies during premalignancy. J. natl Cancer Inst., 39, 663-679

Brand, K.G., Buoen, L.C. & Brand, I. (1975) Foreign-body tumorigenesis by vinyl chloride vinyl acetate copolymer: no evidence for chemical cocarcinogenesis. J. natl Cancer Inst., 54, 1259-1262

Braun, D. & Nixdorf, G. (1972) Separation scheme for plastics analysis. 2. Soluble polymers with acidic pyrolysis products (Ger.). Kunststoffe, 62, 187-189 [Chem. Abstr., 77, 34989j]

Breder, C.V., Dennison, J.L. & Brown, M.E. (1975) Gas-liquid chromatographic determination of vinyl chloride in vinyl chloride polymers, food-simulating solvents, and other samples. J. Assoc. off. anal. Chem., 58, 1214-1220

Brookman, R.S. (1974) Analysis of PVC resins. CHEMTECH, December, pp. 741-743

Brooks, S.M. & Vandervort, R. (1977) Polyvinyl chloride film thermal decomposition products as an occupational illness. 2. Clinical studies. J. occup. Med., 19, 192-196

Byrén, D. & Holmberg, B. (1975) Two possible cases of angiosarcoma of the liver in a group of Swedish vinyl chloride-polyvinyl chloride workers. Ann. NY Acad. Sci., 246, 249-250

Byrén, D., Engholm, G., Englund, A. & Westerholm, P. (1976) Mortality and cancer morbidity in a group of Swedish VCM and PVC production workers. Environ. Health Perspect., 17, 167-170

Calnan, J. (1963) The use of inert plastic material in reconstructive surgery. I. A biological test for tissue acceptance. II. Tissue reactions to commonly used materials. Br. J. Plast. Surg., 16, 1-22

Caputo, A., Viola, P.L. & Bigotti, A. (1974)  Oncogenicity of vinyl chloride at low concentrations in rats and rabbits.  Int. Res. Communs, 2, 1582

Casterline, C.L., Casterline, P.F. & Jaques, D.A. (1977)  Squamous cell carcinoma of the buccal mucosa associated with chronic oral polyvinyl chloride exposure.  Report of a case.  Cancer, 39, 1686-1688

Chiazze, L., Jr, Nichols, W.E. & Wong, O. (1977)  Mortality among employees of PVC fabricators.  J. occup. Med., 19, 623-628

Commission of the European Communities (1977a)  Modifications to the proposed Council Directive for coordination of the legislative, regulatory and administrative provisions in force in Member States with regard to the health protection of workers exposed occupationally to vinyl chloride monomer (Fr.).  J. off. Communautés Eur., No. C219, 2-3

Commission of the European Communities (1977b)  Proposal for a Council Directive on the approximation of the laws of the Member States relating to materials and articles containing vinyl chloride monomer and intended to come into contact with foodstuffs.  Off. J. Eur. Communities, No. C16, 8-12

Commission of the European Communities (1978)  Annexe I et Annexe II. J. off. Communautés Eur., No. L44, 17

Conolly, R.B. & Jaeger, R.J. (1977)  Acute hepatotoxicity of ethylene and halogenated ethylenes after PCB pretreatment.  Environ. Health Perspect., 21, 131-135

Conolly, R.B., Jaeger, R.J. & Szabo, S. (1977)  Acute hepatotoxicity of ethylene, vinyl fluoride, vinyl chloride, and vinyl bromide after Aroclor 1254 pretreatment (Abstract No. 36).  Toxicol. appl. Pharmacol., 41, 146

Cook, W.A., Giever, P.M., Dinman, B.D. & Magnuson, H.J. (1971)  Occupational acroosteolysis.  II.  An industrial hygiene study.  Arch. environ. Health, 22, 74-82

Cornish, H.H. & Abar, E.L. (1969)  Toxicity of pyrolysis products of vinyl plastics.  Arch. environ. Health, 19, 15-21

Couderc, P., Panh, M.-H., Pasquier, B., Pasquier, D., N'Golet, A. & Faure, H. (1976)  Angiosarcoma of the bone indicating a hepatic tumour in a worker exposed to vinyl chloride (Fr.).  Semin. Hôp. Paris, 52, 1721-1722

Creech, J.L., Jr & Johnson, M.N. (1974)  Angiosarcoma of liver in the manufacture of polyvinyl chloride.  J. occup. Med., 16, 150-151

Darby, J.R. & Sears, J.K. (1968)  Plasticizers.  In:  Kirk, R.E. &
    Othmer, D.F., eds, Encyclopedia of Chemical Technology, 2nd ed.,
    Vol. 15, New York, John Wiley and Sons, p. 798

Delorme, F. & Thériault, G. (1978)  Ten cases of angiosarcoma of the liver
    in Shawinigan, Quebec.  J. occup. Med., 20, 338-340

Deutsche Industrie Normen Ausschuss (1977)  Gas Chromatographic Determina-
    tion of Vinyl Chloride (VC) in Polyvinyl Chloride (PVC) (Ger.).
    Deutsche Normen, DIN 53743, Berlin, Beuth

Drevon, C., Kuroki, T. & Montesano, R. (1977)  Microsome-mediated muta-
    genesis of a Chinese hamster cell line by various chemicals (Abstract).
    In:  2nd International Conference on Environmental Mutagens, Edinburgh,
    1977, p. 150

Drew, R.T., Harper, C., Gupta, B.N. & Talley, F.A. (1975)  Effects of
    vinyl chloride exposures to rats pretreated with phenobarbital.
    Environ. Health Perspect., 11, 235-242

Drozdowicz, B.Z. & Huang, P.C. (1977)  Lack of mutagenicity of vinyl
    chloride in two strains of Neurospora crassa.  Mutat. Res., 48, 43-50

Ducatman, A., Hirschhorn, K. & Selikoff, I.J. (1975)  Vinyl chloride expo-
    sure and human chromosome aberrations.  Mutat. Res., 31, 163-168

Duck, B.W. & Carter, J.T. (1976)  Vinyl chloride and mortality?  Lancet,
    ii, 195

Duck, B.W., Carter, J.T. & Coombes, E.J. (1975)  Mortality study of workers
    in a polyvinyl-chloride production plant.  Lancet, ii, 1197-1199

Dyer, R.F. & Esch, V.H. (1976)  Polyvinyl chloride toxicity in fires.
    Hydrogen chloride toxicity in fire fighters.  J. Am. med. Assoc.,
    235, 393-397

Eckardt, R.E. & Hindin, R. (1973)  The health hazards of plastics.
    J. occup. Med., 15, 808-819

Edmonds, L. (1977)  Birth defects and vinyl chloride.  In:  Proceedings of
    the Conference on Women and the Workplace, Washington DC, Society for
    Occupational and Environmental Health, pp. 114-139

Edmonds, L.D., Falk, H. & Nissim, J.E. (1975)  Congenital malformations
    and vinyl chloride.  Lancet, ii, 1098

Edmonds, L.D., Anderson, C.E., Flynt, J.W., Jr & James, L.M. (1978)
    Congenital central nervous system malformations and vinyl chloride
    monomer exposure:  a community study.  Teratology, 17, 137-142

Egan, H., Squirrell, D.C.M. & Thain, W., eds (1979)  Environmental Carcino-
    gens - Selected Methods of Analysis, Vol. 2, Vinyl Chloride (IARC
    Scientific Publications No. 22), Lyon (in press)

Falk, H. & Portnoy, B. (1976)  Respiratory tract illness in meat wrappers.
    J. Am. med. Assoc., 235, 915-917

Falk, H., Creech, J.L., Jr, Heath, C.W., Jr, Johnson, M.N. & Key, M.M.
    (1974a)  Hepatic disease among workers at a vinyl chloride polymeriz-
    ation plant.  J. Am. med. Assoc., 230, 59-63

Falk, H., Heath, C.W., Jr, Carter, C.D., Wagoner, J.K., Waxweiler, R.J.
    & Stringer, W.T. (1974b)  Mortality among vinyl-chloride workers.
    Lancet, ii, 784

Filatova, V.S. & Gronsberg, E.S. (1957)  Sanitary-hygienic conditions of
    work in the production of polychlorvinylic tar and measures of
    improvement (Russ.).  Gig. i Sanit., 22, 38-42

Filatova, V.S., Gronsberg, E.S., Radzyukevich, T.M., Reznik, N.D. &
    Tomichev, A.I. (1974)  Hygienic assessment of working conditions
    and health status of workers in the production of block polyvinyl
    chloride (Russ.).  Gig. Tr. Prof. Zabol., 1, 3-6

Fischer, W.G. (1967)  Pyrolytic gas-chromatography (Ger.).  Glas-Instrum.-
    Tech., 11, 562, 567-570, 775-780, 1086-1088, 1091-1095 [Chem. Abstr.,
    68, 78636k]

Fishbein, L. (1976)  Industrial mutagens and potential mutagens. I.
    Halogenated aliphatic derivatives.  Mutat. Res., 32, 267-308

Fox, A.J. & Collier, P.F. (1976)  Low mortality rates in industrial cohort
    studies due to selection for work and survival in the industry.
    Br. J. prev. soc. Med., 30, 225-230

Fox, A.J. & Collier, P.F. (1977)  Mortality experience of workers exposed
    to vinyl chloride monomer in the manufacture of polyvinyl chloride
    in Great Britain.  Br. J. ind. Med., 34, 1-10

Frongia, N., Spinazzola, A. & Bucarelli, A. (1974)  Experimental lung
    damage from prolonged inhalation of airborne PVC dust (Ital.).
    Med. Lav., 65, 321-342

Fuchs, G., Gawell, B.M., Albanus, L. & Slorach, S. (1975)  Vinyl chloride
    monomer levels in edible fats (Swed.).  Var Foeda, 27, 134-145
    [Chem. Abstr., 83, 145870g]

Funes-Cravioto, F., Lambert, B., Lindsten, J., Ehrenberg, L., Natarajan, A.T.
    & Osterman-Golkar, S. (1975)  Chromosome aberrations in workers
    exposed to vinyl chloride.  Lancet, i, 459

Gamble, J., Liu, S., McMichael, A.J. & Waxweiler, R.J. (1976) Effect of occupational and nonoccupational factors on the respiratory system of vinyl chloride and other workers. J. occup. Med., 18, 659-670

Garro, A.J., Guttenplan, J.B. & Milvy, P. (1976) Vinyl chloride dependent mutagenesis: effects of liver extracts and free radicals. Mutat. Res., 38, 81-88

Gilbert, S.G., Giacin, J.R., Morano, J.R. & Rosen, J.D. (1975) Detecting small quantities of residual vinyl chloride monomer. Package Developments, July/August, pp. 20-24

Going, J.E. (1976) Sampling and Analysis of Selected Toxic Substances. Task III - Vinyl Chloride, Secondary Sources, EPA 560/6-76-002, Springfield, Va, National Technical Information Service

Gordon, S.J. & Meeks, S.A. (1977) A study of gaseous pollutants in the Houston, Texas area. Am. Inst. chem. Eng. Symp. Ser., 73, 84-94

Göthe, R., Calleman, C.J., Ehrenberg, L. & Wachtmeister, C.A. (1974) Trapping with 3,4-dichlorobenzenethiol of reactive metabolites formed *in vitro* from the carcinogen vinyl chloride. Ambio, 3, 234-236

Grasselli, J.G. & Ritchey, W.M., eds (1975) CRC Atlas of Spectral Data and Physical Constants for Organic Compounds, 2nd ed., Vol. III, Cleveland, Ohio, Chemical Rubber Co., p. 279

Green, T. & Hathway, D.E. (1975) The biological fate in rats of vinyl chloride in relation to its oncogenicity. Chem.-biol. Interact., 11, 545-562

Green, T. & Hathway, D.E. (1977) The chemistry and biogenesis of the *S*-containing metabolites of vinyl chloride in rats. Chem.-biol. Interact., 17, 137-150

Green, T. & Hathway, D.E. (1978) Interactions of vinyl chloride with rat-liver DNA *in vivo*. Chem.-biol. Interact., 22, 211-224

Greim, H., Bonse, G., Radwan, Z., Reichert, D. & Henschler, D. (1975) Mutagenicity *in vitro* and potential carcinogenicity of chlorinated ethylenes as a function of metabolic oxirane formation. Biochem. Pharmacol., 24, 2013-2017

Guess, W.L. & Stetson, J.B. (1968) Tissue reactions to organotin-stabilized polyvinyl chloride (PVC) catheters. J. Am. med. Assoc., 204, 118-122

Haley, T.J. (1975) Vinyl chloride: how many unknown problems? J. Toxicol. environ. Health, 1, 47-73

Halpern, B.D. & Karo, W. (1977) Medical applications. In: Bikales, N.M., ed., Encyclopedia of Polymer Science and Technology, Plastics, Resins, Rubbers, Fibers, Suppl. Vol. 2, New York, Interscience, pp. 369, 386-387

Hansteen, I.L., Hillestad, L. & Thiis-Evensen, E. (1976) Chromosome studies in workers exposed to vinyl-chloride (Abstract No. 21). Mutat. Res., 38, 112

Hardie, D.W.F. (1964) Chlorocarbons and chlorohydrocarbons. Vinyl chloride. In: Kirk, R.E. & Othmer, D.F., eds, Encyclopedia of Chemical Technology, 2nd ed., Vol. 5, New York, John Wiley and Sons, pp. 171-178

Harrison, J.H., Swanson, D.S. & Lincoln, A.F. (1957) A comparison of the tissue reactions to plastic materials. Arch. Surg., 74, 139-144

Hawley, G.G., ed. (1971) The Condensed Chemical Dictionary, 8th ed., New York, Van Nostrand-Reinhold, p. 714

Heath, C.W., Jr, Falk, H. & Creech, J.L., Jr (1975) Characteristics of cases of angiosarcoma of the liver among vinyl chloride workers in the United States. Ann. NY Acad. Sci., 246, 231-236

Heath, C.W., Jr, Dumont, C.R., Gamble, J. & Waxweiler, R.J. (1977) Chromosomal damage in men occupationally exposed to vinyl chloride monomer and other chemicals. Environ. Res., 14, 68-72

Hedley, W.H., Cheng, J.T., McCormick, R.J. & Lewis, W.A. (1976) Sampling of Automobile Interiors for Vinyl Chloride Monomer, EPA-600/2-76-124, Springfield, Va, National Technical Information Service

Hefner, R.E., Jr, Watanabe, P.G. & Gehring, P.J. (1975) Preliminary studies on the fate of inhaled vinyl chloride monomer (VCM) in rats. Environ. Health Perspect., 11, 85-95

Hoffmann, D., Patrianakos, C., Brunnemann, K.D. & Gori, G.B. (1976) Chromatographic determination of vinyl chloride in tobacco smoke. Anal. Chem., 48, 47-50

Holmberg, B., Kronevi, T. & Winell, M. (1976) The pathology of vinyl chloride exposed mice. Acta vet. scand., 17, 328-342

Huberman, E., Bartsch, H. & Sachs, L. (1975) Mutation induction in Chinese hamster V79 cells by two vinyl chloride metabolites, chloroethylene oxide and 2-chloroacetaldehyde. Int. J. Cancer, 16, 639-644

Hussain, S. & Osterman-Golkar, S. (1976) Comment on the mutagenic effectiveness of vinyl chloride metabolites. Chem.-biol. Interact., 12, 265-267

IARC (1974)  IARC Monographs on the Evaluation of Carcinogenic Risk of
    Chemicals to Man, 7, Some Anti-thyroid and Related Substances,
    Nitrofurans and Industrial Chemicals, Lyon, pp. 291-318

IARC (1978a)  Information Bulletin on the Survey of Chemicals Being
    Tested for Carcinogenicity, No. 7, Lyon, pp. 159, 183, 194, 382

IARC (1978b)  Directory of On-Going Research in Cancer Epidemiology, 1978
    (IARC Scientific Publications No. 26), Lyon, pp. 67, 70, 71-72, 79,
    120, 129, 148-149, 173, 216-217, 242, 249, 254-255, 348-349 (Abstract
    Nos 169, 179, 183, 202, 308, 329, 378, 435, 549, 556, 635, 653, 667,
    924, 927)

IARC (1978c)  Directory of On-Going Research in Cancer Epidemiology, 1978
    (IARC Scientific Publications No. 26), Lyon, p. 290 (Abstract No. 764)

Infante, P.F. (1976)  Oncogenic and mutagenic risks in communities with
    polyvinyl chloride production facilities. Ann. NY Acad. Sci., 271,
    49-57

Infante, P.F. (1977)  Mutagenic and carcinogenic risks associated with
    some halogenated olefins. Environ. Health Perspect., 21, 251-254

Infante, P.F., Wagoner, J.K., McMichael, A.J., Waxweiler, R.J. & Falk, H.
    (1976a)  Genetic risks of vinyl chloride. Lancet, i, 734-735

Infante, P.F., Wagoner, J.K., McMichael, A.J., Waxweiler, R.J. & Falk, H.
    (1976b)  Genetic risks of vinyl chloride. Lancet, i, 1289-1290

Ivanetich, K.M., Aronson, I. & Katz, I.D. (1977)  The interaction of
    vinyl chloride with rat hepatic microsomal cytochrome P-450 in vitro.
    Biochem. biophys. Res. Commun., 74, 1411-1418

Ivanova, E.V. & Shamina, M.P. (1973)  Toxicological evaluation of an
    aqueous dispersion of a vinyl chloride-vinyl acetate copolymer (Russ.).
    In:  Korotkikh, G.L., ed., Proceedings of the 3rd Conference on Actual
    Problems in Laboratory Practices, Voronezh District Conference of
    Laboratory Physicians, Voronezh, USSR, Department of Public Health,
    pp. 221-222 [Chem. Abstr., 83, 109400v]

Jaeger, R.J., Reynolds, E.S., Conolly, R.B., Moslen, M.T., Szabo, S. &
    Murphy, S.D. (1974)  Acute hepatic injury by vinyl chloride in rats
    pretreated with phenobarbital. Nature (Lond.), 252, 724-726

Jaeger, R.J., Conolly, R.B. & Murphy, S.D. (1975a)  Short-term inhalation
    toxicity of halogenated hydrocarbons. Effects on fasting rats.
    Arch. environ. Health, 30, 26-31

Jaeger, R.J., Conolly, R.B., Reynolds, E.S. & Murphy, S.D. (1975b)  Bio-
    chemical toxicology of unsaturated halogenated monomers. Environ.
    Health Perspect., 11, 121-128

John, J.A., Smith, F.A., Leong, B.K.J. & Schwetz, B.A. (1977) The effects of maternally inhaled vinyl chloride on embryonal and fetal development in mice, rats, and rabbits. Toxicol. appl. Pharmacol., 39, 497-513

Jühe, S. & Lange, C.-E. (1972) Sclerodermal skin changes, Raynaud's syndrome and acro-osteolyses in workers in the PVC-producing industry (Ger.). Dtsch. med. Wschr., 97, 1922-1923

Kappus, H., Bolt, H.M., Buchter, A. & Bolt, W. (1975) Rat liver microsomes catalyse covalent binding of [14]C-vinyl chloride to macromolecules. Nature (Lond.), 257, 134-135

Kappus, H., Bolt, H.M., Buchter, A. & Bolt, W. (1976) Liver microsomal uptake of [14C]vinyl chloride and transformation to protein alkylating metabolites in vitro. Toxicol. appl. Pharmacol., 37, 461-471

Keplinger, M.L., Goode, J.W., Gordon, D.E. & Calandra, J.C. (1975) Interim results of exposure of rats, hamsters, and mice to vinyl chloride. Ann. NY Acad. Sci., 246, 219-224

Kogan, A.K. & Tugarinova, V.N. (1959) On the blastomogenic action of polyvinyl chloride (Russ.). Vop. Onkol., 5, 540-545

Laib, R.J. & Bolt, H.M. (1977) Formation of imidazol derivatives of nucleic acid bases (DNA and RNA) by metabolites of vinyl chloride in vivo and in vitro (Abstract P 26). In: Proceedings of the 4th Meeting of the European Association for Cancer Research, Lyon, 1977, Lyon, University of Lyon, Faculty of Medicine, p. 84

Lange, C.-E., Jühe, S., Stein, G. & Veltman, G. (1974a) Vinyl chloride disease - a systemic sclerosis due to occupational exposure? (Ger.) Int. Arch. Arbeitsmed., 32, 1-32

Lange, C.-E., Jühe, S. & Veltman, G. (1974b) Appearance of angiosarcomas of the liver in two workers in the PVC production industry (Ger.). Dtsch. med. Wschr., 99, 1598-1599

Lange, C.-E., Jühe, S., Stein, G. & Veltman, G. (1975) Further results in polyvinyl chloride production workers. Ann. NY Acad. Sci., 246, 18-21

Laramy, R.E. (1977) Analytical chemistry of vinyl chloride - a survey. American Laboratory, December, pp. 17-27

Lee, C.C., Bhandari, J.C., Winston, J.M., House, W.B., Peters, P.J., Dixon, R.L. & Woods, J.S. (1977) Inhalation toxicity of vinyl chloride and vinylidene chloride. Environ. Health Perspect., 21, 25-32

Lee, C.C., Bhandari, J.C., Winston, J.M., House, W.B., Dixon, R.L. & Woods, J.S. (1978) Carcinogenicity of vinyl chloride and vinylidene chloride. J. Toxicol. environ. Health, 4, 15-30

Lee, F.I. & Harry, D.S. (1974) Angiosarcoma of the liver in a vinyl-chloride worker. Lancet, i, 1316-1318

Léonard, A., Decat, G., Léonard, E.D., Lefèvre, M.J., Decuyper, L.J. & Nicaise, C. (1977) Cytogenetic investigations on lymphocytes from workers exposed to vinyl chloride. J. Toxicol. environ. Health, 2, 1135-1141

Lilis, R., Anderson, H., Miller, A. & Selikoff, I.J. (1976) Pulmonary changes among vinyl chloride polymerization workers. Chest, 69, 299-303

Lillian, D., Singh, H.B., Appleby, A., Lobban, L., Arnts, R., Gumpert, R., Hague, R., Toomey, J., Kazazis, J., Antell, M., Hansen, D. & Scott, B. (1975) Atmospheric fates of halogenated compounds. Environ. Sci. Technol., 9, 1042-1048

Lloyd, J.W. (1975) Angiosarcoma of the liver in vinyl chloride/polyvinyl chloride workers. J. occup. Med., 17, 333-334

Loprieno, N., Barale, R., Baroncelli, S., Bauer, C., Bronzetti, G., Cammellini, A., Cercignani, G., Corsi, C., Gervasi, G., Leporini, C., Nieri, R., Rossi, A.M., Stretti, G. & Turchi, G. (1976) Evaluation of the genetic effects induced by vinyl chloride monomer (VCM) under mammalian metabolic activation: studies *in vitro* and *in vivo*. Mutat. Res., 40, 85-96

Loprieno, N., Barale, R., Baroncelli, S., Bartsch, H., Bronzetti, G., Cammellini, A., Corsi, C., Frozza, D., Nieri, R., Leporini, C., Rosellini, D. & Rossi, A.M. (1977) Induction of gene mutations and gene conversions by vinyl chloride metabolites in yeast. Cancer Res., 36, 253-257

Magnusson, J. & Ramel, C. (1976) Mutagenic effects of vinyl chloride in *Drosophila melanogaster* (Abstract No. 27). Mutat. Res., 38, 115

Makk, L., Creech, J.L., Whelan, J.G., Jr & Johnson, M.N. (1974) Liver damage and angiosarcoma in vinyl chloride workers. A systematic detection program. J. Am. med. Assoc., 230, 64-68

Malaveille, C., Bartsch, H., Barbin, A., Camus, A.M., Montesano, R., Croisy, A. & Jacquignon, P. (1975) Mutagenicity of vinyl chloride, chloroethyleneoxide, chloroacetaldehyde, and chloroethanol. Biochem. biophys. Res. Commun., 63, 363-370

Maltoni, C. (1974)  Angiosarcoma of the liver in workers exposed to vinyl
    chloride.  First two cases found in Italy (Ital.).  Med. Lav., 65,
    445-450

Maltoni, C. (1976)  Precursor lesions in exposed populations as indicators
    of occupational cancer risk.  Ann. NY Acad. Sci., 271, 444-447

Maltoni, C. (1977a)  Vinyl chloride carcinogenicity:  an experimental
    model for carcinogenesis studies.  In:  Hiatt, H.H., Watson, J.D. &
    Winsten, J.A., eds, Origins of Human Cancer, Book A, Cold Spring
    Harbor, NY, Cold Spring Harbor Laboratory, pp. 119-146

Maltoni, C. (1977b)  Recent findings on the carcinogenicity of chlorinated
    olefins.  Environ. Health Perspect., 21, 1-5

Maltoni, C. & Lefemine, G. (1974)  Competency of experimental tests to
    predict environmental carcinogenic risks.  An example:  vinyl chloride
    (Ital.).  Red. Clas. Sci. fis. mat. nat. (Lincei), 56, 1-10

Maltoni, C., Lefemine, G., Chieco, P. & Carretti, D. (1974)  Vinyl chloride
    carcinogenesis:  current results and perspectives.  Med. Lav., 65,
    421-444

Maltoni, C., Ciliberti, A., Gianni, L. & Chieco, P. (1975)  Carcinogenicity
    of vinyl chloride administered by the oral route in rats (Ital.).
    Osp. Vita, 2, 102-109

May, R.W., Pearson, E.F., Porter, J. & Scothern, M.D. (1973)  Reproducible
    pyrolysis gas-chromatographic system for the analysis of paints and
    plastics.  Analyst (Lond.), 98, 364-371 [Chem. Abstr., 79, 93484e]

McCann, J., Simmon, V., Streitwieser, D. & Ames, B.N. (1975)  Mutagenicity
    of chloroacetaldehyde, a possible metabolic product of 1,2-dichloro-
    ethane (ethylene dichloride), chloroethanol (ethylene chlorohydrin),
    vinyl chloride, and cyclophosphamide.  Proc. natl Acad. Sci. (Wash.),
    72, 3190-3193

Milby, T.H. (1977)  Cancer Control Monograph:  Vinyl Chloride, Menlo Park,
    California, SRI International

Miller, A. (1975)  Pulmonary function defects in nonsmoking vinyl chloride
    workers.  Environ. Health Perspect., 11, 247-250

Miller, A., Teirstein, A.S., Chuang, M. & Selikoff, I.J. (1975)  Changes
    in pulmonary function in workers exposed to vinyl chloride and
    polyvinyl chloride.  Ann. NY Acad. Sci., 246, 42-52

Miller, S.A. (1969)  Ethylene and Its Industrial Derivatives, London, Benn

Monson, R.R., Peters, J.M. & Johnson, M.N. (1974) Proportional mortality among vinyl-chloride workers. Lancet, ii, 397-398

Morris, G.E. (1953) Vinyl plastics. Their dermatological and chemical aspects. Arch. ind. Hyg. Occup. Med., 8, 535-539

Müller, G. & Norpoth, K. (1975) Determination of two urinary metabolites of vinyl chloride (Ger.). Naturwissenschaften, 62, 541

Müller, G., Norpoth, K. & Eckard, R. (1976) Identification of two urine metabolites of vinyl chloride by GC-MS-investigations. Int. Arch. occup. Environ. Health, 38, 69-75

Murdoch, I.A. & Hammond, A.R. (1977) A practical method for the measurement of vinyl chloride monomer (VCM) in air. Ann. occup. Hyg., 20, 55-61

National Field Investigations Center (1974) Evaluation of Vinyl Chloride Emissions in the Long Beach Area, California, EPA/330/2-74/002, Springfield, Va, National Technical Information Service

National Institute for Occupational Safety and Health (1977) NIOSH Manual of Analytical Methods, 2nd ed., Vol. 2, Vinyl Chloride in Air, Method No. P&CAM 178, Department of Health, Education, and Welfare (NIOSH) Publ. No. 77-157-B, Washington DC, US Government Printing Office, pp. 178-1-178-10

Nematollahi, J., Guess, W. & Autian, J. (1970) Pyrolytic characterization of some plastics by a modified gas chromatography. Microchem. J., 15, 53-59

Nicholson, W.J., Hammond, E.C., Seidman, H. & Selikoff, I.J. (1975) Mortality experience of a cohort of vinyl chloride-polyvinyl chloride workers. Ann. NY Acad. Sci., 246, 225-230

Noria, D.F., Ritchie, S. & Silver, M.D. (1976) Angiosarcoma of the liver after vinyl chloride exposure: report of a case and review of the literature (Abstract). Lab. Invest., 34, 346

Okumoto, T. & Takeuchi, T. (1972) Rapid characterization of polymeric materials by pyrolysis-gas chromatography (Jap.) Nippon Kagaku Kaishi, 1, 71-78 [Chem. Abstr., 76, 141459n]

O'Mara, M.M., Crider, L.B. & Daniel, R.L. (1971) Combustion products from vinyl chloride monomer. Am. ind. Hyg. Assoc. J., 32, 153-156

Oppenheimer, B.S., Oppenheimer, E.T. & Stout, A.P. (1952) Sarcomas induced in rodents by embedding various plastic films. Proc. Soc. exp. Biol. (NY), 49, 366-369

Oppenheimer, B.S., Oppenheimer, E.T., Danishefsky, I., Stout, A.P. &
    Eirich, F.R. (1955) Further studies of polymers as carcinogenic
    agents in animals. Cancer Res., 15, 333-340

Orusev, T., Popovski, P., Bauer, S. & Nikolova, K. (1976) Occupational
    risk in the production of poly(vinyl chloride) (Macd.). God. Zb.
    Med. Fak. Skopje, 22, 33-38 [Chem. Abstr., 86, 194336h]

Osterman-Golkar, S., Hultmark, D., Segerbäck, D., Calleman, C.J., Güthe, R.,
    Ehrenberg, L. & Wachtmeister, C.A. (1977) Alkylation of DNA and
    proteins in mice exposed to vinyl chloride. Biochem. biophys. Res.
    Commun., 76, 259-266

Ott, M.G., Langner, R.R. & Holder, B.B. (1975) Vinyl chloride exposure
    in a controlled industrial environment. A long-term mortality
    experience in 594 employees. Arch. environ. Health, 30, 333-339

Paddle, G.M. (1976) Genetic risks of vinyl chloride. Lancet, i, 1079

Pagé, M., Thériault, L. & Delorme, F. (1976) Elevated CEA levels in
    polyvinyl chloride workers. Biomédicine, 25, 279

Pastuska, G. (1969) Pyrolysis thin-layer chromatography of high polymers
    (Ger.). Gummi, Asbest, Kunstst., 22, 718-721 [Chem. Abstr., 71,
    92108h]

Plugge, H. & Safe, S. (1977) Vinylchloride metabolism. A review.
    Chemosphere, 6, 309-325

Polakoff, P.L., Lapp, N.L. & Reger, R. (1975) Polyvinyl chloride pyrolysis
    products. A potential course for respiratory impairment. Arch.
    environ. Health, 30, 269-271

Powell, D.A. (1974) Determination of the vinyl resin content of vinyl
    asbestos floor tiles. Fresenius' Z. Anal. Chem., 268, 279-284
    [Chem. Abstr., 81, 136834e]

Prodan, L., Suciu, I., Pîslaru, V., Ilea, E. & Pascu, L. (1975a) Experi-
    mental acute toxicity of vinyl chloride (monochloroethene). Ann. NY
    Acad. Sci., 246, 154-158

Prodan, L., Suciu, I., Pîslaru, V., Ilea, E. & Pascu, L. (1975b) Experi-
    mental chronic poisoning with vinyl chloride (monochloroethene).
    Ann. NY Acad. Sci., 246, 159-163

Purchase, I.F.H., Richardson, C.R. & Anderson, D. (1975) Chromosomal and
    dominant lethal effects of vinyl chloride. Lancet, ii, 410-411

Radike, M.J., Stemmer, K.L., Brown, P.G., Larson, E. & Bingham, E. (1977)
    Effect of ethanol and vinyl chloride on the induction of liver tumors:
    preliminary report. Environ. Health Perspect., 21, 153-155

Raikhlin, N.T. & Kozan, A.H. (1961)  On the development and malignization
    of connective tissue capsules around plastic implants (Russ.).  Vop.
    Onkol., 7, 13-17

Rannug, U. & Ramel, C. (1977)  Mutagenicity of waste products from vinyl
    chloride industries.  J. Toxicol. environ. Health, 2, 1019-1029

Rannug, U., Johansson, A., Ramel, C. & Wachtmeister, C.A. (1974)  The
    mutagenicity of vinyl chloride after metabolic activation.  Ambio,
    3, 194-197

Rannug, U., Göthe, R. & Wachtmeister, C.A. (1976)  The mutagenicity of
    chloroethylene oxide, chloroacetaldehyde, 2-chloroethanol and chloro-
    acetic acid, conceivable metabolites of vinyl chloride.  Chem.-biol.
    Interact., 12, 251-263

Ravier, E., Diter, J.M. & Pialat, J. (1975)  A case of hepatic angiosar-
    coma in a worker exposed to vinyl chloride monomer (Fr.).  Arch.
    mal. prof., med. trav. Sec. Soc., 36, 171-177

Regnault, V. (1835)  Composition of a chlorinated hydrocarbon (Oils from
    oil-forming gases) (Ger.).  Justus Liebig's Ann. Chem., 14, 22-38

von Reinl, W., Weber, H. & Greiser, E. (1977)  Epidemiological study on
    mortality of VC-exposed workers in the Federal Republic of Germany
    (Ger.).  Medichem, September, pp. 2-8

Reynolds, E.S., Jaeger, R.J. & Murphy, S.D. (1975a)  Acute liver injury
    by vinyl chloride: involvement of endoplasmic reticulum in pheno-
    barbital-pretreated rats.  Environ. Health Perspect., 11, 227-233

Reynolds, E.S., Moslen, M.T., Szabo, S., Jaeger, R.J. & Murphy, S.D.
    (1975b)  Hepatotoxicity of vinyl chloride and 1,1-dichloroethylene;
    role of mixed function oxidase system.  Am. J. Pathol., 81, 219-232

Reynolds, E.S., Moslen, M.T., Szabo, S. & Jaeger, R.J. (1975c)  Vinyl
    chloride-induced deactivation of cytochrome P-450 and other components
    of the liver mixed function oxidase system: an in vivo study.
    Res. Commun. chem. Pathol. Pharmacol., 12, 685-694

Reynolds, E.S., Moslen, M.T., Szabo, S. & Jaeger, R. (1976)  Modulation of
    halothane and vinyl chloride induced acute injury to liver endoplasmic
    reticulum.  Panminerva Med., 18, 367-374

Roche, J., Fournet, J., Hostein, J., Panh, M. & Bonnet-Eymard, J. (1978)
    Hepatic angiosarcoma due to vinyl chloride.  Report of 4 cases (Fr.).
    Gastroenterol. clin. Biol., 2, 669-678

Roesli, M., Zimmerli, B. & Marek, B. (1975)  Residues of vinyl chloride
    monomer in edible oils (Ger.).  Mitt. Geb. Lebensmittelunters. Hyg.,
    66, 507-511 [Chem. Abstr., 84, 163016h]

Rona, A. (1971)  Instrumental investigation of adhesives used in the build-
    ing industry.  In:  Symposium on Synthetic Resins in Building Con-
    struction, Paper RILEM (Reunion Int. Lab. Essais Rech. Mater. Constr.),
    1967, Vol. 2, pp. 464-471 [Chem. Abstr., 76, 100475w]

Rosenkranz, S., Carr, H.S. & Rosenkranz, H.S. (1974)  2-Haloethanols:
    mutagenicity and reactivity with DNA.  Mutat. Res., 26, 367-370

Russell, F.E., Simmers, M.H., Hirst, A.E. & Pudenz, R.H. (1959)  Tumours
    associated with embedded polymers.  J. natl Cancer Inst., 23, 305-315

Safe Drinking Water Committee (1977)  Drinking Water and Health, Washington
    DC, National Academy of Sciences, p. 794

Saggese, M.F., Wakeman, I.B. & Owens, F.V. (1976)  PVC with no VCM.
    Modern Packaging, September, pp. 19-21, 62

Salmon, A.G. (1976)  Cytochrome $P$-450 and the metabolism of vinyl chloride.
    Cancer Lett., 2, 109-114

Šarič, M., Kulčar, Ž., Zorica, M. & Gelić, I. (1976)  Malignant tumors of
    the liver and lungs in an area with a PVC industry.  Environ. Health
    Perspect., 17, 189-192

Schwetz, B.A., Leong, B.K.J., Smith, F.A., Balmer, M. & Gehring, P.J. (1975)
    Results of a vinyl chloride-teratology study in mice, rats, and rabbits
    (Abstract No. 29).  Toxicol. appl. Pharmacol., 33, 134

Shackelford, W.M. & Keith, L.H. (1976)  Frequency of Organic Compounds
    Identified in Water, EPA-600/4-76-062, Athens, Ga, US Environmental
    Protection Agency, pp. 129-130

Smith, P.M., Crossley, I.R. & Williams, D.M.J. (1976a)  Portal hypertension
    in vinyl-chloride production workers.  Lancet, ii, 602-604

Smith, P.M., Williams, D.M.J. & Evans, D.M.D. (1976b)  Hepatic angiosarcoma
    in a vinyl chloride worker.  Bull. NY Acad. Med., 52, 447-452

Smyth, H.F., Jr & Weil, C.S. (1966)  Chronic oral toxicity to rats of a
    vinyl chloride-vinyl acetate copolymer.  Toxicol. appl. Pharmacol.,
    9, 501-504

Sokol, W.N., Aelony, Y. & Beall, G.N. (1973)  Meat-wrapper's asthma.  A
    new syndrome?  J. Am. med. Assoc., 226, 639-641

Spirtas, R. & Kaminski, R. (1978)  Angiosarcoma of the liver in vinyl
    chloride/polyvinyl chloride workers.  1977 Update of the NIOSH
    Register.  J. occup. Med., 20, 427-429

Suciu, I., Prodan, L., Ilea, E., Păduraru, A. & Pascu, L. (1975) Clinical manifestations in vinyl chloride poisoning. Ann. NY Acad. Sci., 246, 53-69

Szende, B., Lapis, K., Nemes, A. & Pinter, A. (1970) Pneumoconiosis caused by the inhalation of polyvinylchloride dust. Med. Lav.. 61, 433-436

Szentesi, I., Hornyák, É., Ungváry, G., Czeizel, A., Bognár, Z. & Timar, M. (1976) High rate of chromosomal aberration in PVC workers. Mutat. Res., 37, 313-316

Tabershaw, I.R. & Gaffey, W.R. (1974) Mortality study of workers in the manufacture of vinyl chloride and its polymers. J. occup. Med., 16, 509-518

Thomas, J.-C. (1977) PVC and security, European regulations (Fr.). Caoutch. Plast., 571, 33-38

Thomas, L.B. & Popper, H. (1975) Pathology of angiosarcoma of the liver among vinyl chloride-polyvinyl chloride workers. Ann. NY Acad. Sci., 246, 268-277

Thomas, L.B., Popper, H., Berk, P.D., Selikoff, I. & Falk, H. (1975) Vinyl-chloride-induced liver disease. From idiopathic portal hypertension (Banti's syndrome) to angiosarcomas. New Engl. J. Med., 292, 17-22

Tsuge, S., Okumoto, T. & Takeuchi, T. (1969) Pyrolysis-gas chromatography of chlorine-containing synthetic polymers (Jap.). Kogyo Kagaku Zasshi, 72, 1274-1278

US Consumer Product Safety Commission (1974a) Self-pressurized household substances containing vinyl chloride monomer, classification as banned hazardous substance. Fed. Regist., 39, 30112-30114

US Consumer Product Safety Commission (1974b) Vinyl chloride as an ingredient of drug and cosmetic aerosol products. Fed. Regist., 39, 30830

US Department of Commerce (1977) US Exports, Schedule B Commodity Groupings, Schedule B Commodity by Country, FT410/December, Bureau of the Census, Washington DC, US Government Printing Office, p. 2-85

US Environmental Protection Agency (1974a) EPA bans use of certain vinyl chloride pesticides. Environmental News, 24 April, pp. 1-2

US Environmental Protection Agency (1974b) Preliminary Assessment of the Environmental Problems Associated with Vinyl Chloride and Polyvinyl Chloride, September, Washington DC

US Environmental Protection Agency (1974c)  Preliminary Assessment of the
    Environmental Problems Associated with Vinyl Chloride and Polyvinyl
    Chloride (Appendices), September, Washington DC

US Environmental Protection Agency (1975a)  Preliminary Assessment of
    Suspected Carcinogens in Drinking Water, Report to Congress,
    Washington DC, p. II-7

US Environmental Protection Agency (1975b)  Scientific and Technical
    Assessment Report on Vinyl Chloride and Polyvinyl Chloride.
    EPA-600/6-75-004, Springfield, Va, National Technical Information
    Service, pp. 7-42

US Environmental Protection Agency (1976)  National emission standards for
    hazardous air pollutants.  Standard for vinyl chloride.  Fed. Regist.,
    41, 46560-46573

US Environmental Protection Agency (1977)  National emission standards for
    hazardous air pollutants.  Fed. Regist., 42, 28154-28159

US Food and Drug Administration (1975)  Vinyl chloride polymers in contact
    with food.  Notice of proposed rulemaking.  Fed. Regist., 40,
    40529-40537

US Food and Drug Administration (1977)  Food and drugs.  US Code Fed. Regul.,
    Title 21, parts 175.105, 175.300, 175.320, 176.170, 176.180, 177.1010,
    pp. 438, 445-446, 452, 455, 465, 467, 482, 486, 489, 496-497

US International Trade Commission (1977)  Synthetic Organic Chemicals,
    US Production and Sales, 1976, USITC Publication 833, Washington DC,
    US Government Printing Office, pp. 183, 187, 303, 332

US Occupational Safety and Health Administration (1974)  Standard for
    exposure to vinyl chloride.  Fed. Regist., 39, 35890-35898

US Tariff Commission (1928)  Census of Dyes and of Other Synthetic Organic
    Chemicals, 1927, Tariff Information Series No. 37, Washington DC,
    US Government Printing Office, p. 139

Van Gieson, P. (1969)  Here's a quick, easy way to identify films.
    Package Eng., 14, 76-77 [Chem. Abstr., 71, 71274u]

Veltman, G., Lange, C.-E., Jühe, S., Stein, G. & Bachner, U. (1975)  Clini-
    cal manifestations and course of vinyl chloride disease.  Ann. NY
    Acad. Sci., 246, 6-17

Verburgt, F.G. & Vogel, E. (1977)  Vinyl chloride mutagenesis in *Drosophila
    melanogaster*.  Mutat. Res., 48, 327-336

Vertkin, Y.I. & Mamontov, Y.R. (1970) On the state of the bronchopulmonary system in workers engaged in the manufacture of articles made of polyvinyl chloride (Russ.). Gig. tr. Prof. Zabol., 19, 29-32

Viola, P.L., Bigotti, A. & Caputo, A. (1971) Oncogenic response of rat skin, lungs, and bones to vinyl chloride. Cancer Res., 31, 516-522

Volkheimer, G. (1975) Hematogenous dissemination of ingested polyvinyl chloride particles. Ann. NY Acad. Sci., 246, 164-171

Wagoner, J.K., Infante, P.F. & Saracci, R. (1976) Vinyl chloride and mortality. Lancet, i, 194-195

Ward, A.M., Udnoon, S., Watkins, J., Walker, A.E. & Darke, C.S. (1976) Immunological mechanisms in the pathogenesis of vinyl chloride disease. Br. med. J., i, 936-938

Warren, H.S., Huff, J.E. & Gerstner, H.B. (1978) Vinyl Chloride - A Review. An Annotated Literature Collection 1835-1975. A Literature Compilation 1976-1977, ORNL/TIRC-78/3, Oak Ridge, Tennessee, Oak Ridge National Laboratory

Watanabe, P.G. & Gehring, P.J. (1976) Dose-dependent fate of vinyl chloride and its possible relationship to oncogenicity in rats. Environ. Health Perspect., 17, 145-152

Watanabe, P.G., Hefner, R.E., Jr & Gehring, P.J. (1976a) Vinyl chloride-induced depression of hepatic non-protein sulfhydryl content and effects on bromosulphalein (BSP) clearance in rats. Toxicology, 6, 1-8

Watanabe, P.G., McGowan, G.R., Madrid, E.O. & Gehring, P.J. (1976b) Fate of [$^{14}$C] vinyl chloride following inhalation exposure in rats. Toxicol. appl. Pharmacol., 37, 49-59

Watanabe, P.G., McGowan, G.R. & Gehring, P.J. (1976c) Fate of [$^{14}$C]vinyl chloride after single oral administration in rats. Toxicol. appl. Pharmacol., 36, 339-352

Waxweiler, R.J., Stringer, W., Wagoner, J.K., Jones, J., Falk, H. & Carter, C. (1976) Neoplastic risk among workers exposed to vinyl chloride. Ann. NY Acad. Sci., 271, 40-48

Weast, R.C., ed. (1976) CRC Handbook of Chemistry and Physics, 57th ed., Cleveland, Ohio, Chemical Rubber Co., p. C-298

Wegman, D. (1975) Discussion to paper of Lange et al. (1975). Further results in polyvinyl chloride production workers. Ann. NY Acad. Sci., 246, 20-21

Wilkinson, L.B., Norman, C.W. & Buettner, J.P. (1964)  Determination of residual monomers in latex by gas chromatography. Analyt. Chem., 36, 1759-1762

Williams, D.M.J., Taylor, K.J.W., Crossley, I.R., Smith, P.M. & Duck, B.W. (1975)  Pre-symptomatic detection of liver changes in vinyl chloride monomer workers (Abstract No. 189). Digestion, 12, 362

Williams, D.M.J., Smith, P.M., Taylor, K.J.W., Crossley, I.R. & Duck, B.W. (1976)  Monitoring liver disorders in vinyl chloride monomer workers using greyscale ultrasonography. Br. J. ind. Med., 33, 152-157

Williams, D.T. (1976a)  Confirmation of vinyl chloride in foods by conversion to 1-chloro-1,2-dibromoethane. J. Assoc. off. anal. Chem., 59, 32-34

Williams, D.T. (1976b)  Gas-liquid chromatographic headspace method for vinyl chloride in vinegars and alcoholic beverages. J. Assoc. off. anal. Chem., 59, 30-31

Williams, D.T. & Miles, W.F. (1975)  Gas-liquid chromatographic determination of vinyl chloride in alcoholic beverages, vegetable oils, and vinegars. J. Assoc. off. anal. Chem., 58, 272-275

Windholz, M., ed. (1976)  The Merck Index, 9th ed., Rahway, NJ, Merck & Co., pp. 986, 1283

Withey, J.R. (1976)  Pharmacodynamics and uptake of vinyl chloride monomer administered by various routes to rats. J. Toxicol. environ. Health, 1, 381-394

Yllner, S. (1971)  Metabolism of chloroacetate-1-$^{14}$C in the mouse. Acta pharmacol. Toxicol., 30, 69-80

Zeisler, E.P. (1940)  Dermatitis from Elasti-glass garters and wristwatch straps. J. Am. med. Assoc., 114, 2540-2542

VINYLIDENE CHLORIDE and
VINYLIDENE CHLORIDE-VINYL CHLORIDE COPOLYMERS

## Vinylidene chloride

### 1. Chemical and Physical Data

#### 1.1 Synonyms and trade names

Chem. Abstr. Services Reg. No.: 75-35-4

Chem. Abstr. Name: 1,1-Dichloroethene

1,1-Dichloroethylene; *asym*-dichloroethylene

Sconatex

#### 1.2 Structural and molecular formulae and molecular weight

$$\underset{H}{\overset{H}{\rangle}} C = C \underset{Cl}{\overset{Cl}{\langle}}$$

$C_2H_2Cl_2$                    Mol. wt: 97.0

#### 1.3 Chemical and physical properties of the pure substance

From Weast (1976), unless otherwise specified

(a) Description: Clear liquid with a sweet odour (Hardie, 1964; Windholz, 1976)

(b) Boiling-point: $32^{\circ}C$ (Windholz, 1976)

(c) Melting-point: $-122.1^{\circ}C$

(d) Density: $d^{20}$ 1.218; vapour density, 3.4 (air = 1) (Anon., 1972)

(e) Refractive index: $n_D^{20}$ 1.4249

(f) Spectroscopy data: $\lambda$ vapour <200 nm; infra-red, nuclear magnetic resonance and mass spectral data have been tabulated (Grasselli & Ritchey, 1975).

(g) <u>Solubility</u>:  Insoluble in water (0.04% wt/vol at 20°C);
miscible with most organic solvents (Hardie, 1964)

(h) <u>Volatility</u>:  Vapour pressure is 400 mm at 14.8°C (Perry &
Chilton, 1973).

(i) <u>Stability</u>:  Flash-point (closed cup), -17°C (Anon., 1972);
easily polymerized at temperatures above 0°C in the presence
of oxygen or other catalysts (Windholz, 1976)

(j) <u>Conversion factor</u>:  1 ppm in air $\simeq$ 4 mg/m$^3$

## 1.4  Technical products and impurities

Vinylidene chloride available commercially in the US has the following
typical specifications:  vinylidene chloride, 99.6 wt %;  acetylene, 25 mg/
kg max;  other chlorinated hydrocarbons, none exceeding 0.25 wt %;  acidity
(as hydrogen chloride), 10 mg/kg max;  peroxide (as hydrogen peroxide),
10 mg/kg max;  water, 50 mg/kg max;  and inhibitor (monomethyl ether of
hydroquinone), 180-220 mg/kg (PPG Industries, Inc., 1975).

Typical specifications for vinylidene chloride produced in Japan are
as follows:  specific gravity (d$_4^{20}$), 1.2129;  melting-point, -122.1°C;
boiling-point, 33.4°C;  and refractive index (n$_D^{20}$), 1.4249.

## 2.  Production, Use, Occurrence and Analysis

## 2.1  Production and use

### (a)  Production

Vinylidene chloride was first prepared by Regnault in 1838 by the
reaction of trichloroethane and alcoholic potassium hydroxide (Reinhardt,
1943).

Although vinylidene chloride may be prepared by several methods, it is
produced commercially in the US and Japan by the dehydrochlorination (using
sodium hydroxide or lime) of 1,1,2-trichloroethane, derived from ethylene
dichloride.  The resulting crude vinylidene chloride is purified by washing,
drying and fractional distillation.  Inhibitors are normally added at this
point (Wessling & Edwards, 1971).

The commercial production of vinylidene chloride was dependent on the
development and commercialization of vinylidene chloride copolymers and
was first reported in the US in 1940 (US Tariff Commission, 1941).  Two US
companies produced a combined total of 70 million kg vinylidene chloride
in 1976;  one of these companies manufactured an additional 50 million kg

for captive use as an unisolated intermediate in the production of 1,1,1-
trichloroethane. US imports and exports of vinylidene chloride are negligible.

It is believed that four companies in western Europe produce vinylidene
chloride, but the quantities produced are not known.

Vinylidene chloride has been produced commercially in Japan since
1951. In 1976, three companies produced a combined total of 28.1 million
kg; imports and exports are negligible.

(b) Use

Excluding the amount used as an unisolated intermediate in the
production of 1,1,1-trichloroethane, more than 90% of the vinylidene
chloride produced in the US and Japan is used in the production of copolymers of high vinylidene chloride content, the other major monomer usually
being vinyl chloride. For a discussion of the uses of vinylidene chloride-
vinyl chloride copolymers and of other vinylidene chloride-based polymers,
see p. 450.

The remaining 10% or less of the vinylidene chloride produced is used
in the manufacture of modacrylic fibres, which are largely based on
acrylonitrile with small amounts of vinylidene chloride and other monomers.
For a discussion of the uses of these fibres, see monograph on acrylic and
modacrylic fibres, p. 73.

The American Conference of Governmental Industrial Hygienists recommends that an employee's exposure to vinylidene chloride not exceed an
eight-hour time-weighted average of 40 mg/m$^3$ (10 ppm) in the workplace air
in any eight-hour work shift of a forty-hour work week. During any 15-
minute period, an absolute ceiling concentration limit of 80 mg/m$^3$ (20 ppm)
is proposed, provided the daily threshold limit value (in terms of eight-
hour time-weighted values) is not exceeded (American Conference of Governmental Industrial Hygienists, 1976).

2.2 Occurrence

Vinylidene chloride is not known to occur as a natural product.

(a) Air

Workers in manufacturing facilities using vinyl chloride in polymerization processes (e.g., polyvinyl chloride) have been reported to be exposed to vinylidene chloride (Jaeger, 1975; Ott et al., 1975) in concentrations of less than 20 mg/m$^3$ (5 ppm) and most frequently in trace amounts
(Kramer & Mutchler, 1972). Levels of 8 mg/m$^3$ (2 ppm) vinylidene chloride
have also been reported to occur as a contaminant in the atmosphere of
submarines, and levels of 0-2 ppm have been found in spacecraft (Altman &
Dittmer, 1966).

Emissions of vinylidene chloride in the US in 1974 were estimated to be 1.52 million kg from monomer synthesis operations (reduced to 277 thousand kg by new controls in late 1975), 308 thousand kg from polymer synthesis operations, and 13.8 thousand kg from polymer fabrication operations (Hushon & Kornreich, 1976).

(b) Water

Vinylidene chloride has been detected in effluent discharged from chemical manufacturing plants in The Netherlands at a concentration of 32 µg/l (Eurocop-Cost, 1976) and in effluent discharged by chemical and latex manufacturing plants in the US. It has also been identified in well, river and other untreated water in the US (Shackelford & Keith, 1976). The highest reported concentration of vinylidene chloride in finished US drinking-water was 0.1 µg/l (US Environmental Protection Agency, 1975).

(c) Other

Vinylidene chloride has been found to occur as an impurity in trichloroethylene (see IARC, 1976) (retention volume, 0.192) (Vlasov & Bodyagin, 1970), in vinyl chloride monomer (see p. 377) (limit of detection, 5 mg/kg) (Kiezel et al., 1975; Sassu et al., 1968), and at a level of 0.011% in commercial chloroprene (see p. 131) (Kurginyan & Shirinyan, 1969).

Household and industrial Saran films have been found to contain residual vinylidene chloride monomer: 6 rolls of household film had monomer concentrations ranging from 6.5-10.4 mg/kg, with an average of 8.8 mg/kg. There were no significant differences in samples taken from the beginning (outside) or the end (inside) of each roll. The industrial film showed levels ranging from 10.8-26.2 mg/kg, with levels increasing from the beginning to the end of the roll (Birkel et al., 1977).

2.3  Analysis

Vinylidene chloride has been identified in air by trapping in pyridine and colorimetric determination of the cyanine obtained by reaction with barbituric acid or aniline. The limit of detection was 10 mg/m³ (2.5 ppm) (Gronsberg, 1975).

Gas chromatography has been used to determine vinylidene chloride as an impurity (1) in trichloroethylene (Vlasov & Bodyagin, 1970) and (2) in vinyl chloride monomer (Sassu et al., 1968), with a limit of detection of 5 mg/kg (Kiezel et al., 1975). The same method has been applied to the detection of free vinylidene chloride in latex (Bollini et al., 1974).

Sampling techniques using activated carbon as adsorbent, with subsequent solvent or thermal desorption and gas chromatographic analysis, have been evaluated for determining vinylidene chloride in industrial atmospheres (Severs & Skory, 1975). A sampling technique for concentrations of air pollutants, including vinylidene chloride, on different gas chromatographic packings has also been evaluated. The compounds were thermally desorbed and analysed by gas chromatography using flame-ionization detection; the limit of detection was 4 μg/m$^3$ (1 ppb) (Russell, 1975).

Vinylidene chloride has been detected in Saran films by gas chromatography, with electron capture detection and mass spectrometry confirmation. The limit of detection of the method was 5 mg/kg (Birkel *et al.*, 1977).

### 3. Biological Data Relevant to the Evaluation
### of Carcinogenic Risk to Humans

## 3.1 Carcinogenicity studies in animals[1]

### (a) Oral administration

Rat: In a preliminary report of a study in progress, groups of 50 male and 50 female Sprague-Dawley rats were administered 5, 10 or 20 mg/kg bw vinylidene chloride in olive oil by stomach tube once daily on 4-5 days/week for 52 weeks; 1 carcinoma of the Zymbal gland was observed in a rat treated with 10 mg/kg bw. At the time of reporting, the rats had been observed for 93 weeks after the start of treatment (Maltoni *et al.*, 1977).

### (b) Inhalation and/or intratracheal administration

Mouse: In an experiment still in progress at the time of reporting, groups of Swiss mice, 9 or 16 weeks of age, were exposed for 4 hours/day on 4-5 days/week to vinylidene chloride vapours in air at concentrations of 800, 400, 200, 100 or 40 mg/m$^3$ (200, 100, 50, 25 or 10 ppm). Due to toxicity, mice treated with 200 (60 males and 60 females) or 100 ppm (30 males and 30 females) were exposed for only 2 days, and those treated with 50 ppm (30 males and 30 females) for one week only. Thirty males and 30 females were initially exposed to 25 ppm, and a further group of 120 male and 120 female mice were added when it appeared that exposure to 50-200 ppm had to be discontinued because of high mortality and severe toxic effects;

---

[1]The Working Group was aware of studies in progress to assess the carcinogenicity of vinylidene chloride in mice by skin application and s.c. injection and in mice and rats by oral administration (IARC, 1978). The Working Group was also aware of oral (drinking-water) and inhalation studies in progress in rats, in which analysis of data was not yet complete (Rampy *et al.*, 1977). Furthermore, they knew of inhalation studies in two strains of rats, which were also incomplete (Viola & Caputo, 1977).

treatment of both groups continued for 52 weeks. At the time of reporting, 98 weeks, 24/150 males and 1/150 females had developed adenocarcinomas of the kidney, often bilateral. One male of the group treated with 50 ppm for one week had a kidney adenocarcinoma. No such tumours had occurred in mice exposed to 10 ppm for 52 weeks or in 380 controls (both groups observed until 98 weeks of age) (Maltoni, 1977; Maltoni *et al.*, 1977).

A group of 36 male and 36 female CD-1 mice, 2 months of age, were exposed to 220 mg/m$^3$ (55 ppm) vinylidene chloride in air for 6 hours/day on 5 days a week for 12 months, at which time the experiment was terminated. Two males died early in the experiment and were replaced by healthy mice; 2 males were killed during the 9th month of treatment and one female during the 10th month. Bronchiolo-alveolar adenomas occurred in 6 mice and angiosarcomas of the liver occurred in 3 mice treated with vinylidene chloride; no such tumours occurred in controls. Three hepatomas and 2 skin keratoacanthomas were also reported to occur in treated mice (Lee *et al.*, 1977, 1978) [The Working Group noted the short duration of the experiment].

Rat: A group of 36 male and 36 female CD rats were exposed to 220 mg/ m$^3$ (55 ppm) vinylidene chloride in air for 6 hours/day on 5 days a week for up to 12 months, at which time the experiment was terminated and all survivors killed. Two rats developed angiosarcomas, one in a mesenteric lymph node and one in the s.c. tissue. No such tumours occurred in controls (Lee *et al.*, 1977, 1978) [The Working Group noted the short duration of the experiment].

A group of 16-week-old 60 male and 60 female Sprague-Dawley rats were exposed to 800 mg/m$^3$ reduced to 600 mg/m$^3$ (200 ppm reduced to 150 ppm), and 4 further groups of 30 female and 30 male Sprague-Dawley rats of the same age were exposed to 40, 100, 200 or 400 mg/m$^3$ (10, 25, 50 or 100 ppm) vinylidene chloride in air for 4 hours/day on 4-5 days a week for 52 weeks and observed for up to 82 weeks (time of reporting). An increased incidence of mammary fibroadenomas and carcinomas (40-60%) was reported, in comparison with 100 male and 100 female controls (32%), although no dose-response relationship was found. In addition, one Zymbal gland carcinoma was seen in one rat treated with 100 ppm (Maltoni *et al.*, 1977).

Hamster: In a study still in progress, no tumours had occurred at 74 weeks among a group of 30 male and 30 female Chinese hamsters, 28-weeks of age, exposed to 100 mg/m$^3$ (25 ppm) vinylidene chloride in air for 4 hours/ day on 4-5 days a week for 52 weeks (Maltoni *et al.*, 1977).

## 3.2 Other relevant biological data

The adverse biological effects of vinylidene chloride have been reviewed (Haley, 1975; US Environmental Protection Agency, 1976; Warren & Ricci, 1978).

(a)  Experimental systems

Toxic effects

Results reported for acute toxicity studies on vinylidene chloride have been highly variable;  the lethal concentrations are dependent on dietary parameters (fed or fasted animals) and on the hepatic glutathione content, which exhibits significant diurnal variations (Jaeger et al., 1973a, 1974).  The $LC_{50}$ by inhalation for a 4-hour exposure was 40-60 $g/m^3$ (10 000-15 000 ppm) in fed rats and 2-10 $g/m^3$ (500-2500 ppm) in fasted rats (Jaeger et al., 1973b);  the minimum lethal concentration in fed rats was 40 $g/m^3$ (10 000 ppm) for a 24-hour exposure (Jaeger et al., 1974).  The $LC_{50}$ of vinylidene chloride in rats, following exposure for 4 hours and observation for 2 weeks, was 25.4 $g/m^3$ (6350 ppm) (Siegel et al., 1971).

The oral $LD_{50}$ in mice is 200 mg/kg bw (Jones & Hathway, 1978a);  that in normal rats is 1500 mg/kg bw and that in adrenalectomized rats 80 mg/kg bw (Jenkins et al., 1972).  In dogs, the minimal oral lethal dose was 5750 mg/kg bw, and the minimal i.v. lethal dose was 225 mg/kg bw.  The minimal s.c. lethal dose in rabbits was 3900 mg/kg bw (Barsoum & Saad, 1934). Death is due to vascular collapse and shock (Jaeger et al., 1973b).

Inhalation studies using rats, guinea-pigs, dogs, rabbits and monkeys exposed to a mean level of 189 $mg/m^3$ (48 ppm) for 90 days showed significant mortality and liver damage but no changes in haematological parameters (Prendergast et al., 1967).  Inhalation of 2000 $mg/m^3$ (500 ppm) vinylidene chloride during twenty 6-hour exposures caused nasal irritation, reduced weight gain and induction of hepatic histopathological changes in rats (Gage, 1970).  Liver parenchymal-cell injury was observed in fasted rats exposed to 800 $mg/m^3$ (200 ppm) for 4 hours (Reynolds et al., 1975).

Minimal liver changes, characterized by an increase in cytoplasmic vacuolization of occasional individual hepatocytes, were noted in Sprague-Dawley rats given 6-8 mg/kg bw/day (200 mg/l) vinylidene chloride in their drinking-water for 90 days.  In a status report on a two-year study with male and female Sprague-Dawley rats receiving 16-40 mg/kg bw/day (200-230 mg/l), 8-20 mg/kg bw/day (100-120 mg/l) or 5-12 mg/kg bw/day (60-70 mg/l) in their drinking-water, no toxicological effects were noted except for a non-dose-related decrease in survival of male rats at 18 and 24 months. Rats exposed for 30 or 90 days to doses of 0.1-0.3 mg/l (25-75 ppm) in air showed minimal toxicological effects in the liver (Norris, 1977).

Vinylidene chloride affects the activity of several liver enzymes; notably, it decreases hepatic glucose-6-phosphatase and increases serum alanine $\alpha$-ketoglutarate transaminase.  It increases the liver content of triglycerides and decreases that of glutathione.  Decreased hepatic gluta-thione concentrations (Jaeger et al., 1973a,c) and the microsomal enzyme inducers, phenobarbital and 3-methylcholanthrene (Carlson & Fuller, 1972), increase the lethality and hepatotoxicity of vinylidene chloride.

Vinyl chloride, when administered simultaneously with vinylidene chloride, prevented the hepatotoxicity associated with vinylidene chloride inhalation in fasted rats (Jaeger, 1975).

Various epoxides (1,1,1-trichloropropane-2,3-oxide;  2,3-epoxypropan-1-ol;  styrene oxide;  butadiene monoxide;  and cyclohexene oxide) enhanced the hepatoxicity of vinylidene chloride in male rats and decreased the acute oral $LD_{50}$ (Andersen & Jenkins, 1977).

Embryotoxicity and teratogenicity

Rats were given vinylidene chloride either as 200 mg/l in the drinking-water or as 80-640 mg/m$^3$ (20-160 ppm) by inhalation for 7 hours/day on days 6-15 of gestation;  rabbits were given the same dose by inhalation on days 6-18 of gestation.  No teratogenic effect was seen in either rats or rabbits, although some evidence of embryotoxicity and foetotoxicity was observed in both species exposed by inhalation;  these effects were associated with maternally toxic levels of exposure (Norris, 1977).

Absorption, distribution, excretion and metabolism

As the dose level of radioactive vinylidene chloride is increased in rats from 1-50 mg/kg bw orally, or from 40-800 mg/m$^3$ (10-200 ppm) by inhalation, the metabolic pathway becomes saturated, so that a smaller percentage of the dose administered is metabolized and more is eliminated *via* the lungs as vinylidene chloride. With the 1 mg/kg bw oral dose and the 10 ppm inhalation dose, there was no difference in elimination by fed *versus* fasted rats. At 50 mg/kg bw orally or 200 ppm by inhalation, there was a significant increase in the excretion of vinylidene chloride *via* the lungs and a decrease in urinary excretion of radioactivity in fed *versus* fasted rats (Norris, 1977). The main excretory route for $^{14}$C-vinylidene chloride after i.g., i.v. or i.p. administration to rats is pulmonary: both unchanged vinylidene chloride and related $CO_2$ are excreted by that route;  other vinylidene chloride metabolites are eliminated *via* the kidneys. Biotransformation of vinylidene chloride gives thiodihydroxy-acetic acid and an *N*-acetyl-*S*-cysteinylacetyl derivative as major urinary metabolites, together with substantial amounts of chloroacetic acid, di-thiohydroxyacetic acid (dithioglycolic acid) and thiohydroxyacetic acid (thioglycolic acid) (Jones & Hathway, 1978b).

Mice metabolize a greater proportion of an oral dose of 50 mg/kg bw vinylidene chloride than rats;  and mice (but not rats) excrete a small amount of *N*-acetyl-*S*-(2-carboxymethyl)cysteine and excrete more *N*-acetyl-*S*-cysteinylacetyl derivative than do rats (Jones & Hathway, 1978a).

Metabolic conversion of vinylidene chloride into an epoxide which can rearrange to the corresponding acyl chloride has been proposed (Henschler, 1978;  Jones & Hathway, 1978a,b).

Mutagenicity and other short-term tests

Concentrations of 2 and 20% (20 000 and 200 000 ppm) vinylidene chloride in air produced reverse mutations in *Salmonella typhimurium* TA100 and TA1530 in the presence of 9000 x *g* supernatants from liver, lung and kidneys of mice and rats (Bartsch *et al.*, 1975) and from one human liver biopsy specimen (Bartsch *et al.*, 1976). At a concentration of 5% (50 000 ppm) in air, it is mutagenic in *S. typhimurium* TA1535 in the presence of a 9000 x *g* supernatant of liver or kidney from mice and rats pretreated with Aroclor 1254. It was weakly mutagenic in the presence of a 9000 x *g* supernatant of liver from a human subject who had been receiving long-term phenobarbital medication (Jones & Hathway, 1978c). Reverse mutations were induced in *Escherichia coli* K12 by vinylidene chloride solution in the presence of liver microsomes from mice pretreated with phenobarbital (Greim *et al.*, 1975).

Vinylidene chloride was not mutagenic in the dominant lethal test in male CD-1 mice exposed by inhalation to 40, 120 and 200 mg/m$^3$ (10, 30 and 50 ppm) for 6 hours/day for 5 days (Anderson *et al.*, 1977).

(b)  Humans

Acute exposure to high concentrations of vinylidene chloride in air results in central nervous system depression and narcosis. Repeated exposures to low concentrations are associated with liver and renal dysfunction. Skin contact with vinylidene chloride causes irritation, which may partly be due to the hydroquinone monomethyl ether inhibitor. Contact with the eye causes conjunctivitis and transient corneal injury (Irish, 1963).

3.3  Case reports and epidemiological studies[1]

Ott *et al.* (1976) investigated the cancer risk among a cohort of 138 workers exposed to vinylidene chloride, where vinyl chloride was not used as a copolymer. The authors reported that no findings were statistically related or individually attributable to vinylidene chloride exposure in this cohort [The Working Group noted that 27 workers were lost to follow-up but considered to be alive in the analyses, and that 55 people had less than 15 years since first exposure, and only 5 deaths were observed; these factors precluded any judgement on the findings].

---

[1]A preliminary mortality study has been reported on 629 workers from a vinylidene chloride production and polymerization plant. Exposure to vinyl chloride and acrylonitrile also occurred. There were 39 deaths, 7 of which were from malignant tumours, but this was not greater than the expected value. In persons aged 35-39 years, 2 bronchial carcinomas were observed, whereas 0.08 were expected; however, there was no information on smoking habits (Thiess *et al.*, 1979).

Vinylidene chloride-vinyl chloride copolymers

## 1.  Chemical and Physical Data

### 1.1  Synonyms and trade names

Chem. Abstr. Services Reg. No.:  9011-06-7

Chem. Abstr. Name:  1,1-Dichloroethene polymer with chloroethene

Chloroethylene-1,1-dichloroethylene polymer;  1,1-dichloroethylene-monochloroethylene polymer;  1,1-dichloroethylene polymer with chloroethylene;  vinyl chloride copolymer with vinylidene chloride; vinyl chloride-1,1-dichloroethylene copolymer;  vinyl chloride-vinylidene chloride copolymer;  vinyl chloride-vinylidene chloride polymer;  vinylidene chloride-vinyl chloride polymer

Breon 202;  Breon CS 100/30;  Daran;  Daran CR 6795H;  Dow 874; Dow Latex 874;  ET 67;  Geon 222;  Geon 652;  IKhS 1;  KhS 596; Kurehalon AO;  Laplen;  Latex SVKh;  Polyco 2611;  QX 2168; Saran 683;  Saran 746;  Saran Resin 683;  SP 489;  SVKh 1; SVKh 40;  UP 925;  Velon;  VIKh 65;  Viniden 60;  VKhVD 40; Winiden 60

### 1.2  Structural and molecular formulae and molecular weight

$$\left[\begin{array}{cc} H & Cl \\ | & | \\ C & - C \\ | & | \\ H & Cl \end{array}\right]_x \quad \text{in combination with} \quad \left[\begin{array}{cc} H & Cl \\ | & | \\ C & - C \\ | & | \\ H & H \end{array}\right]_y$$

$$(C_2H_2Cl_2)_x - (C_2H_3Cl)_y \qquad \text{Mol. wt:  10 000-100 000}$$

### 1.3  Chemical and physical properties of the copolymers

(a)  Description:  Crystalline or amorphous powder, depending upon the content of vinylidene chloride (Anon., 1973)

(b)  Melting-point:  183-195°C (Wessling & Edwards, 1971)

(c) <u>Solubility</u>:  Soluble in tetrahydrofuran, 1,4-dioxane, cyclohexanone, cyclopentanone, chlorobenzene and dichloro-benzene (Wessling & Edwards, 1971).

(d) <u>Stability</u>:  Resistant to sunlight and weathering; $\gamma$-rays cause cross-linking and chain scission (Wessling & Edwards, 1971).

## 1.4  Technical products and impurities

Vinylidene chloride-vinyl chloride copolymers are available commer-cially in the US as resins, latexes, films and fibres.  The identity and amounts of impurities in these products are not published and no detailed information on the possible presence of unreacted monomers in the polymers was available to the Working Group (but see section (c), p. 442).  In general, products obtained by emulsion polymerization (i.e., latexes) con-tain varying amounts of additives used in the polymerization process, such as initiators, activators and surface-active agents.

The vinylidene chloride-vinyl chloride copolymers commercially available in Japan are believed to be based on 80-90% vinylidene chloride units.


## 2.  Production, Use, Occurrence and Analysis

## 2.1  Production and use

### (a)  Production

The polymerization of vinylidene chloride was first observed by Regnault in 1838.  Commercial development of the polymer in the US began during the 1930's.  The pure homopolymer is difficult to fabricate, because its softening point is very close to its decomposition point.  The discovery that inclusion of small amounts of other monomers lowered the softening point led to the commercial introduction in the US in 1940 of the family of vinylidene chloride copolymers now known as Saran (Gabbett & Smith, 1964). The copolymers of current commercial interest in the US are:  vinylidene chloride-vinyl chloride (Saran B), vinylidene chloride-alkyl acrylate (Saran C) and vinylidene chloride-acrylonitrile (Saran F).  Because 'Saran' has now come to be used in the US as a generic term for all copolymers of high vinylidene chloride content, and because these copolymers are also often referred to simply as 'polyvinylidene chloride', the composition of the copolymers described in the literature is not always known.

Vinylidene chloride-vinyl chloride copolymers are now produced in the US by free-radical processes, emulsion or suspension.  In Japan, they are produced by an emulsion process.  The emulsion process produces a polymer latex which can be used directly (usually with additional stabilizing ingredients); alternatively, the polymer can be recovered, usually by coagulation with an electrolyte, followed by washing and drying. The emulsion process has the advantage of producing a higher molecular weight polymer than the suspension process and the disadvantage that a relatively high concentration of additives must be used, which may affect some of the properties of the polymer. Suspension polymerization is usually employed for copolymers to be used as moulding and extruding resins.

Four US manufacturers now produce vinylidene chloride-vinyl chloride copolymer resins, latexes and films, and one manufacturer produces vinylidene chloride-vinyl chloride fibre. US production of vinylidene chloride copolymers in 1977 was 68 million kg (Anon., 1977).

Vinylidene chloride-vinyl chloride copolymers were first produced commercially in Japan in 1951. In 1976, four companies produced an estimated 31.9 million kg, 2.7 million kg of which were fibre and the remainder, latex and film.

(b) Use

Vinylidene chloride-vinyl chloride copolymers have become widely used, due to the fact that they are impermeable to water and gases, resistant to oil, grease, chemicals and sunlight, flexible and can be heat-sealed. In addition, their high chlorine content gives them the property of fire retardants.

Vinylidene chloride-vinyl chloride copolymers are used in the form of films for food packaging (the largest use); coatings for cellophane, paper and other surfaces; fibres; and tubes and pipes. In food packaging they are used in household food wraps; industrial food wraps for drum liners, cheese, luncheon meat and sausage; shrink film for beef, poultry and cheese; and in laminations for cap liners, cosmetics and luncheon meat.

A relatively new use is in a coextruded, multi-layered film of polyethylene on a vinylidene chloride-vinyl chloride copolymer core, which is used in colostomy bags (Roth, 1976).

Vinylidene chloride-vinyl chloride copolymers are used as coatings in many applications, and as such are used in two forms: solvent-soluble resins, and water dispersions or latexes. The solvent-soluble resins are used to coat other polymer films such as cellophane (the largest single application), paper drinking cups and plates, and paperboard cartons. Other uses include interior coatings for ship tanks, railroad tank cars and fuel storage tanks, coatings for steel piles and structures, and binders in coatings for magnetic tapes, audio tapes, video tapes and computer tapes (Roth, 1976; Wessling & Edwards, 1971).

The latexes are employed for coating paper used in packaging potato crisps, pretzels, cereal and cake mixes; for coating polypropylene and other plastics for packaging and single serving containers; and for coating

paperboard for packaging sweets, baked goods and frozen and refrigerated
items. Other applications include use as binders for paints and nonwoven
fabrics and as an additive to cement to make high-strength mortars and
concretes (Roth, 1976; Wessling & Edwards, 1971).

Extruded fibres made from vinylidene chloride-vinyl chloride copolymer
resins are used in a wide variety of applications where resistance to
sunlight and chemicals is required (e.g., automotive seat covers, outdoor
furniture, agricultural shade cloth and filter fabrics) (Wessling &
Edwards, 1971).

Vinylidene chloride-vinyl chloride copolymer resins are also extruded
into tubes, rods, pipes and pipe liners for use in contact with chemicals
and other corrosive media (Wessling & Edwards, 1971).

In Japan, approximately 8% of the vinylidene chloride-vinyl chloride
copolymers produced are in the form of fibres used for fishing nets,
interior furnishings and construction appliances. Approximately 75% are
used in film applications, 13% in latex applications and 4% in other
unspecified applications.

The US Food and Drug Administration permits the use of vinylidene
chloride copolymers (including the copolymers with vinyl chloride) as
components of the following products when they are intended for use in
contact with food: (1) adhesives; (2) resinous and polymer coatings;
(3) paper and paperboard; (4) rigid and semirigid acrylic and modified
acrylic plastics; (5) polyethylene-phthalate polymers; and (6) packaging material for use during the irradiation of prepackaged foods (US Food
and Drug Administration, 1977).

## 2.2 Occurrence

Vinylidene chloride-vinyl chloride copolymers are not known to occur
as natural products.

## 2.3 Analysis

The analytical chemistry of vinyl polymers, including vinylidene
chloride-vinyl chloride copolymers, has been reviewed (Cobler *et al.*, 1968).
Methods of detecting surface finishing agents, such as vinylidene chloride
polymers, on paper have also been reviewed (Proksch, 1969).

Methods of identifying polymer films, including vinylidene chloride
copolymers, are based on physical and chemical properties (Briston, 1974;
Van Gieson, 1969).

### 3. Biological Data Relevant to the Evaluation
### of Carcinogenic Risk to Humans

#### 3.1 Carcinogenicity studies in animals

No data were available to the Working Group.

#### 3.2 Other relevant biological data

(a) Experimental systems

Rats and dogs fed a diet containing 5% of a vinylidene chloride-vinyl chloride copolymer for two years showed no toxic effects (Seeler et al., unpublished, cited by Wilson & McCormick, 1954).

Rabbits treated for three months with i.v. injections of 1 ml/kg bw of a 1% solution of a vinylidene chloride-vinyl chloride copolymer exhibited hypertrophy of the reticuloendothelial cells of the spleen, bone marrow, liver, lymphatic tissue and lungs (Miyasaki, 1959).

No data on the embryotoxicity, teratogenicity, metabolism or mutagenicity of this compound were available to the Working Group.

(b) Humans

One case of contact dermatitis, limited to the area of its application, has been reported after use of Saran wrap (a vinylidene chloride-vinyl chloride copolymer); a positive patch test was also obtained (Osbourn, 1964).

Two workers developed persistent cranial nerve disorders after cleaning out tank cars in which an aqueous dispersion of vinylidene chloride copolymers had been transported. The trigeminal nerve was principally involved, and to a lesser degree the occipital auricular and cervical cutaneous nerves as well as the muscles of mastication, the eye muscles and the hypoglossus (Henschler et al., 1970).

#### 3.3 Case reports and epidemiological studies

No data were available to the Working Group.

### 4. Summary of Data Reported and Evaluation

#### 4.1 Experimental data

Vinylidene chloride was tested in rats by oral administration and in mice, rats and hamsters by inhalation exposure. When given by inhalation in rats and mice, it induced malignant tumours, including angiosarcomas.

The preliminary results of another inhalation study in rats and mice indicate the induction of malignant tumours of the kidney in mice, mostly males, and an increased incidence of mammary tumours in rats. No carcinogenic effect was observed in a study in progress in hamsters exposed to vinylidene chloride by inhalation. The study by oral administration in rats is still underway and cannot be evaluated.

Vinylidene chloride is mutagenic.

No data on the carcinogenicity of vinylidene chloride-vinyl chloride copolymers were available to the Working Group.

## 4.2 Human data

The production volume of vinylidene chloride is high, and the material is utilized almost entirely in the production of copolymers. This suggests that occupationally exposed groups might be identified for epidemiological investigation. Production of vinylidene chloride-vinyl chloride copolymers is extensive, and their use in consumer products (including food packaging) indicates the possibility of widespread human exposure.

The only epidemiological study available to the Working Group reported that no tumours were associated with exposure to vinylidene chloride, but the data were not adequate to permit an assessment of carcinogenicity.

No case reports or epidemiological studies relevant to the carcinogenicity of vinylidene chloride-vinyl chloride copolymers were available to the Working Group.

## 4.3 Evaluation

The single epidemiological study on vinylidene chloride available to the Working Group was not adequate to permit an assessment of human carcinogenicity.

In view of the substantial volume of vinylidene chloride manufactured, the use of this compound in copolymers, the identification of the material in industrial emissions and in drinking-water, and its presence in some trichloroethylene, some chloroprene and in household materials, the lack of human epidemiological studies is serious.

The available experimental evidence indicates that vinylidene chloride produces malignant tumours in mice and rats and that some of the tumours are similar to those produced by vinyl chloride. This evidence is, however, limited by the fact that it is based partly on studies which were still in progress. An evaluation of the carcinogenicity of vinylidene chloride will be made when studies known to be underway are completed.

## 5. References

Altman, P.L. & Dittmer, D.S. (1966)  Environmental Biology, Bethesda, MD, Federation of American Societies for Experimental Biology, pp. 326, 328

American Conference of Governmental Industrial Hygienists (1976)  TLVs ®  Threshold Limit Values for Chemical Substances in Workroom Air Adopted by ACGIH for 1976, Cincinnati, Ohio, p. 30

Anon. (1972)  Fire Protection Guide on Hazardous Materials, 4th ed., Boston, Mass., National Fire Protection Association, pp. 42-229, 325M-138

Anon. (1973)  Other vinyl polymers. In:  Chemical Technology:  An Encyclopedic Treatment, Vol. VI, New York, Barnes & Noble, pp. 540-543

Anon. (1977)  Vinylidene chloride linked to cancer.  Chemical Engineering News, 28 February, pp. 6-7

Andersen, M.E. & Jenkins, L.J., Jr (1977)  Enhancement of 1,1-dichloroethylene hepatotoxicity by pretreatment with low molecular weight epoxides (Abstract No. 41).  Toxicol. appl. Pharmacol., 41, 148

Anderson, D., Hodge, M.C.E. & Purchase, I.F.H. (1977)  Dominant lethal studies with the halogenated olefins vinyl chloride and vinylidene dichloride in male CD-1 mice.  Environ. Health Perspect., 21, 71-78

Barsoum, G.S. & Saad, K. (1934)  Relative toxicity of certain chlorine derivatives of the aliphatic series.  Q. J. Pharm. Pharmacol., 7, 205-214

Bartsch, H., Malaveille, C., Montesano, R. & Tomatis, L. (1975)  Tissue-mediated mutagenicity of vinylidene chloride and 2-chlorobutadiene in Salmonella typhimurium.  Nature (Lond.), 255, 641-643

Bartsch, H., Malaveille, C. & Montesano, R. (1976)  The predictive value of tissue-mediated mutagenicity assays to assess the carcinogenic risk of chemicals.  In: Montesano, R., Bartsch, H. & Tomatis, L., eds, Screening Tests in Chemical Carcinogenesis (IARC Scientific Publications No. 12), Lyon, pp. 467-491

Birkel, T.J., Roach, J.A.G. & Sphon, J.A. (1977)  Determination of vinylidene chloride in Saran films by electron capture gas-solid chromatography and confirmation by mass spectrometry.  J. Assoc. off. anal. Chem., 60, 1210-1213

Bollini, M., Seves, A. & Focher, B. (1974)  Determination of free monomers in water emulsions of synthetic polymers or copolymers (Ital).  Ind. Carta, 12, 234-240 [Chem. Abstr., 81, 121672b]

Briston, J.H. (1974)  Appendix B.  Identification of film materials.  In:
Plastics Films, New York, John Wiley and Sons, pp. 287-293

Carlson, G.P. & Fuller, G.C. (1972)  Interaction of modifiers of hepatic
microsomal drug metabolism and the inhalation toxicity of 1,1-dichloro-
ethylene.  Res. Comm. chem. Pathol. Pharmacol., 4, 553-559

Cobler, J.G., Long, M.W. & Owens, E.G. (1968)  Analytical chemistry of
vinyl film-forming polymers.  In:  Sweeting, O.J., ed., Sci. Technol.
Polym. Films, Vol. 1, New York, Interscience, pp. 703-812 [Chem. Abstr.,
70, 78587m]

Eurocop-Cost (1976)  A Comprehensive List of Polluting Substances which
have been Identified in Various Fresh Waters, Effluent Discharges,
Aquatic Animals and Plants and Bottom Sediments, 2nd ed., EUCO/MDU/
73/76, X11/476/76, Luxembourg, Commission of the European Communities,
p. 41

Gabbett, J.F. & Smith, W.M. (1964)  Copolymerizations employing vinyl
chloride or vinylidene chloride as principal components.  In:
Ham, G.E., ed., Copolymerization, Ch. X, New York, Interscience,
p. 609

Gage, J.C. (1970)  The subacute inhalation toxicity of 109 industrial
chemicals.  Br. J. ind. Med., 27, 1-18

Grasselli, J.G. & Ritchey, W.M., eds (1975)  CRC Atlas of Spectral Data and
Physical Constants for Organic Compounds, 2nd ed., Vol. III, Cleveland,
Ohio, Chemical Rubber Co., p. 281

Greim, H., Bonse, G., Radwan, Z., Reichert, D. & Henschler, D. (1975)
Mutagenicity in vitro and potential carcinogenicity of chlorinated
ethylenes as a function of metabolic oxirane formation.  Biochem.
Pharmacol., 24, 2013-2017

Gronsberg, E.S. (1975)  Determination of vinylidene chloride in the air
(Russ.).  Gig. i Sanit., 7, 77-79

Haley, T.J. (1975)  Vinylidene chloride:  a review of the literature.
Clin. Toxicol., 8, 633-643

Hardie, D.W.F. (1964)  Chlorocarbons and chlorohydrocarbons.  Dichloro-
ethylenes.  In:  Kirk, R.E. & Othmer, D.F., eds, Encyclopedia of
Chemical Technology, 2nd ed., Vol. 5, New York, John Wiley and Sons,
pp. 178-180

Henschler, D. (1978)  Metabolism and mutagenicity of halogenated olefins.
A comparison of structure and activity.  Environ. Health Perspect.,
21, 61-64

Henschler, D., Broser, F. & Hopf, H.C. (1970) 'Polyneuritis cranialis' following poisoning with chlorinated acetylenes while handling vinylidene copolymers (Ger.). Arch. Toxikol., 26, 62-75

Hushon, J. & Kornreich, M. (1976) Air Pollution Assessment of Vinylidene Chloride, Springfield, Va, US National Technical Information Service, PB 256 738, p. 40

IARC (1976) IARC Monographs on the Evaluation of Carcinogenic Risk of Chemicals to Man, 11, Cadmium, Nickel, Some Epoxides, Miscellaneous Industrial Chemicals and General Considerations on Volatile Anaesthetics, Lyon, p. 263

IARC (1978) Information Bulletin on the Survey of Chemicals Being Tested for Carcinogenicity, No. 7, Lyon, pp. 70, 257, 272, 278

Irish, D.D. (1963) Aliphatic halogenated hydrocarbons. In: Patty, F.A., ed., Industrial Hygiene and Toxicology, Vol. II, 2nd revised ed., New York, Interscience, pp. 1305-1307

Jaeger, R.J. (1975) Vinyl chloride monomer: comments on its hepatotoxicity and interaction with 1,1-dichloroethylene. Ann. NY Acad. Sci., 246, 150-151

Jaeger, R.J., Conolly, R.B. & Murphy, S.D. (1973a) Diurnal variation of hepatic glutathione concentration and its correlation with 1,1-dichloroethylene inhalation toxicity in rats. Res. Comm. chem. Pathol. Pharmacol., 6, 465-471

Jaeger, R.J., Trabulus, M.J. & Murphy, S.D. (1973b) The interaction of adrenalectomy, partial adrenal replacement therapy, and starvation with hepatotoxicity and lethality of 1,1-dichloroethylene intoxication (Abstract No. 133). Toxicol. appl. Pharmacol., 25, 491

Jaeger, R.J., Trabulus, M,J. & Murphy, S.D. (1973c) Biochemical effects of 1,1-dichloroethylene in rats: dissociation of its hepatotoxicity from a lipoperoxidative mechanism. Toxicol. appl. Pharmacol., 24, 457-467

Jaeger, R.J., Conolly, R.B. & Murphy, S.D. (1974) Effect of 18 hr fast and glutathione depletion on 1,1-dichloroethylene-induced hepatotoxicity and lethality in rats. Exp. mol. Pathol., 20, 187-198

Jenkins, L.J., Jr, Trabulus, M.J. & Murphy, S.D. (1972) Biochemical effects of 1,1-dichloroethylene in rats: comparison with carbon tetrachloride and 1,2-dichloroethylene. Toxicol. appl. Pharmacol., 23, 501-510

Jones, B.K. & Hathway, D.E. (1978a) Differences in metabolism of vinylidene chloride between mice and rats. Br. J. Cancer, 37, 411-417

Jones, B.K. & Hathway, D.E. (1978b)  The biological fate of vinylidene
    chloride in rats.  Chem.-biol. Interact., 20, 27-41

Jones, B.K. & Hathway, D.E. (1978c)  Tissue-mediated mutagenicity of
    vinylidene chloride in Salmonella typhimurium TA1535.  Cancer Lett.,
    5, 1-6

Kiezel, L., Liszka, M. & Rutkowski, M. (1975)  Gas chromatographic deter-
    mination of trace impurities in distillates of vinyl chloride
    monomer (Pol.).  Chem. Anal. (Warsaw), 20, 555-562 [Chem. Abstr.,
    83, 212233s]

Kramer, C.G. & Mutchler, J.E. (1972)  The correlation of clinical and
    environmental measurements for workers exposed to vinyl chloride.
    Am. ind. Hyg. Assoc. J., 33, 19-30

Kurginyan, K.A. & Shirinyan, V.T. (1969)  Identification and quantitative
    determination of some impurities in chloroprene (Russ.).  Arm. Khim.
    Zh., 22, 61-65 [Chem. Abstr., 71, 29974x]

Lee, C.C., Bhandari, J.C., Winston, J.M., House, W.B., Peters, P.J.,
    Dixon, R.L. & Woods, J.S. (1977)  Inhalation toxicity of vinyl
    chloride and vinylidene chloride.  Environ. Health Perspect., 21,
    25-32

Lee, C.C., Bhandari, J.C., Winston, J.M., House, W.B., Dixon, R.L. &
    Woods, J.S. (1978)  Carcinogenicity of vinyl chloride and vinylidene
    chloride.  J. Toxicol. environ. Health, 4, 15-30

Maltoni, C. (1977)  Recent findings on the carcinogenicity of chlorinated
    olefins.  Environ. Health Perspect., 21, 1-5

Maltoni, C., Cotti, G., Morisi, L. & Chieco, P. (1977)  Carcinogenicity
    bioassays of vinylidene chloride.  Research plan and early results.
    Med. Lav., 68, 241-262

Miyasaki, K. (1959)  Experimental studies on the reticulo-endothelial
    system by intravenous injection of high molecular synthetic vinyl
    compounds in rabbits.  Acta pathol. jpn., 9, 109-131

Norris, J.M. (1977)  Toxicological and pharmacokinetic studies on inhaled
    and ingested vinylidene chloride in laboratory animals.  In:  Proceed-
    ings of the Technical Association of the Pulp and Paper Industry (TAPPI)
    Paper Synthetics Conference, Chicago, Ill., 1977

Osbourn, R.A. (1964)  Contact dermatitis caused by Saran wrap.  J. Am.
    med. Assoc., 188, 1159

Ott, M.G., Langner, R.R. & Holder, B.B. (1975)  Vinyl chloride exposure in
    a controlled industrial environment.  A long-term mortality experience
    in 594 employees.  Arch. environ. Health, 30, 333-339

Ott, M.G., Fishbeck, W.A., Townsend, J.C. & Schneider, E.J. (1976)  A
    health study of employees exposed to vinylidene chloride. J. occup.
    Med., 18, 735-738

Perry, R.H. & Chilton, C.H., eds (1973)  Chemical Engineers' Handbook,
    5th ed., New York, McGraw-Hill, p. 3-61

PPG Industries, Inc. (1975)  Vinylidene Chloride, Bulletin 120A, Pittsburgh,
    Pa

Prendergast, J.A., Jones, R.A., Jenkins, L.J., Jr & Siegel, J. (1967)
    Effects on experimental animals of long-term inhalation of trichloro-
    ethylene, carbon tetrachloride, 1,1,1-trichloroethane, dichlorodi-
    fluoromethane, and 1,1-dichloroethylene. Toxicol. appl. Pharmacol.,
    10, 270-289

Proksch, A. (1969)  Determination of chemical auxiliary and finishing
    agents [for paper] by rapid methods (Ger.). Allg. Pap.-Rundsch., 35,
    1207-1208 [Chem. Abstr., 72, 4461k]

Rampy, L.W., Quast, J.F., Humiston, C.G., Balmer, M.F. & Schwetz, B.A.
    (1977)  Interim results of two-year toxicological studies in rats of
    vinylidene chloride incorporated in the drinking water or administered
    by repeated inhalation. Environ. Health Perspect., 21, 33-43

Reinhardt, R.C. (1943)  Vinylidene chloride polymers. Ind. Eng. Chem.,
    35, 422-428

Reynolds, E.S., Moslen, M.T., Szabo, S., Jaeger, R.J. & Murphy, S.D. (1975)
    Hepatotoxicity of vinyl chloride and 1,1-dichloroethylene. Am. J.
    Pathol., 81, 219-236

Roth, S.F. (1976)  Saran coatings - latex or lacquer?  In:  Chemical
    Marketing and Economics Reprints, Staten Island, New York, Chemical
    Marketing and Economics Division of the American Chemical Society,
    pp. 29-36

Russell, J.W. (1975)  Analysis of air pollutants using sampling tubes and
    gas chromatography. Environ. Sci. Technol., 9, 1175-1178

Sassu, G.M., Zilio-Grandi, F. & Conte, A. (1968)  Gas chromatographic
    determination of impurities in vinyl chloride. J. Chromatogr., 34,
    394-398

Severs, L.W. & Skory, L.K. (1975)  Monitoring personnel exposure to vinyl
    chloride, vinylidene chloride and methyl chloride in an industrial
    work environment. Am. ind. Hyg. Assoc. J., 39, 669-676

Shackelford, W.M. & Keith, L.H. (1976)  Frequency of Organic Compounds
    Identified in Water, EPA-600/4-76-062, Athens, Ga, US Environmental
    Protection Agency, pp. 130, 133-134

Siegel, J., Jones, R.A., Coon, R.A. & Lyon, J.P. (1971) Effects on experimental animals of acute, repeated and continuous inhalation exposures to dichloroacetylene mixtures. Toxicol. appl. Pharmacol., 18, 168-174

Thiess, A.M., Frentzel-Beyme, R. & Penning, E. (1979) Mortality study of vinylidene chloride exposed persons in the BASF. In: Proceedings of the Vth Medichem Congress, San Francisco, 1977 (in press)

US Environmental Protection Agency (1975) Preliminary Assessment of Suspected Carcinogens in Drinking Water, Washington DC, p. II-3

US Environmental Protection Agency (1976) Health and Environmental Impacts, Task 1, Vinylidene Chloride, EPA-560/6-76-023, Washington DC

US Food and Drug Administration (1977) Food and drugs. US Code Fed. Regul., Title 21, Parts 175.105, 175.300, 175.320, 175.360, 175.365, 176.170, 176.180, 177.1010, 177.1630, 178.3790, 179.45, pp. 438, 446, 452, 455, 465, 467-469, 471, 482, 486, 489, 496, 530, 596, 607-608

US Tariff Commission (1941) Synthetic Organic Chemicals, US Production and Sales, 1940, Report No. 148, Second Series, Washington DC, US Government Printing Office, p. 58

Van Gieson, P. (1969) Here's a quick, easy way to identify films. Package Eng., 14, 76-77 [Chem. Abstr., 71, 71274u]

Viola, P.L. & Caputo, A. (1977) Carcinogenicity studies on vinylidene chloride. Environ. Health Perspect., 21, 45-47

Vlasov, S.M. & Bodyagin, G.N. (1970) Gas chromatographic analysis of trichloroethylene (Russ.). Tr. Khim. Khim. Tekhnol., 1, 161-162 [Chem. Abstr., 75, 71124c]

Warren, H.S. & Ricci, B.E. (1978) Vinylidene Chloride. I. An Overview. II. A Literature Collection 1947 to 1977, ORNL/TIRC-77/3, Oak Ridge, Tenn., Oak Ridge National Laboratory

Weast, R.C., ed. (1976) CRC Handbook of Chemistry and Physics, 57th ed., Cleveland, Ohio, Chemical Rubber Co., p. C-298

Wessling, R.A. & Edwards, F.G. (1971) Vinylidene chloride polymers. In: Bikales, N.M., ed., Encyclopedia of Polymer Science and Technology, Plastics, Resins, Rubbers, Fibers, Vol. 14, New York, Interscience, pp. 540-579

Wilson, R.H. & McCormick, W.E. (1954) Toxicology of plastics and rubber plastomers and monomers. Ind. Med. Surg., 23, 479-486

Windholz, M., ed. (1976) The Merck Index, 9th ed., Rahway, NJ, Merck & Co., p. 1283

N-VINYL-2-PYRROLIDONE and POLYVINYL PYRROLIDONE

N-Vinyl-2-pyrrolidone

1.  Chemical and Physical Data

1.1  Synonyms and trade names

Chem. Abstr. Services Reg. No.:  88-12-0

Chem. Abstr. Name:  1-Ethenyl-2-pyrrolidinone

Vinylbutyrolactam;  vinylpyrrolidinone;  1-vinylpyrrolidinone;
N-vinylpyrrolidinone;  1-vinyl-2-pyrrolidinone;  N-vinyl-2-
pyrrolidinone;  vinylpyrrolidone;  N-vinylpyrrolidone;  1-vinyl-2-
pyrrolidone

1.2  Structural and molecular formulae and molecular weight

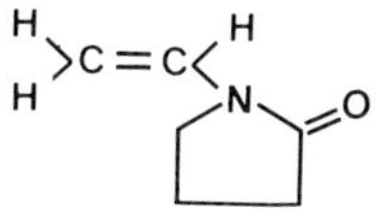

$C_6H_9NO$                 Mol. wt:  111.1

1.3  Chemical and physical properties of the pure substance

From Hort & Smith (1968) and Wood (1970), unless otherwise specified

(a)  Description:  Colourless liquid

(b)  Boiling-point:  $193^\circ C$ (400 mm);  $96^\circ C$ (14 mm)

(c)  Melting-point:  $13.5^\circ C$

(d)  Density:  $d_4^{25}$ 1.04

(e)  Refractive index:  $n_D^{25}$ 1.511

(f)  Spectroscopy data:  Infra-red, nuclear magnetic resonance
and mass spectral data have been tabulated (Grasselli &
Ritchey, 1975).

(g) Solubility: Miscible with water, ether, alcohols, esters, ketones, chlorinated hydrocarbons and aromatic hydrocarbons

(h) Viscosity: 2.07 cP (25°C)

(i) Stability: Flash-point, 98.4°C; polymerizes readily in presence of oxygen

## 1.4 Technical products and impurities

N-Vinyl-2-pyrrolidone available in the US as a commercial grade is stabilized with 100 mg/l (ppm) of N,N'-di-sec-butyl-para-phenylenediamine or caustic pellets (GAF Corporation, 1973).

## 2. Production, Use, Occurrence and Analysis

### 2.1 Production and use

#### (a) Production

N-Vinyl-2-pyrrolidone was first prepared from butyrolactone during World War II (Lorenz, 1971; Puetzer et al., 1952; Timell, 1946). It is manufactured commercially by the vinylation of 2-pyrrolidone with acetylene (Wood, 1970).

N-Vinyl-2-pyrrolidone has been produced commercially in the US since 1955 (US Tariff Commission, 1956). Only one company reported commercial production in 1976, of an undisclosed amount (see preamble, p. 22) (US International Trade Commission, 1977). US imports of N-vinyl-2-pyrrolidone, monomer and polymer combined, amounted to 716 thousand kg in 1976 and were from the Federal Republic of Germany (95%), France (2.5%), the German Democratic Republic (2.2%) and Sweden (0.3%) (US Department of Commerce, 1977).

One company in the Federal Republic of Germany and two companies in the UK manufacture N-vinyl-2-pyrrolidone.

No evidence was found that N-vinyl-2-pyrrolidone has ever been produced commercially in Japan.

#### (b) Use

Use of N-vinyl-2-pyrrolidone in the US in 1974 is estimated to have been 4.5-5.5 million kg. It is used to manufacture its homopolymer, poly-vinyl pyrrolidone, to make copolymers with other monomers and as a chemical intermediate. For information on the uses of polyvinyl pyrrolidone, see p. 466.

Copolymers are made using *N*-vinyl-2-pyrrolidone (usually at a concentration of 1-20%) with many other comonomers (e.g., acrylic acid and esters (see p. 47), vinyl acetate (see p. 341), acrylonitrile (see p. 73), etc). *N*-Vinyl-2-pyrrolidone copolymers are used in various applications, including drilling fluids (Huebotter & Gray, 1965), paints, lube oil additives, adhesives (Hort & Smith, 1968), coatings, cosmetics, textile finishes, synthetic fibres and protective colloids (GAF Corporation, 1973).

Hydrogels based on cross-linked copolymers of *N*-vinyl-2-pyrrolidone and 2-hydroxyethyl methacrylate are used in soft contact lenses (Halpern & Karo, 1977).

*N*-Vinyl-2-pyrrolidone is also used as an intermediate in the manufacture of modified phenolic resins that are used as plasticizers and of dyes and textile assistants (GAF Corporation, 1973)

The US Food and Drug Administration has ruled that *N*-vinyl-2-pyrrolidone may be used in adhesives for use in contact with food provided the level does not exceed that which is reasonably required to produce the intended effect (US Food and Drug Administration, 1977).

## 2.2  Occurrence

*N*-Vinyl-2-pyrrolidone is not known to occur as a natural product. No information on its occurrence in the environment was available to the Working Group.

## 2.3  Analysis

Gas chromatography has been used to determine *N*-vinyl-2-pyrrolidone in a mixture obtained during its synthesis (Arakelyan *et al.*, 1967).

## 3.  Biological Data Relevant to the Evaluation
## of Carcinogenic Risk to Humans

No data were available to the Working Group.


## Polyvinyl pyrrolidone

## 1.  Chemical and Physical Data

## 1.1  Synonyms and trade names

Chem. Abstr. Services Reg. No.:  9003-39-8

Chem. Abstr. Name:  1-Ethenyl-2-pyrrolidinone homopolymer

Poly[1-(2-oxo-1-pyrrolidinyl)ethylene]; polyvidone; poly(*N*-vinylbutyrolactam); poly(1-vinyl-2-pyrrolidinone); poly(vinyl-pyrrolidone); poly(1-vinyl-2-pyrrolidone); PVP; *N*-vinylbutyro-lactam polymer; vinylpyrrolidinone polymer; 1-vinyl-2-pyrrolidinone polymer; vinylpyrrolidone polymer

Albigen A; AT 717; Antaron P804; Bolinan; Charlab Palenine; Ganex P 804; Hemodesis; Hemodez; Igecoll; K 15; K 25; K 25 (polymer); K 30; K 30 (polymer); K 60; K 90; K 115; K 115 (polyamide); Kollidon; Kollidon 17; Kollidon 30; Luviskol; Luviskol K; Luviskol K 30; Luviskol K 90; MPK 90; Neocompensan; Palenine; Peragal ST; Peregal ST; Periston; Periston-n; Peviston; Plasdone; Plasdone K 29-32; Plasdone No. 4; Plasdone XL; Plasmosan; Polyclar; Polyclar AT; Polyclar H; Polyclar L; Polyvidone-Excipient; Polyvidonium; Povidone; Protagent; PVP; PVP 40; PVP-K 3; PVP-K 30; PVP-K 60; PVP-K 90; 143 RP; Subtosan; Vinisil

## 1.2  Structural and molecular formulae and molecular weight

$(C_6H_9NO)_n$          Mol. wt:  10 000-700 000

## 1.3  Chemical and physical properties of the water-soluble polymer

(a)  Description: Yellow solid (Windholz, 1976)

(b)  Density: d 1.23-1.29 (Hawley, 1971)

(c)  Spectroscopy data: Infra-red carbonyl band at 1680 cm$^{-1}$ (Ridgway & Rubinstein, 1971)

(d)  Solubility: Soluble in water, ethanol and chloroform; insoluble in ether (US Pharmacopeial Convention, 1975)

(e) <u>Stability</u>: Powder is relatively stable under normal conditions; aqueous solutions are stable for extended periods when protected from mould (Lorenz, 1971).

(f) <u>Reactivity</u>: Forms complexes with a great many substances (e.g., iodine, polyacids, toxins, drugs, toxic chemicals and dyes) (Lorenz, 1971)

## 1.4  Technical products and impurities

Polyvinyl pyrrolidone is available in the US as commercial and US Pharmacopeial (USP) grades.  There are four commercial viscosity grades, containing a maximum of 1% residual, unreacted monomer as *N*-vinyl-2-pyrrolidone and 0.02% ash (on a dry basis).  Powdered forms contain a maximum of 5% water, and aqueous solutions contain 55-80% water (Wood, 1970).

USP grade polyvinyl pyrrolidone contains 12-13% nitrogen on an anhydrous basis and a maximum of 0.00015% arsenic, 0.001% lead, 0.5% aldehyde (as acetaldehyde) and 1% unreacted *N*-vinyl-2-pyrrolidone (US Pharmacopeial Convention, 1975).

A high-molecular-weight cross-linked grade of polyvinyl pyrrolidone, which is insoluble in water, is available as a powder containing less than 5% water (Wood, 1970).

In Japan, polyvinyl pyrrolidone has a solid content of at least 98% and contains unreacted *N*-vinyl-2-pyrrolidone monomer as an impurity.

## 2.  Production, Use, Occurrence and Analysis

A review article on polyvinyl pyrrolidone has been published (Wood, 1970).

## 2.1  Production and use

### (a)  Production

Polyvinyl pyrrolidone was first prepared in Germany in the 1930s (Wood, 1970).  *N*-Vinyl-2-pyrrolidone monomer is polymerized to polyvinyl pyrrolidone by heating it in the presence of hydrogen peroxide and ammonia (Windholz, 1976).

Commercial production of polyvinyl pyrrolidone in the US was first reported in 1955 (US Tariff Commission, 1956).  One company reported production of an undisclosed amount of polyvinyl pyrrolidone in 1976 (see preamble, p. 22) (US International Trade Commission, 1977).  US imports of

the polymer and its monomer amounted to 716 thousand kg in 1976 and were
from the Federal Republic of Germany (95%), France (2.5%), the German
Democratic Republic (2.2%) and Sweden (0.3%) (US Department of Commerce,
1977).

Polyvinyl pyrrolidone is produced in the following countries in
western Europe (number of manufacturers): the Federal Republic of Germany
(1), France (2), Italy (1) and the UK (3), for a total annual production
of 2-20 million kg.

Polyvinyl pyrrolidone has never been produced commercially in Japan,
but it has been imported since 1961; imports in 1976 amounted to 180
thousand kg.

### (b) Use

At least 5 million kg of polyvinyl pyrrolidone were used in the US in
1974.

It has found numerous industrial applications due to its film-forming
and adhesive properties, its colloidal and dispersing abilities and its
capacity to form complexes with certain chemicals. It is thus used in
aerosol hair sprays, adhesives and lithographic solutions, and in the cosmetics, pharmaceutical, plastic, ink, and other industries (Wood, 1970).

In the cosmetics industry, polyvinyl pyrrolidone is used in shampoos,
hair tints and rinses, hair lotions, shaving creams, pre-electric and
after-shave lotions, pomades, hand lotions and toothpastes. In the pharmaceutical industry it is used in tablet manufacture as a binder and
coating agent; in injection preparations of antibiotics, hormones and
analgesics; and in ophthalmic and topical preparations. Polyvinyl pyrrolidone has been used as a plasma volume expander in the treatment of shock
due to severe blood loss, burns, accidents or surgical procedures; however,
it is now used under emergency conditions only, when blood and plasma
are not available (Lorenz, 1971; Wood, 1970).

In the plastics industry, polyvinyl pyrrolidone is used as a particle-
size regulator, suspending agent and viscosity modifier in two-phase polymerization systems for vinyl chloride, vinyl esters, styrene, acrylics
and other monomers. As a post-polymerization additive, it improves the
dye receptivity and stability of various latexes. When added to acetal
resins, polyvinyl pyrrolidone improves the heat stability of the dried
polymer (Wood, 1970).

Polyvinyl pyrrolidone improves the solubility of dye-based inks,
giving greater colour value per weight of dye; in pigmented inks it
increases tinctorial strength, dispersion stability and gloss (Wood, 1970).
It is also used as a pigment dispersant in paper and to improve dye receptivity in paper coatings (Lorenz, 1971).

It is used in wax and polish formulations; to retard the separation of water in cement mixtures; to prevent caking of fertilizer mixes; and in the preparation of conductive coatings for television or cathode-ray tubes. In heavy-duty detergent formulations, polyvinyl pyrrolidone prevents soil redeposition, especially on synthetic fabrics (Wood, 1970).

Hydrogels based on graft copolymers made of polyvinyl pyrrolidone and poly(2-hydroxyethyl methacrylate) are used in soft contact lenses (Halpern & Karo, 1977).

The ability of polyvinyl pyrrolidone to form complexes is the basis for several applications in the pharmaceutical, textile and beverage industries. It has been investigated for use as a detoxifying agent: thus, a polyvinyl pyrrolidone-iodine complex is used as a germicide (Wood, 1970). It is used in the textile industry as a stripping and colour-lightening agent, since it forms stable complexes with direct, vat or sulphur dyes on cotton and rayon fabric and yarn. It has been incorporated into hydrophobic fibres (e.g., polyacrylonitrile, polyesters, nylon, viscose, natural rubber and polypropylene (see p. 213)) to facilitate dyeing (Wood, 1970).

Polyvinyl pyrrolidone is used in the beverage industry because it forms complexes with many phenols and polyacids, including certain tannins, thereby improving the clarity and stability of vegetable beverages and beer, wine, whiskey, vinegar, tea and fruit juice (Lorenz, 1971). In 1971, polyvinyl pyrrolidone was reportedly used to treat over 60 million bottles of domestic US wine (Anon., 1972).

The US Food and Drug Administration has ruled that polyvinyl pyrrolidone polymers/copolymers may be used in: defoaming agents used in the manufacture of paper and paperboard (not to exceed the amount necessary to accomplish the intended technical effect), as a defoamer and dispersant adjuvant (on fresh citrus fruit only), in vinyl resinous coatings and as a defoamer in paper and paperboard components (aqueous and fatty foods only) intended for use in contact with food in amounts not to exceed that which is reasonably required to produce the intended effect unless otherwise stated. Polyvinyl pyrrolidone may also be used as a clarifying agent in beer (10 mg/1), vinegar (40 mg/1) and wine (60 mg/1); and as a stabilizer, bodying agent, dispersant and adjuvant in tablet and liquid flavour concentrates, nonnutritive sweeteners, vitamins and minerals within the limits of good manufacturing practice. When polyvinyl pyrrolidone is used as a food additive it must be as an insoluble cross-linked polymer of a grade such that, after 3 hours of refluxing with water, 5% acetic acid and 50% alcohol, no more than 50 mg/kg (ppm) extractables may be obtained with each solvent; and after it has been used to clarify a beverage, it must be removed by filtration (US Food and Drug Administration, 1977).

In western Europe, polyvinyl pyrrolidone is used in the manufacture of cosmetics such as hair lacquers, barrier creams, shaving products and shampoos; as a dye-stripping agent for textiles; as an anti-soil-redeposition agent in soaps and detergents; and in the manufacture of a number of other miscellaneous products such as adhesives, photographic chemicals, agricultural chemicals, polishes, paints and dyestuffs.

In Japan, polyvinyl pyrrolidone is used in medicinal chemicals (50%), cosmetics (20%) and other applications, primarily in adhesives (30%).

## 2.2 Occurrence

Polyvinyl pyrrolidone is not known to occur as a natural product. No information on its occurrence in the environment was available to the Working Group.

## 2.3 Analysis

Tests for the identification and purity of polyvinyl pyrrolidone are described in the US Pharmacopeia (US Pharmacopeial Convention, Inc., 1975).

Insoluble polyvinyl pyrrolidone residues in solutions of plant extracts may be determined by a method based on the capacity of the polyvinyl pyrrolidone to absorb tannic acid from solution. The proportion of added tannic acid remaining in solution is measured colorimetrically. The method is applicable in the range of 1-10 mg/ml (Dazzo & Hubbell, 1974).

A method for measuring concentrations of polyvinyl pyrrolidone as low as $10^{-6}$ M, with 2-3% precision, is based on its effect on the voltametric curves of vigorously stirred solutions of electroreducible ions (Verdier *et al.*, 1971).

Polyvinyl pyrrolidone in plasma, urine and faeces was determined spectrophotometrically by measuring the absorbance at 370 nm due to the turbidity of a solution of polyvinyl pyrrolidone produced by the addition of perchloric acid and barium chloride. The method was applicable in the range of 1-4 mg polyvinyl pyrrolidone/100 ml (Ishikawa *et al.*, 1972).

An automated nephelometric method has been described for the determination of polyvinyl pyrrolidone in the antibacterial preparation Salazopyrin, with a relative standard deviation of 0.5% (Hagel & Andersson, 1976).

A method for detecting concentrations of polyvinyl pyrrolidone in dilute solution (0.1% wt/vol) with ± 1% accuracy is based on the infra-red absorption peak at 1680 $cm^{-1}$ due to the carbonyl group (Ridgway & Rubinstein, 1971).

Residual polyvinyl pyrrolidone in beverages after its use as a clarifying agent has been determined in amounts as low as 0.1 mg/l (ppm) with a reproducibility of ±5%. The polymer is adsorbed on a column of silica gel, if the compound is soluble in 40% acetic acid solution, or on Micro-Cel E if the sample is soluble in 50% ethanol solution, and complexed *in situ* with Vital Red dye; after excess dye is eluted, the polyvinyl pyrrolidone-dye complex is eluted and determined colorimetrically (Frauenfelder, 1974).

When applied to beer, using silica gel, the method has a limit of detection of 0.6 mg/1 (ppm) (Postel, 1973).

### 3.   Biological Data Relevant to the Evaluation
### of Carcinogenic Risk to Humans

## 3.1   Carcinogenicity studies in animals[1]

### (a)   Subcutaneous and/or intramuscular administration

Mouse:  Four polyvinyl pyrrolidones (PVP), I, II, III and IV, with average molecular weights of 20 000, 22 000, 50 000 and 300 000, respectively, were implanted subcutaneously as powders into groups of 25 male and 25 female 6-week-old C57BL mice, at doses of about 200 mg/animal. Surviving mice were killed 23 months after the start of the experiment. Of mice treated with PVP IV, 1/50 developed a reticulum-cell sarcoma;  and of mice treated with PVP II, 3/50 developed lymphosarcomas.  Among 75 untreated controls, no lymphosarcomas or reticulum-cell sarcomas were noted within the 25 months of observation (Hueper, 1957).  No tumours were observed within 2 years in a further study, in which 30 C57BL mice received a s.c. implant of a PVP powder with an average molecular weight of 10 000 (200 mg dose) (Hueper, 1959).

Rat:  The same samples of PVPs, I, II, III and IV, described above were implanted subcutaneously as powders (500 mg dose) into groups of 30 3-month-old female Bethesda black rats;  1 squamous-cell carcinoma of the skin at the site of implantation was observed in the PVP IV group.  In addition, a total of 14 benign and 24 malignant neoplasms were observed in treated animals after 26 months (mainly reticulum-cell sarcomas or lymphosarcomas, Kupffer-cell sarcomas, adenocarcinomas or squamous-cell carcinomas of the uterus and adenocarcinomas of the ovary);  they were distributed similarly in the groups treated with PVPs I, III and IV, but not in the group treated with PVP II.  One reticulum-cell sarcoma was observed among 23 female untreated rats during an observation period of 13 months (Hueper, 1957) [The Working Group noted the short observation period for control rats].

---

[1]The Working Group was aware of a study by oral administration in rats, reported in WHO (1974), in which no tumours were reported to occur following administration of up to 10% PVP in the diet for 2 years.  However, full details were not available.

A sample of PVP (average molecular weight, 10 000) was administered subcutaneously as a powder (500 mg/animal) to 20 female Bethesda black rats; 4 reticulum-cell sarcomas were found. Two further PVPs (PVP 6 and 7, average molecular weight, 50 000) were administered as 200 mg of powder, either as single or thrice-repeated implants; 5/30 rats that received a single implant and 2/30 that received repeated implants developed reticulum-cell sarcomas. Malignant tumours, mainly reticulum-cell sarcomas (11) and carcinomas of the uterus, were found in 17/200 untreated rats (Hueper, 1959).

Injection-site sarcomas were observed in 13/30 rats (10 male and 10 female Osborne-Mendel rats and 10 male Bethesda black rats) that received s.c. injections of 1 ml of a 6% solution of a PVP in water weekly for 73 weeks. No local tumours were observed in rats given 0.9% saline solutions. The incidence of spontaneous tumours was unchanged (Lusky & Nelson, 1957).

(b)  Intraperitoneal administration

Mouse:  Four groups of 50 C57BL mice of both sexes received single i.p. implants of 200 mg of powder of the four PVPs described above. Within 23 months, 1 lymphosarcoma was observed in the PVP II group and 2 lymphosarcomas and 1 reticulum-cell sarcoma in the PVP III group. No lymphosarcomas or reticulum-cell sarcomas were noted among 75 untreated controls within the 25 months of observation (Hueper, 1957). Following i.p. implantation of 200 mg PVP powder with a molecular weight of 10 000, 1 lymphoma and 1 mesothelioma of the pericardium were seen in 30 experimental mice (Hueper, 1959).

Rat:  Four groups of 30 female Bethesda black rats were given i.p. implantations by laporotomy of 500 mg of the four PVPs, I, II, III and IV, described above. A squamous-cell carcinoma of the skin occurred at the incision site in the PVP I group. A total of 13 benign and 29 malignant neoplasms (mainly reticulum-cell sarcomas and lymphosarcomas, Kupffer-cell sarcomas, adenocarcinomas and squamous-cell carcinomas of the uterus) were found. One reticulum-cell sarcoma was observed among 23 untreated female rats during the observation period of 13 months (Hueper, 1957). Following i.p. injection of a PVP with a molecular weight of 10 000, 3 reticulum-cell sarcomas were seen in 20 rats. Malignant tumours, mainly reticulum-cell sarcomas (11) and carcinomas of the uterus, were found in 17/200 untreated controls (Hueper, 1959).

Two specially prepared PVPs, one with a molecular weight between about 2000 and 38 000 and the other between 4000 and 80 000, were compared with the PVPs 6 and 7, of average molecular weight 50 000, which had been used in the previous experiments. The two new PVPs were administered as 2 ml of 25% aqueous solutions 4 times at fortnightly intervals to groups of 35 3-month-old female NIH black rats to a total dose of 2 g PVP/animal. PVPs 6 and 7 were injected intraperitoneally to 20 and 30 female rats as 5 ml of 20% solutions, 3 times a week, until 9 injections or 9 g of PVP had been injected into each rat. The treatment was discontinued for one month and then resumed until a total of 15 g had been administered to each rat. All experimental animals that survived an observation period of 2 years were killed and examined *post mortem*. The various types of cancers observed in the experimental series treated with the four PVPs were identical or very close in number, location and structure to those seen among untreated control rats (Hueper, 1961).

### (c)   Intravenous administration

Rat:   The four samples of PVPs described above were injected into groups of 15 female rats as 2.5 ml of a 7% solution given 8 times at weekly intervals. Two benign and 14 malignant tumours (mainly reticulum-cell sarcomas) occurred at different sites. One reticulum-cell sarcoma was observed among 23 untreated female rats during an observation period of 13 months (Hueper, 1957) [The Working Group noted the small number of animals and the short observation period of control rats].

Rabbit:   PVPs I, II, III, IV, 6 and 7 (average molecular weights ranging between 20 000 and 300 000) were injected as 7% saline solutions to 27 Dutch rabbits (2500-3500 mg/injection;   total dose, 22 000-56 000 mg in the different groups). No tumours were seen within 4 years (Hueper, 1959). Groups of 6 rabbits received up to 5 injections of 50 ml of a 25% solution in water containing a total of 62.2 g PVP (molecular weight 2000-38 000 and 4000-80 000). No tumours were seen within 28 months (Hueper, 1961).

## 3.2   Other relevant biological data

### (a)   Experimental systems

### Toxic effects

With doses of up to 40 000 mg/k bw PVP (molecular weight >10 000) no acute oral $LD_{50}$ could be established in rats (Scheffner, cited in WHO, 1974). In groups of rats fed diets containing 1 and 10% PVP (molecular weight 38 000) for 2 years, no toxic effects or gross or histological changes were noted;   and there was no evidence that PVP was absorbed from the intestinal tract (Burnette, cited in WHO, 1974).

The morphological changes following PVP administration were the same in mice, rats, rabbits and dogs. Single or repeated i.v. doses of PVP evoked no gross pathological changes, except for enlargement of the spleen. Microscopically, the principal lesion is a thesaurismotic reaction, a foam-cell, storage phenomenon characterized by the appearance of swollen cells with reticular-type nuclei loaded with vacuoles or deposits of PVP. Some of these cells are large and multinucleated. They are found in many organs but most typically in the spleen (Ammon & Muller, 1949;   Bargmann, 1947;   Fresen & Weese, 1952;   Hartman, 1951;   Hueper, 1959;   Nelson & Lusky, 1951).

Embryotoxicity and teratogenicity

No teratogenic effect was observed after injection of 500 µg PVP (molecular weight, 11 500) in 0.01 ml saline into the yolk sac of rabbits on the 9th day of gestation (Claussen, 1975;  Claussen & Breuer, 1975).

Absorption, distribution, excretion and metabolism

PVP labelled with [14]C or [131]I was not metabolized to any significant degree by rats, rabbits or dogs following its i.v. injection.  The retention of PVP in the body is proportional to its molecular size, since only that of low molecular weight can be excreted.  The reticuloendothelial system retains PVP with a molecular weight in excess of 110 000 (Hespe et al., 1977;  Ravin et al., 1952).

No data on the mutagenicity of this compound were available to the Working Group.

(b)  Humans

PVP with a molecular weight of less than 25 000 is excreted via the kidney (Ravin et al., 1952).  The excretion rate and distribution of [14]C-PVP with an average molecular weight of 40 000 administered by i.v. infusion was studied in 4 terminal cancer patients;  about 1/3 was excreted in the urine in the first 6 hours and 1/3 in the following 18 hours.  Small amounts were excreted in the faeces.  At autopsy, PVP was found to be accumulated in kidneys, lungs, liver, spleen and lymph nodes (Loeffler & Scudder, 1953).

Liver biopsies were obtained from 22 patients who received i.v. infusions of 3.5 or 4.5% PVP.  Basophilic globular deposits were seen within Kupffer cells or free in the sinusoids of the liver and were occasionally accompanied by a mild inflammation (Gall et al., 1953).

Thesaurismosis (storage disease) was also reported following inhalation of hair spray containing PVP.  Lymph-node biopsies from 6 such patients showed pathological changes varying from slight hyperplasia to marked granuloma formation resembling sarcoidosis.  In some patients, lung lesions such as fibrosis or pneumonia were found, with hyperplasia of alveolar lining cells and an accumulation of macrophages.  Three of the patients died (Bergmann et al., 1962).

3.3  Case reports and epidemiological studies

No data were available to the Working Group.

## 4.  Summary of Data Reported and Evaluation

### 4.1  Experimental data

No data on the carcinogenicity or mutagenicity of $N$-vinyl-2-pyrrolidone were available to the Working Group.

Polyvinyl pyrrolidone was tested in mice, rats and rabbits by several routes of administration, using materials of various molecular weights. Repeated subcutaneous injections of an aqueous solution of polyvinyl pyrrolidone to rats resulted in local sarcomas.  Single or several subcutaneous or intraperitoneal implantations of polyvinyl pyrrolidone powder resulted in a low incidence of local tumours.  After several intravenous injections or after intraperitoneal implantation of polyvinyl pyrrolidone, tumours occurred in rats at distant sites, including the reticuloendothelial system;  the results of these experiments do not allow an evaluation of a possible association of these distant tumours with such treatment.

### 4.2  Human data

No case reports or epidemiological studies directly related to the carcinogenicity of polyvinyl pyrrolidone were available to the Working Group.  However, cosmetologists may represent an occupational group repeatedly exposed to polyvinyl pyrrolidone.  The extensive use of polyvinyl pyrrolidone in industry, in a variety of consumer products and, in the past, as a plasma expander indicates that widespread human exposure has and does occur.

### 4.3  Evaluation

The available data do not permit an evaluation of the carcinogenicity of $N$-vinyl-2-pyrrolidone or of polyvinyl pyrrolidone to humans.  The *limited evidence* of the carcinogenicity of polyvinyl pyrrolidone in experimental animals, together with the widespread human exposure to both compounds, suggest the need for epidemiological studies and for animal studies using the dermal, inhalational and oral routes (see also 'General Remarks on the Substances Considered', p. 35).

## 5. References

Ammon, R. & Müller, W. (1949)  The influence of high doses of Periston on the rabbit, with special consideration of the spleen (Ger.).  Dtsch. med. Wschr., 74, 465-468

Anon. (1972)  Polyvinylpyrrolidone helping the little old winemaker. Chemical Marketing Reporter, 24 April, pp. 5, 46

Arakelyan, V.G., Sarycheva, L.S., Zarutskii, V.V., Ostrovskii, S.A. & Golovkin, G.B. (1967)  Nitrogen-containing compounds. III. Chroma-tographic determination of vinylpyrrolidinone and pyrrolidinone (Russ.). Gazov. Khromatogr., 7, 147-149 [Chem. Abstr., 71, 45627s]

Bargmann, W. (1947)  Changes in the spleen after administration of Periston as a plasma volume expander (Ger.).  Virchows Arch. path. Anat., 314, 162-166

Bergmann, M., Flance, I.J., Cruz, P.T., Klam, N., Aronson, P.R., Joshi, R.A. & Blumenthal, H.T. (1962)  Thesaurosis due to inhalation of hair spray. Report of twelve new cases, including three autopsies.  New Engl. J. Med., 266, 750-755

Claussen, U. (1975)  Teratological experiments using the yolk-sac-method on rabbits (Abstract).  Teratology, 12, 327

Claussen, U. & Breuer, H.-W. (1975)  The teratogenic effects in rabbits of doxycycline, dissolved in polyvinylpyrrolidone, injected into the yolk sac.  Teratology, 12, 297-301

Dazzo, F. & Hubbell, D. (1974)  A quantitative assay of insoluble polyvinyl-pyrrolidone.  Plant Soil, 40, 435-439

Frauenfelder, L.J. (1974)  Universal chromatographic-colorimetric method for the determination of trace amounts of polyvinylpyrrolidone and its copolymers in foods, beverages, laundry products, and cosmetics. J. Assoc. off. anal. Chem., 57, 796-800

Fresen, O. & Weese, H. (1952)  IV. Aspect of the tissues after infusion of different fractions of Kollidon (Periston N, Periston, Periston of high viscosity) in animals (Ger.).  Beitr. path. Anat., 112, 44-62

GAF Corporation (1973)  Chemical Catalog, Calvert City, Ky, USA, pp. 2-6

Gall, E.A., Altemeier, W.A., Schiff, L., Hamilton, D.L., Braunstein, H., Giuseffi, J., Jr & Freiman, D.G. (1953)  Liver lesions following intravenous administration of polyvinyl pyrrolidone (PVP).  Am. J. clin. Path., 23, 1187-1198

Grasselli, J.G. & Ritchey, W.M., eds (1975)  CRC Atlas of Spectral Data
    and Physical Constants for Organic Compounds, 2nd ed., Vol. IV,
    Cleveland, Ohio, Chemical Rubber Co., p. 446

Hagel, L. & Andersson, R. (1976)  Automated nephelometric determination
    of poly(vinylpyrrolidone) in Salazopyrin. Anal. chim. acta, 86,
    69-77 [Chem. Abstr., 85, 198224x]

Halpern, B.D. & Karo, W. (1977)  Medical applications.  In: Bikales, N.M.,
    ed., Encyclopedia of Polymer Science and Technology, Plastics, Resins,
    Rubbers, Fibers, Vol. 2, Suppl., New York, Interscience, p. 391

Hartman, F.W. (1951)  Tissue changes following the use of plasma substitutes.
    Arch. Surg., 63, 728-738

Hawley, G.G., ed. (1971)  The Condensed Chemical Dictionary, 8th ed., New
    York, Van Nostrand-Reinhold, p. 715

Hespe, W., Meier, A.M. & Blankwater, Y.J. (1977)  Excretion and distribution
    studies in rats with two forms of $^{14}$carbon-labelled polyvinylpyrroli-
    done with a relatively low mean molecular weight after intravenous
    administration. Arzneimittel-Forsch., 27, 1158-1162

Hort, E.V. & Smith, R.F. (1968)  Pyrrole and pyrrole derivatives.  In:
    Kirk, R.E. & Othmer, D.F., eds, Encyclopedia of Chemical Technology,
    2nd ed., Vol. 16, New York, John Wiley and Sons, p. 853

Huebotter, E.E. & Gray, G.R. (1965)  Drilling fluids.  In: Kirk, R.E. &
    Othmer, D.F., eds, Encyclopedia of Chemical Technology, 2nd ed.,
    Vol. 7, New York, John Wiley and Sons, pp. 300-301

Hueper, W.C. (1957)  Experimental carcinogenic studies in macromolecular
    chemicals.  I.  Neoplastic reactions in rats and mice after parenteral
    introduction of polyvinyl pyrrolidones.  Cancer, 10, 8-18

Hueper, W.C. (1959)  Carcinogenic studies on water-soluble and insoluble
    macromolecules. Arch. Path., 67, 589-617

Hueper, W.C. (1961)  Bioassay on polyvinylpyrrolidones with limited molecular
    weight range. J. natl Cancer Inst., 26, 229-237

Ishikawa, S., Furuichi, Y. & Nakamura, S. (1972)  Determination of poly(vinyl
    pyrrolidinone) (Jap.).  Nippon Nogei Kagaku Kaishi, 46, 267-271 [Chem.
    Abstr., 77, 137024v]

Loeffler, R.K. & Scudder, J. (1953)  Excretion and distribution of polyvinyl
    pyrrolidone in man as determined by use of radiocarbon as a tracer.
    Am. J. clin. Path., 23, 311-321

Lorenz, D.H. (1971) *N-Vinyl amide polymers*. In: Bikales, N.M., ed., Encyclopedia of Polymer Science and Technology, Plastics, Resins, Rubbers, Fibers, Vol. 14, New York, Interscience, pp. 239-251

Lusky, L.M. & Nelson, A.A. (1957) Fibrosarcomas induced by multiple subcutaneous injections of carboxymethylcellulose (CMC), polyvinylpyrrolidone (PVP), and polyoxyethylene sorbitan monostearate (Tween 60) (Abstract No. I363). Fed. Proc., 16, 318

Nelson, A.A. & Lusky, L.M. (1951) Pathological changes in rabbits from repeated intravenous injections of Periston (polyvinyl pyrrolidone) or dextran. Proc. Soc. exp. Biol. (N.Y.), 76, 765-767

Postel, W. (1973) Detection and estimation of poly(vinylpyrrolidone) in beer (Ger.). Brauwissenschaft, 26, 337-340

Puetzer, B., Katz, L. & Horwitz, L. (1952) Preparatory method for 1-vinyl-2-pyrrolidinone. J. Am. chem. Soc., 74, 4959-4960 [Chem. Abstr., 48, 13682a]

Ravin, H.A., Seligman, A.M. & Fine, J. (1952) Polyvinyl pyrrolidone as a plasma expander. Studies on its excretion, distribution and metabolism. New Engl. J. Med., 247, 921-929

Ridgway, K. & Rubinstein, M.H. (1971) The quantitative analysis of polyvinylpyrrolidone by infrared spectrophotometry. J. Pharm. Pharmacol., 23, 587-589

Timell, T. (1946) Recent developments in acetylene chemistry. Tek. Tid., 76, 578-579 [Chem. Abstr., 39, 5693]

US Department of Commerce (1977) US Imports for Consumption and General Imports, TSUSA Commodity by Country of Origin, FT 246/Annual 1976, Bureau of the Census, Washington DC, US Government Printing Office, p. 227

US Food and Drug Administration (1977) Food and drugs. US Code Fed. Regul., Title 21, parts 172.210, 173.55, 175.105, 175.300, 176.170, 176.210, pp. 363-364, 425, 438, 446, 452, 455, 471, 481, 491, 493

US International Trade Commission (1977) Synthetic Organic Chemicals, US Production and Sales, 1976, USITC Publication 833, Washington DC, US Government Printing Office, p. 308

US Pharmacopeial Convention, Inc. (1975) The US Pharmacopeia, 19th rev., Rockville, Md, pp. 395-396

US Tariff Commission (1956) Synthetic Organic Chemicals, US Production and Sales, 1955, Report No. 198, Second Series, Washington DC, US Government Printing Office, p. 143

Verdier, E., Piro, J. & Garcia Montelongo, F. (1971) Quantitative determination of surface-active agents by electroadsorption (Fr.). *Talanta*,
**18**, 1237-1241

WHO (1974) Toxicological evaluation of some food additives including
anticaking agents, antimicrobials, antioxidants, emulsifiers and
thickening agents. *WHO Food Addit. Ser.*, *No. 5*, 486-489

Windholz, M., ed. (1976) *The Merck Index*, 9th ed., Rahway, NJ, Merck & Co.,
p. 996

Wood, A.S. (1970) *Vinyl polymers (pyrrolidone)*. In: Kirk, R.E. &
Othmer, D.F., eds, *Encyclopedia of Chemical Technology*, 2nd ed.,
Vol. 21, New York, John Wiley and Sons, pp. 427-440

## ACROLEIN

### 1.  Chemical and Physical Data

1.1  Synonyms and trade names

Chem. Abstr. Services Reg. No.:  107-02-8

Chem. Abstr. Name:  2-Propenal

Acraldehyde;  acrylaldehyde;  acrylic aldehyde;  allyl aldehyde; propenal;  prop-2-en-1-al;  2-propen-1-one

Aqualin;  NSC 8819

1.2  Structural and molecular formulae and molecular weight

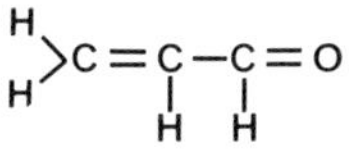

$$\begin{array}{c} H \\ H \end{array}\!\!>\!\!C = \underset{\underset{H}{|}}{C} - \underset{\underset{H}{|}}{C} = O$$

$C_3H_4O$                    Mol. wt:  56.1

1.3  Chemical and physical properties of the pure substance

From Weast (1976), unless otherwise specified

(a)  Description:  Colourless liquid with a pungent odour (Guest *et al.*, 1963;  Windholz, 1976)

(b)  Boiling-point:  52.5-53.5°C

(c)  Melting-point:  -86.95°C

(d)  Density:  $d_4^{20}$ 0.8410;  vapour-air density at 37.7°C, 1.6; vapour density, 1.9 (air = 1) (Anon., 1972)

(e)  Refractive index:  $n_D^{20}$ 1.4017

(f)  Spectroscopy data:  $\lambda_{max}$ 207 nm ($E_1^1$ = 2000);  infra-red, Raman, nuclear magnetic resonance and mass spectral data have been tabulated (Grasselli & Ritchey, 1975).

(g) Solubility: Soluble in water, ethanol, ether and acetone

(h) Volatility: Vapour pressure is 200 mm at 17.5°C (Perry & Chilton, 1973).

(i) Stability: Flash-point, -26.1°C (Anon., 1972); polymerizes spontaneously, particularly in the presence of light, alkali or strong acid (Windholz, 1976)

(j) Conversion factor: 1 ppm in air = 2.3 mg/m³

## 1.4 Technical products and impurities

Acrolein is available in the US as a commercial grade with a minimum purity of 92% and contains 0.1-0.25% hydroquinone (see IARC, 1977) as an ihibitor. Impurities include water, 4.0% max, and small amounts of acetaldehyde and propionaldehyde (Guest *et al.*, 1963). The grade of acrolein used as an intermediate in glycerine manufacture is at least 99% pure.

In Japan, acrolein available commercially has the following specifications: purity, 96% min; water content, 1.5% max; hydroquinone, 0.1-0.3%. It also contains acetaldehyde and acetone as impurities.

## 2. Production, Use, Occurrence and Analysis

A review on acrolein has been published (Guest *et al.*, 1963).

## 2.1 Production and use

### (a) Production

Acrolein was first prepared by Redtenbacher in 1843 by the dry distillation of fat (Prager *et al.*, 1918). All acrolein produced in the Federal Republic of Germany, France, Japan and the US is made by the catalytic vapour phase oxidation of propylene (Anon., 1971; Schaal, 1973). Acrolein was manufactured in the Federal Republic of Germany and the US prior to 1967 and 1970, respectively, by the cross-condensation of acetaldehyde and formaldehyde (Anon., 1971).

Commercial production of acrolein in the US was first reported in 1955 (US Tariff Commission, 1956). In 1976, two US companies reported production of an undisclosed amount (see preamble, p. 22) (US International Trade Commission, 1977). US production in 1974 amounted to 27.7 million kg; this did not include an estimated 45-68 million kg produced captively from propylene as a transitory, unisolated intermediate in the production of acrylic acid (see also p. 47).

One French company was reported to have an annual capacity of 24 million kg acrolein in 1973 and was expected to increase this to 50 million kg/year (Schaal, 1973). One company in the Federal Republic of Germany produces acrolein (Anon., 1971). Western European production of acrolein in 1977 was 50-60 million kg.

Acrolein has been produced commercially in Japan since 1960. Three companies produced a total of about 18 million kg in 1976.

Worldwide production of acrolein in 1977 is estimated to have been 100-120 million kg.

(b)  Use

Use of acrolein in the US in 1974 (excluding that as an unisolated intermediate for acrylic acid) was as follows: for the production of glycerine (50%), for the production of synthetic methionine (25%) and for other applications (25%).

Glycerine, an important derivative of acrolein in the US, is used in a variety of products, including drugs, cosmetics, tobacco, food and beverages, in the production of alkyd resins, polyether polyols and explosives, and as a plasticizer in cellophane film.

Another important derivative of acrolein is the amino acid, *dl*-methionine, a poultry feed additive, which is widely used to promote improved feeding efficiency and to accelerate growth (Anon., 1971; Guest *et al.*, 1963). Worldwide demand for synthetic methionine in 1972 amounted to 65-70 million kg, and this is the fastest growing end use for acrolein (Anon., 1973). The hydroxy analogue of *dl*-methionine, produced in the US, is also made from acrolein and used in poultry feedstuffs.

Other chemicals and chemical products made from acrolein include: glutaraldehyde, 1,2,6-hexanetriol, 2-hydroxyadipaldehyde (Guest *et al.*, 1963), quinoline, pentaerythritol (Schaal, 1973), cycloaliphatic epoxy resins (Weschler, 1965), oil-well additives and water-treatment formulae (Anon., 1976).

Acrolein has also been used to modify food starch (Chapman & Kertesz, 1966) and as an aquatic herbicide, biocide and slimicide (Berg, 1977), and has reportedly been used in the manufacture of colloidal forms of metals and perfumes and as a warning agent in methyl chloride refrigerants (Windholz, 1976).

During World War I, acrolein was used as a poison gas (Izard & Libermann, 1978); 183 thousand kg were produced between 1914-1918 (Champeix & Catilina, 1967).

It has been tested for homopolymerization to polyacrolein; however, the brittle nature of the polymer makes it unattractive for commercial applications and is not used (Guest *et al.*, 1963).

Use of acrolein in western Europe in 1977 was in methionine (70%), glycerine (20%), glutaraldehyde (5%) and other uses (5%).

In Japan, acrolein is used as a raw material for the production of methionine (80%) and other chemicals (20%).

The US Food and Drug Administration permits the use of up to 0.6% acrolein to modify food starch. It also allows the use of acrolein as a slimicide in the manufacture of paper and paperboard used in contact with food (US Food & Drug Administration, 1977).

The US Occupational Safety and Health Administration's health standards for exposure to air contaminants require that an employee's exposure to acrolein not exceed an eight-hour time-weighted average of $0.25$ mg/m$^3$ (0.1 ppm) in the workplace air in any eight-hour work shift of a forty-hour work week (US Occupational Safety and Health Administration, 1976).

The work environment hygiene standards (in terms of an eight-hour time-weighted average) for acrolein reported by Winell (1975) are $0.25$ mg/m$^3$ (0.1 ppm) in the Federal Republic of Germany, the German Democratic Republic and Sweden, and $0.5$ mg/m$^3$ (0.2 ppm) in Czechoslovakia. The acceptable ceiling concentration of acrolein in the USSR is $0.7$ mg/m$^3$ (0.3 ppm).

## 2.2 Occurrence

### (a) Air

It was estimated that acrolein, acetone and low fatty acids are emitted at the rate of 1 million kg/year during the manufacture of oxidation-hardening enamels in The Netherlands (Doorgeest, 1970). Acrolein has been determined in the exhaust gases from a passenger car diesel engine in concentrations of 0.5-0.8 mg/m$^3$ (0.2-0.3 ppm) (Smythe & Karasek, 1973) and in the exhaust gases from an automobile rotary engine at a level of 0.2 ppm (Hoshika & Takata, 1976).

### (b) Food

Acrolein has been separated from sugar-cane molasses (Hardlicka & Janicek, 1968). It has also been detected in: (1) souring salted pork (Cantoni et al., 1969); (2) the fish odour of cooked horse mackerel (Shimomura et al., 1971); (3) the aroma volatiles of white bread (Mulders & Dhont, 1972); (4) the volatile components of raw chicken breast muscle (Grey & Shrimpton, 1967); (5) the aroma volatiles of ripe arctic bramble berries (Kallio & Linko, 1973); and (6) the products from heating fats (Bauer et al., 1977).

(c) Occupational exposure

The following exposures to acrolein in workplace air have been reported: (1) levels of 0.44-1.5 mg/m$^3$ (0.2-0.6 ppm) in a Russian rubber vulcanization plant producing styrene-butadiene rubber footwear components (Volkova & Bagdinov, 1969); (2) 0.11-1.04 mg/m$^3$ (0.05-0.4 ppm) during the welding of metals coated with anti-corrosion primers (Protsenko *et al.*, 1973); (3) 0.322 mg/m$^3$ (0.14 ppm) in pitch-coking plants (Masek, 1972); and (4) less than 0.1 mg/m$^3$ (0.04 ppm) from diesel train engine exhaust during repair and servicing (Apol, 1973).

(d) Other

Acrolein has been detected in cigarette smoke at a mean level of 65.9 μg in a cigarette made from black tobacco (Testa & Joigny, 1972) and at levels of 51-102 μg in 85-mm non-filter cigarettes made from four Bright tobacco varieties (Rathkamp *et al.*, 1973).

It has been identified as a volatile component of essential oils extracted from the wood of oak trees (Egorov *et al.*, 1976); and it has been found in the smoke resulting from combustion of wood (110 mg/m$^3$, 50 ppm), kerosene (<2.5 mg/m$^3$, < 1 ppm) and cotton (140 mg/m$^3$, 60 ppm) (Einhorn, 1975).

2.3 Analysis

Gas chromatography has been used to measure trace amounts of acrolein in the volatile components of raw chicken muscle (Grey & Shrimpton, 1967) and in tobacco smoke (Rathkamp *et al.*, 1973).

Acrolein has also been determined as its 2,4-dinitrophenylhydrazone derivative using gas chromatography with flame-ionization detection in: (1) diesel automobile engine exhaust (Smythe & Karasek, 1973); (2) automobile engine exhaust (Hoshika & Takata, 1976); and (3) the aroma volatiles of ripe arctic bramble berries, using thin-layer and gas chromatography with mass spectrometry confirmation (Kallio & Linko, 1973). Gas chromatography with flame-ionization detection has also been used to determine the content of acrolein in waste-water, with a limit of detection of 0.5 mg/l (Voloshina, 1971).

Spectrophotometry in the visible or 450 nm range or colorimetry using chromotropic acid can be used to determine the acrolein content of air, with a limit of detection of 0.5 mg/m$^3$ (Gronsberg, 1974). Spectrophotocolorimetry using 4-hexylresorcinol has been used to detect acrolein in industrial atmospheres (Ionescu Nipal *et al.*, 1968); and ultra-violet spectrophotometry using thiosemicarbazone at 290 nm has been used to detect it in the atmosphere of open-cut mines containing exhaust vehicle gases, with a level of detection of 0.4 μg/sample (Shadrin, 1970).

A tentative spectrophotometric colorimetric method at 605 nm has been described using 4-hexylresorcinol for determination of acrolein in air, with a limit of detection of 0.023 mg/m$^3$ (<0.01 ppm) (Intersociety Committee, 1972).

A microwave spectrophotometric method has been used to determine acrolein in automobile exhaust (Tanimoto & Uehara, 1975).

Fluorescence spectroscopy has been used to determine the acrolein present in biological systems (Alarcon, 1968) and in air (Sawicki *et al.*, 1967). Fluorescence spectroscopy has also been used to determine acrolein applied as a herbicide in irrigation waters in the range of 4 µg/l (ppb)- 2 mg/l (ppm) (Hopkins & Hattrup, 1974).

A polarographic method has been evaluated for determing acrolein at concentrations of 0.05-0.5 mg/l (ppm) in surface waters (Howe, 1976).

Thin-layer chromatography can be used to determine acrolein as an impurity in commercial isoprene, with a limit of detection of 3 mg/kg (ppm) (Kuznetsova *et al.*, 1973).

### 3. Biological Data Relevant to the Evaluation of Carcinogenic Risk to Humans

### 3.1 Carcinogenicity studies in animals[1]

#### (a) Skin application

Mouse: A group of 15 S mice (sex unspecified) received 10 weekly applications of a 0.5% solution of acrolein in acetone (total dose, 12.6 mg/animal). Twenty-five days after the first acrolein application, the mice received weekly skin applications of 0.17% croton oil for 18 weeks; during the second and third weeks the concentration was reduced to 0.085%. When croton oil and acrolein were administered together, each compound was given alternately at 3- or 4-day intervals. At the end of the croton-oil treatment, all 15 mice were still alive, and 2 had a total of 3 skin papillomas, compared with 4/19 controls that received the croton-oil treatment alone (Salaman & Roe, 1956) [The Working Group noted the short duration of the experiment].

---

[1]The Working Group was aware of studies in progress to assess the carcinogenicity of acrolein in hamsters by inhalation and in rats by administration in the drinking-water (IARC, 1978).

(b)  Subcutaneous and/or intramuscular administration

Mouse:  Fifteen female stock mice were injected once weekly with 0.2 mg acrolein in 0.1 ml sesame oil for 24 weeks.  Eleven mice were still alive at 12 months, 3 at 18 months and 1 at 21 months.  No local sarcomas were reported to occur (Steiner *et al*., 1943) [The Working Group noted the lack of complete pathological examination and the small number of animals used].

(c)  Inhalation and/or intratracheal administration

Hamster:  A group of 18 male and 18 female 6-week-old Syrian golden hamsters were exposed to 9.2 mg/m$^3$ (4 ppm) acrolein in air for 7 hours a day on 5 days/week for 52 weeks.  Another group of 18 males and 18 females received the same acrolein treatment plus intratracheal instillation of 0.9% saline.  At 52 weeks, 3 males and 3 females in each group were killed; the surviving animals were killed at 81 weeks.  Among 57 animals examined in both groups, 1 female killed at 74 weeks had a papilloma of the trachea. Tumours at other sites were not increased in comparison with untreated controls (Feron & Kruysse, 1977).

3.2  Other relevant biological data

Two reviews have been published on the biological effects of acrolein (Champeix & Catilina, 1967;  Izard & Libermann, 1978).

(a)  Experimental systems

Toxic effects

The oral LD$_{50}$ is 28 mg/kg bw in mice (Safe Drinking Water Committee, 1977), 46 mg/kg bw in rats and 7 mg/kg bw in rabbits (International Technical Information Institute, 1975).  The s.c. LD$_{50}$ is 30 mg/kg bw in mice and 50 mg/kg bw in rats (International Technical Information Institute, 1975;  Skog, 1950).  The inhalation LD$_{50}$ in rats is 300 mg/m$^3$ (130 ppm) (Skog, 1950).

In rats, the lowest lethal concentration for a 4-hour exposure period, which killed 2-4/6 animals, was 18.4 mg/m$^3$ (8 ppm) in air (Carpenter *et al*., 1949).  The LC$_{50}$ in rats for a 30-minute exposure was 300 mg/m$^3$ (130 ppm) (Fassett, 1963);  the lowest lethal concentration for a 6-hour exposure was 24 mg/m$^3$ (10 ppm) in mice, rabbits and guinea-pigs;  in cats, it was 1570 mg/m$^3$ (680 ppm) for an 8-hour period (International Technical Information Institute, 1975).  The LC$_{50}$ in hamsters was 58.4 mg/m$^3$ (25.4 ppm) for a 4-hour period (Kruysse, 1971).

In rats exposed to 0.55 ppm (v/v) acrolein in air for 24 hours/day on 7 days/week for 180 days, irritation of the nasal mucosa was observed between days 7-21 and then disappeared, in spite of continuation of exposure.  Lower body weight and differences in certain biochemical parameters persisted (Bouley *et al*., 1975).

Rats, hamsters and rabbits were exposed to 0.9-11 mg/m³ (0.4-4.9 ppm) acrolein in air for 6 hours a day on 5 days/week for 13 weeks. In animals given the highest level, eye and nasal irritation and hyperplasia and metaplasia of the epithelial lining of the respiratory tract were observed in all species. The lowest exposure level (0.4 ppm) produced no toxic effects in rabbits or hamsters (Feron *et al.*, 1978).

In dogs and monkeys exposed to 8.5 mg/m³ (3.7 ppm) acrolein in air for 8 hours a day on 5 days/week for 6 weeks, squamous metaplasa and basal-cell hyperplasia occurred in the trachea; squamous metaplasia of the lung was seen in 7/9 monkeys (Lyon *et al.*, 1970).

In rats, inhalation exposure for 41 hours to acrolein at concentrations of 4.8 mg/m³ (2.1 ppm) or for 20 hours at a concentration of 9.4 mg/m³ (4.1 ppm) as well as an i.p. injection of 3 mg/kg bw caused elevated hepatic alkaline phosphatase activity (Murphy *et al.*, 1964). One i.p. injection of 3 mg/kg bw in rats caused a prolongation of both pentobarbital and hexobarbital sleeping times (Jaeger & Murphy, 1973).

No data on the embryotoxicity or teratogenicity of this compound were available to the Working Group.

### Metabolism

Rats metabolized 10.5% of a s.c. dose of 1 ml of a 1% solution of acrolein in arachis oil to *N*-acetyl-*S*-(3-hydroxypropyl)-L-cysteine, which was isolated from the urine (Kaye, 1973).

Acrolein (0.165-0.270 mg/kg bw) given intraperitoneally to partly hepatectomized adult rats inhibited DNA and RNA synthesis in the liver and lungs (Munsch & Frayssinet, 1971). Addition of acrolein to isolated nuclei of liver cells from rats led to an inhibition of their transcriptional ability (Moulé & Frayssinet, 1971).

### Mutagenicity and other short-term tests

The genetic effects of acrolein have been reviewed by Izard & Libermann (1978).

In the earliest reported study, acrolein induced mutations in *Drosophila melanogaster* (2.23% compared to 0.19% in the controls) (Rapoport, 1948).

It was claimed in an abstract that acrolein had no mutagenic activity in *Escherichia coli* K-12/343/113 (including two forward- and one back-mutation markers) in the presence or absence of 9000 x *g* supernatant from mouse liver (Ellenberger & Mohn, 1976). Results reported in another abstract indicate that acrolein is mutagenic in an *E. coli* strain deficient in DNA polymerase without metabolic activation (Bilimoria, 1975).

Acrolein did not induce cytoplasmic respiration deficiency in
*Saccharomyces cerevisiae* N123. It was also negative in a back-mutation
test (spot test) with two yeast strains, one sensitive to base substitution (S211) and one to frameshift mutation (S138). The epoxides, glycidol
and glycidaldehyde (see also IARC, 1976), possible metabolites of acrolein,
were positive in the base substitution strain (S211). Glycidaldehyde was
a strong inducer of respiratory deficient mutants in N123 (Izard, 1973).
It is negative in the dominant lethal test in male mice given i.p. doses
of 1.5 or 2.2 mg/kg bw (Epstein *et al.*, 1972).

(b) Humans

Acrolein is a powerful lachrymogen, even at concentrations as low as
7 mg/m$^3$ (3 ppm), and greatly irritates the conjunctiva and the mucous
membranes of the respiratory organs (nasal cavities and throat) (Prentiss,
1937). Exposure to acrolein in air at a level of 2.5 mg/m$^3$ (1 ppm) is
intolerable, causing lachrymation and marked eye, nose and throat irritation within a period of 5 minutes (Fassett, 1963; Sim & Pattle, 1957).

In higher concentrations, it also causes injury to the lung;
respiratory insufficiency may persist for at least 18 months after exposure
(Champeix & Catilina, 1967). A concentration of 350 mg/m$^3$ (150 ppm) is
lethal after 10-minutes' exposure (Prentiss, 1937).

3.3 Case reports and epidemiological studies

No data were available to the Working Group.

4. Summary of Data Reported and Evaluation

4.1 Experimental data

Acrolein was tested in mice by skin application and subcutaneous
injection and in hamsters by inhalation exposure. The two studies in mice
suffer from several limitations, making them inadequate for evaluation of
carcinogenicity. No carcinogenic effects were detected in hamsters.

The irritating properties of this compound limit the dose levels that
can be used in animal testing.

The preliminary and conflicting nature of the available data precludes
an evaluation of the mutagenicity of acrolein.

4.2 Human data

No case reports or epidemiological studies regarding the carcinogenicity of acrolein were available to the Working Group. The large amounts of
acrolein produced, its use as a final product and as an intermediate in the
synthesis of other compounds, and its occurrence in the workplace and in

the general environment (e.g., air and food) may permit the identification of exposed groups for epidemiological investigation.

4.3 Evaluation

The data from two inadequate animal studies of local (skin and subcutaneous) carcinogenesis and from one negative inhalation study, together with the absence of human data, preclude an evaluation of the carcinogenicity of acrolein.

# 5. References

Alarcon, R.A. (1968) Fluorometric determination of acrolein and related compounds with $m$-aminophenol. Anal. Chem., 40, 1704-1708

Anon. (1971) Degussa brings in new acrolein capacity. European Chemical News, 16 July, p. 10

Anon. (1972) Fire Protection Guide on Hazardous Materials, 4th ed., Boston, Mass., National Fire Protection Association, pp. 325M-19, 49-29-49-30

Anon. (1973) World shortage looming for amino acids. Chemical Engineering News, 24 December, pp. 18-19

Anon. (1976) UCC finishes first phase in Louisiana expansion. Chemical Marketing Reporter, 4 October, pp. 3, 35

Apol, A.G. (1973) Health Hazard Evaluation/Toxicity Determination, Union Pacific Railroad, Pocatello, Idaho, PB-229 161, National Institute of Occupational Safety and Health, Health Hazard Evaluation Report 72-32, Springfield, Va, National Technical Information Service

Bauer, K., Czech, K. & Porter, A. (1977) Severe accidental acrolein intoxication at home (Ger.). Wien. klin. Wschr., 89, 243-244

Berg, G.L., ed. (1977) 1977 Farm Chemicals Handbook, 63rd Issue, Willoughby, Ohio, Meister Publishing Co., p. D19

Bilimoria, M.H. (1975) The detection of mutagenic activity of chemicals and tobacco smoke in a bacterial system (Abstract No. 39). Mutat. Res., 31, 328

Bouley, G., Dubreuil, A., Godin, J. & Boudène, C. (1975) Effects of a weak dose of continuously inhaled acrolein in rats (Fr.). Eur. J. Toxicol., 8, 291-297

Cantoni, C., Bianchi, M.A., Renon, P. & Calcinardi, C. (1969) Bacterial and chemical alterations during souring in salted pork (Ital.). Atti Soc. Ital. Sci. Vet., 23, 752-756 [Chem. Abstr., 73, 129686q]

Carpenter, C.P., Smyth, H.F., Jr & Pozzani, U.C. (1949) The assay of acute vapor toxicity, and the grading and interpretation of results on 96 chemical compounds. J. ind. Hyg. Toxicol., 31, 343-346

Champeix, J. & Catilina, P. (1967) Acrolein Poisoning (Fr.), Paris, Masson

Chapman, D.G. & Kertesz, Z.I. (1966) Food additives. In: Kirk, R.E. & Othmer, D.F., eds, Encyclopedia of Chemical Technology, 2nd ed., Vol. 10, New York, John Wiley and Sons, p. 17

Doorgeest, T. (1970) Paint and air pollution (Dutch). TNO Nieuws, 25, 37-42 [Chem. Abstr., 72, 136075x]

Egorov, I.A., Pisarnitskii, A.F., Zinkevich, E.P. & Gavrilov, A.I. (1976) Study of some volatile components of oak wood (Russ.). Prikl. Biokhim. Mikrobiol., 12, 108-112 [Chem. Abstr., 85, 182256y]

Einhorn, I.N. (1975) Physiological and toxicological aspects of smoke produced during the combustion of polymeric materials. Environ. Health Perspect., 11, 163-189

Ellenberger, J. & Mohn, G.R. (1976) Comparative mutagenicity testing of cyclophosphamide and some of its metabolites (Abstract No. 36). Mutat. Res., 38, 120-121

Epstein, S.S., Arnold, E., Andrea, J., Bass, W. & Bishop, Y. (1972) Detection of chemical mutagens by the dominant lethal assay in the mouse. Toxicol. appl. Pharmacol., 23, 288-325

Fassett, D.W. (1963) Aldehydes and acetals. In: Patty, F.A., ed., Industrial Hygiene and Toxicology, 2nd revised ed., Vol. II, Toxicology, New York, Interscience, pp. 1978-1979

Feron, V.J. & Kruysse, A. (1977) Effects of exposure to acrolein vapor in hamsters simultaneously treated with benzo[$a$]pyrene or diethyl-nitrosamine. J. Toxicol. environ. Health, 3, 379-394

Feron, V.J., Kruysse, A., Til, H.P. & Immel, H.R. (1978) Repeated exposure to acrolein vapour: subacute studies in hamsters, rats and rabbits. Toxicology, 9, 47-57

Grasselli, J.G. & Ritchey, W.M., eds (1975) CRC Atlas of Spectral Data and Physical Constants for Organic Compounds, 2nd ed., Vol. IV, Cleveland, Ohio, Chemical Rubber Co., p. 297

Grey, T.C. & Shrimpton, D.H. (1967) Volatile components of raw chicken breast muscle. Br. Poult. Sci., 8, 23-33

Gronsberg, Y.S. (1974) Determination of acrolein in air. Khim. prom. (Moscow), 5, 394 [translation in Soviet Chem. Ind., 6, 337-338]

Guest, H.R., Kiff, B.W. & Stansbury, H.A., Jr (1963) Acrolein and deri-vatives. In: Kirk, R.E. & Othmer, D.F., eds, Encyclopedia of Chemical Technology, 2nd ed., Vol. 1, New York, John Wiley and Sons, pp. 255-274

Hardlicka, J. & Janicek, G. (1968) Volatile carbonyl compounds isolated from sugar-cane molasses (Czech.). Sb. Vys. Sk. Chem. Technol. Praze. Potraviny, E21, 77-79

Hopkins, D.M. & Hattrup, A.R. (1974)  Field Evaluation of a Method to Detect Acrolein in Irrigation Canals, REC-ERC-74-8, PB Rep. No. 234926/4GA, Springfield, Va, National Technical Information Service

Hoshika, Y. & Takata, Y. (1976)  Gas chromatographic separation of carbonyl compounds as their 2,4-dinitrophenylhydrazones using glass capillary columns. J. Chromatogr., 120, 379-389

Howe, L.H. (1976)  Differential pulse polarographic determination of acrolein in water samples. Anal. Chem., 48, 2167-2169

IARC (1976)  IARC Monographs on the Evaluation of Carcinogenic Risk of Chemicals to Man, 11, Cadmium, Nickel, Some Epoxides, Miscellaneous Industrial Chemicals and General Considerations on Volatile Anaesthetics, Lyon, pp. 175-181

IARC (1977)  IARC Monographs on the Evaluation of the Carcinogenic Risk of Chemicals to Man, 15, Some Fumigants, the Herbicides 2,4-D and 2,4,5-T, Chlorinated Dibenzodioxins and Miscellaneous Industrial Chemicals, Lyon, pp. 155-175

IARC (1978)  Information Bulletin on the Survey of Chemicals Being Tested for Carcinogenicity, No. 7  Lyon, pp. 219, 281

International Technical Information Institute (1975)  Toxic and Hazardous Industrial Chemicals Safety Manual for Handling and Disposal with Toxicity and Hazard Data, Tokyo, p. AI-35

Intersociety Committee (1972)  Tentative method of analysis for acrolein content of the atmosphere (colorimetric). In: Methods of Air Sampling and Analysis, Washington DC, American Public Health Association, pp. 187-189

Ionescu Nipal, F., Iftode, M., Legun, I. & Duluta, V. (1968)  Spectrophotometric determination of acrolein (Rom.). Rev. Chim. (Bucharest), 19, 172-173 [Chem. Abstr., 69, 54111e]

Izard, C. (1973)  Mutagenic effects of acrolein and of its two epoxides: glycidol and glycidal, on Saccharomyces cerevisiae (Fr.). C.R. Acad. Sci. (Paris), Ser. D, 276, 3037-3040

Izard, C. & Libermann, C. (1978)  Acrolein. Mutat. Res., 47, 115-138

Jaeger, R.J. & Murphy, S.D. (1973)  Alterations of barbiturate action following 1,1-dichloroethylene, corticosterone, or acrolein. Arch. int. Pharmacodyn., 205, 281-292

Kallio, H. & Linko, R.R. (1973)  Volatile monocarbonyl compounds of arctic bramble (Rubus arcticus L.) at various stages of ripeness. Z. Lebensm. Unters.-Forsch., 153, 23-30

Kaye, C.M. (1973)  Biosynthesis of mercapturic acids from allyl alcohol, allyl esters and acrolein. Biochem. J., 134, 1093-1101

Kruysse, A. (1971)  Acute Inhalation Toxicity of Acrolein in Hamsters, Report R3516, Zeist, The Netherlands, Central Institute for Nutrition and Food Research TNO [cited in Feron & Kruysse, 1977]

Kuznetsova, E.V., Turgel, E.O. & Taranenko, S.A. (1973)  Determination of trace amounts of carbonyl compounds in isoprene by continuous flow thin-layer chromatography. Zh. anal. Khim., 28, 1582-1587

Lyon, J.P., Jenkins, L.J., Jr, Jones, R.A., Coon, R.A. & Siegel, J. (1970)  Repeated and continuous exposure of laboratory animals to acrolein. Toxicol. appl. Pharmacol., 17, 726-732

Masek, V. (1972)  Aldehydes in the air in coal and pitch coking plants (Ger.). Staub-Reinhalt. Luft, 32, 335-336 [Chem. Abstr., 77, 143521w]

Moulé, Y. & Frayssinet, C. (1971)  Effects of acrolein on transcription in vitro. FEBS Lett., 16, 216-218

Mulders, E.J. & Dhont, J.H. (1972)  Odor of white bread. III. Identification of volatile carbonyl compounds and fatty acids (Ger.). Z. Lebensm. Unters.-Forsch., 150, 228-232 [Chem. Abstr., 78, 83052c]

Munsch, N. & Frayssinet, C. (1971)  Action of acrolein on nucleic acid synthesis in vivo (Fr.). Biochimie, 53, 243-248

Murphy, S.D., Davis, H.V. & Zaratzian, V.L. (1964)  Biochemical effects in rats from irritating air contaminants. Toxicol. appl. Pharmacol., 6, 520-528

Perry, R.H. & Chilton, C.H., eds (1973)  Chemical Engineers' Handbook, 5th ed., New York, McGraw-Hill, p. 3-49

Prager, B., Jacobson, P., Schmidt, P. & Stern, D., eds (1918)  Beilsteins Handbuch der Organischen Chemie, 4th ed., Vol. 1, Syst. No. 90, Berlin, Springer, p. 725

Prentiss, A.M. (1937)  Chemicals in War. A Treatise on Chemical Warfare, 1st ed., New York, McGraw-Hill, pp. 139-140

Protsenko, G.A., Danilov, V.I., Timchenko, A.N., Nenartovich, A.V., Trubilko, V.I. & Savchenkov, V.A. (1973)  Working conditions when metals to which primer has been applied are welded evaluated from the health and hygiene aspect. Avt. Svarka., 2, 65-68

Rapoport, I.A. (1948) Mutatations under the influence of unsaturated aldehydes (Russ.). Dokl. Akad. Nauk SSR, 61, 713-715 [cited in Izard & Libermann, 1978]

Rathkamp, G., Tso, T.C. & Hoffmann, D. (1973) Chemical studies on tobacco smoke. XX. Smoke analysis of cigarettes made from Bright tobaccos differing in variety and stalk positions. Beitr. Tabakforsch., 7, 179-189

Safe Drinking Water Committee (1977) Drinking Water and Health, Washington DC, National Academy of Sciences, pp. 553-556, 798

Salaman, M.H. & Roe, F.J.C. (1956) Further tests for tumour-initiating activity: N,N-di-(2-chloroethyl)-p-aminophenylbutyric acid (CB1348) as an initiator of skin tumour formation in the mouse. Br. J. Cancer, 10, 363-378

Sawicki, E., Carnes, R.A. & Schumacher, R. (1967) Spectrophotofluorimetric determination of 3-carbon fragments and their precursors with anthrone. Application to air pollution. Mikrochim. acta, 5, 929-935

Schaal, G.E. (1973) Make acrolein from propylene. Hydrocarbon Processing, September, pp. 218-220

Shadrin, A.S. (1970) Spectrophotometric determination of acrolein in the atmosphere of open-cut mines with truck transportation (Russ.). Tr. Inst. Gorn. Dela. Min. Chern. Met. SSSR, 24, 27-32 [Chem. Abstr., 76, 131082v]

Shimomura, M., Yoshimatsu, F. & Matsumoto, F. (1971) Fish odor of cooked horse mackerel (Jap.). Kaseigaku Zasshi, 22, 106-112 [Chem. Abstr., 75, 62292d]

Sim, V.M. & Pattle, R.E. (1957) Effect of possible smog irritants on human subjects. J. Am. med. Assoc., 165, 1908-1913

Skog, E. (1950) A toxicological investigation of lower aliphatic aldehydes. I. Toxicity of formaldehyde, acetaldehyde, propionaldehyde and butyraldehyde; as well as of acrolein, and crotonaldehyde. Acta pharmacol., 6, 299-318

Smythe, R.J. & Karasek, F.W. (1973) The analysis of diesel engine exhausts for low-molecular-weight carbonyl compounds. J. Chromatogr., 86, 228-231

Steiner, P.E., Steele, R. & Koch, F.C. (1943) The possible carcinogenicity of overcooked meats, heated cholesterol, acrolein and heated sesame oil. Cancer Res., 3, 100-107

Tanimoto, M. & Uehara, H. (1975)  Detection of acrolein in engine exhaust with microwave cavity spectrometer of Stark voltage sweep type. Environ. Sci. Tech., 9, 153-154

Testa, A. & Joigny, C. (1972)  Gas-layer chromatographic determination of acrolein and other α,β/unsaturated compounds in the gas phase of cigarette smoke (Fr.). Ann. Serv. Exploit. Ind. Tab. Allumettes-Div. Etud. Equip., Sect. 1, 10, 67-81

US Food and Drug Administration (1977)  Food starch - modified. Slimicides, US Code Fed. Regul., Title 21, parts 172.892, 176.300, pp. 419-420, 494

US International Trade Commission (1977)  Synthetic Organic Chemicals, US Production and Sales, 1976, USITC Publication 833, Washington DC, US Government Printing Office, p. 321

US Occupational Safety and Health Administration (1976)  Occupational safety and health standards subpart Z - toxic and hazardous substances. US Code Fed. Regul., Title 29, Chapter XVII, Section 1910.1000, p. 31:8302

US Tariff Commission (1956)  Synthetic Organic Chemicals, US Production and Sales, 1955, Report No. 198, Second Series, Washington DC, US Government Printing Office, p. 143

Volkova, Z.A. & Bagdinov, Z.M. (1969)  Industrial hygiene problems in vulcanization processes of rubber production (Russ.). Gig. i Sanit., 34, 33-40 [Chem. Abstr., 71, 128354b]

Voloshina, A. (1971)  Determination of some organic compounds in waste waters by a gas-liquid chromatographic method (Russ.). In: Dorofeenko, G.N., ed., Methods of Chemical Analysis of Effluent Waters from Chemical Industries, Rostov-on-Don, USSR, Rostov University, pp. 6-17 [Chem. Abstr., 78, 88404d]

Weast, R.C., ed. (1976)  CRC Handbook of Chemistry and Physics, 57th ed., Cleveland, Ohio, Chemical Rubber Co., p. C-463

Weschler, J.R. (1965)  Epoxy resins. In: Kirk, R.E. & Othmer, D.F., eds, Encyclopedia of Chemical Technology, 2nd ed., Vol. 8, New York, John Wiley and Sons, pp. 299-300

Windholz, M., ed. (1976)  The Merck Index, 9th ed., Rahway, NJ, Merck & Co., p. 17

Winell, M. (1975)  An international comparison of hygienic standards for chemicals in the work environment. Ambio, 4, 34-36

Corrigenda covering Volumes 1 - 6 appeared in Volume 7, others appeared in Volumes 8, 10, 11, 12, 13, 15, 16, 17 and 18.

## Volume 8

p. 101          *replace*

*by*

CUMULATIVE INDEX TO IARC MONOGRAPHS ON THE EVALUATION

OF THE CARCINOGENIC RISK OF CHEMICALS TO HUMANS

Numbers underlined indicate volume, and numbers in italics indicate page. References to corrigenda are given in parentheses. Compounds marked with an asterisk (*) were considered by the Working Groups, but monographs were not prepared because adequate data on their carcinogenicity were not available.

A

2-Amino-5-nitrophenol*

Amitrole                                          7,31

Amobarbital*

Anaesthetics, volatile                            11,285

Anthranilic acid                                  16,265

Aniline                                           4,27  (corr. 7,320)

Apholate                                          9,31

Aramite Ⓡ                                         5,39

Arsenic and inorganic arsenic compounds           2,48
  Arsenic pentoxide
  Arsenic trioxide
  Calcium arsenate
  Calcium arsenite
  Potassium arsenate
  Potassium arsenite
  Sodium arsenate
  Sodium arsenite

Asbestos                                          2,17  (corr. 7,319)
                                                  14    (corr. 15,341)
                                                        (corr. 17,351)

  Actinolite
  Amosite
  Anthophyllite
  Chrysotile
  Crocidolite
  Tremolite

Auramine                                          1,69  (corr. 7,319)

Aurothioglucose                                   13,39

Azaserine                                         10,73

Aziridine                                         9,37

2-(1-Aziridinyl)ethanol                           9,47

Aziridyl benzoquinone                             9,51

Azobenzene                                        8,75

Azothioprine*

B

Benz[c]acridine                                   3,241

Benz[a]anthracene                                 3,45

Benzene                                           7,203 (corr. 11,295)

Cantharidin                                                    10,79

Caprolactam                                                    19,115

Carbaryl                                                       12,37

Carbon tetrachloride                                           1,53

Carmoisine                                                     8,83

Catechol                                                       15,155

Chlorambucil                                                   9,125

Chloramphenicol                                               10,85

Chlorinated dibenzodioxins                                    15,41

Chlormadinone acetate                                          6,149

Chlorobenzilate                                                5,75

Chloroform                                                     1,61

Chloromethyl methyl ether                                      4,239

Chloroprene                                                    19,131

Chloropropham                                                 12,55

Chloroquine                                                   13,47

para-Chloro-ortho-toluidine and its hydrochloride            16,277

5-Chloro-ortho-toluidine*

Chlorpromazine*

Cholesterol                                                   10,99

Chromium and inorganic chromium compounds                     2,100
    Barium chromate
    Calcium chromate
    Chromic chromate
    Chromic oxide
    Chromium acetate
    Chromium carbonate
    Chromium dioxide
    Chromium phosphate
    Chromium trioxide
    Lead chromate
    Potassium chromate
    Potassium dichromate
    Sodium chromate
    Sodium dichromate
    Strontium chromate
    Zinc chromate hydroxide

Chrysene                                                       3,159

Chrysoidine                                                    8,91

Fluorescein disodium*

2-(2-Formylhydrazino)-4-(5-nitro-2-furyl)thiazole        *7*,*151* (corr. *11*,*295*)

Fusarenon-X                                              *11*,*169*

G

Glycidaldehyde                                           *11*,*175*

Glycidyl oleate                                          *11*,*183*

Glycidyl stearate                                        *11*,*187*

Griseofulvin                                             *10*,*153*

Guinea green B                                           *16*,*199*

H

Haematite                                                *1*,*29*

Heptachlor and its epoxide                               *5*,*173*

Hexamethylenediamine*

Hexamethylphosphoramide                                  *15*,*211*

Hycanthone and its mesylate                              *13*,*91*

Hydrazine                                                *4*,*127*

Hydroquinone                                             *15*,*155*

4-Hydroxyazobenzene                                      *8*,*157*

8-Hydroxyquinoline                                       *13*,*101*

Hydroxysenkirkine                                        *10*,*265*

I

Indeno[1,2,3-*cd*]pyrene                                 *3*,*229*

Iron-dextran complex                                     *2*,*161*

Iron-dextrin complex                                     *2*,*161* (corr. *7*,*319*)

Iron oxide                                               *1*,*29*

Iron sorbitol-citric acid complex                        *2*,*161*

Isatidine                                                *10*,*269*

Isonicotinic acid hydrazide                              *4*,*159*

Isoprene*

Isopropyl alcohol                                        *15*,*223*

Isopropyl oils                                           *15*,*223*

Isosafrole                                               *1*,*169*
                                                         *10*,*232*

| | |
|---|---|
| *N*-Methyl-*N*,4-dinitrosoaniline | 1,*141* |
| 4,4'-Methylene bis(2-chloroaniline) | 4,*65* |
| 4,4'-Methylene bis(2-methylaniline) | 4,*73* |
| 4,4'-Methylenedianiline | 4,*79*  (corr. 7,*320*) |
| 4,4'-Methylenediphenyl diisocyanate | 19,*314* |
| Methyl iodide | 15,*245* |
| Methyl methacrylate | 19,*187* |
| Methyl methanesulphonate | 7,*253* |
| *N*-Methyl-*N*'-nitro-*N*-nitrosoguanidine | 4,*183* |
| Methyl red | 8,*161* |
| Methyl selenac | 12,*161* |
| Methylthiouracil | 7,*53* |
| Metronidazole | 13,*113* |
| Mirex | 5,*203* |
| Mitomycin C | 10,*171* |
| Modacrylic fibres | 19,*86* |
| Monocrotaline | 10,*291* |
| Monuron | 12,*167* |
| 5-(Morpholinomethyl)-3-[(5-nitrofurfurylidene)-<br>  amino]-2-oxazolidinone | 7,*161* |
| Mustard gas | 9,*181* (corr. 13,*243*) |

N

| | |
|---|---|
| 1,5-Naphthalene diisocyanate | 19,*311* |
| 1-Naphthylamine | 4,*87*  (corr. 8,*349*) |
| 2-Naphthylamine | 4,*97* |
| Native carrageenans | 10,*181* (corr. 11,*295*) |
| Nickel and nickel compounds | 2,*126* (corr. 7,*319*)<br>11,*75* |

   Nickel acetate
   Nickel carbonate
   Nickel carbonyl
   Nickelocene
   Nickel oxide
   Nickel powder
   Nickel subsulphide
   Nickel sulphate